FOUNDATIONS OF SCIENCE

FOUNDATIONS OF SCIENCE

The Philosophy of Theory and Experiment

(Formerly Titled: PHYSICS THE ELEMENTS)

By

NORMAN
ROBERT
CAMPBELL

Dover Publications, Inc. New York

This new Dover edition first published in 1957 is an unabridged and unaltered republication of the first edition of the work formerly published under the title, *PHYSICS THE ELEMENTS*.

It is published through special arrangement with Cambridge University Press.

Library of Congress Catalog Card Number: 57-13303

Manufactured in the United States of America.

PREFACE

THE object and nature of this book is sufficiently explained in the introduction; here I will only warn the reader who gets no further that, in spite of its title, it is not an elementary treatise on physics. On the other hand, although there is a just prejudice against an author who seeks to disarm criticism, I would explain here how the book came to be written—not in order to explain its faults away, but in order, by giving notice of them, to render them less harmful.

The book was planned in 1904; and from that time onward parts of it were written in the form of separate essays as various problems forced themselves on my attention in the course of the ordinary scientific work which occupied most of my time. Some of these essays have been already published in their original form in various Reviews and in a little book called *The Principles of Electricity* (Jack, 1912). At the end of 1912 all the present chapters, and some others, were written in that form; but since they had been written independently and my views had naturally developed in the writing of them, coordination was needed. I began the work, but was interrupted, first by the preparation of a new edition of another book, and then by the war.

In 1919 an opportunity for completing the book occurred, better than was ever likely to occur again. But it was not entirely favourable; time was limited to eight or nine months, and the work had to be done in the country, without access to libraries or even to my own collection of books. Moreover, I found that I had forgotten about the matter so completely that, at the outset, the manuscript might have been that of an unknown author. It would have been wiser to read it, burn it, and start afresh; but in a mistaken attempt to save time, the old material was used; and though everything except the Introduction has been re-written, at least half of it is practically a mere transcript. There were two reasons for preserving the Introduction with as few alterations as possible. First though, unlike most introductions, it was actually written before the rest of the book, I found that I had really carried out my plan and had stated my intention as well as I could state it now. The second reason is personal piety. When the chapter was first written it was sent to my friend, Charles Donald Robertson, with whom, although his tastes were literary rather than scientific, I had often discussed with much profit the principles of science. It was found among his papers after his death in 1910, and returned to me.

Two faults arise from these circumstances. The coordination of the separate essays is still incomplete, and there are several instances (which I leave the reader to discover, if he is sufficiently interested) where the point of view is rather different in different parts of the book. On the whole I attach more value to the later portions. The most serious inconsistency arises in a reference in the earlier chapters to Part III, which is not included in the present volume; it was only when half the book was in type that it was decided to omit this Part, both on account of lack of time and because the volume would be too bulky. A summary of some of the conclusions of that Part are given in an appendix.

And here perhaps a brief account should be given of the plan of the remainder of the treatise. Part III, under the title Motion, deals with temporal and spatial conceptions. Part IV, Force, with statics and dynamics, both classical and modern. Part V, Energy, with the doctrine of energy, especially in its application to heat, thermodynamics and radiation. The remaining great branches of Physics, Electricity and other parts of Radiation, do not seem to raise so many fundamental questions as those dealt with in these Parts, and the original plan did not include them. Of these Parts, III is complete in substance but not in form (except for some of the more recent developments of the Theory of Relativity—most of which, however, belong to Part IV); and isolated chapters of Parts IV and V are also done. I have not the remotest idea when, if ever, they will be published. I have been tempted to publish what is already written, after suitable revision, in another volume of about the same size as this. But as it would consist of isolated essays and would not be a complete treatise, it would be so directly contrary to my original idea that I have determined not to abandon the plan, although at present there seems little prospect of carrying it out.

The other fault is a complete lack of reference to the work of others. My large index of references was lost in the disorder of war-time removals, and I had no chance, and no time, to replace it. But perhaps the omission is not an unmixed evil. As is pointed out in the Introduction, there is very little original in the substance of the book; there is hardly a paragraph which is not a paraphrase of something that can be found in well-known treatises or papers. If complete references were given, the notes would be almost as bulky as the text, and the book would be quite unreadable; if they were incomplete, they would probably be misleading and might cause offence. Moreover if anything valuable has been added to a mere compilation of what everyone knew before, it arises from a unity conferred by the passage of all this matter through a single mind; for though the conclusions reached are seldom new, they have not been easy to reach, but represent many hours of strenuous thought and result from many changes of opinion. Such unity, it seems to me, might be destroyed if the reader were constantly reminded of what others have said on the matter, even if they only said the same things in rather different words.

For the same reason I find it difficult to make the usual acknowledgements of prefaces. I have probably read as widely as most people in the ordinary literature of physics and in discussions of the principles of science; and there is none of it to which I am prepared to say that I do not owe valuable ideas. If anybody thinks that anything in the book is of sufficient worth for them to claim the right to it, I shall gladly acknowledge the claim, and ask them to accept the reasons that have been given for not admitting it beforehand. But for the general train of thought which inspires the whole I can make acknowledgements to my masters, Henri Poincaré and Mr Bertrand Russell; but I fear that the latter (at any rate) will think his pupil anything but a credit to him. Lastly, I would render thanks to a source which does not receive thanks as often as it should. The inspiring authors of *The King's English* would doubtless find the book a mine of the blunders which they hold to scorn so amiably; but it would have been even more fruitful if they had not written.

N. R. C.

KETTLEWELL,
October 1919

Ταράσσει τοὺς ἀνθρώπους οὐ τὰ πράγματα
ἀλλὰ τὰ περὶ τῶν πραγμάτων δόγματα

It is not the facts, but the explanation of them, that matters

CONTENTS

INTRODUCTION

Summary. It is explained that the book, of which this is the introductory volume, is intended to be a complete treatise on physics of which the main object is criticism. Criticism does not involve adverse judgement, but only analysis, which is more likely to strengthen than to weaken the evidence for the propositions criticised. It is suggested that such criticism may have a value, though an indirect value, for those pursuing original researches as well as for teachers and students. The general plan of the work is sketched and some of the main questions which are considered mentioned.

Criticism of this kind is not novel, but it has not been applied to experimental science as fully as to mathematics. Such criticism as has been applied to physics has almost always come from mathematicians. It is suggested that criticism by one interested in the experimental rather than the mathematical side of the subject may have some special interest.

One reason why criticism has been left so largely to mathematicians is that physicists are afraid of being led into any discussion which they regard as philosophical. Some remarks are made on the origin and basis of this attitude: the obvious fact is pointed out that, if it is true that fundamental scientific discussion necessarily lands us in philosophy, then philosophy must be a part of science and merits our attention. The opinion is, however, expressed that the fear is not justified and that science can be adequately discussed without any philosophy at all. On the other hand, there are connections between science and philosophy which it has seemed desirable to notice in a special chapter sharply distinguished from the rest of the book.

The object of the book. I want to explain rather carefully what is the object of this book; for if the reader does not understand that object thoroughly, he will not be able to utilise whatever value the book may possess.

The book aspires to be a treatise on physics, complete within its limits, written by a serious student of the science for other serious students. It is not in any sense a popular work addressed to those whose chief intellectual interests lie elsewhere; it assumes throughout entire familiarity with all the facts and theories of physics, ancient and modern. Its primary purpose does not exclude the possibility that some portions of it may be comprehensible and even mildly interesting to those who have not such familiarity; for even when reference is made to matters beyond their knowledge, the context will sometimes show what the example is intended to illustrate. But I must insist that any value of this kind which the book may have is purely incidental; the needs of professional physicists and their needs alone have been considered in writing it.

Nevertheless its object is not the same as that of most of the works which are addressed to professional physicists. The work is neither an original memoir, a description of original investigations in science, nor a standard treatise designed to replace, for example, the monumental *Handbuch* of Winkelmann. It does not pretend to add to the sum of distinctively scientific knowledge; indeed, if there is in it any scientific statement which is not perfectly familiar to those for whom it is written, that statement can hardly be anything but a blunder. On the other hand it is not a mere compilation of information already existing; large tracts of knowledge will be passed by without mention and those which are selected for the most detailed examination will not always be those which are generally considered of the greatest scientific importance or interest. And again it is not a text-book for students or their teachers. Its subjects have not been chosen because they fall within the syllabus of any Board of Examiners, actual or such as might exist in an ideal world; they are not those which are most suitable for immature minds.

Criticism. It is easier thus to explain what the book is not than to explain what it is. For it is only because the questions which it discusses are not usually asked and because the bare possibility of asking them is often not recognised that there is any need to enter on this explanation. Briefly it may be said that what is aimed at here is not investigation or exposition, but criticism. In addition to the attitudes towards physics of the original investigator and the teacher there is possible another, the attitude of the critic. The teacher does not want criticism in his text-books, because the faculty of appreciating it is one of the latest to appear in the process of education; a critical attitude towards a subject can only be adopted usefully when a complete mastery of its content has been attained. So long as the pupil is in the text-book stage he is prepared to accept, and is usually only too ready to accept, statements without any very searching inquiry into their foundation. The original investigator, on the other hand, does not want criticism in his treatises, since the exercise of the critical faculty is a necessary part of investigation; he feels perfectly prepared to provide it for himself and would rather resent having it offered to him, cut and dried, by others.

It is, I think, largely because scientific literature is usually designed to meet directly the needs of one or other of these great classes that criticism in science has been neglected—so neglected, indeed, that everyone does not realise what it involves. It seems often to be thought that to criticise a proposition is merely to judge whether it is true or false, with a strong bias in favour of the second alternative. But before such a judgement can be passed reasonably an important process must be carried out which is applicable just as much to the most certainly established as to the most dubitable statement, the process of analysis. The critic must determine exactly what the statement means, on what evidence it is advanced, what relation it bears to other statements either involved in it as assumptions or derived from it as consequences. It is only when these matters have been decided that judgement can be passed, and in many cases the preliminary analysis will be found a much more important part of the criticism than the final judgement.

Criticism of this nature has secured a large part of the attention of pure mathematicians for the last 30 years and has become almost a new branch of their study. In this treatise on physics I hope to extend in some measure such criticism to a portion of experimental science. Our inquiries will speedily discover to us reasons why criticism can never be as complete or as fundamental in an experimental science as in one based on pure logic; the necessary limitations which we shall find provide another reason why this branch of the study has received so little attention. But it seems worth while to make the attempt. I want to inquire into the precise meaning of the many propositions which make up the science of physics and into the evidence on which they are based; I want to examine the significance and connotation of the ideas in terms of which its results are expressed and into the character of their mutual relations.

These inquiries will be clearly the more interesting the more fundamental are the propositions and the ideas concerning which they are made; the investigations will be chiefly directed to those basic principles of each department of the science which are so firmly established that criticism of them, in the narrower sense of a judgement of their truth or validity, is not generally thought necessary. In examining these fundamental matters it will not be our object to raise doubts concerning them; it will be rather to examine why no doubts are possible. The further developments of the science will not require so much notice; the nature of their connection with the fundamental principles is more generally understood and more adequately treated in text-books of the usual type. Least attention of all will be required for those branches of our knowledge where opinion is still not wholly agreed; to examine in detail propositions which may yet be rejected would be waste of time.

The value of criticism. But of what use is such criticism if it is to add nothing to the established doctrines of physics and subtract nothing from them? What is the use of criticism, in any sense of the word, applied to matters concerning which everyone is perfectly agreed? Such questions are sure to be asked. The most direct answer that I can give, and the only one on which I am prepared to insist, is that criticism of this kind is to me intrinsically interesting; I want to undertake it for its own sake and not for any ulterior object. I express my thoughts in the form of a book, chiefly because the best way to clear them from confusion is to explain them to others, but also because others may possibly have the same interests. But I venture also to think that greater attention to these matters on the part of the two main classes of professed physicists, who are at present satisfied with treatises of a more ordinary type, might sometimes help them in their own special work, even if it were not worth giving for its own sake.

Nothing that I have to say is likely to offer any direct help in the solution of the problems of original research. The physical propositions about which most discussion will range are so fundamental, so long and so solidly established, that it is in the highest degree unlikely that an attack upon any new or outstanding question would be aided by a reconsideration of their meaning or validity. And while they remain undoubted a detailed analysis of them has no immediate bearing on the progress of the science. But it is always possible that some unforeseen development may drag once more into the arena of discussion laws and theories which nobody dreams of doubting to-day. Poincaré has pointed out that it might become more convenient to deny that "space is Euclidean"; if once the validity of that proposition were called in question a discussion of its precise meaning, of the evidence on which it is based, and of its relation to other propositions which must stand or fall with it—such a discussion might become of very immediate practical interest. It is not certain that even those who stand in the forefront of original investigation would be able to answer all the questions that might be raised without a good deal of thought and trouble[1].

But any value that criticism may have for the "practising physicist" will probably be more indirect and arise from a better understanding of the methods that he practises. Measurement and calculation are two of the most important weapons in the armoury of physical research, and though it is not suggested that actual errors in their use are frequent or, if they were, would be avoided by such discussions as are to be offered, I cannot help thinking that a complete inquiry into their nature and relations may be useful. What is meant by an arbitrary scale of measurement? Why is Mohs' scale of hardness more "arbitrary" than the Centigrade scale of temperature or the metric system of length? What conditions must be fulfilled before a scale of hardness which is not arbitrary can be substituted? What is the basis of the "argument from dimensions"? Why are the dimensions of a magnitude always expressible by rational indices? If a magnitude can have a dimension $T^{-\frac{1}{2}}$, why should it not have a dimension $\log T$? What are the assumptions added in direct calculation to those employed in the argument from dimensions, the assumptions which permit the determination of the "undetermined constant"? Why is the undetermined constant never very different from 1?[2] How far is the method applicable to electrical quantities which have two different dimensions? These questions are such as men of science may properly ask.

The benefits which a teacher of science might derive from criticism is more direct and obvious. A complete logical and analytical view of science may not be of benefit to his pupils, but he is less likely to puzzle them if he has himself the clearest possible view of the matters he teaches. That he

[1] See Preface. When Einstein's Principle of Relativity first provoked discussion, several physicists of the first rank condemned some of the propositions, involving notions of "time" and "space," implied by it on the ground, not that they were actually false, but that they were self-inconsistent and contradictory. Even those who regard the Principle as nothing more than an elegant mathematical device admit now that such criticisms were misdirected. If Part III of this volume had been written at that time, doubtless it would not have prevented these errors directly; it is far more likely that I should have made the blunders or worse blunders myself. But perhaps the mere raising of the questions, which could hardly have been avoided, would have helped others to escape them.

[2] This question has been asked and not answered by a physicist no less distinguished than Einstein (*Ann. d. Phys.* 35. 687. 1911). Of course the constant does sometimes differ considerably from 1: in one actual application of the argument it is as great as $6\pi^2$, and other applications could be devised in which it would be still greater. But there is some truth in the statement for which the question seeks an answer.

often has not such a view is apparent to everyone who has done much reviewing of elementary text-books. Whenever any fundamental matter is approached there is a tendency to repeat, with hardly verbal alteration, statements of which the original source is now difficult to trace; they may have been lucid and true in their original context, but now they are merely confusing or deliberately misleading. That delightfully naïve definition of mass as "quantity of matter", so redolent of the 18th century, is fortunately vanishing from our text-books, but students are still told that "matter is that which occupies space", and are left to gasp when they learn later, probably from some other book, that the "aether which pervades all space" is not matter. The prevalent explanation of the paradox: The day is the unit of time, but the length of the day is increasing, can deceive few intelligent pupils, but they may well think that it is their imagination which is at fault, and not that of the author of the phrase (surely the least imaginative of mankind), when they are surprised to learn that "negative weight is inconceivable."

Of course these are extreme instances, and most teachers are able to supply the deficiencies of their text-books; but if such obvious absurdities can pass almost unchallenged, it is likely that minor errors or, what is worse, ambiguities escape detection. They would be avoided if writers would not write anything unless they are quite sure what it means themselves; if they are not sure, the cause is much more likely to be found in some real obscurity than in their own stupidity. Once it is clear what a scientific statement means, it is seldom difficult to determine whether it is true or false; the elucidation of meaning is one of the chief tasks which this book is designed to undertake.

The order of criticism. However, in this volume of the treatise detailed criticism of actual scientific propositions will hardly be attempted; its purpose is wholly introductory. There are certain matters which are common to all branches of the science and certain features common to all physical propositions. It is more convenient to discuss them once and for all before beginning detailed inquiry than to discuss them one by one as they arise. For instance, almost all scientific propositions involve to some extent temporal and spatial ideas, and their proof depends on measurements of times and distances. They would not be significant and would not be true unless certain other propositions, involving these ideas and these measurements, were also true. In Part III of this volume we examine the temporal and spatial propositions on which all other physical propositions are based; they are not usually regarded themselves as physical propositions; indeed it seems not always to be recognised that there are such propositions. In Part II we recede yet a further stage into the foundations of science. The propositions of Part III, like those that are based on them, involve the conceptions of measurement and calculation. It is the use of these conceptions which distinguishes physics from all other sciences[1]. Our inquiry therefore is conveniently prefaced

[1] This statement may be disputed, but I think it is true. Measurements in all other sciences are those of magnitudes for which a method of measurement has been developed

by a discussion of these conceptions and a consideration of what is common to all systems of measurement and of calculation; we ask what distinguishes measurable properties from those which are not measurable and exactly how or why measurement leads to the introduction of mathematical calculation.

In Part I we again proceed in the same direction. Measurement and calculation are possible because certain laws and theories are true. Before we can understand measurement we must understand how laws and theories are established and precisely what they assert.

I do not mean that in this introduction no questions are raised which will not turn out to be of importance later in connection with definitely scientific propositions. There are many digressions which do not lead to the main goal of the inquiry; and it must be admitted that there is a danger that these side tracks may sometimes obscure the straight road. But I have endeavoured consistently to refrain from the discussion of any matters which do not arise directly from some strictly scientific question. Some of the discussions may have an interest apart from their bearing on the problems of modern physics, but that interest, I would repeat, is incidental. This volume is introductory and nothing more; it will have little value apart from its successors. Why it is issued without them is explained in the preface.

In describing the purpose of this introductory volume the three parts have been mentioned in reverse order. It may well be urged that this reverse order is logical and that it should have been adopted in writing. If our object is only to examine actual physical propositions, it would appear better to start with those propositions and to answer any questions about their derivation or foundation as they appear. Further by that process a grave danger might be avoided. Our introduction, if it comes first, must consist of the statement of general principles; only a few examples of their application can be given, and the choice of them will be determined by their simplicity or their aptness in illustration rather than for their intrinsic importance. There can be no guarantee that these principles are really those involved in much more important but much more complicated examples. There is clearly a grave risk that we shall be led into the error of laying down general rules about science without a sufficiently wide basis. This is an objection to our procedure which is not to be lightly brushed aside. Many awful examples could be quoted as a warning of the danger of laying down *a priori* doctrines about the nature of science and then considering how far science can be twisted into agreement with those doctrines. But forewarned is forearmed, and there is no alternative but to face this danger. For no criticism can proceed except on some predetermined principles; the critic must have some foreknowledge of the qualities he expects to find in the thing criticised. Even if these principles are not stated beforehand, they must necessarily be present in the critic's mind; and if they are erroneous, they are likely to be less harmful if attention is drawn to them. Before he discusses any particular

---

by researches which are distinctly physical. It is noteworthy that the portion of chemistry which involves accurate measurement and mathematical calculation, so closely associated with measurement, is called "physical chemistry."

example, the critic should consider in his own mind whether the principles he is about to apply are applicable also to other examples over as wide a range as possible; but, even if it were possible, it is not certain that he ought to bring all these examples to the reader's notice before he considers any one of them. I venture to claim that I have not neglected my duty in this matter. Every question which will be raised in this volume has been suggested by what appears to be a direct train of thought, starting from some definitely scientific problem which has occurred in thinking or writing about a considerable range of scientific topics. During the period between the inception of the work and its publication I have been led by ordinary scientific work to consider with some care many branches of the science far apart. Wherever a new branch has been considered, it has always been viewed in the light of the principles on which this treatise is based. It has usually happened that the examination has led to some revision of views previously expressed, and many portions of the book (especially in the second part) have had to be rewritten several times; but the main ideas have remained unaltered.

Relation to previous work. This then is the intention of the book. It may very well seem that there has been much ado about nothing and that the intention is far from being novel. Criticism is not new in physics. Mach's classical work on Mechanics is just such criticism as has been described; much of Thomson and Tait's *Natural Philosophy* and of the physical writings of Helmholtz is critical in this sense. Volumes and essays on the principles of science and on their application to particular problems are, or ought to be, on the bookshelf of every physicist; he cannot afford to neglect Poincaré any more than Landolt and Börnstein. Where such reapers have passed, what room is there for gleaners?

Of course I should be proud if my work were classed with theirs; but I think there is a difference of degree which almost amounts to a difference in kind. All the writings which have just been mentioned are more or less fragmentary; they consider either one particular scientific problem and do not consider how far the principles applied in its solution are applicable elsewhere; or they consider one particular principle and do not trace its application to more than a few isolated examples. Mach's *Mechanics* taken in conjunction with his lectures on Heat provides a more complete criticism of physics than the works of any other writer; but there is a large range, especially in the later developments of the subject, to which he makes no reference. If therefore this book were nothing but a compilation of the views of others with a slight extension of them to problems which have arisen since their day, it would probably have a value different from, but not necessarily greater than, that of the writings from which it would be compiled; it would represent a treatise as compared with original monographs. I have not attempted to give the book this value; the views of others are expressed indirectly through their influence on my own rather than directly; but I think the book has a special character through aiming at the completeness of a treatise rather than the detail of a monograph.

However that is not to my mind the chief difference. It is remarkable, though readily explicable, that all the writings that have been mentioned and most of those on similar lines are the work of those who were primarily mathematicians and not experimenters. They were either, like Kelvin or Helmholtz, members of the old school of physicists who always approached that science through the avenue of mathematics, or, like Mach and Poincaré, mathematicians by profession. Now of course mathematics is essential to physics, but nevertheless it is not physics; it is for the physicist a tool, a means to an end and not an end in itself. Nobody can hope to advance physical knowledge greatly unless he has at his disposal, either in himself or in another, some portion of the skill of the mathematician; but neither can he hope to advance it to-day unless he has also at his disposal the skill of the glass-blower[1]. It is hardly possible for a physicist to be wholly ignorant of mathematics—it is only if he is a Faraday that he can achieve that feat; but it is quite possible for a mathematician to be wholly ignorant of physics, especially in its more modern developments. The importance of experimental relatively to mathematical physics has increased very greatly, and on this account alone it is desirable that a criticism of the science should be undertaken by somebody whose knowledge and interests lie on that side; he is sure to see problems which the mathematician has overlooked.

But that is not all. It will be urged very strongly in what follows that, though a great part of science is independent of personality and derives its value from the fact that all men can agree about it, there is another part, not less important, which is valuable because it is personal. The very significance of this part depends upon personal intellectual tastes, upon things which are valuable just because men differ in them. Now the intellectual tastes of a mathematician necessarily differ from those of the experimental physicist; to the latter the mere handling of apparatus and the exercise of ingenuity in the overcoming of mechanical difficulties is a source of intense pleasure; to the former they are to be avoided. It is doubtless ridiculous to maintain that the practice of the experimental art confers in some mysterious fashion a power of appreciating science which is not to be attained by any other means; but it is not ridiculous to maintain that the enjoyment of that art indicates mental qualities different from those which make it seem simply laborious. And as the physicist possesses intellectual interests which the mathematician lacks, so the reverse is also true. The difference between them, quite unimportant in the normal course of scientific investigation, is vital when we come to inquire into fundamentals; for in such an inquiry a stage must ultimately be reached at which we have to accept without argument propositions as ultimate. What propositions we shall be prepared so to accept must depend in some measure on our intellectual tastes. In

---

[1] I hope I need hardly explain that I do not mean to place mathematics and glass-blowing on the same level. The difference is, of course, that the former, but not the latter, has an intrinsic value as an end as well as a value as a means. Nor do I mean by "either in himself or in another" that it is possible to hand over mathematical work to an assistant as completely as the making of apparatus. But it will generally be admitted that a man will be a better experimentalist if he can do his own instrument-making, even if he does not actually do it.

order to indicate how a difference may arise between physicists and mathematicians, it may be suggested that it will come from a different estimate of the relative importance and ultimate value of two processes of thought, Deduction and Induction. "Induction", says the mathematician[1], "appears to me either disguised deduction or a mere method of making plausible guesses." A physicist would be more likely to interchange the two terms in that statement.

Science and metaphysics. But the very fact is significant that those interested in experimental science have left to mathematicians the more fundamental inquiries into their study. Does it mean that criticism of science is impossible or even that it is undesirable? The possibility can only be decided by an attempt; it will be discussed better at the end of the treatise than at the beginning. But the desirability may be called in question here. There is no good in refusing to recognise that many physicists are not merely uninterested in fundamental criticism, but are positively hostile to it. If an attempt is made to introduce into any physical discussion considerations more general or more fundamental than would be appropriate to an ordinary text-book, it is apt to be met with some sneer about "philosophical" or "metaphysical" arguments, and with a suggestion that such matters are unworthy of the attention of a serious man of science.

These terms are not likely to be used unless controversy has become heated. In our calmer moments we do not follow the practice of politicians who dismiss, by the attachment of a label, views which they find it inconvenient either to accept or refute. It is only rude and senselessly rude to call a man by a name which he does not accept. Nevertheless the feelings which inspire such outbursts are not to be neglected lightly, and it is worth while to consider for a moment whether there is any basis for the prejudice.

It has, of course, an historical origin. Science, unlike mathematics, had for a time to struggle against philosophers for recognition as an independent and important branch of learning. The battle is won, and it is now rather the philosopher who walks warily lest he bring on his head the contempt of firmly established science. But the memory of it remains in a reluctance to discuss quite freely the subjects (largely those of the third part of this volume) which once formed part of the exclusive province of philosophy. Those who attacked science—and their example is followed by those who to-day adopt the yet more offensive method of patronising it—seldom took the trouble to understand what they attacked; a discussion of such subjects came to be associated with an attack on firmly established propositions by persons with a complete and impenetrable ignorance of everything scientific.

But "fas est et ab hoste doceri" does not mean that it is always wise to adopt the errors of a defeated foe. Because philosophers have talked nonsense (as it seems to us) about "space" and "time," there is no reason why we should follow their example; because they would not take the trouble to find out what we mean, there is no reason why we should not find out what they mean, or even what we mean ourselves. It cannot be denied

[1] Mr Bertrand Russell, *The principles of mathematics*, Ch. II.

that science does state and use important propositions about space, time and motion; we say that space is three-dimensional, time one-dimensional and that motion can be compounded according to the parallelogram law[1]. And if we make such statements and believe them, it is allowable to ask exactly what we mean when we state them and on what grounds we believe them. They are not so simple as to be incapable of analysis, and if the evidence on which we base them has anything to do with experiment or observation we ought to be able to give some idea of what that evidence is. I have already explained that in applying criticism to them I do not mean to dispute, but rather to confirm, their value; it is possible that we shall discover limits to their truth, but that will only make their truth within those limits more certain. And if anybody thinks that, if they are not to be disputed, nobody who is not either stupid or ignorant could imagine that there is anything interesting or relevant to say about them—well, he might at least read what I have to say before coming to that conclusion.

And what applies to the discussions of time, space, and motion applies equally to other parts of the book. If anyone chooses to call them metaphysical, there is nothing to prevent him; but he must not fall into the egregious error of supposing that thereby he renders them unworthy of consideration; the question remains whether metaphysics, in his sense, is relevant to science. If it is found that propositions and conceptions which are distinctively scientific are based on other propositions and conceptions and derive from them their truth and significance, then, even though some people choose to term them metaphysical and not scientific, it remains the fact that these other propositions are essential to science. I am sorry to have to insist on considerations so simple and elementary; but even those who do not share the prejudice against which I am contending will admit that it exists. Now whatever faults this book may possess, they do not include that of being metaphysical in any reasonable sense. For one of the chief characteristics which distinguishes science from metaphysics, and the feature which makes men of science so averse from the latter, is that in science, but not in metaphysics, it is possible to obtain universal assent for conclusions, and to present results which do not lose their value because, when they are presented, they are so obvious as to be indubitable. I maintain that the results presented in this work are of that nature. I am quite prepared to find that the vast majority of men of science find everything I have to say dull and trite and so familiar that it is not worth saying; but if that should be their

[1] It is interesting to note as an illustration of the perversity of the prejudice that though everyone would state cheerfully that space is three-dimensional, many would feel that the corresponding statement about time is already beginning to have a dangerous taint of metaphysics. Accordingly I will substitute for "time is one-dimensional" another proposition closely allied to it: If an event C happens between two events A and B, and D happens also between A and B, then D must happen either simultaneously with C, or between A and C or between C and B. It will not be denied that this proposition is important and true; and nobody would, I think, call it metaphysical. The corresponding proposition concerning space is not true. Both London and New York are between the north and south poles: but London is neither coincident with New York, nor between New York and the north pole, nor between New York and the south pole.

judgement, I shall not be wholly disappointed. It will show at least that I have avoided metaphysics successfully. I am not sure that the most handsome compliment that anyone could pay my work would be to say that he knew it all before.

But is it true that metaphysics can be avoided wholly in an attempt to probe to the foundations of science? (Now and henceforward I propose to use the word metaphysics, not as a mere term of abuse, but to denote the study which those who accept the status of metaphysician think valuable. So far as I can make out, the study consists in the investigation of reality and existence.) At some stage in our inquiry we must stop and accept judgements without argument; is it certain that these judgements will not be found to be metaphysical? Or again, are we sure that the process of reasoning by which we develop our conclusions from these fundamental judgements does not depend on the acceptance of doctrines that are distinctively metaphysical? The general opinion to-day is that science is in no way dependent on metaphysics; and the proof of independence which seems generally to be thought the most convincing is that persons holding the most diverse metaphysical views all agree in accepting the same scientific conclusion. Personally I accept the opinion, but the reason by which it is so often supported seems to me quite inadequate; that a man, even a highly educated and intelligent man, holds two opinions simultaneously, does not seem to me to prove at all that they are not inconsistent. Moreover the opinion is not perfectly general; some men of science[1] hold that science depends on the proposition, apparently metaphysical, that matter is real and exists; and many of those who are ready to assent verbally to the independence are apt to show great annoyance if any one dares to deny that proposition. Again many metaphysicians agree that science and metaphysics are independent only because they believe that science is not true in the same sense as is their own study; they grant its independence only at the sacrifice of its value. Accordingly it has seemed necessary to inquire into the matter rather more closely, and one chapter (Chapter IX) has been devoted to some discussion of it. I want to insist very strongly that this chapter differs from the rest of the book. I do not pretend that it deals with scientific matters, and I have tried to show by the whole tone of it that the universal agreement which elsewhere is the test of truth cannot be applied; I am expressing my personal opinions and nothing more. I believe that those opinions are shared by many other men of science and that even those who do not share them will be able to understand the point of view that they represent. But if anyone should differ entirely from what is said in that chapter, there is no reason whatever why he should not agree with everything that is said elsewhere. At one time I thought of making still more evident the distinction between this chapter and the rest of the book by putting it as an appendix; but though that plan has been abandoned, I still want the reader to realise its entire independence.

This is not the place to anticipate the conclusions that will be reached;

[1] E.g. E. Wiechert, *Phys. Zeit.* 12. 702. 1911.

but perhaps the confidence of some timid persons will be restored if I assure them that they are not going to be asked to accept doctrines which, even though they are formally independent of science, are abhorrent to them. I would call attention therefore to two considerations which are likely to affect our judgement of the relations between science and metaphysics.

First, it is by no means certain that when two people use the same words they mean the same thing; in particular it is not certain that when a physicist says that matter is real he is referring at all to the proposition which the metaphysician asserts by the same phrase. There is an obvious indication that they do not mean the same thing; for the metaphysician would also assert (or deny) that time is real and that space is real, but no physicist would ever think of using those phrases. It is not that he thinks time and space unreal, but he does not think that time and space, as he uses the words, are subjects to which the predicates real and unreal are applicable at all; it seems to him no more sensible to say that time is real than to say that to-morrow is rectangular.

Second, we are all metaphysicians, physicists included. We are all interested in problems which the metaphysician attempts to solve. Metaphysics, like science, has developed out of the mass of common unorganised knowledge; and just as the least scientific people hold, with an intensity varying inversely as their information, views about matters which are definitely in the province of science—about the weather, the proper way to draw up a fire, and the peculiar efficacy of red flannel—so also the least metaphysical people hold opinions about matters definitely within the province of metaphysics. And again the less attention they have given to the forming of those opinions and the less the study on which they are based, the more fiery is apt to be the faith in them and the fiercer the resentment if they are questioned. The world is not divided into those who do and those who do not hold metaphysical doctrines, but rather into those who hold them for some reason and those who hold them for none. Nothing is further from my intention than to imply that the mere study of questions is bound to lead to the right answer, or that those who have studied them most are sure to be right as against those who have studied them less. There is danger in too close study which I have no desire whatever to overlook in this connection; it is that the student will become so immersed in his study that he will forget the questions from which it originally arose, and will so simplify it that it ceases to have any content for less sophisticated people. Nevertheless when the man of science is roused to anger by some especially distressing ineptitude, he will do well to inquire whether he is protesting as a man of science or whether his momentary lapse from scientific calm does not indicate that he too is among the metaphysicians.

PART I

THE PROPOSITIONS OF SCIENCE

CHAPTER I

THE SUBJECT MATTER OF SCIENCE

Summary. Science is distinguished from mathematics and philosophy by its attitude towards judgements of the material world. It accepts such judgements as ultimate and fundamental.

However it does not accept *all* such judgements, but selects from them. How is the selection made?

The answer is, by a refinement of the criterion by which judgements of the external world are distinguished from those of the internal world. This criterion is universal assent. The subject matter of science consists of those immediate judgements for which universal assent can be obtained.

Various objections to this view are considered: (1) There are differences of opinion in science as in other studies. Agreed; but they do not concern fundamentals. (2) A single bold denier could upset all science. No; he could not maintain his denial; here science is distinguished from mathematics. (3) What of "abnormal sensations," e.g. colour blindness? Judgements of colour are not fundamental; they are eliminated by a process which is considered in some detail. (4) If this answer is accepted, are there any universally admitted judgements left? Yes; judgements of "time," "space," "number," "identity," and perhaps others.

What is the distinction between physics and other sciences? The distinction is one of method rather than of matter. Physics is the science of measurement.

Is the criterion of universal assent ultimate or only an indication of something more fundamental? It is suggested for future consideration that it is not ultimate, but that the truly ultimate is one that is scarcely capable of precise expression.

Lastly, what would happen to science if the prevailing agreement failed? Such questions are unanswerable. We are discussing science as it is, not as it might be.

Science, mathematics and philosophy. Science, mathematics and philosophy are three branches sprung from a common stem; they bear marks of their common origin, and, indeed, it is only during the past hundred years that they have been clearly distinguished. Each of them presents a more or less ordered series of propositions derived by some process of reasoning from another set of propositions expressing judgements which, for the purposes of that study, are regarded as fundamental, subject to no doubt and capable of no proof. The propositions which represent the result of the study depend, of course, on the fundamental judgements on which they are based and on the process of reasoning by which they are derived; in respect of both of these characteristics the three studies differ widely. The difference in respect of the fundamental judgements, the subject matter of the study, is more clearly recognised than the difference in respect of the process of reasoning; by stating very briefly that difference we shall distinguish at once science from other studies with which it has sometimes been confused and open in the most suitable manner our discussion of its peculiar characteristics.

The recognition of the distinction between science and other branches of learning is based, historically and logically, on the recognition of the part played in it by judgements of the material world. In mathematics such judgements play no part at all; in philosophy they are regarded as of neither more nor less importance than other judgements which are regarded as immediate and fundamental; in science they are the only source of knowledge and no proposition is to be regarded as valid which is not directly based upon them. When it was accepted that science was nothing more and nothing less than the study of the material world, science was freed from the connection with transcendental philosophy which had hitherto hampered its development; and when it was accepted that mathematics was quite independent of that study the way was opened to that advance in certainty and lucidity which, in the last fifty years, has converted it almost into a new branch of learning.

Science and the material world. However, this acceptance of the definition of science as the study of the material world may appear surprising to those familiar with recent writings on the principles of science; it may seem to indicate a crudity of view which has long been antiquated. The tendency in more recent times has been to avoid any reference to "matter" or "the material world," and to define the judgements which form the basis of science as those which are derived from "sensations" or from "routines of sensation" or some similar phrase with a psychological flavour. I have preferred the older phrase, not because I believe it is adequate, but because I believe that it is not less adequate than the later and because I desire to enter a protest against the attitude which led to its abandonment.

The abandonment of the term "matter" in the definition of the judgements which form the basis of science was due in the first instance to attacks on it made by idealist philosophers. They urged that their studies had led them to the conclusion that "matter" did not "exist," or, at least, that, if it existed, its nature was wholly different from that which seemed to be indicated by scientific studies. Some of them adopted a definitely hostile attitude to science, attempting to depreciate its conclusions, and asserting that, while science might serve some useful object in describing the sequence of phenomena, it was presumptuously trespassing beyond its province in propounding any ultimate interpretation of them. Now, even if we agreed that such assertions are true, they provide no reason for abandoning the older definition of the province of science. When we say that science is the study of matter, we are not committing ourselves to any statement concerning the result to which those studies will lead; we are only saying that the judgements which science investigates are those which have led, rightly or wrongly, to a belief in the existence of matter or to the attribution to it of certain properties. Nobody doubts the fact of certain judgements; difference of opinion concerns only the interpretation of them; and it is only the fact that we assert when we say that they are to form the basis of our study.

But no student of science does really admit that such assertions are true; none will admit that his study is in any way subordinate to philosophy, or that, if the conclusions of science and philosophy conflict, it is science rather than philosophy which has to give way. To admit in the determination of our attitude towards science arguments which are confessedly based on considerations foreign to science is not only to be guilty of intellectual cowardice but also to prejudice from the outset the inquiry in which we are about to engage. Our business at present is to decide what science is, and nothing is more likely to lead us into error than preconceived notions, derived from studies other than science, of what science ought to be. Moreover we are for the moment concerned only with the question, what are the judgements which science regards as fundamental? To analyse those judgements would lead us at once beyond the province of science; we require merely to identify them. For the purposes of identification a description which has no pretensions to logical accuracy may often be the most useful. If I ask where a certain house is I shall probably prefer to be told that it is nearly opposite the house of the man with the red whiskers than to be given its precise co-ordinates on the 25-inch survey map. In just the same way, most of my readers will probably gain a much clearer idea of what class of judgements is intended if they are described as judgements of the material world than they would if they were described by means of the much less familiar conceptions of sensations or sense-perceptions.

Selection of material judgements. However, while I maintain that to state that science is the study of the material world is to give a perfectly definite description of its subject matter and one which leaves as little ambiguity as any other, I do not think that the description is quite accurate. It errs in being both too inclusive and too exclusive. Not all judgements concerning the material world are the proper subject matter of science, and it is possible that there are judgements which are not strictly concerning the material world and yet are proper subject matter. This last error is the less important, but deserves passing notice. If only judgements of the material world are the proper subject matter of science, it is doubtful whether experimental psychology can claim to be a science, and yet that claim would probably be admitted; for instance, propositions stating the effect on the minimum sound which is audible of the simultaneous perception of strong sensations of other kinds seem to be properly regarded as scientific laws, but the judgements on which they are based concern events in the consciousness of the percipient which can hardly be regarded as part of the material world. And here we may note another objection to a definition of science as the study of routines of sensation or any similar phrase; if such a definition were accepted, it would become rather difficult to avoid the conclusion, erring in the opposite extreme, that psychology, rather than physics, is to be regarded as the *scientia scientiarum*, the fundamental science on the results of which all others build their structure.

But for the present it is more important to consider the first objection which was raised, namely that all judgements of the material world are not the proper subject matter of science. The student of science, like every other human being, occupies practically the whole of his conscious life in making judgements of the material world; he makes them from the moment he hunts for his slippers as he gets out of bed to the moment when he switches off the electric light as he returns to it; but he does not regard these operations as forming part of his scientific researches. It is only when he is in his laboratory and consciously arranging his environment for that specific purpose that the judgements of the material world which he makes become of any value for the increase of scientific knowledge. The recognition of this obvious and familiar fact does not involve any denial of the applicability of scientific knowledge to the affairs of daily life; it is not inconsistent with the belief, more often expressed in the age of youthful enthusiasm of the last century when science first began to make rapid strides, that the time may come when all our experiences, important or trivial, will be seen to be mere examples of universal scientific laws. Such laws, when they are discovered, are always found to have a range far greater than that of the evidence on which they were based; they are usually found to explain phenomena which had never been recorded until the possibility of explanation called attention to them. But before these experiences can thus be brought within the range of science, science must have completed her task and the laws must have been formulated; the extension of science to affairs outside the laboratory is the last and not the first stage in the development; such affairs do not provide the primary and fundamental judgements on which science is based, but only a final and unessential illustration that the structure is finished.

But perhaps it will be objected that the distinction made in the last paragraph, between the experiences of our daily life which do not provide subject matter for science and the experiences of the laboratory which do, is too rigid and indicates no important difference. It will not be denied, of course, that the distinction is actually made in the practice of modern physics, but it may be urged that it is much less notable in sciences in an earlier stage of development; it is less obvious in the observational sciences, and, even as regards physics,—what should we have lost if Newton had not sat in his orchard and Archimedes gone to his bath! After all, the finitude of our powers makes it necessary that we should impose some limitations on the range of phenomena which we submit to detailed consideration; we select from our experience the simpler elements and those which seem to offer the best opportunities for analysis.

Such is the account which is often offered of the reasons which govern the choice of the subject matter of our scientific investigations. I believe that it is inadequate, and that, if we do not push further our inquiry into the characteristics which mark the judgements which can properly become the basis of scientific conclusions, we shall overlook a feature which determines directly the whole process of scientific reasoning and gives to its results their peculiar value. It is not chance or caprice which has led us to the actual choice of our subject matter; it is not even a desire for "simplicity"; experiences which for their attainment need the erection of vast buildings, the accumulation of the most costly apparatus and materials in comparison with which gold is worthless dirt do not form part of any ordinary conception of the simple life. There is a very definite criterion, instinctively recognised by everyone who appreciates the spirit of science, which demands open expression.

Evidence for an external world. What this criterion is will be easily seen if we ask ourselves why the particular class of immediate judgements, of which those that are the basis of science form part, are described as judgements of the material or of the external world. (For our present purpose we may regard "material" and "external" as identical, for our knowledge of any external objects which are not material is based on our knowledge of those which are material.) We all realise instinctively that the judgements which compose our conscious life can be divided into two classes, those which represent events happening within ourselves and those which represent events in the external world. The first class includes our judgements concerning our tastes and our desires and our purely logical judgements; the second class the judgements we associate with sense-perceptions. The distinction between these two classes arises from a difference in the extent to which the judgements are common to persons other than ourselves. In respect of the first class of judgements we find that other persons often dissent entirely from us; in respect of the second class we find there is something common between ourselves and any other person with whom we can enter into communication. It is the community of our judgements of the second class with those of others that leads us to attribute them to some agency which is neither we nor they, but something external to all; it is the divergence of our judgements of the first class from those of others which leads us to attribute them to something inherent in our own personality.

An example will perhaps help to make my meaning clearer. Dr Johnson thought he could confute Berkeley and prove the existence of matter by kicking the table. No doubt he was utterly wrong and only made his mistake because he quite misunderstood what the bishop had intended to assert; but he was at least right in this, that the judgements which he could not refrain from making when his foot hit the table are among the judgements which have led plain men of all times to believe in the existence of matter. That belief is connected with the judgements of sensation that he made then much more intimately than it is connected with the intellectual judgements that he made when he decided that he could confute his opponent by kicking the table, or with the voluntary judgement that he made when he decided that he would kick it. We shall see what that difference of connection is if we consider the part that might have been played in the incident by some other person, say the worthy Boswell. If Boswell had ventured to express his judgement that kicking the table was quite irrelevant to the discussion and that, however often it was kicked, Berkeley's argument would remain unanswered; or if, agreeing that refutation by kicking was possible, he had decided that it was undignified and had decided not to kick; in either case, we may be perfectly sure that Johnson's judgement in the matter would have been perfectly unaffected; he would not have cared in the least whether Boswell agreed with him or no. But now suppose that Boswell had concurred in his master's intellectual and voluntary judgements, had kicked, had found that his foot went through the table and that he experienced no sensation of impact; then it is certain that Johnson's belief in the existence of matter would have received, for the moment at least, a grave shock. It was essential to that belief, not only that he should experience a certain sensation when he kicked the table, but also that everyone else, even Boswell, for whose attainments he had so well-founded a disdain, should experience the sensation; the community of the sensation was the very foundation of his belief.

There is another difference between the two classes of judgements which confirms their classification as external and internal; it is a difference in the degree to which they are subject to the control of our wills. Dr Johnson could, of course, refrain from kicking the table if he desired, but, if he decided to kick and began to make the complex series of judgements of sensation involved in the act of kicking, no effort of his will could prevent him from completing that series and experiencing the impact of his foot on the wood. The elements of this series of judgements are connected by a bond of necessity, independent of and unalterable by volition, which is not found to connect a series of judgements of the intellect involved in a train of reasoning. I can easily contemplate the facts that men are mortal and that Caesar is a man without proceeding to conclude anything about the mortality of Caesar. Now volition is intimately connected with the personality which we distinguish from the external world; that "I" should be subject to "my" will seems involved in the very meaning of those words; one of our chief reasons for attributing externality to our judgements of sensation is their greater independence of volition.

The criterion of scientific judgements. Universal assent. This very superficial discussion of a very abtruse matter is not, of course, intended to prove anything; it is only intended to recall to the mind certain ideas which are closely connected with the customary division of the world into external and internal, into matter and personality. The reason for recalling them is that the criteria which are used in distinguishing the subject matter of science from the remainder of our experience are simply a development of the criteria used in distinguishing matter from personality. The latter depend in some manner, very complex and very difficult to state precisely, on differences in the degree to which judgements are shared by all sentient personalities and on differences in the extent to which they are subject to volition. The former are free from these difficulties and complexities because they take account of these differences only in their extreme form. Judgements do not form part of the proper subject matter of science until they are free from the smallest taint of personality, unless they are wholly independent of volition and unless universal assent can be obtained for them. In practice the last criterion is applied almost exclusively; the subject matter of science may be defined as those immediate judgements concerning which universal agreement can be obtained.

This conclusion may seem so familiar that it was hardly worth while to have engaged in such a long discussion to arrive at it. That science is something strictly impersonal is recognised universally. The term "scientific," when applied as a qualifying adjective to matters which do not lie wholly within the realm of science, often denotes independence of personality. "Scientific" history is history freed (it is supposed) from all personal prejudices, written so that it cannot be told whether the author is French or German, Catholic or Protestant. The "scientific management" of factories is strenuously opposed on the ground that it allows no scope for the exercise of personality. Again everyone admits that "scientific" knowledge is in some way peculiarly positive and free from differences of opinion; that there is an agreement about scientific propositions which cannot be obtained for those of any other branch of learning except mathematics—and in this connection mathematics is hardly distinguished from science.

But these facts, so trite as to be unworthy of formal statement, are not at all what I am concerned here to assert. They all refer to the results of scientific investigations, the propositions which result from the long process of experiment and reasoning; what we are concerned with here is the foundations of scientific investigations, the propositions from which that long process starts. Moreover I am not at all disposed to admit that these familiar facts are facts, or that the statements that have just been quoted are true in the absolutely unqualified sense on which it is important to insist in connection with the proposed definition of the subject matter of science. It is true, of course, that there is a consensus of opinion about scientific matters which there is not, for instance, about artistic or religious matters; but there is by no means universal agreement. In the first place, a scientific proposition cannot receive assent until it is understood, and the number of persons who have received the education necessary for comprehension is not large; it is not even as great as that of the persons who think they have received it. The consensus, if it exists, is only a consensus of experts. And it does not exist. Doctors differ, whatever their faculty; and most of us have attended meetings of grave professors of science at which feeling ran as high as at any Church Congress. The general and uninstructed opinion seems to be that science, starting from the unorganised mass of conflicting judgements which represents the results of our individual experience reaches by some wonderful process of reasoning results free from all element of doubt, free from all personal difference, unchanging and universal. The view that I wish to assert is the precise opposite. It is that science starts by selecting for its consideration those judgements alone concerning which absolutely universal agreement can be obtained, rejecting unhesitatingly any concerning which there can be any doubt or any personal opinion; that at every stage of the reasoning to which it submits these judgements a personal element is introduced and with it the possibility of error and of difference of opinion; and that its final results, those which represent its greatest achievements and possess the greatest intellectual value, are almost as individual and as personal as the greatest achievements of art.

Is universal assent obtainable? Let us then examine the definition rather more closely. The subject matter of science consists of those judgements for which universal assent can be obtained. By universal assent is meant the assent of all intelligences whose opinion on the matter can be ascertained at all. An obvious objection apparently arises at once. If the assent must be absolutely universal, the whole fabric of science could be overthrown by a single bold denier who took on himself, for the sake of notoriety or any other equally unworthy motive, to dispute what all others accept.

The answer to the objection will appear if we inquire how we ascertain the judgement of any other person. Normally, of course, we ask them in words and judge their opinion from the words which they utter in reply. But we may sometimes doubt their truthfulness, doubt whether their reply "really" represents their judgement. What do we mean by "really represents"? We must look a little deeper.

The principle underlying our decisions as to what other people are thinking is analogy with our own conduct. We know that certain judgements in our own minds are associated with certain movements of our own bodies, that is of those portions of the "external world" which are in a peculiar manner directly under the control of our wills. We see also that other people's bodies, that is portions of the external world essentially similar in appearance but not under the control of our will, behave in a manner closely resembling that in which our body behaves when we make a certain judgement. Accordingly we infer that other people's bodies are under the control of other people's wills and that the minds of which those wills are parts are making judgements of the same nature. And this inference leads to generally consistent results; judging the working of other people's minds by means of it, we find that their minds work in much the same way as our own. That is the foundation of our method of knowing what other people think and, indeed, our reason for believing at all that there are other people.

Now among the actions or bodily movements which thus reveal mental judgements, speech is usually the most important; but it is by no means the only revealing action. Speech fails us with the deaf or with foreigners, and we have recourse to gesticulation. Moreover we know that we sometimes use words to conceal our thoughts and are not without suspicions that others may do the same. Accordingly when a man's judgements, as revealed by his speech, are such as to be generally discordant with what we had expected from our previous experience, the possibility occurs to us that it is not his judgement, but only the relation between his judgement and his speech which is abnormal; we turn our attention to his actions other than his speech and try to use them to deduce his judgements. In many cases we find that his judgements as revealed by his other actions are quite different from those revealed by his speech; that the former and not the latter are in accordance with what we had expected; and accordingly we conclude that the man is lying or, perhaps, honestly mistaken. In fact, if any question arises, we usually regard speech as the least and not the most reliable indication of a man's judgements; because we know from our own experience that it is much easier to speak in a manner which does not correspond to our judgements than to maintain the deception, intentional or unintentional, in other forms of action. It is easier to assure our hostess that our tea is exactly as we like it than to swallow without a grimace the cup into which she has put salt in mistake for sugar.

It is by such means that the impostors have been detected who from time to time have claimed that they possessed special senses lacked by the rest of mankind. And the process of detection deserves the brief attention that has been given to it because it illustrates so well the foundation for the belief that the judgements for which universal assent can be obtained are those which concern the external world. It is because he is brought into contact with an external world over which he has no control that in such cases the impostor is unable to maintain by his actions the deception which he attempts to maintain in his speech. Moreover the fact that, when judgements of the external world are concerned, we can ascertain the real opinion of any person by examining his actions rather than his speech suggests two other remarks of some interest.

First, by this method we are enabled to ascertain the judgements of beings who cannot speak, infants and animals; and I think we must and can push the application of the criterion so far as to maintain that judgements of the external world are not the proper subject matter of science unless not only adult and reasonable men but also infants and animals agree in them, so far as their opinion is ascertainable. Secondly, we can exclude from the subject matter of science judgements which clearly ought to be excluded, but yet are such that universal agreement concerning them appears to be obtainable. The chief judgements of this nature are the conclusions of pure logic and pure mathematics[1]. It is improbable that anyone will seriously deny the Law of the Excluded Middle or the proposition that two and two make four, but if he did out of sheer perversity, I do not see what means there would be of convincing the rest of the world that he was

---

[1] It is not asserted, of course, that these conclusions are not accepted by science or that their acceptance is not essential to the process of reasoning by which science develops its conclusions from its fundamental judgements. It is only asserted that these conclusions are not themselves fundamental judgements.

perverse. (Of course I am referring to the pure logical and arithmetical propositions. We shall see later that there is a sense in which the statement that "two stones and two stones make four stones" is a judgement of the external world; an impostor who denied this proposition could be detected.) For his judgement, not concerning the external world at all, would not necessarily affect his actions; his speech is the only means we have of ascertaining his thoughts. Accordingly the universal acceptance of the propositions of pure logic and mathematics, though they may never be actually denied, is rather more precarious than that of the fundamental scientific judgements, and the criterion which we are proposing to apply will exclude them without further discussion.

Apart from imposture, honest self-delusion may sometimes give rise to conflicts of judgement. In such cases the self-deluded person has become convinced that a phenomenon B is invariably associated with another A; accordingly whenever he knows that A has occurred he will assert that he has also observed B, even when other observers are quite unable to observe B at all. It is almost always possible to convince the person of error and thus to bring his judgements into accordance with those of others by showing him that his assertion of B is associated, not with the occurrence of A, but only with his belief in the occurrence of A. When the conditions are such that he thinks that A has occurred, although he has not observed it directly and, as we know, it has not occurred, we ask him whether he observes B; if he says that he observes B, we draw his attention to the fact that A has not occurred. He then realises that he has been deluded and the delusion is removed. The process deserves this brief notice, because it illustrates once more the connection between universal agreement and the attribution of judgements to the external, rather than to the internal, world. In most cases, we decide that a judgement is "external" because there is universal agreement about it; here the recognition that a judgement is internal rather than external explains the failure to obtain universal agreement, and so removes the discrepancy.

Is universal agreement possible? Abnormal sensations. A far more serious source of disagreement and one which seems at first sight more difficult to explain away is to be found in the existence of persons whose sensations are, temporarily or permanently, abnormal. Thus, if I gaze steadily for some time at a red patch on a white ground and then turn my eyes to a uniformly white surface, I see on it a green patch of the same shape as the red patch at which I had been looking previously. Other persons, who have not looked at the red patch, fail to see the green patch; my judgement in a matter of pure sensation, which seems to bear all the marks of a judgement of the external world, is not shared by others. The tests for imposture and self-delusion fail; there is no doubt that I really do observe what I say that I observe. An even more striking example is, of course, provided by persons whose colour sensations are permanently abnormal, colour-blind persons as they are usually called. Here we cannot even trace any connection between the abnormal sensations and the previous experience of the person affected; his sensations of colour always differ from those of the majority, and, even when his whole material prosperity depends on his ability to agree with the rest of mankind in his colour judgements, the disagreement still persists. Similar abnormalities occur in connection with judgements of sensations other than colour; some persons, for example, are almost tone-deaf and unable to distinguish notes of different pitch. And if, as has been suggested, we push our demand for universal agreement so far as to demand the agreement of animals before we admit judgements as proper for the subject matter of science, we should probably find that abnormality was the rule and normality the exception, if by normal judgements we mean those made by the majority of adult human beings.

Accordingly if we are to maintain our criterion that universal agreement about any judgement must be obtained before it can be admitted as part of the subject matter of science, we must simply exclude from that subject matter all these judgements concerning which an irresoluble difference exists. These judgements include all those connected with colour, pitch, taste, smell; consequently there can be no science of colour and no science of musical tone. Can such a conclusion be seriously pressed?

If we confine our attention to the science of physics, which is alone our true concern in this volume, there is no difficulty in accepting that conclusion. Colour and pitch are not in any way fundamental in physics; it would be perfectly possible to leave out of our treatises any mention of them and out of our experiments any use of them, and yet to leave the science of physics essentially unchanged. So far as I can see, persons totally blind and totally deaf from birth could appreciate as well as anyone else the significance of all the propositions of physics and could be as good a judge as anyone else of their value.

It is true, of course, that we habitually use our senses of colour and pitch in our experimental work and that we may say that the spectrum of sodium is characterised by a brilliant doublet in the yellow; but if the value of any of our experimental work were challenged or if we were asked to explain further the meaning of our statement, we should find no difficulty whatever in abandoning altogether our experimental methods and our form of statement; and in so doing we should feel that we were adding to the trustworthiness of the work and the lucidity of the statement. We recognise that there is no distinction which is of the least importance for physics—whatever its importance for other sciences or studies may be—between those portions of the spectrum which are just within and just without the visible range or between those tones which are and those which are not audible.

Nor is there any obscurity about the manner in which we thus make ourselves independent of direct judgements of colour and pitch. Our only reason for taking any interest in any observations is our desire to discover laws. If in abandoning judgements of colour as proper subject matter we were forced also to abandon laws which could only be stated in terms of such judgements, then indeed we should feel that, if colour was not a proper subject for scientific judgement, it ought to be, and that in excluding it we were depriving our science of a real part of its value. If on the other hand we can substitute for laws involving colour judgements other laws which cover the same range of phenomena and seem precisely equivalent to them, then there is no loss in abandoning them. But in all the cases we are considering we can find such equivalent laws. At this stage in our inquiry we cannot say precisely what we mean by "equivalent" laws, but the general nature of the procedure adopted is quite simple. It has been found, say, that a phenomenon A is always associated with a colour judgement B made by most people, though there are some who dissent from that judgement. We now discover that, among the normal majority, the colour judgement B is always associated with some other judgement C; and further that everyone, including the abnormal minority, agree in the judgement that C is always associated with A. Then for normal persons the law that A is always associated with C is equivalent to the law that A is associated with B; whenever an instance of one law is found, a slight alteration of the conditions of observation will enable an instance of the other to be found. For the abnormal persons the two laws are not equivalent, but for them the substitution of the new law for the old is no loss, but an unbalanced gain, for the law that A is associated with B was one which they could not appreciate at all.

Moreover it usually turns out that the new law, about which everyone agrees, is a more than adequate substitute for the old; it brings to light new relations which were not suspected so long as attention was directed to the old. Thus, when we find (say) that the appearance of yellow to all normal persons is associated with a particular refrangibility of the light received and that agreement can be obtained about refrangibility when it is not obtainable about yellowness, we substitute for the law that the sodium flame is yellow the law that the sodium flame emits light of a particular refrangibility[1]; this law is not less satisfactory to normal people than the old, for it covers exactly the same ground. It is more satisfactory to the abnormal, for it gives them a means which they did not previously possess for distinguishing between the sodium and the calcium flame. But further inquiry shows that it is more satisfactory also to the normal people, for the test of refrangibility enables them also to distinguish lights of which the colour appears the same; it shows that coloured light is often complex and so on; and it enables a host of new laws to be discovered which would never have been suspected had we been content to rely wholly on colour sensations. Other examples of this procedure, such as that whereby we substitute frequency of vibration for pitch, are so obvious that they need not be enumerated.

When such a law about which universal agreement can be obtained has

---

[1] Of course now-a-days we talk about wave-length or frequency rather than refrangibility; but the principles involved in this further transformation of the law are too important to be discussed at this stage.

been substituted for one about which judgements differ, decisions what is normal sensation and what is abnormal are revised. The substituted law is regarded as fundamental and sensations are regarded as normal or abnormal according as they agree with this law; a person is regarded as the more "normal" according as the relations which are exhibited by his judgements coincide with those asserted by the substituted law. It is usually found that normality is a matter of degree. Thus the persons who can detect directly differences of pitch of less than half a semitone are certainly a minority of mankind; but they are regarded as more normal than the rest of mankind, who are classed as more or less tone-deaf, because the differences which they can detect are actually found to correspond accurately to differences in frequency of vibration. An even more striking example is provided by Cavendish, who could measure accurately quantities of electricity by the sensation which he experienced when a condenser was discharged through his body. Most people would be quite unable to appreciate the differences which he could detect with such certainty, but we know now that it is the judgements of Cavendish rather than those of the rest of mankind which accord with the differences shown by a ballistic galvanometer. Since we now measure quantities of electricity by that instrument rather than by direct sensation, we judge that in this matter the sensations of Cavendish were much more normal, much more true, than those of the rest of us.

It seems then permissible to conclude that judgements concerning such matters as colour or pitch, which show differences of opinion, are not regarded as fundamental by the science of physics and form no part of its ultimate subject matter. When students of that science make such a statement as: The spectrum of sodium is characterised by a brilliant yellow doublet, it is to be regarded merely as an abbreviation for a statement that the wave-length of this doublet lies within a certain range, that range, namely, which in normal persons corresponds to yellow light. If the significance or the truth of the statement is challenged we are always perfectly ready to abandon it, to omit all mention of colour sensations and to refer only to refrangibility or wave-length.

But perhaps it may be argued that this conclusion does not really remove the difficulty, because, before the substitution of refrangibility for colour can be made, the science of colour must have been developed in the manner that has been indicated and a relation between colour and refrangibility established. This science is therefore more fundamental than physics, and it is illegitimate to argue that a judgement is not fundamental to physics merely because we choose to relegate it to a science which may be designated by a different name but still is absolutely necessary to the development of physics.

This contention is perfectly valid, but one essential matter has been overlooked. The science of colour may be more fundamental than physics but it does not take as fundamental or, indeed, employ in any way the judgement concerning which there is the difference of opinion. When we are investigating the relation between colour and refrangibility we are not forced to choose between the two conflicting judgements; we admit both equally. What interests us is the fact that the normal person makes one kind of judgement and that the abnormal person makes another; concerning this fact there is no disagreement. Everyone agrees that the diverse judgements are made; the difference of opinion that exists until the science of colour is developed concerns the choice which of the two judgements is to be accepted. On this question the science of colour expresses no opinion at all; it merely shows that the judgements of normal persons bear a relation to refrangibility which is not borne by the judgements of abnormal people. The choice between the two judgements is first made by the physicist; he makes the choice by rejecting both and substituting for them observations on refrangibility. The fact that these observations happen to agree with those of normal persons may be useful to him in some of his investigations, but it does not form in any way an essential part of his science.

In the same way any difficulty can be removed that might affect such sciences as anatomy, physiology or psychology which desire to develop the science of colour beyond the point where the interest of the physicist ceases. The anatomist or physiologist may desire to establish a relation between the difference of normal from abnormal sensations and differences in the structure or function of sense-organs; the psychologist may desire to establish a relation between sensations which are temporarily abnormal and the previous sensations or other mental experiences of the percipient. But again all these persons are not in the least concerned to decide whether the abnormal or the normal judgements are "true"; all that they are concerned with is the fact that normal and abnormal judgements occur, and concerning this fact there is no difference of opinion. If in any part of the investigation of this or other sciences a decision has to be made between the divergent judgements (for instance, when the physiologist is concerned with differences in the colour of blood), they refer to physics for the decision. They either abandon the colour-judgement in favour of an observation of refrangibility, or they accept the conclusion, indicated but not asserted by the conclusions of physics, that the observations of normal persons are in some way more true than those of abnormal persons, and take care that the observations on which they rely are those of normal observers.

In this discussion all the examples have been taken from judgements of colour and pitch; if we had referred to judgements of taste or smell the position would have appeared less clear. For we have not at present any science of taste or smell; we have not been able to correlate such judgements with the "physical properties" of the objects concerning which there is no difference of opinion. Now I cannot think of any proposition which can reasonably be regarded as part of physics in which such judgements play any part at all; but they undoubtedly do play a part in the science of chemistry. Watts' *Dictionary* is full of statements concerning the taste and smell of various compounds, and these qualities are undoubtedly used by chemists in identification. I do not know whether there is any evidence that different observers do differ in their sense of smell; it may be that the variations of odour on which chemists rely are so extreme that they are much wider than any differences between individual observers; but it will probably be admitted that such differences might arise and that the possibility of them ought to be faced. If they did arise, chemists would probably abandon all judgements of smell as unreliable, until and unless an adequate science of smell could be developed which would correlate judgements of smell with properties concerning which no difference of opinion could arise. Accordingly though it may not be actually true that no science uses any judgements as fundamental unless universal agreement in them can be secured, it is probably true that no science so uses any judgements concerning which differences of opinion are known to exist. The principle which we are discussing is admitted, and if any deviation from it is allowed it is recognised as a source of grave weakness and danger to the science concerned. Nobody pretends that men of science are incapable of passing error; we are concerned only with the principles which they would consciously admit, not with those which they are tempted in moments of weakness to substitute.

Judgements for which universal assent can be obtained. The detail in which abnormal sensations have been discussed and the insistence with which the necessity for a perfectly strict fulfilment of the criterion has been pressed will perhaps suggest the question, Are there any sensations which are universally normal? If we inquire with sufficient care shall we not always find some differences of judgement about any other kind of sensation? Is it possible to find any judgement of sensation concerning which all sentient beings whose opinion can be ascertained are always and absolutely in agreement?

The best answer that can be given is to state at once what judgements appear to be absolutely free from contradictions such as we have been considering. I believe there are at least three groups of such judgements:

(1) Judgements of simultaneity, consecutiveness and "betweenness" in time. I believe that it is possible to obtain absolutely universal agreement for judgements such as, The event A happened at the same time as B, or A happened between B and C.

(2) Judgements of coincidence and "betweenness" in space.

(3) Judgements of number, such as, The number of the group A is equal to, greater than or less than, the number of the group B.

These three groups will be termed respectively time-, space- and number-judgements.

It will probably be recognised, as soon as these three groups are mentioned, that the agreement which can be obtained in respect of them is more complete than in the case of any other judgements. It appears almost inconceivable to us that anyone could judge that B happens between A and C when we judge that A happens between B and C, or that anyone could judge that A is coincident in space with B when we judge that it is separated from it.

Perhaps divergences in respect of number-judgements may appear rather more possible, but I think that is only because it is not always fully realised in what such judgements consist; after the discussion of the matter which will be undertaken in a later chapter any doubts on the matter should be removed. Now inconceivability is not, of course, any indication of impossibility, but it is a very good test of unfamiliarity; and the fact that we find it difficult to imagine a difference of opinion on these matters is as good a proof as can be offered of the fact that such difference of opinion has never yet been encountered. The general agreement seems to extend far beyond the range of normal human beings; so far as we can ascertain them, the judgements of infants, imbeciles, and animals appear to coincide with our own.

It is a familiar remark that most of the observations which we make in our laboratory work consist of judgements of one of these three classes. When we read a graduated instrument, observe the deflection of a spot of light, or measure a length with a scale, we make a space-judgement; when we "time" any process with a stop-watch we make a time-judgement. Number-judgements may seem less prominent, but that is, as we shall see, only because we rely upon our instrument makers to make them for us. The standardisation of every instrument requires number-judgements; but instead of weighing a body by placing gramme-weights on the pan until a balance is obtained and then counting the number of the weights, we use larger bodies which have previously been determined to be equivalent to some assigned number of gramme-weights. The reason for this choice of observations does not seem always to be recognised; I have seen it suggested that we choose length and time-judgements because length and time are among the three "fundamental units." Such a view I believe to be utterly mistaken; the matter will be discussed in a later chapter, but surely to dispose of the suggestion it is sufficient to point out that we never make direct observations of the third "fundamental unit," mass[1]. I would urge that the choice is dictated by the knowledge that judgements of space and time are those concerning which the most universal agreement can be obtained and that everyone is "normal" in respect of the observations concerned in them.

Further it seems to be felt generally that judgements of the three classes which have been named are in some way more fundamental than others. A distinction was suggested incidentally in a previous paragraph between such properties as "colour" and the "physical properties" which are ultimately substituted for it. Now spatial, temporal and numerical properties are essentially "physical properties"; they appear to us more definitely properties of the bodies concerned and less functions of the observer or conditions of observation than such things as colour. The exact significance of the phrase is difficult to analyse, but it is worth noting that its use coincides

---

[1] The writer to whom I refer seemed to be guilty of the schoolboy blunder of confusing weight with mass when he urged, in support of his view, that the third class of observation, ranking with determinations of length and time, consisted of measurements with the balance!

nearly with that of a much older phrase, namely the "primary qualities" which were distinguished by Locke from the "secondary qualities" of matter; the qualities which are observed when we make time-, space- and number-judgements are all "primary qualities" (such as "extension" or "impenetrability," to quote from Locke's list). According to Locke and his followers, the primary qualities were all true properties of the matter, remaining quite unchanged when the matter was not observed; the secondary qualities only came into existence with observation. I am entirely unable to appreciate this distinction; with the best will in the world I cannot attribute any meaning whatever to the statement that a body has certain properties, except that somebody has observed them or does or can or will observe them; the conception of a property which never is or can be observed is beyond my comprehension. I am inclined to believe that the basis of Locke's distinction between primary qualities, independent of observation, and secondary qualities, dependent on observation, is simply the distinction between qualities which, if they are observed at all, will always be observed to be the same and those which may appear different to different observers. This distinction, like that of the "physical properties," is valuable because it shows how important in the analysis of our sensations and in the selection of the subject matter of science is the test of universal agreement.

The three classes of time-, space- and number-judgements probably do not include all of those concerning which universal agreement can be obtained. They have been selected for mention because they appear all quite distinct from each other and because each of them appears ultimate and incapable of further analysis. It would be desirable to give a complete list of fundamental and ultimate judgements, but, for reasons which will appear in the next chapter, that does not seem possible. There is no difficulty in finding other judgements concerning which no difference appears to exist and which are therefore fundamental; but it is not easy to be sure that they are ultimate and irresolvable into the other classes or even to state them with precision. But one group of such judgements is of sufficient importance to deserve some notice here; it is that which consists in the identification of objects. The meaning of this phrase can be explained best by an example.

Suppose that we are weighing a body or measuring the resistance of a wire with a Post Office Box and a galvanometer. Then one of the judgements on which we base our conclusion as to the resistance or the weight is a space-judgement, a judgement of the coincidence of the pointer of the balance scale or the spot of the galvanometer with its zero. But another judgement concerned is the identification of the weights which are in the balance pan or the plugs which are out of the Post Office Box when that coincidence is secured; our decision depends on something which we know about the weights or the box as well as on our observation of the scales. If we are asked why the weight or the plug which produces a balance is marked 200 and why we say it represents 200 grammes or 200 ohms, we shall of course refer to the experiments by which the weights and the box were calibrated; and we shall be able to analyse these experiments to a very large extent into space-, time- and number-judgements. But the application of the calibration to our new observations obviously involves one assumption, namely that the weight or coil which we have calibrated is the same as that which is now placed on the balance or short-circuited by the plug which has been removed; it would obviously be possible for somebody who had not kept his eye on the apparatus during the whole process of calibration and use to doubt whether some other weight or coil had not been substituted after the calibration had been performed.

If doubts were expressed on the matter, they could certainly be removed by allowing the doubter to watch the whole process of calibration and subsequent use, unless he suspected us of being conjurers with a deliberate intention to deceive. The judgement is one concerning which universal agreement is possible. But is it incapable of further analysis? Probably not; it seems likely that space-judgements are concerned in it. But it is useless to ask questions to which at present no answer can be given; the object in mentioning the matter is only to show that our list of fundamental and immediate judgements probably requires extension, and that any additions which may be made to it will satisfy the same criterion as that which is satisfied by the list already given, that the judgements should be such that truly universal assent for them can be obtained.

Physics and other sciences. The question which was asked on p. 18 is now answered. Science has undoubtedly originated from observations made in the course of daily life; attention has been directed to some part of our experience, either because it is extremely common and therefore important, or because it is rare and curious. From the interest thus aroused scientific investigation has sprung, but the first and necessary stage in that investigation is the selection of the matter which shall receive detailed consideration. This selection is made by applying the criterion that our subject matter must be such that there is no difference of opinion concerning it. If portions of experience can be found among the observations of daily life which satisfy this criterion, they will serve as well as any other; most sciences have passed through an "observational" stage in which all the requisite subject matter can be obtained by selection. But the growth of the science, developed from this matter in ways which we shall consider in later chapters, either exhausts this matter or, more often, shows that it does not satisfy the criterion as accurately as was at first supposed. The science then proceeds to the "experimental" stage in which experience is deliberately produced for no other reason than that it may form the subject matter of the science. But whether the science is in the observational or the experimental stage the criterion of universal assent determines whether any part of experience is to be rejected or accepted.

These statements have been made generally about "science"; no attempt has been made to confine them to physics, and the only suggestion that has been made for a distinction between the subject matter of the different sciences has been rejected. Is there then no difference between the subject matter of physics and that of other sciences? Of course there is a difference, but I think the difference is exactly what it appears to be and that therefore there is no reason to discuss it with readers who are supposed to be generally conversant with the sciences. The differentiation of the sciences is mainly historical; at a time when the sciences were still undistinguished from each other, the attention of different observers was called by chance or personal predilection to different phenomena in daily life. One happened to be interested in the motion of rigid bodies, another in the curious properties of the loadstone or the rubbed amber, a third in combustion, a fourth in the processes of the human body; the distinctions which were thus established in subject matter have persisted because each road, starting from a different point, has led to different country. Of late many of the roads have given off side-tracks and these side-tracks have tended to converge. It would be impossible now to say exactly what part of the subject matter of spectroscopy is to be allotted respectively to astronomy, physics and chemistry; when the bio-chemist becomes a chemist and ceases to be a physiologist; or where the boundary between the geologist and the geophysicist is to be drawn. History and history alone can decide these questions. In subject matter there is no distinction of any importance for our present purpose between the sciences; all accept the criterion which has been enunciated.

Physics is often regarded as more fundamental than the other sciences, and there is certainly good ground for this view. Almost all other sciences base their conclusions to some degree on those of physics, and a reversal of accepted propositions of physics, if it were sufficiently extensive, would render it necessary for almost all other sciences to revise their conclusions. This predominance of physics is sometimes attributed to its special concern with the "laws of time and space"; the Kantian doctrine that spatial and temporal concepts are fundamental to all knowledge still exerts great influence on the imagination of those who pride themselves on their freedom from all "metaphysical nonsense." The fact of the predominance I am not disposed to dispute, nor yet its association with such concepts as length and time[1]; but I believe that the association is not due in the least to the choice of subject matter made by students of physics, but entirely to the manner in which they treat it; for the distinctions between the methods by which different sciences treat exactly the same subject matter are very striking and very important. The predominance of physics is, I believe, due to its consistent determination to introduce measurement into its discussions at the very earliest stage; it is because physics alone is concerned with the fundamental processes of measurement, and because all other sciences rely on work which is essentially physical for all their reliable methods of measurement, that its conclusions are bound to exert a certain influence over theirs. The

---

[1] Even at this stage it is desirable to protest against the ambiguity of the word "time." I would use "duration" here, if it were not for the fear of being dubbed a Bergsonian.

influence is really much more noticeable in connection with laws other than those of space and time; the electrochemist is probably not aware that he is depending on essentially physical knowledge when he is measuring a length or a time, but he is aware of it when he is measuring a resistance. However, these are matters which properly belong to a much later stage of our discussion.

Is the criterion of universal assent ultimate? A few further remarks are necessary to avoid misconception. It must be insisted again that our object in this discussion is merely to ascertain what is the criterion which science applies in the selection of its subject matter; we are not concerned to ask why it applies that criterion. If these judgements which are selected are indeed ultimate and fundamental, to ask such a question would be to trespass beyond the province of science; ultimate judgements are those for the acceptance of which no reason can be alleged. We must be extremely careful not to assert that universal assent is a test of " truth " or that our fundamental judgements are " true " because they are universally accepted. If such an assertion were made, the door would be opened to all kinds of objections which might appear very trivial to students of science, but yet would have to be faced and answered. For instance, it might be urged that the discussion of the method of detecting imposture on p. 23 only served to show that there is no such thing as universal assent; that in the last resort all the judgements which I accept are my judgements, and that the phrase "the judgements of others" merely serves to disguise an essential similarity in origin between these judgements and those which I term my own. The assumption that there are other people would appear to be merely one of the derivative propositions of science and one on which it would be quite illegitimate to base any support for our fundamental judgements.

Such objections—and many others of the same kind might be raised— are quite without force if it is realised that we are only attempting to describe a certain class of judgements and not to justify them. If anyone asserts that he does not know what I mean when I speak of the judgements of others, that the phrase conveys no ideas to his mind, and that he is quite unable to distinguish between his judgements and those of others, then I admit that these pages have been written in vain, so far as he is concerned. But their value for others who do know what I mean and do appreciate the distinction will be quite unaltered. And since the objector will be trying to convince us that our " other people ", including himself, do not exist, he will scarcely be able to complain if his objections are ignored.

But though it would be unwise to base the validity of the criterion of universal assent on some more fundamental principle, it is quite permissible to inquire whether there is any other criterion which, up to the present, has led to the same result and might be substituted for it without alteration in actual science ; or whether, if there is such a criterion and it should disagree in the future with that of universal assent, one criterion would be preferred to the other and would be regarded as truly ultimate. One way in which we may seek an answer is to ask what we should do if the opportunity for applying our criterion failed. If we were isolated from all other living beings and so unable to ascertain their assent or dissent from our judgements, would it become impossible for us to select judgements on which a study of science might be based? If it would not be impossible, then there must be some other criterion by which selection can be made.

The supposed natural history of the man on the desert island is a fruitful source of fallacy, and grave dangers attend the use of the fiction; it is so difficult to be sure that he does not carry with him into isolation some ideas and knowledge derived from the busy world. And certainly if he went to his island after having practised science elsewhere, he would have no difficulty in continuing his researches, if he found a laboratory awaiting him. We who have access to our fellows do not actually appeal to outsiders to have all our observations confirmed; we have already learnt by experience the kind of observation which others will confirm, and we ask others to repeat them only when doubt arises. But the experience by which we avoid the necessity of constant appeals to the ultimate criterion is, of course, derivative; we must suppose that our islander does not possess it. How then would he fare?

He would certainly be faced by some difficulties which cause us no trouble, especially such as arise from temporary abnormality of his sensations. Thus, when the patch on the ceiling turned green after he had gazed at a red patch the change would appear to him of precisely the same nature as the turning green of a bunsen flame when a copper wire is heated in it. We, on the other hand, by comparing the sensations of others know (as we put it) that the change of colour, in one case, is due to a real change in the observer, not in the ceiling, and, in the other case, is due to a real change in the flame, not in the observer. Could the islander ever detect his error, and, if he did not, into what further errors would it lead him?

So long as he believed that the red patch really turned a corresponding patch on the ceiling green, the science which he developed would certainly be very different from our own. But it may be urged plausibly that he could not remain long under that delusion; he would discover the relation between colour and refrangibility. He would find that the refrangibility of the light from the bunsen did change when the copper wire is inserted in it, but that the refrangibility of the light from the ceiling did not change after he had looked at the red patch. But it must be remembered that, even if he made this discovery, he would still not have the reason which we have for abandoning judgements of colour in favour of those of refrangibility. If he did abandon them it would be in virtue of some other criterion than that of universal assent. Our previous discussion has indicated what this criterion might be. The laws based on refrangibility are much more satisfactory, regarded simply as laws, than those based on colour; by abandoning his colour-judgements as unreliable he would get rid of the necessity of recognising laws which he would already have had reason to suspect. For he would have found that the turning green of the ceiling did not depend on the proximity of the red patch or on any of the circumstances which usually determine change of colour. The law of colour-change in this instance would be totally different from almost all other laws of similar phenomena.

This is the conclusion that I want to suggest. The history of physics as developed by the islander indicates that there is a criterion which may be applied in the selection of the subject matter of science to replace that of universal assent; it is the criterion of the satisfactoriness and coherence of the laws which can be derived from the subject matter. Now is this criterion more or less fundamental than the other? Is our real and ultimate reason for choosing to consider certain judgements and refusing to recognise others that the former, but not the latter, lead to the kind of results which we desire? If so, what is the difference between our practice and that of the dishonest observer who "cooks" his results and says nothing about those which do not support the conclusion at which he wishes to arrive?

These are important and suggestive questions. Before we answer them we must consider more closely the nature of the propositions which we derive from our subject matter.

If universal agreement failed? But before we leave the matter one question must be asked and settled which will reappear in many forms throughout our discussion.

We have concluded that the subject matter of science consists of judgements concerning which universal agreement can be obtained, and that judgements of the external world received through the sensations are especially important for science because universal agreement can be obtained for them. What would happen if this universal agreement ceased, if we were unable to find any judgements which everyone would accept, or (more probably) if we found differences arising concerning space-, time- and number-judgements on which hitherto everyone has been agreed? Would science lose all its value or would it be able to substitute such a criterion as has been suggested in the last paragraph? Even if it is true that "satisfactoriness" rather than universal assent is the ultimate criterion, would the satisfactoriness remain if the universal assent was removed?

I must insist here, and shall often insist again, that such questions are meaningless and that to attempt to give any answer to them would lead us into error. The practice of science has been developed in order to deal with certain portions of our experience; and doubtless the form that it has taken has been determined largely by the nature of that experience. If the experience had been different, the practice would probably be different; and in some matters we shall be able later to trace a change in the methods and principles of physics introduced by new discoveries. But the change in the experience suggested here is far more fundamental than any which has actually occurred; not only our formal science but our whole process of thought of every kind is intimately connected with the possibility of the universal agreement which has been discussed. If it failed, not only would science fail but every process of thought would have to be altered fundamentally. If there were no agreement, there would be no reason for believing that there are other people, and therefore no reason for believing that they differ in opinion from us. Perhaps others with minds differently constituted can consider and discuss with profit such hypotheses, but to one trained in the school of science they produce nothing but bewilderment.

And even if the question were significant, any attempt to answer it would lead us to violate the fundamental principles of this volume. We are concerned to consider only what science is. If we considered what it might be, we should be forced to base the discussion on some doctrine more fundamental and more ultimate than any involved in actual science. For our present purpose it is necessary to deny that there is such a doctrine. Science is what it is; it is a law to itself and admits no inquiry why it is what it is.

CHAPTER II

THE NATURE OF LAWS

Summary. A definition of a law is offered for discussion, namely that it is a proposition, asserting a relation of uniform association, which can be established by experiment.

We start with the inquiry between what terms the uniformity of association is asserted.

These terms are usually complex and depend for their significance on other laws. Hooke's Law is taken as an example and subjected to a preliminary analysis.

The discovery of the complexity of the terms involved in laws leads to the recognition as laws of propositions which are not usually called by that name, e.g. those asserting the association of the properties of a substance.

The term "concept" is defined as an idea depending for its significance on the truth of some law.

The use of single words to denote concepts raises some difficulties in the expression of laws. The discussion of these difficulties brings to light sundry features of laws which are important at later stages.

It is insisted that the grammatical form of a scientific proposition is not a certain guide to its nature, and that the reasoning processes of classical logic have no application to science.

The general nature of laws. It has been remarked already that the interest which we take in the judgements which form the subject matter of science is that we use them to state laws. Laws are undoubtedly one characteristic class of scientific proposition, according to some writers the only characteristic class. Part of our inquiry then must be in what way laws are derived from the fundamental subject matter; and since it does not seem that there is any characteristic class of scientific proposition intermediate between laws and the fundamental propositions, this part must be the next to engage our attention. If it were possible to develop our investigation in a strictly logical manner, we should expound directly the process of reasoning by which laws are derived from fundamental judgements; but that ideal is at present unattainable and there is some reason to believe that it will always remain unattainable. Accordingly we shall proceed in the reverse direction, start with propositions which are undoubtedly laws, attempt to analyse them, and thus to display their connection with the original subject matter of science. Again, there will be no attempt at complete analysis. Certain features which seem to have especial interest will be selected for discussion; it is hoped thus to raise and settle all the questions which are important for future inquiry. The justification of this mode of procedure will appear when the inquiry is ended.

Laws are propositions asserting relations which can be established by experiments or observation. The terms between which the relations are asserted consist largely or entirely of judgements of the material world, immediate or derivative, simple or complex; the relations asserted, if not always the same, have always a common feature which may be described as "uniformity of association." In other words, a law always asserts that A is uniformly associated with B, where A and B are "phenomena," knowledge of which is derived from judgements of the external world. The term "uniformly" is to be interpreted as a generalisation of "always"; it means not only "at all times" but also something more, the exact nature of which we shall have to investigate. Both the nature of the terms and the nature of the relation are characteristic of a scientific law, but the relation may be regarded as even more characteristic than the terms. For this relation, at least to the extent that the conception of uniformity is involved in it, is characteristic of other propositions which, though they concern terms of a different nature, are still called "laws," though not scientific laws. Legal laws, for example, prescribe uniformity in the acts of the persons on whom they are binding; it is only in an essentially law-abiding community, where duty and practice are closely assimilated, that it would ever have occurred to anyone to describe the uniform association which is described by scientific laws by the same name as the dictates of an arbitrary despot[1].

This description, superficial though it is and subject to later revision, will serve as a guide to our discussion. It suggests that there will be two main questions to be answered, What are the terms between which the relation is asserted, and What exactly is the relation asserted between the terms? Neither of these questions seem to me to have received the attention which they deserve; both of them are immensely difficult and to neither can a complete answer be given. But it is possible to draw attention to some points connected with both questions which are often overlooked and concerning which much misconception exists, at any rate among those who are not versed in the practice of science.

The complexity of laws. We will start then with a consideration of the nature of the terms between which the relation characteristic of laws is asserted. The first point to which attention should be directed is that these terms are not usually simple and immediate judgements of sensations but complex collections of such judgements. In fact in most laws these collections imply by their nature the truth of other laws, so that all the propositions which are ordinarily recognised as laws and are actually called by that name depend both for their proof and their significance on other laws. This feature of laws, if it can be established, is clearly of the first importance for our inquiry; for if we were to confine our consideration to recognised laws, we should only solve a very small part of the problem before us; even if we discovered exactly what they meant and on what evidence they were asserted, we should still have to face the question again in connection with those other laws on which they depend so intimately.

---

[1] I believe that the term "laws of nature" is based historically on the belief that they are the dictates of an arbitrary despot, namely the laws of God.

An example will show best what is meant. Let us imagine that we have to explain what some law means and on what evidence it is asserted to a person of average intelligence but wholly devoid of scientific knowledge— say the minister in charge of a Government department; and let us choose for explanation a definite law, say Hooke's Law, stated in the form that the extension of a body is proportional to the force acting upon it. Our minister will probably not at first raise any question as to the meaning of the law, for the ideas of extension, force and proportionality will appear familiar to him; his questions will be rather directed towards the evidence for the law. Accordingly we shall take him into the laboratory and show him the experiments by which we establish it; we shall hang weights on the rod and measure its extension, perhaps with a scale, but more probably with some more delicate device, such as an optical lever. If we use such a device, the question will immediately be asked why we consider the deflections of the spot of light on the scale proportional to (or connected by some other relation with) the extension of the rod; and when we answer the question we shall find ourselves explaining the laws of reflection of light and perhaps demonstrating them. The assumption of the truth of these laws is therefore involved in our proof of Hooke's Law.

Now this conclusion is very obvious and may seem very unimportant. Everyone knows that we apply the results of one branch of science to promote the knowledge of another. The experimental art consists not merely in manipulative dexterity but much more in ingenuity in devising experimental methods and in applying laws already known to the discovery of others. But it will be urged that the use of such experimental devices is a mere matter of convenience and has nothing really to do with the laws which they are employed to establish. The truth of Hooke's Law does not depend on the truth of the laws of reflection, because, if there were any doubt about those laws, we could easily prove the law by other means; we could, for example, substitute a level and micrometer screw for the optical lever.

But I do not think that the matter is quite so simple as is suggested here. What we mean by extension seems to be what we measure with a millimetre scale; that method is ultimate ; if we employ it, it would seem that our method is as direct as it can be and that no subsidiary laws are involved. But we must recognise that if we confine our proof of Hooke's Law to those cases in which the extension can be measured by a millimetre scale, the scope of the law will be very much restricted; we undoubtedly mean to assert the law in cases to which that measurement is quite inapplicable; and if we mean to assert it over the widest possible range we must have recourse to much more delicate, and much less direct, methods of measuring extension. All such methods, whether they involve the use of the optical lever, interference apparatus, or micrometer screws, depend on the assumption that certain laws are true; and though it may be urged that each of them depends on a different law and that, therefore, none of these laws is essential to Hooke's Law, yet a brief consideration will show that there is one law involved in them all, namely that they all give the same result.

For these reasons it seems impossible to accept the view that the laws involved in the use of experimental devices are in no way essential to the laws which they are employed to prove; it seems to be indicated that a law, namely that different methods of measurement agree, is involved in the use of the term "extension." But the point which I am trying to make will appear more clearly if we consider the other factor which is involved in the statement of Hooke's Law, namely force. The questioner will, no doubt, think at the outset that he has nothing to learn about force; he will believe that force is something inseparably connected with the muscular sensation of effort, and it will seem to him obvious that the weight exerts force on the rod because, if the weight was attached to his hand instead of to the rod, he would experience that sensation of effort. But of course we shall have to point out to him that his knowledge is not so complete as he imagines and, in particular, that if he merely means by force something which leads to the sensation of muscular effort, he has no way of measuring force with any certainty; he may be able to tell roughly whether one force is equal to another, but how can he tell that one force is double another?

If he fails to answer this question[1], we shall expound to him the scientific conception of force and shall explain that by force we mean the product of mass and acceleration. But now it is obviously open to him to inquire why, if we define force in this way, we assert that the weight exerts force on the rod; for the rod has no acceleration and its mass does not seem to affect the extension. We then explain that the force is measured by the mass-acceleration of the weight, not of the rod; that we know the mass of the weight and that, if it were not supported by the rod, it would have a certain acceleration; that the difference between this acceleration and that which it has (namely, zero) is due to the rod, and that it is the mass-acceleration imposed on the weight by the rod that we mean by the force exerted on the rod. Now in this explanation we are clearly assuming the truth of two laws, that of the independence of forces and that of the equality of action and reaction[2]; if we denied the first of these laws, we should have no reason

---

[1] If he is really an intelligent person he will not fail to give an answer; he will say that, if he judges that the force exerted by two weights is equal when tested by muscular sensation, then, when he holds up both weights at the same time, he is supporting double the force. His answer contains the germ of the method of measuring force as a fundamental magnitude (see Chap. X) rather than as a derived magnitude; and in so far as he suggests that force is actually measured as a fundamental magnitude and not as a derived, I believe that he is more correct than the writers of many valued text-books on dynamics. But when we come to consider the matter more nearly we shall find that the method he suggests has already assumed one law, namely the independence of forces, and that if he elaborated it he would have also to assume the equality of action and reaction. The conclusion reached in the text that the notion of force is inseparable from the assumption of the truth of these laws would follow even if we abandoned the prevalent definition of force as a derived magnitude, namely the product of mass and acceleration.

[2] The tendency in modern treatises on the foundations of dynamics is to substitute for the Newtonian laws some other propositions; but these propositions are also of the nature

to believe that the presence of the rod makes no difference to the acceleration which the weight would have had if it were not supported; if we denied the second, we should have no reason to believe that the force exerted by the rod on the weight is equal to that exerted by the weight on the rod.

Accordingly the laws of dynamics are involved in the measurement of the force on the rod (and therefore in any statement concerning that force) at least as intimately as the laws of the reflection of light are involved in the measurement of the extension by means of the optical lever. But really they are involved a great deal more intimately; for consideration will show that there is no means whatever of measuring the force on the rod which does not involve those laws. Whenever we measure a force and apply it, we *first* measure it and *then* apply it, thereby assuming the independence of forces; and if, as we always do, we measure the mass-acceleration of the body *by* which the force is applied rather than that *to* which it is applied, we assume the equality of action and reaction. But the intimate connection between force and the laws of dynamics can best be seen if we inquire why we call by a special term, force, the product of the mass and the acceleration. We have a name for the product of mass and velocity and another for the product of mass and acceleration, but we have none for the product of the mass and "jerk," that is, the rate of change of acceleration. The reason is that we know important laws which relate the mass-velocities or the mass-accelerations of bodies when they react, but we know none concerning the mass-jerks; if we did not know these laws we should not have these special names. Our whole conception of force depends on the truth of the laws of dynamics; if those laws were not true, we should not form that conception. Every statement which we make about forces involves the tacit assumption that the laws of dynamics are true; without that assumption a statement such as that made in Hooke's Law would be neither true nor false; it would be simply meaningless. We might still assert significantly that the body A when hung on the rod produced an extension a, and the body B an extension b; but when we assert the law we mean something much more than that; we mean that A and B have certain properties which we describe by saying that they exert certain forces, and among these properties is that of obeying the laws of dynamics.

The conclusion which I am trying to enforce is that the use of certain words implies the assumption that certain laws are true, and that any statement in which those words are involved is without any meaning whatever if the laws are not true. Consequently any laws in the statement of which those words are used depend entirely, not so much for their truth as for their significance, on these other laws.

of laws. Personally I believe that the reaction from the Newtonian standpoint has gone too far, and that some laws essentially equivalent to Newton's second and third laws are necessary to any adequate statement; it is merely in the way that they are expressed that improvement is desirable. But I fear that the full discussion of the matter must be postponed for the hypothetical second volume of this treatise.

What has been said about "force" applies equally to all the other technical terms of physics and other sciences. We only invent new terms (or give a new meaning to words previously in common use) when we have new facts or ideas to express; these new facts are usually laws or propositions which again depend for their meaning on laws, and the terms are useless and meaningless unless the laws are true. Thus, if we say anything about electrical resistance we assume that Ohm's Law is true; bodies for which Ohm's Law is not true, gases for example, have no electrical resistance[1]. Similarly Hooke's Law, which we have taken as an example of a law which depends on others, in its turn gives rise to a term, "Young's Modulus," which depends for its significance on the truth of that law; no law involving Young's Modulus is significant unless Hooke's Law is true.

Unrecognised laws. An important class of words which in this manner connote laws is that which includes the names of special substances; it suggests further interesting considerations. Thus, whenever we speak of "silver" or "iron," we are implying that certain laws are true, namely the laws asserting the association of the properties of silver or iron. If very high electrical conductivity was not associated with a brilliant white colour and solubility in nitric acid to give a solution in which ammonia forms a precipitate soluble in excess—and so on—we should not speak of silver; and if strong paramagnetism was not associated with the power of combining with carbon to form alloys which can be tempered, we should not speak of iron.

But the suggestion that such names of substances involve laws in the same manner as such terms as "force" or "electrical resistance" leads to new considerations. In all the previous examples which have been given, the proposition which is involved in the use of the word (i.e. Laws of dynamics, Ohm's Law, Hooke's Law) is generally recognised as a law and called by that name; while the propositions stating the association of the properties of silver and iron are not so generally recognised as laws. Does this difference in practice represent any important difference in the nature of the propositions? Are these propositions really laws?

The answer cannot be fully given until we have decided more definitely the nature of the relation which is asserted by the indisputable laws, but it will be admitted that if the characteristic feature of that relation is uniformity of association, there is no important difference in this matter; for the association between the properties of silver is in every sense as uniform as that between the extension and the force which is asserted by Hooke's Law. On the other hand, there may appear to be a difference in the nature of the terms between which the relation is asserted. In the indisputable laws these terms are properties which can be measured and stated in numerical terms, whereas all the properties of silver are not capable of measurement. It has been suggested that all true laws are numerical laws and the possibility that

---

[1] We sometimes use the term when Ohm's law—i.e. that the current is proportional to the potential difference—is only true over a very small range of current; but then we speak of the "resistance for a current i," implying that for currents very near i the law is true.

the distinction thus indicated is fundamentally important must be borne in mind; but it should be noted that the acceptance of such a distinction would exclude from the class of laws a very large number of propositions which are universally admitted as such by other sciences. Moreover some of the properties of silver are measurable, its melting point, its conductivity and so on; on this view part at least of the proposition asserting the association of the properties of silver would have to be admitted as a law.

I believe however that the reason why this and similar propositions are not usually called laws is much simpler, clearer and less abstruse. It is two-fold. In the first place we do not usually assert the association of the properties of silver as a single proposition at all; and it is to single propositions which can be stated adequately in a single grammatical sentence or mathematical equation that the term "law" is confined. The assertion of the properties of silver is not called a law simply because the relations involved are so very complex; they would need a column or more of a chemical dictionary to state with any completeness. A single example will suffice to show that this consideration is of great weight in determining whether a proposition shall be called a law. In the early days of the science of radioactivity it was thought that the alpha rays were absorbed in the same manner as beta rays or X-rays; people spoke of the "exponential law of absorption of alpha rays." When Bragg and Kleeman showed that the relation between the distance travelled and the intensity was quite other than that predicted by the exponential law and very much more complicated, people no longer spoke of the "law of absorption" of alpha rays at all; the relation was so complicated that it could not be stated adequately in a single sentence or formula, and therefore a single name was not applied to it. But when later Geiger showed that the cube of the velocity of the rays was proportional to the distance from the end of their range and thus enabled the absorption to be stated once more in a single manageable formula, then once more the term Geiger's *Law* of absorption came into use. It is simply because numerical laws are capable of compact expression that the idea has gained ground that assertions of numerical relations are alone entitled to the designation of laws.

The second reason is that the properties of silver were discovered to be associated long before the conception of a scientific law was formed. A law conveys the impression of a proposition established by conscious and deliberate scientific investigation, and we are not inclined to give it to a proposition which was familiar before any such investigation was undertaken[1]. If we had lived in the days of the sons of Noah and had watched their earliest attempts at elucidating the properties of iron, it is quite possible that we should call the proposition asserting the association of the properties of iron Tubal-Cain's Law.

[1] Deliberate investigation has, of course, greatly extended our knowledge of the properties of iron or silver and has added to it numbers of associations, representing other elements and materials. But sufficient properties were known to identify silver and distinguish it from all other substances before the scientific era, and the conception of an association of properties distinguishing a substance had gained universal acceptance.

The distinction between those propositions asserting associations which are called laws and those which are not so called would appear therefore not to be essential to our present discussion, but it is nevertheless significant. It is indicated that the relations asserted by propositions which are not usually regarded as laws are often both older and much more complicated than those of recognised laws; and yet, since these laws depend for their significance on the validity of those relations, they are not only older and more complicated but also more fundamental. It seems that as soon as we begin to analyse recognised laws into the elements on which they depend logically or from which they have been developed historically, we discover that these elements are in some sense much more complicated than the laws which depend on them. Instead of finding that the analysis becomes easier as it proceeds it is possible that it will become more difficult.

Concepts. The expression of laws. Thus our first conclusion is that many of the words used in expressing scientific laws denote ideas which depend for their significance on the truth of certain other laws and would lose all meaning if those laws were not true. These words include most of the technical terms of science, but the laws on which they depend for their meaning are often not explicitly recognised as such. It will be convenient to have a name for such words and they will in future be called "concepts." A concept is a word denoting an idea which depends for its meaning or significance on the truth of some law. The conclusion at which we have arrived is that most, if not all, of the recognised laws of physics state relations between concepts, and not between simple judgements of sensation which remain significant even if no relation between them is known.

But the use of concepts in the expression of laws raises some difficulties if we consider more nearly the form in which laws are usually expressed. These difficulties will probably appear at first very trivial and concerned with matters which have not the slightest scientific importance. And this first impression will ultimately turn out to be correct; the difficulties which are raised can be removed. Nevertheless the consideration of them will lead to some conclusions which are not wholly unimportant, and the matter is discussed only because it offers a convenient means of reaching those conclusions.

It has been said that the word "silver" is meaningless unless the proposition asserting the uniform association of the properties of silver is true, and that every statement about silver implies the truth of that proposition. Suppose now that I say that the melting point of silver is 960° C. If it is true that in using the word silver I have assumed the association of its properties, then, since among its properties is its melting point, I have already assumed that its melting point is 960° C. The statement that silver melts at 960° C. is not, therefore, an experimental proposition the truth of which can only be established in the laboratory; it is a mere truism, like the statement that a black cat is black, the truth of which would be immediately recognised by anyone to whom the statement was significant at all.

The conclusion is obviously false, but it does seem to indicate either that our view of the meaning of silver is in error or that some change is required in expressing what is doubtless an experimental statement. The second alternative seems preferable and we may examine whether any simple alternative of the mode of statement will make it more satisfactory. The easiest way to avoid the difficulty would seem to be to omit the melting point from the definition of silver; but if, having done so, we assert some other property of silver, say, that silver has a density of 10·5, the same difficulty will arise in connection with this property. Is the density to be included in the definition? If we now agree to omit the density from the definition, an objector by raising the same point again and again can finally drive us to omit all the properties of silver from its definition and force us to admit that by "silver" we mean just nothing at all. Or if, when we are forced to omit density from the definition, we propose to reinsert the melting point, thus avoiding this conclusion, it may be urged that we employ a different definition when we state the melting point and when we state the density, and that consequently the silver which melts at 960° C. is not the same thing as the silver which has a density of 10·5—again a conclusion we cannot admit.

This objection will doubtless seem to many people a mere quibble and the kind of quibble that makes them unreasonably angry; to mention it is to risk the most violent invective of which scientific men are capable; they might almost call the offender a "metaphysician." But after all the more absurd is a quibble the easier it should be to expose the fallacy on which it rests. I am not really suggesting that the statements which are challenged are valueless or insignificant; I want to only discover precisely where the supposed objector is wrong and so to draw attention to some widely prevalent misconceptions.

First then we may note that an objection of the same kind might be raised to statements of somewhat similar form which are not scientific, statements about the properties of objects which are not scientific concepts. For instance, I might say that William Smith lives next door to me. The objector might ask me to define "William Smith" and inquire whether the property of his living next door to me was part of the definition. If I replied that it was part of the definition, I should be in exactly the same difficulty as occurred in connection with the statement about silver; I should be driven to the conclusion either that the statement was a mere tautology or that, when I made different statements about William Smith, I was in each case referring to a different person. But of course I should say that his dwelling-place was not part of the definition, and that William Smith would remain the same person if he moved a few doors down the road. But, as we saw, if this way out of the difficulty is taken, the objector can ultimately force us to one of two conclusions, either that there are statements about William Smith which are simple definitions and convey information about nothing but the use of words, or that I mean nothing at all by William Smith. But I should now be perfectly prepared to accept the first of these alternatives. I should agree that, if I said that William Smith was the son of John Smith and Eliza (formerly Jones) his wife, I was stating a mere definition; if William Smith were not the son of these persons I should not call him William Smith and he would be a different person. In fact, I should evade the objection by dividing roughly William Smith's properties into two classes, one class defining the person and such that, if he did not have them, he would not be the same person; the other class such that he would remain the same person even if he did not have those properties.

Defining and non-defining properties. Now can we evade the difficulty about silver in the same manner? Are there properties of silver which simply define what we mean by silver and such that, if they were altered, the substance would not be silver; and are there on the other hand non-defining properties, such that they might be changed without affecting the fact that the substance in question is silver?

There may seem at first sight certainly to be properties of the second class, namely properties which have just been discovered and are attributed to silver for the first time. Before (let us say) the X-ray spectrum of silver was discovered, it would have been absurd (and indeed impossible) to maintain that this spectrum was part of the defining properties of silver; and yet when the spectrum was discovered we did not cease to call the substance silver. Accordingly the first attribution, at any rate, of the spectrum was the statement of an experimental fact which was not implied by the mention of the word silver and yet was a true property of silver; it was a non-defining property. But a little further consideration will make the matter rather more doubtful. We are not really concerned with what word we use but with what we mean by the word. If we agreed in future to use only Latin for scientific purposes and to call silver "argentum," it would be obvious that the scientific significance of our propositions would be entirely unaffected by the change. And so, conversely, the fact that we continue to call a substance by the same name does not imply necessarily that the substance is the same or that we mean precisely the same by our propositions about it. The question which is really asked is whether, when we have attributed a new property to silver, we mean exactly the same thing by silver as we did before; and the answer to this question is rather more doubtful. Let us therefore leave new properties out of account for the moment and return to that which has served as an example hitherto.

If there are defining and non-defining properties of silver we must be able to assign any given property to one class or the other. To which class then does the melting point belong? If we found that the melting point of silver was not 960° but 962°, should we cease to call the substance silver or regard it as a different substance?[1] Of course we should regard it as the same substance; we should simply suppose a slight error to have been made in the determination. The melting point, then, is a non-defining property.

[1] As a matter of fact it appears not to be known which of the suggested values is the more accurate.

But consider now a property in which an error of this sort is impossible, say the property of dissolving in nitric acid. If we went down to our laboratory one day and found that all the substances which had been called silver and had dissolved in nitric acid would no longer dissolve, what should we say? I do not think the question can be answered. It must be insisted again that it is quite useless to ask what would happen if the judgements on which all scientific knowledge is based were different from what they are; the methods of science have been elaborated to deal with facts as they are, and if they were very different there would either be no science, or at least there would be a science very different from anything that we recognise now by that term. Such events as have been supposed simply do not happen, and there is an end of the matter. But so far as an answer can be given, it is that we should say that silver had changed and that, though we might use the same name for the new substance as for the old, the substance was new and different from the old. Solubility in nitric acid is then a defining property.

However, there is really no difference in this respect between the melting point and the solubility in nitric acid. If we insist on contemplating the possibility that silver might cease to dissolve in nitric acid, we should also contemplate the possibility that it might change its melting point to some figure (say 100°) differing from that now accepted by something far greater than any possible error of experiment. And if the change did take place we should be in the same difficulty in deciding whether or no the substance had changed. So far as this test is concerned, both melting point and solubility are defining properties or neither of them is. The apparent difference, which might make us think at first that solubility is a defining and melting point a non-defining property, arises only from the fact that the latter is the more precise and therefore more likely to be affected by errors of observation. If we had stated, not simply that silver dissolves, but had stated the rate of dissolution, the two properties would have been on exactly the same footing.

So far then it does not seem clear whether any property is defining or non-defining. The only distinction which can be made is that a property appears to be more nearly defining according as an error concerning it is less probable; but since the probability of an error increases with the accuracy of statement, such a distinction would lead to the conclusion, which is quite as paradoxical as the quibbling objection from which we started, that the more accurately a property is stated the less characteristic of the substance it is; and that the only properties which are so characteristic as to be completely defining are those which are stated with such latitude that any possible error of experiment would fall within the definition. In other words, the more we know of a property the less we can use it for defining the substance of which it is a property!

But we have omitted from consideration a very important possibility. In the discussion we have tacitly supposed that all substances which have previously been called silver and given the melting point 960° are now found to melt at 962°. Suppose however that we found that the substances which we had previously called silver could be divided into two classes, those in each class having exactly the same properties in every respect but one, while one class melts at 960° and the other at 962°; then we should not regard them as the same substance and should not call them by the same name In such circumstances the melting point would be a defining property, such that a change in it indicated a change in the nature of the substance And here we are at the root of the matter; indeed it may seem that an unnecessarily long discussion has only led to a conclusion obvious from the outset. We call a substance silver so long as it is distinguished from other substances and we call all substances silver which are indistinguishable from each other. The test whether a property is a defining or a non-defining property rests simply on the distinction between those properties which serve to distinguish the substance from others and those which it possesses in common with others. Any set of properties which serve to distinguish silver from all other substances will serve to define it.

But we are yet not free from our difficulties. We may choose several sets of properties to distinguish silver from all other substances; in fact there is probably no property, except the mere possession of weight, which might not be used, either alone or in conjunction with others, to define silver. All properties may therefore be defining properties, and yet none of them is such that we should be prepared to admit that the assertion of the property is not the statement of an experimental fact. Again there is hardly any property which might not be excluded from the defining properties, for the remainder would always serve the purpose of definition. However, though in the present state of our knowledge there is no difficulty in distinguishing silver from all other substances, it is not inconceivable that another substance might be found which, though possessing all the properties which we at present attribute to silver, differed from it in respect of some property which is as yet unknown[1]. If such a discovery were made the newly discovered property would be necessarily a defining property, and yet it would be ridiculous to say that we asserted nothing experimental when we said that silver had the property or to maintain that silver since its discovery was an essentially different substance from silver before its discovery.

These considerations suffice to show that an escape from the objection raised by a division of properties into defining and non-defining is impossible; any such division would be purely artificial and would represent no distinction between the properties which is of the least value to science. But before we turn to the other possible means of escape which was indicated, one conclusion may be drawn from the discussion.

All laws are connected. This conclusion is that statements about silver

[1] Since this sentence was first written the possibility suggested has become a fact. Ionium shares with thorium all the properties known twenty years ago and differs from it only in properties which were not suspected then.

cannot strictly be separated from statements about every other kind of substance. In order to define silver we have to state sufficient of its properties to distinguish it from everything else; and so before we can give an adequate definition we must know the properties of everything else. In fact it is a property of silver, and one of its most important properties, that it is different from mercury or lead; if, in order that a statement about silver may be significant, silver must first be defined, then before such a statement can be made we must know all the properties of mercury and lead. But the same consideration applies with equal force to mercury or lead; before we can make any significant statement about them we must know all the properties of silver. Accordingly statements about silver, mercury and lead are not independent statements; each depends for its meaning (and not only for its truth) on the truth of all the remainder; each statement about any particular substance is only part of a universal statement which includes the assertion of all the properties of all substances.

These considerations apply not only to silver in its relations to other substances, but also to all laws in their relation to all other laws. If we consider any law very carefully we shall find that there is somehow involved in it a reference to any other law, and that its significance would be changed to some small degree if any other law whatever ceased to be true or if any new law were discovered. The change would usually be extremely small and utterly unappreciable in the ordinary pursuit of science, but it will be recognised by a sufficiently careful investigation. Thus we saw that Hooke's Law, because it involves the concept force, depends for its significance on the laws of dynamics, and in particular on the law of the equality of action and reaction. Now this law is asserted to be true for all forms of force and applies therefore, let us say, to the force which we call the pressure of radiation; in its application to radiation the law involves again the laws of radiation and, through them, the laws of electrodynamics. Hence there is a connection between Hooke's Law and any law in which the laws of electrodynamics are involved. No doubt this conclusion seems fanciful and it is not pretended that it is of the slightest importance in the practice of physical investigation; there is no danger that we shall be led into any scientific error by our usual neglect of the connection. But it seems a necessary result of the view (which again is unavoidable) that laws often, if not always, relate concepts, depending for their significance on the truth of other laws. The recognition that laws are not entirely independent of each other, that each assumes in some measure the truth of the others, that all science is intimately cross-connected by innumerable ties, real though slight—these conclusions cannot be neglected in any inquiry into the origin of laws and the means by which they are established.

Science and logic. Such are the views to which we are led by endeavouring to avoid one horn of the dilemma presented to us by the supposed objector. The other alternative which he offered to us was the admission that in two assertions of different properties of silver we mean

different things by the term silver. I do not see any way of escaping from
the admission if we allow the argument to proceed so far, but on the other
hand, our previous discussion should show that there is no harm in making
it. The statements that silver melts at 960° and that its density is 10·5 are
logically equivalent; it is impossible to explain fully and adequately the
meaning of one of them except in such a way as to show that they are both
assertions of the law of the association of all the properties of silver; if they
are logically significant at all, then they are logically the same statement,
and if one is true the other follows without any experimental inquiry. On
the other hand, we all know that they do not mean the same thing; and if
anyone cares to assert this indubitable fact in the form that we mean different
things by silver in the two cases, I see no reason why we should quarrel
with him. We need only quarrel if he proposes to draw further conclusions
which we are indisposed to admit.

One conclusion which was threatened we have already prevented by our
admission, namely, that in asserting some or all of the properties of silver
we were stating something which does not require experimental inquiry
for its establishment. The only other dangerous conclusion that is possible
is that some process of argument which we employ is unreliable and leads
to false results. But we could only be convicted of error if in some later
stage in the development of science it was found that we based on the statement which we have made some conclusion which was fallacious or ambiguous
owing to our use of the term silver in two senses; for instance, if from two
propositions involving the word silver we deduced a third which would
follow only if it were certain that the word was used in exactly the same
sense in each of them. Now I do not think that we shall ever be caught
in such an error; and it is for this reason that the matter has been discussed
so fully. There seems to be a very important distinction between the use
of words in science and their use in any logical study. The logician needs
accurate and unique definitions of the words which he employs, because
he uses them, not merely to record for subsequent reference or to convey
to others thoughts which have passed through his mind, but also as instruments in the process of deduction. Words, or some equivalent symbols,
are essential, for example, in the syllogism; the processes of thought involved
in it cannot take place at all without them; the conclusion from the major
and minor premisses will not follow in our minds unless we think of the words
in which they are expressed; and the conclusion will not be true unless the
predicate of the minor premiss means exactly the same thing as the subject
of the major. It is because words are the tools of thought, and not merely
a means of registering its conclusions, that logicians have found that the
further they proceed in the direction of subtlety of thought the greater the care
they must exercise in the definition of their words, until finally they have to
reject altogether the words of common speech, on account of the vague and
indeterminate associations from which they cannot be freed wholly, and have
recourse to artificial symbols which can be made entirely unambiguous.

The only penalty of using the same word in different senses is that we cannot employ it as an instrument of logical thought; we cannot apply to our propositions the logical processes which need the use of words as instruments It is undoubted that we can study science with perfect satisfaction to ourselves (and nobody else matters) although we commit the heinous offence of using ambiguous terms. And this fact is simply an indication that we do not use in the course of our study any processes which require words to be un-ambiguous. This conclusion I believe to be true and very important. Logic was the first form of accurate and systematic thought to be developed, and hence an impression has arisen that no thought can be accurate or systematic which does not employ the processes of formal logic. Of course the province and power of logic have been very greatly extended in recent years, but some of its essential features, including that which has raised the difficulty we are considering, have remained unchanged; and any process of thought which does not show those features is still illogical. But illogical is not synonymous with erroneous. I believe that all important scientific thought is illogical, and that we shall be led into nothing but error if we try to force scientific reasoning into the forms prescribed by logical canons. It is for this reason that the analysis of scientific propositions which we are attempting is so difficult; all the methods which have been developed for the analysis of logical thought are inapplicable; the task requires a second Aristotle. Until the task is completed it is impossible to show that scientific thought is fundamentally different from logical thought, but the fact that we can violate important rules of logical thought without suffering any inconvenience is strong evidence that the fundamental difference exists[1].

Definitions. If we boldly refuse to pay any attention to logical canons our difficulties vanish at once. Our words then are not instruments by means of which the process of thought is conducted, but merely convenient means of recalling to our minds thoughts which have once passed through them or of calling up in the minds of others thoughts which are passing through our own. They have nothing whatever to do with the operation by means of which we pass from one set of thoughts to another. The meaning of a proposition—a phrase which I have often used without explaining it—is simply the set of thoughts which it calls to mind; the meaning of two propositions is different if they call up different thoughts. Now it is meaning in this sense which alone is important to science, and since it will be readily admitted that meaning in this sense has little or nothing to do with logical form, such form is of very little importance for science.

Indeed we should have saved ourselves much trouble—but lost the opportunity for useful discussion—if we had stopped our objector at the outset. He raised his difficulty first by asking for a definition. We should

---

[1] The application of these remarks must be with caution. Because we are not bound by the rules of formal logic it does not follow that we are not liable to error similar to that which attends, in other studies, their neglect. Cases can be indicated in which a failure to observe the implication of words used has led to error, but the error is not that of a false logical deduction.

have refused to give one. No student of science has ever felt the smallest need for a formal definition of silver; our words are perfectly effective in calling up the thoughts we desire without one, and in admitting the right of anyone to ask for one we were encouraging a very dangerous delusion. And it is a delusion which has caused a good deal of trouble to scientific people. There are few of us who have not been asked, and considerably puzzled, by a familiar question from unscientific acquaintances, What is electricity? The most accomplished physicists are seldom ready with an answer; the right answer is that the question is unanswerable because it does not mean anything at all. The question is suggested only by the idea that sentences are capable of being analysed into constituents each of which has a separate significance and, in particular, that any word which is grammatically a noun is capable of being the subject in some significant statement in the subject-predicate form. Our friend has heard statements made in which the word Electricity is used; and he jumps to the conclusion that this word can be extracted from the sentence, placed in another beginning, "Electricity is...," and that some sentence of this form must have a clear meaning.

His idea, though it would probably not be approved by modern logic, has undoubtedly much in common with the ideas of that study. Logic does undoubtedly analyse sentences into their constituents and builds up fresh significant statements by recombining them in a different manner. But if our conclusions as to the nature of scientific statements is correct, the idea is false. Such statements are not necessarily analysable into constituents. A sentence is a single whole framed for a single purpose, namely the bringing of certain ideas into the mind of the hearer; and even if the ideas which it is intended should be called up are capable of analysis, it by no means follows that the words used must be capable of a similar analysis; still less does it follow that the analysis of the ideas must be followed step by step in an analysis of the words. When we are merely trying to call up ideas, a jumble of words quite outside all the rules of grammar may often be more effective than the most accurately turned sentence. Many slang catch-words and our usual practice in talking to children or to dogs provide excellent illustrations of that fact.

On the other hand it would be absurd to pretend that grammatical construction or the use of words which are common to other statements are no guide to the meaning of a scientific statement. When we say that silver melts at 960° and that ice melts at 0°, the ideas which we wish to evoke have doubtless much in common; and again when we say that a current of water is flowing in a tube there is some similarity between the ideas conveyed and those conveyed by the statement that a current of electricity is flowing in a wire. But it is equally absurd to suppose that the common element in either pair of statements can be ascertained by studying their grammatical form, or that the relation between the ideas conveyed by one pair of statements is at all similar to that conveyed by the other pair. In the first pair it is probably true that to every statement about silver corresponds a significant statement in very nearly the same form about ice, but it is certainly not true that to every statement about water corresponds a significant statement of the same form about electricity.

The latitude which men of science allow themselves in expressing essentially similar ideas in entirely different grammatical form and, on the other hand, expressing essentially different ideas in the same form has many advantages. It allows us to suggest loose analogies and subtle differences which would be very cumbrous to express more definitely in language which could not be mistaken. But it has also disadvantages. The practice confuses outsiders—perhaps not so unimportant a matter as we are sometimes inclined to think—and it sometimes confuses ourselves. I think, for instance, that the mere introduction into physics of the words "time" and "space" has led to the creation of many quite unnecessary difficulties which might have been avoided if grammatical form had always been more closely assimilated to the thought expressed. Examples of this nature will occur in our subsequent inquiry. For the present it is only necessary to insist on the general conclusion to which we have been led, namely that the processes involved in scientific inquiry are not only or mainly those which are studied by traditional logic and that therefore our statements need not be expressed in the form suitable for the application of those processes.

But before we leave the matter it may be well to note that we can express our propositions about silver in a manner which will satisfy the logician. The difficulty was that since, in order to define silver it is necessary to state some, if not all, of its properties, any statement asserting these properties follows immediately from the definition and requires no experimental proof. Accordingly unless there are properties of silver the attribution of which requires no experimental proof, no statement about silver can be made which is an experimental proposition. But further consideration will show that there is one such proposition, namely that asserting the uniform association of all the properties of silver; this proposition may be asserted in the words that "silver exists." This proposition requires experimental proof and can be asserted logically after the definition of silver by the mention of all its properties. All other propositions, such as that silver has a density of 10·5, are logically equivalent to it; if it is true that silver (as defined) exists, then it follows immediately and without any further experimental inquiry that silver has a density of 10·5 or that silver melts at 960°. Moreover both these propositions are logically equivalent; if one is true, so is the other. We shall avoid all the difficulties which have been raised, if we are content to assert any property of silver by the simple statement that silver exists, followed by a clause, added for emphasis or reminder, that among the properties which have been stated to define silver and are now stated to be associated there is that one to which attention now is drawn, a certain melting point, for example.

It has been convenient to base the later part of our discussion on the "law" of the properties of silver, but we ought to return and consider how our conclusions apply to undoubted laws. We have concluded that though a law involving concepts has a definite meaning, it does not follow that formal definitions of those concepts can be given. A law is a single whole, or at least, if it is capable of analysis, the parts into which it can be analysed are not those into which it can be divided grammatically. These considerations apply to "force" as much as to "silver." Because we state that the force on a certain body is 1 dyne or that extension is proportional to force, it does not follow that we can state significantly that force "is" something or other. Though laws state relations between concepts, the significance of those concepts can hardly be separated from that of the laws they are used to state.

CHAPTER III

THE NATURE OF LAWS (*continued*)

Summary. We now ask what is the nature of the relation asserted by laws between the terms we have considered.

The "orthodox" view that laws assert a relation of cause and effect is considered and rejected. Many laws assert relations which are not, like the causal relation, dual, temporal and asymmetrical.

The origin of the view which is rejected is traced to a confusion between psychological relations involved in the experiment which proves a law and the materia relation asserted by the law which is proved, not only by that experiment but also by many others.

So far from all laws asserting causal relations, it is doubtful whether any assert them. Temporal order appears to be introduced by the conception of "processes" rather than by that of cause and effect.

But if the relation asserted by laws is not causal, what is it? The consideration of this question requires first a decision what is the fundamental characteristic of laws. It is suggested that a proposition is to be regarded as a law if it has an importance for science which is of a special kind.

If this conclusion is accepted, it follows that the relation asserted by a law must be some form of "uniformity," a term which includes invariability and generality.

The forms of uniformity asserted by actual laws are probably divisible into two classes, which are termed "uniform association" and "functionality." The latter is a mathematical conception the discussion of which is beyond our scope at present; but it is necessary to inquire further into the nature of uniform association (U.A.).

It is asked (1) whether U.A. is a dual relation; and, if so, whether it is (2) symmetrical, and (3) transitive. These questions are not answered definitely; they require a complete analysis of the relations stated by laws, which has not been achieved. But various points are raised which seem of special interest, either intrinsically or because of the further considerations which they raise.

The conclusion which seems to be indicated is that no uniform association can be completely expressed in the dual form, except that characteristic of the laws asserting the existence of substances. This relation may also be symmetrical. Uniform association can never be truly transitive, but there is an approximately transitive form which is of considerable importance.

These conclusions lead to inquiries how individual bodies and systems are to be distinguished from substances and what exactly is the difference (noted at the beginning of the preceding chapter) between subsidiary laws which define concepts and those which do not.

The question, so far avoided, of the nature of those laws which are more elementary than any concepts is raised. It is probable that these laws assert uniform associations of the kind characteristic of substances.

Finally, it is suggested that the importance of a law and the decision whether or no a given proposition is to be regarded as a law is determined not only by the considerations of its formal nature, but rather by its connection with theories. Just as the choice of our subject matter is determined largely by the possibility of ordering it in laws, so the selection of laws is determined largely by the possibility of ordering them in theories.

Cause and effect. So far our discussion has been based on a consideration of the nature of the terms between which laws assert the relation of uniformity. We must now turn to the second branch of inquiry and seek to ascertain more definitely what is the nature of this relation, whether it is the same in all laws or, if not, how it differs in different laws.

Half a century ago this question would have received a ready answer. The nineteenth century philosophers who so gaily instructed men of science in their business had no doubt what was the essential characteristic of scientific laws; in this matter Whewell, Hamilton, Mill and Jevons were agreed. "The expression Laws of Nature", Mill tells us, "means nothing but the uniformities which exist among natural phenomena when reduced to their simplest expression"; and a few pages later informs us that the uniformity which exists among natural phenomena is nothing but the relation of Cause and Effect. Doubtless nowadays the views of Mill are completely discredited, and he is regarded as an awful warning to those who would pronounce sweeping judgements about science without studying it themselves rather than as the infallible mentor and doughty protagonist that he appeared to an earlier generation. But reaction always swings too far, and we are apt to forget that the intellect of one who influenced his generation so profoundly cannot have been altogether contemptible. It is worth while therefore to consider his views with some care; even if we ultimately reject them, they are likely to contain a grain of truth, the search for which will lead us to explore our subject thoroughly.

The precise investigation of the properties of the relation of cause and effect has filled so many pages that it would be a crime to add to their number. And after all since we are examining Mill's views the only matter that interests us is the properties which he attributed to that relation. Accordingly let Mill speak for himself. "To certain facts certain facts do, and, as we believe, always will, succeed. The invariable antecedent is called the cause; the invariable consequent, the effect."

These ideas are so familiar and so closely connected with all that we say and think about the external world that it would be paradoxical to dispute their validity. Accordingly, since they are to be criticised, it will be well at the outset to point out the limits of the criticism, in order that the appearance of extravagance may be avoided. There is, then, no intention to dispute that our experience of the external world may be, and often is, ordered in the form suggested by the causal relation; we do habitually divide that experience into portions one of which is prior to and regarded as the cause of the other; and this method of division not only leads to no error, but is the indispensable means to practical results of the highest importance. All this is agreed. What will be disputed is that the division of experience in accordance with the causal relation is the only kind of division which will reduce it to order, or that it is the division actually adopted in most scientific investigation. Again, since experience *can* be divided up according to the causal relation, there must be a great significance in the causal relation, even if the experience is divided in some other way. This again is agreed. What is disputed is the exact nature of that significance. To deny that the causal relation is as important in connection with scientific laws as was imagined by Mill is not to fly in the face of common sense. There is no need to dispute the common sense view of the matter. But science and common sense are not identical and would not be so even if it were true—as it is not—that science is nothing but organised common sense; for if they were identical, where would be the value of science?

But the most superficial examination by common sense shows that the realm of the relation of cause and effect is not quite so wide as is suggested by Mill's definition. The firmest believers in the universality of the causal relation admit difficulties. Thus, there is the hackneyed instance of the relation of day and night; each day invariably precedes the following night, and yet we do not regard that day as the cause of that night. Or, to take an even simpler example, if we allow a body to fall freely, its fall through the first foot precedes invariably its fall through the second; and yet the fall through the first foot is not usually regarded as the cause of the fall through the second. Every fact which precedes invariably another fact is not its cause. And that admission, which is made universally, opens the way to doubts whether the subject of cause and effect is quite as free from doubt as appears at first sight.

Do laws assert cause and effect? Let us then examine without prejudice a few examples of laws and discover whether they do indeed state relations of cause and effect defined as Mill defines it. But first it will be convenient to subject that relation to a slight analysis.

There are four elements in the relation of cause and effect which call for our special attention. First, the relation is invariable; second, it is temporal; third, it is asymmetrical, that is to say, it is such that if A has the relation to B, B has not the relation to A, so that if A is the cause and not the effect of B, B is not the cause but the effect of A; fourth, it is dual, that is to say, it is a relation between two terms only. The first element is probably identical with that which we intended when we spoke of the association asserted by laws being "uniform." Neither adjective, invariable or uniform, is so perfectly unambiguous that further inquiry is unnecessary or impossible; we shall have to inquire later whether the meaning which Mill attaches to the term, as indicated by his use of it, is such as we can accept and whether his word is preferable to that used here. But for the moment we may accept it as meaning nothing more nor less than the quality which it is agreed is most definitely characteristic of laws. It is only the second, third and fourth elements of the causal relation, as explained by Mill, which require our immediate attention.

Of the three laws which have served as examples so often, it is clear that one, the law of the association of the properties of silver, is not characterised by the causal relation. Not even Mill could maintain that one property of silver is the cause or the effect of another property[1]; but then Mill would doubtless have denied that the proposition, Silver exists, is a law, and we have not yet decided definitely that he is wrong. It may be that he is right, and that we are wrong in regarding it as a law. But it will be well to note exactly how the relation asserted by the proposition differs from the causal relation. In the first place, in our discussion of defining and non-defining qualities, we have seen that the third and fourth conditions cannot be fulfilled in this case at the same time; if the relation is expressed in the dual form it is symmetrical. In the second place—and this is far more important—it is not temporal. There is no necessary temporal relation whatever between the observation of the properties; we can observe that the substance melts at 960° either before or after, and at any interval before or after, observing that its density is 10·5. If, Silver exists, is indeed a law, it contains none of the elements of the causal relation except invariability.

Our next example is Ohm's Law. The relation here is certainly dual; it is stated between two terms, the current and the potential difference[2]. On the other hand, part, at least, of it is certainly symmetrical. The relation of proportionality asserted between current and potential difference is such that if the current bears it to the potential difference then the potential difference bears it to the current. The question whether the relation is temporal is rather more difficult. There is certainly a temporal relation between current and potential difference more definite than that between the melting point and density of silver. In fact we often assume (e.g. in the treatment of electric waves incident on a conductor) that changes of current and potential difference, or electric intensity, are simultaneous. If that is true, the relation, though temporal, will not be that characteristic of cause and effect, for it is symmetrical. But perhaps, if conduction is to be interpreted by the action of electrons possessing inertia, the strict truth of that statement is doubtful. However I do not think that the temporal relation is involved in Ohm's Law at all. Even if changes in current and changes in potential are not strictly simultaneous, Ohm's Law certainly does not state

[1] There is a sense in which one property may be the cause of another; for instance, it would not be unreasonable to say that the high electrical conductivity of silver is the cause of its good reflecting power. We shall have to inquire later what "cause" in this sense means, but for the present I think everyone will recognise that it does not mean what we are discussing here.

[2] In very bad text-books Ohm's Law is sometimes stated in the form that the current is proportional to the potential difference and inversely proportional to the resistance. Of course the latter part of this statement is either a tautology or meaningless; resistance has no meaning except the constant ratio of potential difference to current. If it means that, the second half of the statement means exactly the same thing as the first; if it does not mean that, it means nothing at all which is relevant to Ohm's Law. It is no excuse for the confusion created by such blunders that they have been committed by many eminent persons, even if the original author of the law is among the number—but I do not think he was.

which precedes the other; even if the temporal relation is not quite certain, the uncertainty introduces not the smallest doubt in our belief in the truth of the law, which cannot therefore be concerned with that relation. So far as Ohm's Law is concerned, the relation between current and potential difference is no more temporal than that between the melting point and density of silver.

On the other hand, there does appear to be some temporal element and some asymmetry in the relation asserted by Hooke's Law. The asymmetry is the more obvious, for it certainly seems that the force "produces" the extension in a manner in which the extension does not "produce" the force. Nor is it certain that the asymmetry is not temporal, for, while the extension can be reasonably thought to be produced after the application of the force, it is difficult to conceive of the force being produced after the occurrence of the extension. However, even if the causal relation is part of the relation asserted by Hooke's Law, it is not the whole of the relation. If we examine more closely we shall see that the causal relation is involved only in that part of the law which consists in stating that a given force A produces a given extension B. But this is not all that the law states; not the least important part of it states something which is concerned not with any special A and B, but with the whole possible series of A's and B's; it is this part that we assert when we say that the extension is proportional to the force. It would be perfectly possible for an observer to be aware of every special relation between a given A and the corresponding B, and yet not to be aware of the relation of proportionality which connects all of the special cases. Now this relation of proportionality is not causal, for it is not temporal and it is symmetrical; accordingly, even in the case of Hooke's Law, cause and effect, though they may represent part of the law, do not represent the whole of it.

This conclusion is so obvious that it is difficult to imagine how anybody could overlook it. On the one hand we have a very common suggestion that all true laws are numerical laws (see p. 43), and on the other the suggestion that the characteristic relation of all laws is that of cause and effect. The two views are directly contradictory; the more completely numerical is a law, the less is the causal relation involved in it. How then did so acute a person as Mill overlook this plain conclusion? Chiefly doubtless because he failed to recognise, as his writings show, that the assertion of proportionality was something different from and additional to the assertion of the particular magnitudes related in every special case; when he said that all laws were causal he was thinking of them as stating merely a set of relations, each between a given A and a given B. But even then it might have been expected that the example of Ohm's Law would have convinced him of his error; for this law also can be partially and incompletely stated in the form of a set of relations each between a given current and a given potential difference; and yet even in this part of the law the relation does not appear to be causal.

Experiments and causes. If, however, we regard the matter in a different light, the distinction between Ohm's Law and Hooke's Law in the matter of causality will almost vanish. We might carry out our experiments to prove Ohm's Law in two ways. In our first experiment, we might connect in series a wire of constant resistance, an ammeter and a constant battery; we might then vary the current by inserting shunts in parallel with the wire and the ammeter. In the second experiment, instead of inserting shunts, we might change the number of cells in the battery. In both experiments, after the adjustment was made, we should take readings of the ammeter and of a voltmeter connected in parallel with the wire. Now the results of the first experiment we should probably describe by saying that changes in the current produce proportional changes in the potential difference between the ends of the wire; those of the second by saying that changes in the potential difference produce proportional changes in the current. If we express the law in either of these two ways we seem to introduce the causal relation; for "produced by" is a relation from which it is difficult to dissociate the temporal and asymmetrical character which determines the causal relation. That relation does not appear in the law stated simply in the form that current and potential difference are proportional, because, if we state the law in that form, we are not thinking about the way the experiment is made but only about its result; we are implying that the two methods of conducting the experiment are precisely equivalent and that there is no real distinction of any importance between them. If one of the methods appeared in any way more fundamental than the other, the relation between current and potential difference would not be symmetrical; but as both appear equally fundamental and it makes not the slightest difference whether current is regarded temporarily as cause or as effect, the causal relation is immaterial and must be omitted in the complete statement of the law.

But now let us turn to Hooke's Law. Here only one method of experiment seems possible. We may apply the force to the rod in many different ways, but in all of them we have to apply the force and then observe the extension; there seems no second method in which we can make the extension and then observe the force, for there is no way of extending the rod except by applying force to it[1]. But without making any change in the experimental

---

[1] Of course the rod can be extended by heating it, but this violates the conditions for the law, which is only true if the temperature is constant. Nevertheless a method is suggested by which, as in Ohm's Law, the direction of the causal relation might be reversed; for we can make the rod produce force by heating it, fixing the end and allowing it to contract. But I do not think this really provides a way out of the difficulty. When the rod has cooled and contracted and is exerting force, what Hooke's Law states is a relation between this force and the excess of the length of the rod over that which it would have if the force were removed. To state that the rod produces force on contracting is not to state Hooke's Law, for, according to that law, force on the rod in the direction produced by contraction (i.e. tension) is associated with expansion and not with contraction. If we are to regard the process as an example of Hooke's Law it must be in this fashion. The rod cools; its natural length diminishes; an obstacle prevents its attaining its natural length; and a force produced by the obstacle pulls the rod out to more than its natural length. In that process it is, as before, the force which produces the extension, not the extension which produces the force.

I insert this note because it was only in the last revision of this chapter that I found that some serious fallacies had been based on the idea that by this process a second method could be found of proving Hooke's Law in which, as for Ohm's Law, the apparent relation of cause and effect was reversed.

arrangements, I think it is possible to reverse the apparent direction of cause and effect simply by putting the matter in rather a different way. It will make no material difference to the meaning of the law if we consider the force exerted by the rod rather than the force exerted on the rod; for the use of the word force implies that these two are equal. If there were some word which denoted the two indifferently we should be perfectly willing to substitute it for force in the statement of the law; perhaps such a word may be found in "stress[1]". Consider now what happens when we place a weight on the end of the rod and remove the support of our hand. The weight begins to fall; in so doing it stretches the rod and the extension of the rod produces a force which brings the weight to rest. If we look at the matter in that light, it appears that the extension produces the force and not the force the extension; the direction of the causal relation is reversed.

These considerations are intended to indicate that, even when the law can be so expressed as to make a causal relation evident, a slight alteration in the method of statement reverses the direction of that relation without making any important change in the law; and that, consequently, the causal relation is in no way essential to the law, but arises from circumstances that are really irrelevant to it. To confirm this conclusion we must examine what are these circumstances. The example of Ohm's Law shows that they are connected with the precise manner in which the experiment proving the law is made. Now that we are familiar with Ohm's Law, we are perfectly aware that, whether we change the circuit by means of a shunt or by inserting more cells in the battery, we are changing at the same time both the current and the potential difference. But if we did not know that law, we should not know that the two kinds of change were equivalent. We can attribute to both current and potential difference a meaning quite apart from the truth of the law; we need not inquire what those meanings are; it is sufficient to observe that they are such that the current through a circuit is changed by a shunt and the potential difference across it by inserting cells. In the investigation of Ohm's Law, current or potential difference appears as the cause, according as the change made in the circuit is such that, even if the law were not true, the current or the potential difference would be altered by that change; in the investigation of Hooke's Law, extension or force appears as the cause according as the change is regarded so that, even if the law were not true, extension or force would be expected as a result of the change. The direction of the causal relation depends entirely on the ideas which are in our mind when we begin the experiment. If we are thinking of current or of force on the rod when we design the experiment, then current or force appears as the cause; if we are thinking of potential difference or extension then potential difference or extension appears as the cause.

Is cause and effect a relation of thought? Here, I think, we arrive at the matters which lie at the base of the conception of cause and effect. A great many changes which we observe, including all those concerned in any experiment (as distinct from observation), are the result of our voluntary

---

[1] Hooke's original statement, Sic tensio ut vis, seems to meet the case.

action exerted through the muscles of our limbs; and in all such changes one part is psychologically prior to another. We say to ourselves, I will make such and such a change and observe what happens; and if we say that, the idea of the change that we make voluntarily is necessarily in our minds before the remainder of the change which we observe. For even if the two parts of the change occur really simultaneously (as they do in Ohm's Law or Hooke's Law), one part is present in our mind before either of the changes happens, while the other is not. If we regard only the course of our thoughts, the changes are connected by a temporal and asymmetrical relation; one change enters our thoughts before the other; the relation between our thoughts about the change is to this extent similar to the causal relation.

But it is not similar to the causal relation in respect of the first element which we noted on p. 58; the relation is not invariable. For mere thinking about one part of the change is not invariably or uniformly connected with thinking about the other. I may think about the first change, decide to make it and then change my mind and not make it; or I may make it, and then my attention may be distracted and I may fail to observe or think about the other part of the change. The relation about the thoughts of the change, though temporal and asymmetrical, is not invariable; it is not therefore the causal relation. Moreover it should be noted that the relation is temporal and asymmetrical only because it is associated with voluntary action; it is only because I voluntarily decide to make the first change, and therefore am forced to contemplate it before I make it, that I think about it before the second. Now voluntary action is inseparably connected with personality; it is the possibility of voluntary action which makes personality interesting and important. But we have agreed that nothing can be scientific or a proper basis for the investigations of science unless it is wholly freed from any taint of personality. Accordingly the relation between the thought which we are considering would not be in any case one that is important for science; even if it were in some sense a causal relation it would not be the causal relation with which science is concerned. Of course, if relations established voluntarily were invariable and uniform, we should probably not form the conception of personality and should have no reason not to include such relations in the study of science, for universal agreement about them would probably be obtainable. What we are saying is only that the relation is no more invariable when its occurrence in different people is concerned than when its occurrence in ourselves is concerned. But the distinction is sufficiently important to deserve separate expression.

The intimate relation between voluntary action and cause and effect probably accounts for the importance that has been attributed to that relation. All early thought on natural phenomena was anthropomorphic; the actions taking place in the natural world were always assimilated to actions in which men were concerned. It was observed that a great many changes which took place were the result of the voluntary action of men, and it was concluded that those changes which were not obviously produced by human action were produced by the action of beings, demons or gods, not very different from men. In all human action the psychological relation of cause and effect was evident; one part of the change was prior to another in the sense that it was thought of earlier, and it was therefore supposed that the same relation obtained in the actions of non-human beings. Now, interpreted in this manner, the voluntary actions of non-human beings appeared slightly (but only slightly) more uniform and invariable than those of men, and hence invariability, as well as temporal asymmetry, came to be associated with the relation underlying natural, as distinct from human, phenomena. The Laws of Nature were the Laws of God; and such uniformity as could be expressed by them were only an indication of the invariability of God's wishes; their vagaries—miracles and such like—represented the results of His occasional moods of ill-temper and wilfulness or His still more occasional moods of beneficence.

Of course nobody would venture to express such views to-day even from the security of the pulpit; but their effect survives in our language and to a much slighter extent in our thought. It is only, I believe, because all changes are still associated vaguely and loosely in our minds with changes produced by voluntary action that it is not perfectly evident that the relation of cause and effect, characterised by temporal asymmetry, plays a very small part in those natural uniformities which are expressed by laws.

Our conclusion is then that, in the case of Ohm's Law and Hooke's Law, the relation between the concepts concerned does not satisfy at once all the conditions for the causal relation. If we consider only our thoughts about the concepts then the relation is temporal and asymmetrical, but not invariable; if we consider the concepts themselves then it is invariable, but not temporal and asymmetrical. For if we neglect everything which passes through our minds as we decide to bring about the changes, and consider only our observations of the changes when they occur, we shall be quite unable to decide whether one occurs before or after the other. If the law means, as it does, that a certain change observed in the ammeter is invariably associated with a certain change observed in the voltmeter, then however carefully we observe the changes we shall be unable to decide that they are not simultaneous. Similarly in Hooke's Law, the occurrence of the extension is simultaneous with the application of the force. The only difference between the laws is this. Owing to certain associations of ideas we find no difficulty whatever in thinking either about the current before the potential or about the potential before the current; whereas we do find difficulty in thinking about the extension before the force, while there is no difficulty in thinking about the force before the extension. The reason is largely historical; we have clear conceptions of what is meant by a current and a potential difference which are quite independent of Ohm's Law, and were developed before Ohm's Law was known; so that we can think of either without thinking of the other and can devise experiments in which, apart from Ohm's Law, one can be changed without the other. On the other hand, the notion of the extension of a rod (at constant temperature) or of any change of its size or shape is very difficult to separate from the notion of the application of force to it, because none of us have passed through a period in which we were aware that rods could be extended without being also aware that such extension could be and usually is produced by the application of force. Moreover the very phrase "force *on* the rod" suggests that the force is the "cause" of some change in the rod; the suggestion was reversed, as we saw, if we spoke of force *by* the rod. Though we know now that force and extension are simultaneous, we are so accustomed to think of extension as produced by force that it is always force which occurs first to our mind when we think of any connection between the two.

Mill's error arose from the fact that, since he was not a man of science and had not his instinctive knowledge of what laws mean, he attributed far too much importance to the details of the experiment by which a law is proved. He thought that each law was proved by one experiment and one only, and quite overlooked the fact that entirely different experiments are precisely equivalent in the proof of the same law. In any given experiment the psychological causal relation can nearly always be traced, for the word experiment connotes something undertaken voluntarily, and voluntary action always implies that the change which is made voluntarily is thought about before it actually occurs. But this voluntary priority of part of the change is entirely irrelevant to the purposes of science; it can be directly reversed without changing in any way the significance of the law which is proved.

Are any laws causal? Processes. All laws then do not state the relation of cause and effect. Do any laws state it? It may seem that our answer here must be in the affirmative, for the invariable temporal sequences which common sense recognises as cause and effect have to be introduced somehow into our laws. If we rule out from our laws all causal relations, how are we to express in them the undoubted fact that some processes take time for their accomplishment?

Now there certainly are propositions, which may be regarded as laws, which do state undeniable relations of cause and effect. Thus when we say that the passage of a certain spark through a mixture of hydrogen and oxygen produces an explosion, we certainly mean that the spark must pass before the explosion occurs; and there is no means of varying the way the experiment is conducted, or even the way in which it is thought about, which will make the explosion occur before the spark passes or appear to produce the spark. And if we inquire carefully we shall find that there is a definite time interval which can be measured between the passage of the spark and the occurrence of the explosion. Whenever it appears impossible to reverse the apparent relation of cause and effect we shall find the same feature, namely that there is evidence to believe that there is a measurable interval between the two connected changes; and conversely when there is no reason to believe that there is such a measurable interval we can always by changing the experiment, or the way we think about it, reverse the apparent causal relation. It would seem then that the original expectation was correct and that laws dealing with phenomena which take time must involve the causal relation.

But further inquiry makes even this conclusion doubtful. Consider the very simple example which was quoted at the beginning of our inquiry, the law of a falling body. We say that a body falls 490 cm. in the first second after it is released, 1470 cm. in the next second and, generally, $490(2n-1)$ cm. in the nth second. Here we are stating an undeniable temporal asymmetrical relation between the distances fallen in the first and subsequent seconds; the fall of 1470 cm. is necessarily after the fall of 490 cm. And yet we do not regard the fall in the first second as the cause of the fall in the subsequent seconds. That is to say, even when we obtain an undoubted case of invariable temporal asymmetry, we do not always call it cause and effect; we may call it an instance of two effects of the same cause. Further we do not usually state the law of falling bodies in the form that the distance fallen in the nth second is $490(2n-1)$ cm.; we state it in the form that the acceleration of a falling body is independent of the distance fallen and equal to 980 cm./(sec.)^2. And we do not adopt this form merely because it is a shorter and neater statement; we regard it as altogether a more fundamental statement. But in adopting it we have abandoned altogether the relation of cause and effect. For though it might be possible to express the matter formally so that the acceleration appears as the cause of the distance fallen in any particular second, the ideas associated with a constant acceleration are really directly contradictory to those associated with the causal relation.

For the causal relation, as we have seen, is derived ultimately from the study of those changes in the external world which are the result of voluntary action; it involves necessarily the idea of a sequence of individual events, each connected in a special manner with that which precedes it. But there is another kind of change which is equally noteworthy and characteristic, namely the change which appears to go on of its own accord and without any instigation. Perhaps the most typical instance of such change is the motion of a body with uniform velocity, which Newtonian mechanics regards as essentially spontaneous and "uncaused." A change of this kind, a "process" as it will be called here, may be discontinuous at the beginning and at the end; it may begin with an event, which is its cause, and end with an event, which is its effect; but the process itself is continuous and does not consist of events between which any relation of cause and effect can subsist.

This common sense view of processes leads to a special form of scientific law just as the common sense view of voluntary action leads to the causal form of scientific view. What exactly this form is we shall have to consider more closely when we deal with "time." But it is clear that the idea of a process enables us to order events which are consecutive in time just as well as the idea of cause and effect; and I think it will be judged that, when the two alternatives are both possible, we prefer the idea of a process to that of cause and effect. The preference is illustrated by the falling body, but it may be suspected also in the case of the explosion. We are forced at present, owing to deficiency of knowledge, to state the relation between the spark and the explosion as causal; but we feel that if we knew more about it, we might be able to state it in the form that a process starts in the gas when the spark passes, and, after continuing some time, becomes (not causes) an explosion. If we could state the law in that form it would be more satisfactory; the use of the causal relation in a law is a confession of incomplete knowledge.

The part that causal relations play in actual laws will often be considered in connection with definite examples. But I hope that the observations which have been made are sufficient to convince the reader that such relations are by no means essential to science and that they play a much less important part in it than is often imagined. So little is it our object to order our external judgements in terms of cause and effect that our efforts are consistently directed to ridding ourselves of the necessity for employing cause and effect at all.

But one further point should be noted. It may be suggested that by describing temporal changes in terms of processes, we do not really get rid of the causal relation; for the process is started by an event which is its cause and ends in another which is its effect. In certain cases this is true, but it is not true in all cases. For consider again the case of the falling body; the "cause" of the acceleration, if there is one, is the presence of the body in the earth's gravitational field; since, however, the "cause" is simultaneous with and not precedent to the "effect," the supposed causal relation is not that contemplated by Mill. As a matter of fact some philosophers have been led, by arguments not very different from those which we have just considered, to conclude that Mill was wrong and that cause and effect are generally simultaneous. Now of course if anyone cares to call "cause and effect" a temporally symmetrical relation between simultaneous events it is not worth while to argue with him concerning the mere use of words; but it must be insisted that such a relation is utterly different from that which common sense calls cause and effect. If we are right in believing that the notion is based on the psychological priority of one part of an experiment, temporal asymmetry is absolutely essential to it; and it is only against this special temporal asymmetry of the relation stated by laws that the foregoing criticism has been directed.

The importance of laws. But if the relation asserted by laws is not that of cause and effect, what is it?

A complete answer to this question could only be given as a result of an examination of all the actual laws of physics and their careful analysis. If it were given now it would necessarily anticipate the results of the remainder of this treatise, but since there is no pretence of developing the subject in its logical order, this of itself would be no objection. However, even when our whole inquiry is completed, I fear that we shall not be in a position to give a definite answer. There are probably many different relations asserted by laws, and to distinguish accurately between them would doubtless need skill in logical analysis which is far beyond my reach. I believe that a detailed examination of laws with a view to the elucidation of the nature of the relations involved in them would yield valuable and important results, and I hope that someone else may undertake the task.

There remains however the possibility that all the relations asserted by laws possess some common part or some common feature; the discovery of this common part or feature would serve our immediate purpose almost as well as a complete analysis. For it would enable us to distinguish laws from other propositions, and it would probably enable us to attack successfully the problem to which our present inquiry is really directed, namely that of the method by which laws are established. But before we can achieve even this limited aim one question which has been raised several times and never answered must be definitely settled. Which among known propositions are to be included in the class of laws? Is every proposition a law which is usually so called and none a law to which that name is never given? Among what propositions are we to search for the common part of the relation?

Let us be clear what we are asking. It is not really about the use of words; the fact that two propositions are called by the same term is of no importance to us, unless it indicates that both of them have some common feature and that this feature is the one with which we are concerned. It has been pointed out already that the name Law may be given or refused to a proposition by reason of historical accident or a slight change in complexity; such features are not important. What features are important? Can we find any feature which is possessed by most propositions now called laws and is such that, if it could be established that any other proposition possesses that feature, it would be recognised that its importance for science is the same as that of those propositions? This is really what is asked.

Now when we are discussing the importance of laws, the only verdict which is either possible or necessary is that of the jury of serious students of science. The only persons who are in a position to judge whether a proposition is important for science, or whether it is as important as some other proposition, are those to whom science is the first concern of their intellectual life. No proof of the statements which are about to be made can be offered to those who are not serious students of science and no appeal made against the judgements of those who are; science is simply the study of students of science. I believe that what will be said will be accepted by all such students, and, if it is, their agreement is all that is required.

The object of science is the ordering of natural phenomena, the reduction to a reasoned system of the chaos of individual judgements of the external world. A law is important for science because it represents the achievement of one stage in this ordering; it establishes a connection between a large number of previously disconnected observations. A law is the more important the more complete this achievement, the larger is the number of observations which it connects, and the more "orderly" is the connection. The orderliness of a connection is to be judged primarily and ultimately by the intellectual satisfaction which it gives, for the attainment of intellectual satisfaction is the end of science as of all other branches of pure learning. But, as we know, science has another value which is not purely intellectual; it enables us to exercise some control over natural processes which affect our material comfort and convenience.

Now whether we regard the intellectual value or the practical value of science, it is evident that it arises chiefly from the invariability of the connection established. "Invariability," to my mind, and I think to that of Mill, implies simply the possibility of indefinite repetition; a connection is invariable when, after having observed it on one occasion, I can return later and always observe it again. It is, of course, invariability in this sense which gives to science its practical value; it is because the connections between observations established by science are invariable that they can be used for prediction; and it is the power to predict that gives the power to control. But invariability is also essential to the intellectual value of science. The mass of material which science has to order is not a complete whole; it constantly receives addition with every moment of our conscious existence. If every fresh addition to the material rendered necessary the establishment of fresh connections, the task of science in ordering the material could never be complete; we should be in the position of Tristram Shandy who took three years to write the story of his first three days[1], and we should abandon the task in despair. It is only because the connections which we have found useful in ordering the material that has already accumulated turn out to be equally useful in ordering new material as it accumulates that we are able and willing to engage in the pursuit of science at all. This applicability of relations based on the old material to the new material is what is meant by invariability.

Invariability then is one essential element in the relation established by any law which has importance for science; but it is not the only element. We could always achieve invariability by narrowing sufficiently the observations between which the connection is established. If we established a connection between observations so special that we could be certain that exactly those observations would never occur again, we could be certain that the future accumulation of material would never force us to abandon the connection established. But invariability secured in that manner would be as worthless both for practical and intellectual purposes as variability. The observations between which the invariable connection is established must be so general that we are sure that they will occur again; and the more general they are and the more likely they are to occur again, the more important and valuable will be the invariable relation. Generality, therefore, is as important an element of the relation of laws as invariability.

Further generality in this sense includes definiteness. Just as a relation could always be made invariable by restricting its scope sufficiently, so also it could be made invariable by making it sufficiently vague and indefinite.

[1] Mr Russell, as is well known, maintains that it is untrue that the life would "never" be completed. But his conclusion seems to be based on a meaning attributed to "never" which is quite different from that employed in ordinary discourse.

A law is the more useful and important, the more completely instances are divided up into cases which are so definite that further division is impossible, and the more the number of cases to which the law is applicable is increased by such subdivision; it is through this increase in the number of cases by subdivision that generality and definiteness are associated. The substitution of numerical quantitative laws for merely qualitative laws is an excellent example of the increase in the value of a law due to increase in generality and definiteness. It is much less satisfactory to say that the current through a wire increases with the potential difference across it than to state a numerical relation between the two; for the numerical law allows us to distinguish between different cases, to all of which the law is applicable, which the qualitative law would regard as a single instance. If the view, suggested before, that only numerical laws are entitled to be termed laws means that no law which is not numerical has all the complete characteristics and all the highest value of a law, then it must be admitted. It is only by introducing the definiteness which can be given by measurement alone that the element of invariability can be fully developed. On the other hand definiteness is a matter of degree and is possessed also in some measure by the qualitative law from which the quantitative law is developed. Unless there is some difference in kind in the relation which produces a difference in kind in importance, qualitative as well as quantitative propositions should be admitted for our present purpose to the class of laws.

Invariability and generality are then two of the necessary elements which give to laws their importance. It is the combination of these two closely associated elements which I intend by the word "uniformity"; I prefer that word to invariability, because the latter seems to omit one essential part of the necessary feature. There will probably be no dispute that uniformity is essential to laws and the basis of their importance, but it is still possible that there is some other element which is equally necessary. I cannot discover for myself that there is such an element and I do not feel that it is necessary. It seems to me that the importance of a law is directly proportioned to the degree of uniformity, including both invariability and generality, concerned in the relation asserted by it; and that so long as the relation is characterised by uniformity the rest of its nature is entirely unimportant. I do not feel that I should have any hesitation in accepting as part of a law, ordering natural phenomena, any form of relation whatever so long as it was uniform. It must be admitted, of course, that this feeling may only result from insufficient analysis and imagination, and that it might be possible to suggest a case which would not be covered by the criterion.

But there is this to be said in favour of the opinion, that it is extremely trite and that this long discussion has only established something which nobody ever doubted. We have returned to Mill's definition: "The expression Laws of Nature means nothing but the uniformities which exist among natural phenomena." If he had left it there, we should have been in perfect agreement with him. And his further elaboration of the definition was probably not due to a belief that, out of several kinds of uniformities, only one kind was asserted by laws, but to a belief that there is only one kind of uniformity, namely that consisting of the relation of cause and effect. Our difference from him is merely that we deny that all uniformities consist of causal relations.

Accordingly in future we shall regard as laws all propositions which assert uniformities discovered by experiment or observation, and shall not regard as laws any which do not assert such uniformities. It is clear that the question, which has been left unsettled so long, namely whether the propositions giving rise to the concepts "substances" are truly laws, is to be answered in the affirmative.

The nature of uniformity. But while we admit that any relation of uniformity might characterise a law, we must inquire rather more closely what is the nature of the relations which are actually employed.

In the first place a question may be asked which is of some importance when the method by which laws are established is considered. When a law asserts uniformity, does it assert something additional to any other relation which may be asserted by the law or is the uniformity involved in the nature of the relation asserted? Can the law be analysed into a statement that there is a certain relation between the terms of the law and a further assertion that this relation is uniform, or is the uniformity necessarily asserted by the assertion of the relation?

I think the answer is that both these possibilities may occur, and that they may both occur in the same law. Thus Ohm's Law may be divided into two sections, one of which states a long series of relations between a given current and a given potential difference, while the other states a feature which is characteristic of all these relations and inseparable from the collection of all of them, namely proportionality. The first section states that there is a certain relation between a current i and a potential difference V, which we describe by saying that in certain conditions they are associated; it further states that this relation of association is uniform; that it is invariable in the narrower sense and general over a certain range of the determining conditions. Here the uniformity can be separated from other relations stated by the law; the law states certain relations and then asserts that they are uniform. On the other hand, the second section states a relation in the very meaning of which uniformity is involved; proportionality, like any other mathematical relation involving the conception of a variable, is a relation from which a certain generality is inseparable; if the relation had not this generality which is a form of uniformity, then it would not be proportionality. Here uniformity is inseparable from the relation asserted by the law.

And, as might be expected, it appears that, when the uniformity is separable from the remainder of the law its nature is not the same as when it is inseparable. In the first case invariability is the more important part of the uniformity, although generality is also characteristic; in the second case only generality and not invariability is concerned. Accordingly we distinguish at once two kinds of uniformity; I believe that this division can be applied to all forms of uniformity asserted by laws. Such uniformity is always either of the kind asserted by the first section of Ohm's Law, consisting of what will be termed a "uniform association" (written for brevity U.A.) between certain concepts or collections of observations interconnected by a law, or it is of the kind asserted by the second section and consists of the functionality which is applicable to mathematical variables. Of course it is not pretended that the uniformity of each of these two kinds is always the same; there are multitudes of mathematical uniformities, all distinguishable from each other and each connected with a different function. Similarly there are probably multitudes of uniform associations; they are not so easily distinguished, but the differences are doubtless connected with the differences of the relation which is called association and is asserted to be uniform. All that is meant is that the relation asserted by any law may be classed either as a uniform association or as a functionality, and that it is the common properties of members of these classes and not their differences which are important in any such survey of scientific investigation as is undertaken here. In what follows therefore we need only concern ourselves with these classes, and indeed only with the first of them; for the mathematical conception of functionality has been so completely discussed by competent authorities that I should only blunder if I attempted to add to what they have said.

Uniform association. Is it dual? Uniform association is then a relation characteristic of laws and such that the uniformity can be separated from the rest of the relation. It cannot be defined, for it is one of the most important indefinables of science; we only paraphrase the assertion of it, if we say that it means that certain observations or groups of observations always occur in certain relations, so that if some of them are observed, then the others can be observed. Cause and effect is a special form of uniform association, and the main object of the first part of this chapter was to establish that there are forms other than cause and effect. But though we cannot define it, we may yet ask further questions about its nature, and we may usefully consider how many of the properties of the special form are possessed by all forms.

It has already been decided that U.A. is not always temporal or asymmetrical. The example of the law "Silver exists" shows that it is certainly not always dual. For that law clearly involves many terms, namely all the various properties of silver. We may now go to the other extreme and ask if it is ever temporal or asymmetrical or dual. Laws are obviously sometimes temporal; of the other two qualities duality must receive attention first, for only a dual relation can be either symmetrical or asymmetrical in the simple sense.

Laws are often expressed in a dual form—Ohm's Law and Hooke's Law are obvious examples—and it is this duality which has led largely to the idea that the relation asserted is causal. But this mode of expression is adopted only because a great part of the law is not stated explicitly at all. If Ohm's Law is to be true the statement must be qualified by the assertion that the body to which it is to be applied is one of a certain class, chiefly metals and electrolytes. The full law will therefore include other concepts than the current and the potential; it asserts a relation not between two terms but between many. Similarly Hooke's Law requires the qualification that it shall only be applied to certain bodies and the further qualification that the temperature of the body does not change. In these laws the appearance of duality is misleading. On the other hand the law of the properties of silver, which appears at first sight not to be dual, is seen on closer inspection to be expressible in the dual form. For if we divide the properties of silver into two classes, one of which includes all the properties except one and the other of which includes only the remaining one, then we might assert that the second class was uniformly associated with the first; whenever the first is observed then the second can be observed also. The conventional method of stating laws must clearly be disregarded in answering this question; a deeper inquiry is necessary.

One way may be suggested in which, in spite of the necessity for the introduction of qualifying conditions, it might be possible to state Ohm's Law completely and yet in the dual form. It may be that Ohm's Law may be considered to state that (the current in a metal or electrolyte) is proportional to (the potential difference in the same metal or electrolyte), the words in brackets each representing a single term. But I do not think that this is what the law states; for if it is, our conclusion that laws state relations between concepts would have to be abandoned. The law which gives rise to the concept "current" is just as true in a gas as in a metal or electrolyte; in both mediums certain magnetic actions are associated with the transference of certain quantities of electricity along certain paths. There is no law which defines a current in a metal which is not also true of a current in a gas, and the limitation expressed by the words in the first bracket would indicate that this term did not denote observations interconnected by a law; the term would not be a concept. Since it appears necessary in view of future difficulties to maintain the view that such laws always state relations between concepts, the possibility of converting the relation stated by Ohm's Law into a dual relation in this way must be abandoned. Is there any other way?

The restatement of the law that silver exists was possible because it seems to consist of the assertion that a large number of terms a, b, c, d, ... are uniformly associated together, each term being related to the others in exactly the same way. If this is the nature of the relation stated by the law, then it would seem to follow that the term a is uniformly associated with the complex term (b, c, d, ...). But if the terms are not all involved in the relation in the same way, this conclusion would not seem to follow. Now I do not feel sure that the term (metal or electrolyte) is involved in Ohm's Law in the same way as the terms current and potential difference; or rather, since I am sure that it is not involved in the same way, I am not sure whether the difference is sufficient to prevent the resolution of the complex relation between many terms into a dual relation between two terms. For part of this difference arises only in what has been called the second section of the law, namely that which asserts proportionality; but in this section uniform association is not involved at all; that relation is only involved in the first section which states that a certain current is associated with a certain potential difference. In this section, are the current, the potential difference and the metallic or electrolytic nature of the body associated in the same way as the properties of silver? and, if not, what is the precise nature of the difference?

These questions may be thought too subtle ; but subtlety is no excuse for neglect. The matter has been discussed chiefly in order to show that there are interesting problems connected with the structure of laws which are, as far as I know, still unattacked and unsolved; my object has been chiefly to instigate others to solve them. What we want is an analysis of the relational structure of laws as complete (though not necessarily of the same nature) as that which has been elaborated recently for the propositions of pure mathematics. The solution of these problems would not in any way change the result attained by science and would not influence greatly its future developments, for the basis of the inquiry must be laws as they actually exist. But it would have considerable intrinsic interest and would probably have important consequences. Thus it would aid in the answering of the questions raised in the next chapter, namely those concerning the methods by which laws are established. One view of the nature of this method involves the assumption that laws are always discovered as dual relations; clearly if there are laws which cannot be expressed as dual relations, the whole of that method falls to the ground as applied to such laws.

Uniform association. Is it symmetrical? There is another question of some importance connected with and arising directly out of the question whether laws can be expressed by dual relations. If and when laws can be so expressed, is the dual relation symmetrical? that is to say, if the relation between A and B is such that, if A can be observed, B can be observed, then is it also such that, if B can be observed, A can be observed? The common sense answer to this question is that it is not. This answer does not depend on the assumption that the relation involved is the essentially asymmetrical cause and effect; for U.A. includes both the relation of cause to effect and the relation of effect to cause; and it is generally held that if A is the cause or effect of B, then B is the cause or effect of A. But it is also held that there may be cases in which, though A is the cause of B, B may also be produced by causes other than A, and cases in which, though B is the effect of A, A may have other effects than B. We are really asking whether this view, with the substitution of U.A. for the causal relation, is correct?

The common sense view of the matter is certainly incorrect; it is based simply on the neglect of the qualifying conditions. When it is said that extension may be the effect of force but may also be the effect of other things, such as increase of temperature, it is overlooked that extension is U.A. with force only if the qualifying condition is specified that there is no change of temperature; in any complete statement of the law the matter of temperature must be dealt with. If it is dealt with and the qualifying conditions are such that the extension cannot be produced by anything but force, then, if the law can be asserted in a dual form at all, involving a relation between force and extension, it would seem that the relation must be symmetrical, and that, if a certain extension is uniformly associated with a certain force, then that force is uniformly associated with that extension. However since it is very doubtful whether the relation can be expressed in this manner in a dual form, such considerations are of little use except to show how there enters into our discussion the problems usually raised under the terms "Plurality of Causes" and "Intermixture of Effects."

But the discussion becomes more definite when we turn to laws (which nobody has ever imagined to be causal) defining substances and relating their properties. For here the suggested analysis is probably near the truth, and the fundamental relation of U.A. is one between many terms, representing the many properties, each of which enters into the relation in the same manner as the others. If this is so, the relation can certainly be expressed in the dual form suggested on p. 73; but this form is certainly asymmetrical. Thus, if a body possesses all the other properties of silver, it will be soluble in nitric acid; but if it is soluble in nitric acid it will not necessarily possess all the other properties of silver. However a redistribution of the terms may lead to a symmetrical dual relation; for if two collections of properties $A, B, C, D, \ldots$ and $X, Y, Z, U, \ldots$ can be found such that each collection is characteristic of silver and possessed by no other element, then it will be true that if one collection is observed the other can be observed; if the relation asserted by the law "Silver exists" is taken to be the relation between these two collections, then it will be symmetrical.

Now this division will always be possible unless there are two substances which are distinguished by one property and one property only; so long as there are at least two properties in which a substance differs from any other substance, it is always possible to place one of these properties in one collection and the other in the other; each of the collections will then be characteristic of one substance alone and each will therefore be uniformly associated with the other. The question whether the law asserting that a substance exists can be asserted as a dual symmetrical relation is therefore resolved into the question whether two substances, regarded as distinct, can differ in one property and one only. If we proposed to answer this question in the affirmative it would be necessary to consider very carefully what we mean by a single property; but since, in spite of a tendency at first sight to admit that there might be such substances, it seems that the answer must be in the negative, there is no such necessity.

The example that naturally occurs when this question is asked is that of isomers and isotopes. Such bodies do always differ in respect of more than one property. Isomers differ not only in their chemical reactions but also in their melting points, solubilities and so forth. Isotopes differ not only in their parentage and products, but also in the range of the rays they emit. But suppose that there were only one property different. Suppose for example that the products of chlorinating phenol differed in nothing but their melting point. Then it might be possible to separate out three parts from the chlorinated mixture; but when they were examined they would all prove exactly the same. I think we should prefer to deny that a pure substance had always a constant melting point rather than to imagine three different substances[1]; in order to speak of three different substances, we require two different properties, one to separate them and the other to distinguish them when separated. Again, suppose that two radioactive substances produced exactly the same product; then I think these substances would be called the same in spite of their different parentage. Or if a substance produced two others differing in nothing by the rays they emitted or in the products to which they give rise, then I think we should speak not of different substances, but of the same substance breaking up in two different ways[2]. A closer examination will always show that the statement that there are two substances differing only in a single property is always avoided when the facts might justify it.

It appears then that the law that a substance exists can always be expressed as a symmetrical dual relation. This conclusion is of some importance because it enables a distinction to be made which clearly has to be made and is difficult to make otherwise.

Uniform association. Is it transitive? But before we consider this distinction it will be well to ask and consider another question similar to that which we have just discussed. The consideration will also lead us to some important conclusions. We have just inquired whether, if the law can be expressed in such a form that the relation of U.A. involved is dual, the relation is also symmetrical; we now ask whether, if it can be expressed in that form, the relation is transitive. A relation is said to be transitive if it is such that, if A bears it to B and B bears it to C, then A bears it to C.

It would seem at first sight that the answer must be in the negative. For the statement that A is U.A. with B means that, if A is observed, B can be observed; and that statement would imply that if A is observed, C cannot be observed, if C is different from B; if A is U.A. with B it cannot be U.A. with anything but B. If the U.A. is asymmetrical, it is possible that, though A is U.A. with B, B may still be U.A. with C, for, if the order of the terms is important, B does not bear the same relation to C as to A, and the statement that B is U.A. with C is not inconsistent with the statement that A is U.A.

---

[1] If the proportions in which the three parts occurred were constant then we might speak of different substances; but now there would be a second property in which they differed, namely the proportions in which they occurred in a mixture made by a certain process.

[2] It may be interesting to record that this passage was first written before isotopes were known and was altered later. Since, however, this example has actually become real since the passage was written just after the discovery of isotopes, it has been left.

with B. But the conclusion cannot follow that A is u.a. with C, because this conclusion, once more, is inconsistent with the statement that A is u.a. with B.

On the other hand, common sense certainly regards u.a. as sometimes transitive; indeed this conclusion seems to be involved in the assumptions made in the discussion in the first part of this chapter. For there we concluded that the proof of Hooke's Law by the use of the optical lever was justified on the ground that the application of a certain force was u.a. with a certain deflection of a spot of light, and that this deflection of the spot was u.a. with a certain extension of the rod. The conclusion from these premisses that the application of the force is u.a. with the extension involves necessarily the assumption that the u.a. involved is transitive. And yet argument is certainly valid.

The difficulty vanishes if we remember once more that the expression in the dual form of such laws as are involved here is essentially incomplete, and that the complete law must involve more terms, namely those specifying the qualifying conditions. The conclusion that A is u.a. with C would not be inconsistent with the statement that A is u.a. with B, if C were part of B. But if this were so, the statement that A is u.a. with C would not be a complete statement of the law; other terms (namely the part of B other than C) would be involved, and the full statement of the law would require the assertion of a relation involving these terms as well as A and B. But this observation does not explain immediately the argument under discussion; for C (the extension of the rod) cannot be regarded as part of B (the deflection of the spot). The argument is really this. I observe that, in certain conditions X, the application of the force is u.a. with the deflection of the spot. Now I know that, in certain other conditions Y, the deflection of the spot is u.a. with an extension of the rod. But the conditions Y include the conditions X, which are part of them; therefore in the conditions X the application of the force is u.a. with the extension of the rod.

The argument expressed in this form does not depend on the transitiveness of the relation of u.a.; it is similar rather to syllogistic deduction by means of a more general major premiss and a less general minor. Whenever we are considering any argument involving laws, it must be borne in mind that the expression of them in the conventional dual form is always elliptical and that any deduction which appears to depend on a necessary duality of u.a. cannot be strictly valid. However the expression of the law as a dual relation subject to certain qualifying conditions, though it is doubtless not entirely adequate, has some significance, and, since it is so widely adopted, may be used to raise the questions to which the discussion is intended to lead. We have seen that, if the law is stated by a dual relation, that relation must be regarded as transitive, and that arguments based on the assumption that it is transitive (and on the complete neglect of qualifying conditions) will often lead to true conclusions. Such arguments clearly require caution in their use; they are not likely to mislead those who have a true appreciation of the meaning of laws, but they may mislead and have misled others.

The problem has been raised partly in order to insist again on the need for a much more thorough investigation of the nature of laws than is usually undertaken, partly because it leads to other questions. One of these will be considered in Chapter V; another, which takes us back to the first part of this chapter, may be considered here. We have taken as an example the proof of Hooke's Law by means of the subsidiary laws of the reflection of light. We are led once more to ask what is the precise difference between these laws and the laws of dynamics which give rise to the concept force. I think we shall have to conclude that there is no formal difference whatever between the way that the laws of reflection are involved in Hooke's Law and the way that the laws of dynamics are involved. Just as our conclusion concerning extension is derived from our observation of the deflection of the spot by means of another known law which states in more general conditions a relation between deflection and extension, so our conclusion concerning the force exerted on the rod when the body is hung on it is based on a law which states in more general conditions a relation between this body and the force that it exerts. If it is asked why we say a given weight exerts a force of 2 kilogrammes weight, we shall show that the weight is U.A. with the balancing of two other weights, and that each of these weights again is U.A. with the balancing of the standard kilogramme. When we have established this series of U.A.'s we have done all that is necessary to prove that the given weight does actually exert a force of 2 kilogrammes weight and no other force, and that the relation between this force and the corresponding extension is· that asserted by the law. So far the process is exactly similar to that involved in the use of the optical lever to measure extension. But we noted that the importance of the laws of dynamics in respect of Hooke's Law concerns not so much the truth of the law as its meaning; the series of U.A.'s which has been established is sufficient to prove that the law is true, but it does not indicate why we express the result by the use of the term force. If we ask why we use that term, we shall find that we refer to U.A.'s between the weight and other things which are not examined in the process of establishing the law at all; we shall note the U.A. asserted when we say that the weight falls with a constant acceleration and the U.A. asserted when we describe the results of experiments on it with the ballistic pendulum. It is these U.A.'s which prove that the weight obeys the laws of dynamics, and therefore exerts and is subject to force. These U.A.'s form series which are side-chains to the main series of U.A.'s which establish Hooke's Law. In the main series we have the U.A. between the weight and the balancing of certain other weights; in the side chains the U.A. of constant acceleration under gravity and of conservation of momentum. The introduction of concepts into the statement of laws depends on the fact that a concept may be U.A. with more than one other concept; its U.A. with one other concept proves the truth of the law; its U.A. with others gives the law its significance and importance.

Now such side-chains of U.A.'s are to be found equally in the series involved in the use of the optical lever. The main series consists only in the establishment, for the special experimental arrangement used, of a connection between deflection of the spot and movement of the legs of the lever; the side-chains would establish, among other things, the law of equality of angles of incidence and reflection. Formally there seems no difference whatever between the two main series and the relations of the side-chains to them. The difference lies in the importance of the side-chains. Length and extension would be important physical concepts even if the laws of reflection of light were very different from what they are; but force would not be an important conception if the laws of moving bodies were very greatly changed. But what is the origin of this impotance? It is to be found, I suggest, in the part played by the laws in the process of measuring the concepts. We can measure length and extension without any reference to the laws of optics; we cannot measure force without reference to the laws of dynamics. But since it does not seem to be universally recognised how large a part is played by laws in all processes of measurement, the evidence for this view must be left to a later stage in the volume.

Nature of fundamental laws. One further question must be asked before we leave this branch of the subject. The terms of many laws, between which the laws assert U.A. or other uniform relation, are concepts, depending for their significance upon other laws; in fact in all the laws that have been taken as examples some at least of the terms are concepts. The inquiry into the nature of laws cannot be complete until we have examined the more fundamental laws by which these concepts are connected with terms which are not themselves concepts, but are fundamental judgements implying no other law. Enough has probably been said to show how very difficult any such examination must be. At first view Hooke's Law seemed quite a simple matter, involving only two of the judgements which have been recognised as fundamental and asserting that they are U.A.; there is a space-judgement concerning the position of the spot on the scale and a number-judgement concerning the group of standard kilogrammes balanced by the weight. But on further inquiry it is found that further laws were implied and that the experiments required to establish these laws are much more complex than that required to establish Hooke's Law. It is by no means an easy matter, as many writers have found, to say precisely what are the experiments concerned in the establishment of the laws of dynamics, and it is still less easy, if when we know what these experiments are, to analyse them into fundamental judgements. Moreover, speaking strictly, we should have said that Hooke's Law was true for solids; the law, There are solid bodies, is involved in it. This law, further, will be found to be involved in all the other laws which have been taken as examples; it is certainly involved in the laws of dynamics. The task of deciding what experiments are necessary and sufficient to prove that there are solid bodies is even more formidable than that of finding the experiments on which the laws of dynamics are based. Indeed it appears that the further we probe into laws and the more fundamental the laws which we examine, the greater are the complexities of the relations involved and the more difficult is it to analyse the relations into such as exist between fundamental judgements.

It may be confessed at once that no attempt will be made in this volume to analyse any law right down to the fundamental judgements on which it depends. The task may be possible, but a stage is always reached at which the concepts which it is attempted to analyse are so familiar, and so intimately involved in all our ordinary thoughts and speech, that it is very difficult to know whether any progress is being made; it is always doubtful whether the ideas into which another idea is analysed do not really involve the idea which is under analysis. However in our consideration of "time" and "space" we shall have to make some attempt at analysis, and face some of the very great difficulties which must be encountered. But at present all that we are concerned to know is whether, if the analysis could be completed, we should discover relations, stated by laws, different from and additional to those which have been considered already; or rather, since we have made no pretence to examine all the relations stated by laws, but only those in virtue of which they are laws, we only want to know whether we should find that the more elementary and complex laws, which underlie the apparently simple laws, are laws in virtue of any relation other than the uniformity which we have been discussing.

So far as I can make out, we should not find any such new relations. I think that the more elementary is the law the more important does the relation of uniform association become; and that if laws were analysed into their ultimate constituents the relation between those constituents, in virtue of which they are ordered in laws, would always be uniform association; further that it approaches more nearly to that form of uniform association which is characteristic of substances than to any of the others which we have considered. Now in some ways this form is simpler than any of the others. The terms which it relates are excessively numerous and the relation between them must have the complexity of any highly multiple relation; but on the other hand all the terms seem to be involved in the relation in the same way, and this feature has enabled us to analyse this form rather more satisfactorily than others. It may be therefore that the fundamental laws are really simpler and not more complex than the derivative; the apparent simplicity of the derivative laws is delusive, and only due to the fact that the relations involved in them are so complex that they are never stated in any but an incomplete form. It seems difficult to believe that the ideas of the more advanced portions of science are truly simpler than those of the more elementary portions.

Until the analysis is actually effected, these conclusions must be precarious, but they will be accepted for the purposes of the next stage in our inquiry. This next stage is to ascertain how laws are proved and what evidence is to be accepted for the truth of a law; it is to this problem that all the discussion of this chapter serves as a preliminary. For if we are to decide what evidence is necessary for the establishment of a relation, we must know the nature of the relation to be established. According to the view which we are going to adopt, this relation in the great majority of cases is uniform association, and it is to the establishment of this relation that most of our attention will be directed. In more complex laws, and especially numerical laws, other forms of uniformity are doubtless involved and determine that the proposition in which they are involved is a law. But the consideration of the establishment of these other forms will be postponed until we can examine the nature of the relations more closely.

Individual systems. However, before we pass to this inquiry, we must return to a matter mentioned on p. 76 and consider an important distinction connected with the conclusion that the law that a substance exists can be asserted in the form of a symmetrical dual uniform association of its properties.

This distinction is between substances and individual bodies or systems. I have in my pocket a threepenny bit; I say it is made of silver (not pure silver—but that does not matter). Now when I speak of a silver threepenny bit or say that it is made of silver, I am surely asserting a U.A., an association just as uniform as I assert when I speak of silver. For I mean that if I examine the bit and observe that it has certain properties, its size and shape and so on, then I can also observe the characteristic properties of silver; I am asserting a U.A. of properties just as truly as when I say that silver has a density of 10·5, meaning that this property of density is associated with the remaining characteristic properties of silver. Am I therefore asserting a law when I say that the bit is made of silver, and is there a law of the threepenny bit, the law, This threepenny bit exists? Of course not. But what is the difference? The discussion we have just left gives the answer. Though the association of the properties of the threepenny bit is uniform, the statement of it cannot be put as the assertion of a *symmetrical* dual U.A.; the U.A. is essentially asymmetrical. For there are properties distinguishing threepenny bits from shillings and other things made of silver; further there is some one property, distinguishing this threepenny bit from all other threepenny bits; for if there were not I should not be able to speak of *this* threepenny bit. Here then we do really meet the case of a substance with one and only one distinguishing property, and in this case, as we saw, the U.A. concerned must be asymmetrical. Though, if we observe the threepenny bit, we can observe the characteristic properties of silver, it is not true that if we observe those properties we can always observe the threepenny bit. Individual bodies and systems are then such that their properties are, like those of substances, connected by a U.A.; but the U.A. expressed in the dual form is necessarily asymmetrical[1].

[1] It may be well in order to avoid an appearance of inconsistency, to call attention to statements made on p. 75. It was said there that the laws, involved in the establishment of Hooke's Law, relating deflection of the spot and extension or the hanging of the body on the rod and the application of force, were symmetrical. Yet they are clearly the kind of laws which define individual systems, namely the particular body hung on the rod or the

I can find no other satisfactory way of stating what we mean by individual bodies and avoiding the confusion of them with substances; and since individual bodies are very important conceptions in all science it is necessary to be quite clear what we mean by assertions about them. Accordingly it will be well to answer certain objections which may be raised to the method of distinction offered. First, it may be said that what is characteristic of *this* threepenny bit is not a single property but a whole set of properties; accordingly we may divide these properties into two parts, put one part in one collection and the other part in the other collection, and so make the U.A. symmetrical. Now it must probably be admitted that there are at least two properties characteristic of each individual object and such that no other object possesses them; but I think the objection is answered if we say that a statement of the U.A. which put some of these properties in one group and some in the other, though it would be true and though the U.A. would be symmetrical, would not be what we mean by making any statement about *this* object. When we speak of *this* object we mean to keep together and to regard as inseparable *all* the properties which distinguish that object from anything else. Accordingly though a statement can be made about a symmetrical U.A., it is not the statement which gives rise to the concept *this* object; what we mean when we make any statement about *this* object cannot be asserted as a symmetrical U.A. The second objection is that the property or group of inseparable properties, X, is never constant, and therefore that the supposed U.A. is not a U.A. because the relation is variable. Thus, if X is the property of being in my pocket, the association of X with the properties of silver would cease if I were so misguided as to go to church to-morrow. There is no property distinguishing this bit from all others which remains absolutely constant, for the bit has a finite life and it is only during a limited period that the proposition, This bit exists, is true. Herein undoubtedly lies a difference between the proposition asserting the existence of an individual body and that asserting the existence of a substance; the latter is true over all time, the former only over a limited period. But this difference, though important, is not that which distinguishes an individual body, for we shall see presently that it is found also in connection with systems more general. Further, though no actual individual body is permanent, we can distinctly form the conception of a permanent individual body; we can imagine that there might be a proposition asserting the existence of an individual body which is permanent, and when we ask what we should mean by such a proposition and how it would differ from the law of a substance, a distinction based on variability fails. Moreover individual bodies are generally important for physics in proportion to their permanence, and some individual bodies important for physics are quite permanent so far as our experience goes;

particular arrangement of the optical lever; they should therefore be essentially asymmetrical. But it was insisted that the form in which those laws were stated was not complete; the part of them which characterises the individual system and gives rise to the necessary asymmetry is contained in the qualifying conditions which are not stated explicitly.

the sun or the standard kilogram are examples. In fact when we make any statement about an individual body in the course of scientific inquiry, we are regarding it as permanent; that is to say, we only make such statements as would be true if the body in question were permanent. Impermanence may therefore be a fact, but it is not the fact which is important when we speak of an individual body, and it is not the property which gives its meaning to a statement about an individual body.

I conclude therefore that, though there may be between individual bodies and substances differences other than that of essential asymmetry in the characteristic U.A., yet it is this essential asymmetry which we mean by the difference. An individual body is something possessing a peculiar property X, which defines that body and makes it *this* body; the proposition that the body exists can be expressed, like the proposition that a substance exists, in the form of a dual U.A.; but X is such that the U.A. is asymmetrical, that the group which includes X is not necessarily associated with the group which excludes it. The importance of this conclusion is that it forces us to recognise that any statement about the properties of a body or the properties of a system involves the assertion of a U.A. just as much as a statement about the properties of a substance; and therefore that it involves to much the same extent experimental inquiry. Whenever we speak in later chapters of the "properties of a system" this feature must be borne in mind.

The theoretical criterion of laws. Now let us turn our attention to a proposition slightly more general than that which we have been considering, namely that all threepenny bits are made of silver. We are here considering a property, not of an individual body, but of a large group of individual bodies all possessing a common characteristic. Is this proposition a law? It is certainly not. And yet it appears very similar to another proposition which, according to our criterion, is certainly a law, namely that all rhombohedral crystals with a certain angle are made of calcium carbonate; this proposition is part of, or rather a form of, the law that calcium carbonate exists. There seems hardly any formal difference in the nature of the relations stated by the two propositions, and such difference as there is would seem to make the former more definitely a law than the latter. For while it is true that silver is not always associated with the form of a threepenny bit, it is also true that calcium carbonate is not always associated with the rhombohedral form; for it crystallises also as aragonite in the prismatic system. In both cases the U.A. asserted is not symmetrical; but in both cases the proposition can be altered into the form of a dual symmetrical U.A.; for when we are speaking of threepenny bits in general, we are not forced, as we were in the case of *this* threepenny bit, to maintain inseparable the characteristic properties, in order to preserve the true meaning of the proposition. Just as we can divide up the properties of calcium carbonate into two groups related by a dual symmetrical U.A., so we can also, without great arbitrariness, divide the properties of threepenny bits. On the other hand the association is actually more uniform in the case of the threepenny bits; for while objects of the same shape as calcite crystals are made of substances other than calcium carbonate (models of wood or of glass), it is improbable, since threepenny bits are sufficiently unimportant to escape the attentions of forgers, that objects of the shape of threepenny bits have ever been made or ever will be made of anything but silver.

But it may be said that, while at the present time the association of the form of the threepenny bits with silver is more uniform than that of the crystalline form with calcium carbonate, it is not so invariable if we consider the past; there was a time when there were no threepenny bits. It may be suggested again, as it was in considering individual bodies, that the association does not constitute a law because, though it is invariable and uniform over a certain period, it is not permanently invariable. Even if the suggestion were true, I think such a criterion would be open to the objection which was raised before, namely that such associations are important only in so far as they are permanent and that the position would be unchanged if they were permanent. But here the suggestion is not even true, if we consider only what has actually been observed. It is quite true that there was a time when no threepenny bits had been observed and found to be of silver, but it is equally true that there was a time (though it may not be possible to fix the exact date) when no calcite crystals had been observed and found to consist of calcium carbonate; if the criterion were strictly applied it would only prove that no proposition is a law unless it had always been known! For the whole period during which threepenny bits have been known at all, they have been known to be made of silver.

Yet the criterion of permanent invariability of the association is undoubtedly at the bottom of the refusal to recognise the proposition about threepenny bits as a law; but it is not permanent invariability in the past that is in question. The reason why, in spite of its essential similarity to undoubted laws, we do not regard the proposition about threepenny bits as a law, is indicated by Mill's definition of cause and effect, quoted on p. 57. "To certain facts certain facts do, *and, as we believe, always will*, succeed." If in this sentence we substitute the idea of association for that of succession, we obtain a very adequate statement of what we mean by U.A. Now the basis of the distinction which we are examining lies in the portion in italics. The rhombohedral form may not be associated always and in all cases with the substance calcium carbonate; but we do believe that there will always be cases in which that association can be found. But though the form of the threepenny bit is actually always and in all cases associated with the substance silver, we do not believe that that association always will or must be found. The distinction between the threepenny bits and the rhombohedral crystals is based, not so much on what our actual experience is and has been, but on what it will or might be. But in basing an important distinction on such considerations we seem to be treading on rather dangerous ground; if we begin to consider what would happen if our experience were not what it is, a host of the most serious and difficult questions is raised. We have hitherto refused to consider such questions at all and dismissed them as irrelevant to science; science, once more, is what it is and not what it might be. It seems only permissible to consider what might be, if our ideas on that subject are very firmly based on what is; if we say that threepenny bits might, and rhombohedral crystals of a certain angle might not, be made of other substances, we must be sure that our judgement is nothing but the result of past experience. Now I do not think that we can say that we have such experience, if we confine ourselves entirely to such experience as we have considered so far; if we regard only observation of the threepenny bits, we have no more reason to believe that the association of their shape with silver is not as uniform and invariable as any association asserted by any undoubted law.

But when we say that they might be made of something other than silver, we are referring to our knowledge of the circumstances which brought them into existence. We know that the selection of silver for their material was an arbitrary and voluntary choice. Anything voluntary, as has been decided already, is foreign to science; and it is because there is known to be voluntary element in the association of silver with threepenny bits that we exclude that association from the realm of laws and of science generally, although it is as uniform as many which we admit. The uniformity of an association is not sufficient by itself to make it possible as the relation asserted by a law; something must be known of the origin of the association. Here is clearly a new principle. For when we say that the origin of the association is known, we do not mean that there is a law associating the concept three-penny-bits-made-of-silver with some other concept; indeed it is difficult to see how, according to the conclusion reached already, we could prove that the relation defining a concept was not a law by relating it through a law to some other concept. What we do mean will appear if we consider some other and rather different examples.

Consider the propositions that sea-water contains sodium chloride, that air contains oxygen and nitrogen in certain proportions, that there are eight planets at least as large as Mercury. All these assert uniform associations: are they laws? Judgement perhaps is doubtful; it is felt that these propositions are somehow intermediate between that about the threepenny bits and that about silver. They are more nearly laws than the former, but less clearly laws than the latter. But the distinction here has nothing to do with voluntary action, at least of men; and if we invoke the aid of God, I suppose His choice in making silver what it is was as arbitrary as that in fixing the number of the major planets. And yet we do feel that there is less necessity about the constitution of air or sea-water than about the properties of silver. We believe that this constitution *will* always be found just as surely as the associated properties of silver, but we do not believe as surely that it *must* be found; we can easily conceive of a world the same in all respects as that which we know in which there was a little more oxygen in the air or one more major planet. We can conceive also of a world in which no silver was actually present; but we feel that a world would be very different from our own if there was in it a substance having enough of the properties of silver to distinguish it from all other elements but having a slightly different melting point, and if our silver did not exist in it. If silver is present at all, it must be the silver we know.

Instead of attempting to arrive at the basis of the distinction by analysis, I will state at once what that basis seems to be. It lies in the use of theories to explain laws, a process which we shall examine in a later chapter. Associations which are not the necessary consequences of any theory are such that, though they are always found and, as we believe, will always be found, it does not seem that they must always be found; those of which it appears that they must always be found are necessary consequences of some theory. If the change of some association would not invalidate any theory proposed for the explanation of laws, then we do not feel that that association must always be found; but if it is such that, if it were changed, some theory at present valid would be untrue, then we feel it must be always found.

There are geological and astronomical theories which account for the presence of salt in the sea, for the fact that oxygen and nitrogen, rather than hydrogen, are the chief constituents of the air, and for the presence of some planets in the solar system. But none of these theories are sufficiently definite to predict the exact proportions of salt or oxygen or the precise number of the planets; all these theories would be quite unchanged if these matters were slightly different from what they are[1]. On the other hand, though there is not at present an adequate theory to account in detail for the association of the properties of silver, we feel quite sure that such a theory is possible; all the properties of silver must be the expression of some structure of the atoms of silver. If some of the properties, but not others changed (under such circumstances that we believed the structure to be unaltered), then the general theory that all the properties are determined by a single structure would be false. It is because we believe that such a general theory is true that we believe that any association which is inconsistent with it, not only does not and will not, but cannot occur. The distinction lies not so much in the relation between the doubtful law and any actual theory as in its relation to a possible theory. We feel that a theory which accounts perfectly for the association of all the properties of silver is possible; but we do not yet see our way at all to a theory which accounts for the exact constitution of the sea or the air or the solar system; in all these there is an element of "chance."

---

[1] Would the case be different if there were *no* salt in the sea? Yes; but only if sodium and chlorine were still common constituents of rocks. The geological theory explains the connection between the composition of sea-water and of the rocks; it is only if that relation were very different that the theory would have to be changed. If we express the proposition in such a form that it is a necessary consequence of the theory—if we say, for example, that in a country subject to rain-fall, large enclosed masses of water will have constituents common with those of the rocks surrounding them—then I think the proposition is a law. Such considerations lead directly to the view which is being put forward.

Such a view as is put forward here is impossible to prove, for the decision what is and what is not a law, what is and what is not fundamentally important to science, can only be made by the instinctive judgement of men of science. The view is merely commended to their attention. It explains at once why we reject the proposition about threepenny bits from the class of laws, for the only theory which could account adequately for the association is one which introduces the conception of voluntary action. Now voluntary action and all ideas derived from it (with one exception) are excluded as rigidly from scientific theories as from scientific laws; the proposition cannot therefore be a necessary consequence of any theory. It is only if the ideal indicated by the extreme determinist view of voluntary action were attained, and we could explain why people wished certain things in the same way as we can explain associations in the external world, that the statement about the threepenny bits would become as much a law as that about the calcite crystals.

If this view is correct, it has a very important bearing on our whole conception of the nature of scientific investigation. We have already had reason to suspect that, because our object in selecting judgements of the external world for examination is that we may make laws from them, we refuse to include in our selection any judgements which will not fall neatly and satisfactorily into laws; we accomplish the apparently miraculous feat of reducing a chaotic world to order, because we carefully confine our attention and our efforts only to those portions which we find can be ordered. Now we have reason to believe that we push this process still further. When we have got our laws we want to explain them by theories; and so again we reject from consideration any propositions, however much they may resemble in their structure those which we accept as laws, which refuse to fit in with our theories, the form of which is dictated chiefly by preconceived ideas of what a theory should be. Of course if the matter is put in that way, science appears a very arbitrary study; suspicion may be thrown upon its value. Perhaps it will be well then to explain that it will be urged later that this feature of science, so far from detracting from its value, is precisely what gives to it supreme and unequalled value. At any rate the point of view is one which must be considered in later discussions.

CHAPTER IV

THE DISCOVERY AND PROOF OF LAWS

Summary. The discovery of laws is a special case of Induction or the determination of a general relation from a limited number of particulars.

A familiar solution of the problem is that stated (e.g. by Mill) in the Canons of Induction. Our inquiry will again be conducted in the form of criticism of Mill.

The rejection of the view that the causal relation is characteristic of laws does not of itself imply the rejection of the Canons, for the arguments on which they are based would apply to any dual U.A.

The Canons depend on the Law of Causation. This law depends for its significance on the division of experience into facts; this division must therefore precede the use of the Canons.

How is the division to be made? It is concluded that the only answer consistent with the usefulness of the Canons is that *any* division whatsoever leads to facts to which the Law of Causation is applicable.

The consequences of this answer are examined. It is shown that, if any division into facts is permissible, the Canons may lead to conclusions which are undoubtedly false.

Similar considerations apply to the division of the facts into instances, which again must precede the use of the Canons. It is concluded therefore that some method of dividing experience into facts and instances must be known before the Canons are applied.

What is this method? It is argued that the method actually used involves the knowledge of certain U.A.'s. But the object of the Canons is to determine U.A.'s. Accordingly the Canons alone cannot discover all laws; there must be some more fundamental method.

But can the Canons discover any laws? The answer is no; but they may be useful in indicating in what direction to seek for a law more general or more precise than one previously known.

They may also discover "particular causes." This conception is analysed. It is shown to be important in experiment, but to be quite different from the relation characteristic of laws.

How then are laws discovered? The question is divided into three, based on the fact that laws are always suggested before they are proved. First, how are laws suggested? Second, what is the nature of the experiments which prove them? Third, what is the foundation of the proof?

To the first question it is answered that laws are almost always suggested by theories. In connection with the second some slight analysis of the nature of an experiment is undertaken.

The third question brings us back to Induction. What are we to substitute for the Law of Causation? It is argued that we substitute nothing. We realise that we can never prove a law to be true. On the other hand we can do what the Canons cannot do, namely prove that a suggested law is not true. Laws are proved, if at all, by the exhaustion of other possibilities. It is for this reason that the repetition of experiments gives greater value to a law. The view that repetition gives greater weight owing to reasons connected with Chance and Probability will be considered in a later chapter.

Induction. We need not waste time on preliminaries. The great difficulty which attends the discovery of laws has been discussed in various forms by many philosophers of note; it arises from the necessity that the relation established by a law shall be valid, not only for that portion of experience on which the evidence for the law is based, but also for experience received subsequently and unknown at the time of establishment. Laws predict; and the question which faces us is how prediction is possible and how it can be made certain.

The process of arguing from the particular to the general, or from the small portion of experience of which we have knowledge or record to the much greater portion which is at the time wholly unknown to us, is generally called Induction. Those who have held the opinion concerning the importance of cause and effect in scientific laws which was discussed at the beginning of the preceding chapter have usually also held that the problems of Induction are to be solved by following certain definite rules of experiment and ratiocination. These rules are termed by Mill the Canons of Induction, and there are few of us sufficiently fortunate as to have escaped encounter with them in the examination room. It will be convenient once more to conduct our inquiry under the guise of criticism, and to lead up to the conclusions at which we want to arrive by considering in some details the answer to the problem which was offered by Mill.

The Canons of Induction in the form given by Mill are all based on the assumption that the uniformity which is asserted by laws is the causal relation; it might seem therefore that when we rejected that assumption any further examination of the Canons was rendered unnecessary. But an inquiry would show that the assumption that all physical laws are causal is not really essential to the Canons. They profess to provide a means of establishing that a "fact" A is the cause of the "fact" B, but the method which they provide does not depend for its validity on the assumption that the relation of the cause to the effect is temporal or that it is asymmetrical; it depends for its validity only on the assumption that the relation is dual and is "invariable." For the Canons do not profess to prove that A is definitely the cause or definitely the effect of B; at most they propose to prove that it is *either* the cause *or* the effect, and sometimes they do not propose to prove even as much as that. Accordingly they assume only that the relation between A and B has those characteristics which are possessed equally by cause and effect; these characteristics are duality and invariability. It is true that the Canons are in many cases more easily applied in practice if it is known that the relation sought is temporal and that the effect B is always to be sought among facts which occur after the cause A, but there is nothing in their statement which implies that it must be sought there. It is very remarkable that Mill, having devoted long chapters to elucidation of the exact nature of the causal relation and the establishment of the view that all physical laws are causal, makes no direct use of his conclusions in the chapters dealing with Induction which follow immediately.

Now the relation of uniform association which is to be substituted for that of cause and effect is by no means always dual. But a dual relation can often, if not always, be put in place of the true and more complicated relation without any change in the logical content of the law, although some change in significance is involved. Moreover laws are often discovered or suggested in the first instance by the establishment of dual relations, though the more complex relation, derived from a combination of several dual relations, is afterwards shown to be more appropriate. Indeed it seems that a single experiment, which involves necessarily the psychological relation of cause and effect, seldom establishes directly anything but a dual relation. Accordingly though it is not certain that all the relations asserted by laws are dual or even that they can be obtained by the combination of dual relations, the discovery of a method by which dual relations of uniform association could be established would lead us far on the path of solving completely the problem before us. Again, the uniformity of a uniform association is something rather more general than invariability; it implies not only repetition of the same observation on different occasions, but also a similarity among certain groups of observations. But once more an examination of the use of the Canons will show that they do not distinguish in any way between invariability in time and the more general relation of uniformity; if they can discover dual invariable relations they will also discover the dual uniform relations which we term uniform association. Since therefore dual relations of uniform association possess all the properties on which the use of the Canons of Induction depends, the Canons of Induction, if they provide a method as valid and complete as is often imagined, would be almost exactly what we are seeking, even if we propose later to substitute uniform association for cause and effect.

Before we proceed it will be convenient to introduce a new term to denote the combination of two terms which are related by a dual U.A. or by that special form of it which is the relation of cause and effect. Such combination will be termed a "routine." The problem which the Canons of Induction profess to solve is the discovery of portions of experience which form routines and their analysis into two terms related as cause and effect, or by some other relation which, like cause and effect, is dual and invariable.

The law of causation. But while the Canons of Induction assume nothing about the logical form of the causal relation except that it is dual and invariable, they certainly assume another very important proposition about causality. This proposition is the Law of Causation[1]. I do not know whether the applicability of this proposition is part of the definition of causality, and whether a relation to which it is not applicable would be regarded as causal; nor is inquiry necessary; it suffices to know that the Law is involved inextricably in the Canons. The Law of Causation is some-

---

[1] The question suggests itself whether this "Law" is a law in our sense. The matter will not be considered explicitly, but the answer will probably appear in the course of the discussion.

times stated in the form that every effect has a cause, but in this form it tells us little. For so far we have defined an effect as a fact which is related in a certain way to another fact which is the cause; if no further definition of an "effect" is offered, the proposition would seem to tell us nothing except that there are cases in which this relation is valid; it does not tell us how many such cases there are. But when the Law of Causation is asserted more is usually meant; it is usually meant that every fact is an effect and, consequently, that every fact is related to some other by the causal relation. In this form the proposition will assert something significant, if, and only if, we can give a clear and definite meaning to the term "fact."

The fundamental idea connoted by the word "fact" seems to be independence to some extent of other facts. Experience is supposed to be divided into portions, such that no portions contain anything in common; each such portion is a fact. If we adopt this definition it seems that the Law of Causation, as it is used in the Canons, may be paraphrased thus: Some or all of our experience of the external world can be divided into portions which contain no common part and are such that every such portion can be combined with some other portion to form a routine in which those two portions, or "facts," are the terms related as cause and effect. The possibility is not excluded that a single fact may be combined successively with a number of other facts to form a corresponding number of different routines. It seems generally to be thought that this number is limited to two; a fact can be combined with one other fact as a cause and with a second other fact as an effect. But all thorough discussion of the Canons admits that this limitation cannot be maintained. Moreover, even if it could be maintained, it would have to be admitted that the two routines are indistinguishable by the Canons, for they cannot tell the difference between cause and effect.

It seems to me that only by stating the Law of Causation in this way can the proposition be made significant and at the same time a rigid definition of what is a fact avoided. But if it is stated in this way an obvious question arises. Can the division of our experience into facts, characterised by the necessary properties, be effected in only one way; or is it possible that, by dividing it in different ways, we can arrive at several entirely distinct sets of routines ordering in different ways exactly the same experience? I do not know what is the orthodox answer to this question; common sense would probably reply that the division of experience into facts can be made in many different ways, but that the routines which result from the different ways of division are not mutually inconsistent. It is easy to think of trivial examples in which two men, regarding the same set of events from two different points of view, will describe them in different ways, involving different relations of cause and effect; but the possibility of this difference arises from the complexity of the portions into which both of them divide the experience. The experience really consists of a chain of causes and effects, $ABCD\ldots$, A being the cause of B, B of C, and so on. One observer asserts that AB is the cause of CD, another that A is the cause of BCD.

The analysis in both cases is incomplete; if it were complete there would be only one method of division possible.

Thus, the common sense view seems to be that there is only one method of dividing experience into facts which is really fundamental; and if that is so, it is doubtless this fundamental method which it is the object of science to discover. But if there is only one method it is very doubtful whether the Canons of Induction can discover it. For the Canons undoubtedly assume that the experience is divided into facts before the Canons are applied to it, and accordingly it would seem that it must be known what is the correct method of division and what are truly facts before the Canons can be used to discover which pairs of facts are causally related. On the other hand it may be possible to avoid this conclusion by supposing that, if the Canons indicate a causal relation at all, it is a true one; and that the only penalty which we should incur if we started with a wrong division of the facts would be that we could not discover a causal relation at all. This possibility will have to be examined in the course of our discussion. It will be found that the supposition is certainly not true, because the Canons can undoubtedly lead to wrong conclusions if a wrong division into facts is made.

But even if the supposition were true and facts could always be discovered by finding, through a process of trial and error, a division of the experience which, interpreted by the Canons, led to the indication of a causal relation, it would be still desirable, if it were possible, to define a "fact" in a way which is wholly independent of causal relations and of the use of the Canons. I have never seen such a definition and I do not believe that it is possible to give it. The only definition that I can suggest which, if it were acceptable, would meet the case, would be that the true fundamental facts are the ultimate elements into which experience can be divided, or that each elementary judgement is a fact. But if such a definition is adopted, the Law of Causation is simply untrue. It would be a fundamental fact that a spot of light coincides with a certain mark on a scale[1]; this fact may have a cause, but the cause is not another elementary fact of the same kind; the cause is not, for example, that there is a sensation of red or that two sounds occur simultaneously; the cause, if there is a cause, is something infinitely more complex and would not be found among facts determined according to the proposed definition.

I conclude, therefore, that if there is only one method of dividing experience into facts which obey the Law of Causation, the Canons of Induction are entirely valueless in determining causal relations. They presuppose that the division is made correctly, and the only way of knowing that the division has been made correctly involves a previous knowledge of all causal relations; if the division could be made the problems which the Canons are to solve would have been solved already. But the same objection might not apply if there is some finite number of divisions into facts which are all

---

[1] Even this fact is not really elementary; for, as we have seen, the expression "a certain mark" involves an asymmetrical U.A. Elementary judgements are so simple that they are hardly expressible in words.

satisfactory; for it might turn out that all the alternative divisions into facts which were such that they gave causal relations when the Canons are applied to them were also such that all the causal relations thus obtained were true. However, examination would again prove that the supposition is not tenable and that some criterion, independent of a knowledge of causation, would again be required to distinguish divisions which are satisfactory from those which are not. But the suggestion of a finite number of divisions into facts, all of them equally valid, need not detain us, for it is not likely to be maintained seriously. The only suggestion that is likely to be pressed, if it is agreed that there is more than one valid division into facts, is that there is an infinite number of satisfactory divisions; or, in other words, that any division whatever of experience into portions which include no common part will give facts which are subject to the Law of Causation. This suggestion, that anything is a fact and has a cause or an effect or both, is plausible; indeed common sense would probably decide that it is true, and it seems to be admitted when the Law of Causation is stated in the vague form that every effect has a cause. The admission is in no way inconsistent with the view that there is one and only one ultimate division into facts, for it has been already noted that a collection of elementary facts, interrelated causally among themselves, may bear the causal relation to another similarly constituted collection of elementary facts. And it is quite possible that, by examining the causal relations between such collections of facts, the causal relations between the elementary facts of which the collection consists may be elucidated.

However, the assumption seems self-consistent only if the elementary facts between which the true and fundamental relation of causality subsists are not divisible. If they are not divisible, then any portion of experience must be a collection of elementary facts; each of these facts has a cause (or effect), and the collection of elementary facts which are the causes (or effects) of the first collection bears to the first collection the causal relation. Even if one collection includes two elementary facts a and b which form a routine (ab), a or b will have a cause or effect which is not included in the collection and will bear the causal relation to the whole routine (ab). Every collection of elementary facts and every portion of experience will, therefore, have a cause and an effect. But the assumption cannot be true if the elementary facts between which the fundamental causal relations subsist are divisible. For, if they are divisible, part only of an elementary fact might be included in one collection, and even if the remainder were included in the other collection, the relation between the two collections would not be wholly causal; such a collection, including part only of an elementary fact, would have neither cause nor effect. Since we have seen that it is very doubtful whether facts so simple that they are indivisible are subject to the Law of Causation, and can be taken as such elementary facts, the assumption that every portion of experience is a fact is liable to much suspicion from the outset.

On the other hand if it were true, the difficulties raised in connection with the Canons would vanish. For though the Canons presuppose a division into facts, such a division would not presuppose any knowledge if all division were equally satisfactory. The only difference between different divisions would then be that they would bring to light different routines all of which were equally valid. Accordingly it will be well to examine the consequences of the assumption further.

The Canons of Induction. Of the five Canons of Induction formulated by Mill it is only necessary to examine two, the Method of Agreement and the Method of Difference. Of the others the Joint Method of Agreement and Difference is merely a combination of these two, while the Method of Residues assumes that they have already been fully applied. The Method of Concomitant Variations—in practice the most powerful of all the methods —may seem to be independent of the first two, but I think it can be shown to be merely a brief summary of a large number of successive applications of them. Moreover, even if it does contain some new element, it will readily appear that the criticisms directed against the Methods of Agreement and Difference are directly applicable also to that of Concomitant Variations.

The two Canons are stated by Mill in the following words:

1. *Method of Agreement.* If two or more instances of the phenomenon under investigation have only one circumstance in common, the circumstance in which alone all the instances agree is the cause (or effect) of the given phenomenon.

2. *Method of Difference.* If an instance in which the phenomenon under investigation occurs and an instance in which it does not occur have every circumstance in common save one, that one occurring only in the former; the circumstance in which alone the instances differ is the effect, or the cause, or an indispensable part of the cause of the phenomenon.

The context shows that by the "phenomenon" and the "circumstances" are meant "facts" to which the Law of Causation is applicable. The phenomenon is distinguished from the circumstances only because it is the fact which, in the special conditions of the inquiry, is the prime object of our attention. "Instances" are collections of facts which make up together the phenomenon and the circumstances.

In considering the Canons it will be advisable not to have in our minds any particular application of them, but to treat them as formal rules. For as soon as we direct our attention to a special example the natural association of ideas leads us unawares to make implicitly many assumptions which beg the whole question. The neglect of this precaution is probably the reason why the very obvious criticisms which are about to be made have not received much attention. It is only when we have arrived at general conclusions that it will be desirable to apply them to particular examples in order to discover possible errors. The two rules may therefore be expressed in the following form. The first states that if the two collections of facts

$$(1)\ ABC \text{ and } (2)\ ABC'$$

can be found, then (AB) forms a routine; the second states that if the two collections of facts

$$(1)\ ABC \text{ and } (2)\ C$$

can be found, then (AB) forms a routine. In the first, A, the phenomenon, can occur without either C or C'; it cannot therefore form a routine with either; there is no evidence that it can occur without B, and therefore it does form a routine with B. In the second, C can occur without A and therefore cannot form a routine with it, but B cannot occur without A and therefore forms a routine with it.

The separation of " facts." The conclusion by either of these methods that (AB) is a routine depends entirely upon the truth of two assumptions. First that A and B are "facts," and that each forms one half of a dual routine; second that the other part of the routine of which A is one part is contained in the same instance with A. If either of these assumptions is denied there is not the smallest reason for believing that A is causally connected with B.

The first assumption, that A and B are facts, we have already agreed to accept provisionally, on the ground that any division into facts of the experience constituting the instances is satisfactory. We must now examine the consequences of accepting the assumption.

The best way of examining the matter is to consider what would happen if precisely the same instances were divided into facts in a different manner. The possibility of dividing differently any part of the instance which includes A will be left out of consideration for the moment, for if, assuming that A is a fact, the Canons always lead to the correct indication of the routine of which it forms part, the assumption will have been justified. In that case the only result of sub-dividing A, or of including with it some other portion of experience, would be either to make the discovery of a routine impossible (and so to restrict the usefulness of the Canons, but not to diminish their validity) or to lead to the discovery of some quite different routine. But the possibility of dividing differently B and C must certainly be taken into account.

If B in the Method of Agreement contained *all* that part of the experience which is common to the two instances, and, in the Method of Difference, all that (other than A) which is not common, then the only re-division of the experience which would be possible, subject to the condition that the two instances must retain their form, would be a transference to C of some of the experience contained in B. The conclusion would then be that part of B (say b) and not all B formed a routine with A[1]. The routine (Ab) thus obtained would necessarily be asymmetrical even though the routine (AB) were symmetrical; A would be u.a. with B, but not B with A. But this limitation does not deprive the Canons of all their value even for the discovery of symmetrical routines; for as a matter of fact many complete symmetrical routines are discovered in practice through finding several asymmetrical

---

[1] This possibility is recognised by the words "or an indispensable part of the cause" in the Method of Difference. It would be interesting to inquire why these words are inserted in one Canon and not in the other. The question is dealt with in some fashion in standard treatises; and though the explanation given does not seem complete, there is no need to pursue the matter. There is no intention here of criticising all the ambiguities and errors of the "orthodox" statement, but only those which lead to the conclusions at which it is desired to arrive.

routines which are ultimately combined. The gradual discovery of all the properties of a substance, or of enough to distinguish it from all others, affords an example.

But as the Canons are usually applied B does not contain all that is common (or all that is different) in the two instances. Thus, if the two instances of the Method of Agreement are made on the same day, the portion of experience which we call "making experiments on the same day" is included in C rather than in B; if it were included in B, the routine discovered would not be held to be satisfactory, for it would often not be held that the law involved the necessity of making the observations on the same day. Similarly in the Method of Difference, the exact time at which the experiment is made (different in the two instances) is held to be part of C rather than B, for the exact time of making the experiment is not part of the law. Now if C and C' contain a part (say c) which is the same, we can redivide the experience into facts, so that c takes the part of B, while B is merged in the rest of C and C'; and we should then arrive at the result that the routine of which A forms part is (Ac); in our example we should conclude that the cause of the phenomenon is the fact that the experiment is being made on some particular day. Similarly in the Method of Difference the substitution for B of the part in which the two C's differ would lead us to conclude that the cause of the phenomenon is the fact that it has been made at one hour of the day rather than at another.

Nor is this all. Though strictly B must be exactly the same in the two instances of the first method, it is seldom so in practice. Thus, if we are proving that a spark through a certain mixture is the cause of an explosion, B will be the explosion. But we call "explosions" many events which are not exactly the same; one explosion may be much weaker than another and yet be an "explosion." Once we admit that the B's may be at all different and yet be admitted as the same fact, the way is opened to endless variations in the division of the experience into facts. Unless we have some criterion of differences which may be admitted and those which may not, it seems that we may take out of C any portion we please and make it part of B, and out of B any part we please and make it part of C, so long as we retain something common to the two B's. There is an almost endless series of routines which can be established between which the Canons provide no method of distinction; and yet some of them, most of them in fact, would actually be judged to be false. We conclude that the suggestion of p. 92 is false, and that the possibility of finding a method of division satisfying the conditions of the Canons does not prove that the division is correct.

These are very obvious objections and they have not been entirely neglected by those who have expounded the Canons. Some of them may be countered by asserting that the conditions imagined are not those contemplated by the Canons and that therefore a failure of the Canons in such conditions is only to be expected. But we are not really asking whether the Canons would be true in some ideal conditions; for if we consider carefully what conditions are necessary for the strict application of the Canons we shall very soon conclude that they are quite unattainable in practice. How, for instance, are we to fulfil the condition necessary for the Method of Difference (which is considered a very powerful method) if nothing except B is to be common to the two instances? We are compelled to make all experiments within a few miles of the earth's surface and in the presence of human beings. Are then these conditions necessary parts of every routine which can be established by the Canons? Moreover—and this is more important—the Canons are actually used in conditions which do not come up to the ideal and yet they undoubtedly do lead to some results which are valid, if not very important. That is not disputed. But if they are used successfully in such conditions which do not come up to the ideal, it must be because some assumptions are made in their application which are not stated in the ideal. Our entire object is to discover what are these additional assumptions.

Some of the objections again are considered fully by Mill when he discusses the complications introduced by the possibility of the Plurality of Causes and the Intermixture of Effects[1]. It is not proposed to follow these arguments. Many of them seem to me highly unsatisfactory and to depend simply on the abandonment of the definition of cause and effect. It is supposed, for example, that A may be a cause of B in a particular instance but not generally. Now it has been admitted that an event may be included in a routine with more than one other and may be the cause or effect of more than one other event; and this possibility explains quite truly a large class of cases in which the Method of Agreement fails. But if A is a part of two or more routines, these must still be routines; they must not be statements of what happens in particular instances. It is in this sense that a "particular" cause is a quite unjustifiable conception; and it is used in this sense when, for instance, it is admitted that the hour of the day is in a sense the cause of the phenomenon in one experiment though it is not always the cause. But cause and effect is above all an invariable relation; it is its invariability which gives it its importance for science; and though we do speak of the causes of particular events, we are not in that case using the term cause in the sense which is important for science. "Cause", like many other words, has been fruitful of confusions because it is used in more than one sense.

But if the arguments which remain, when clear errors and misunderstandings are removed, are examined, it will be found that they do not in the least degree affect the contention which is made here, that the failures of the Canons which we are considering are due to the fact that it is not legitimate to divide up the experience into facts in any way whatsoever. Certain limitations must be imposed to obtain permissible methods of division; the arguments to explain the failures of the Canons are simply

---

[1] Again it is instructive to consider why Plurality of Causes and not Plurality of Effects is considered possible.

discussions of what these limitations are. But all that we are concerned with at present is that there must be limitations; that every portion of experience is not a fact subject to the Law of Causation; and that the decision what are facts cannot be made by the Canons themselves, but must be made from some other source of knowledge before the Canons are applied.

Separation of instances. So much for the first assumption concerned in the use of the Canons. The second is that the fact which is part of the same routine with the phenomenon under consideration is contained in the same instance. This assumption clearly affects the division of experience into instances just as the first affected its division into facts; the division into instances must be satisfactory before the Canons are applied. And again the question arises how we are to know the way to divide experience into instances, each of which contains both terms of some routine, before the routines are known.

So far as I can make out nobody has proposed a rule. The conclusion at which we have just arrived, obvious though it is when stated explicitly, appears to have been overlooked completely by those who have formulated the Canons. Of course the fact that Mill gives examples of the application of the Canons, and has not included among them any in which the assumption is violated, proves that he had some kind of tacit rule which served him well in these particular cases; but he has not told us what that rule was and we can only discover by examining his examples. I think we can obtain some idea of what his rule was, and how he came to overlook that it was a rule needing express statement, by displaying in a rather different way the need for some rule and applying our results to a particular example.

The most powerful Canon of Induction, according to Mill, is the Method of Joint Agreement and Difference, which is a combination of the two Canons already stated. In the application of this Canon four instances are required which, in their simplest form, have the following composition: (1) ABC, (2) ABD, (3) C, (4) D. The first two instances have the form suitable for the application of the first Canon, the Method of Agreement; they both contain the phenomenon A and agree only in the single circumstance B; (1) and (3) or (2) and (4) have the form suitable to the application of the Method of Difference; they both contain the phenomenon A and differ only in the presence of B in one and its absence from the other. The four taken together prove that B is the cause or the effect of A in a manner which, according to Mill, is almost free from ambiguities arising from the Plurality of Causes and the Intermixture of Effects.

Now we are asking why the experience which is made up of these four collections has been selected from our experience and divided into four instances; in particular we may inquire why, given the fact that the portion of experience included in the four collections is to be divided into four instances (already a considerable assumption), it has been divided in this particular way. The total experience included may be represented by $AABBCCDD$. Even if we agree to retain the division of this experience into these eight facts, what reason is there for believing that C rather than B, standing alone, is an "instance" or ABD rather than ADC? If we adopted, in place of the classification which has been given, the following: (1') ABC, (2') B, (3') ADC, (4') D, then the application of the Canon in the most orthodox fashion would immediately lead to the conclusion that AC was a routine and that AB was not, that C and not B is the cause or the effect of A.

In order to see why such an obvious criticism of the Canons has not been fully considered, let us apply our arguments to a special example. We may select one that has often been used before, the combination of oxygen and hydrogen under the action of a spark. We are inquiring what is the cause of the combination; A then is this combination; B is the passage of the spark; C and D are circumstances which differ in two experiments; let us suppose that C is the presence of the gases in a glass vessel, D the presence of the gases in a quartz vessel. If we divide our experience into instances in the first manner, we take as our four "instances" the following experiments: (1) the combination of the gases in the glass vessel after the spark has passed, (2) the combination of the gases in the quartz vessel after the spark has passed, (3) the failure of combination in a glass vessel if no spark passes, (4) the failure of combination in a quartz vessel if no spark passes. We conclude that the spark is the cause of the combination and that the material of the vessel is of no account. If we divide our experience in the second manner, we take as our four instances: (1') and (4') the same as (1) and (4), (2') the passage of the spark unattended by combination of the gases or by their presence in either the glass or quartz vessel, (3') the combination of the gases unattended by the spark while the gases are present both in the quartz and the glass vessels. We conclude that the cause of the combination is the presence of the gases in the glass vessel. This conclusion is incorrect. A false division into instances, like a false division into facts, leads to a false conclusion. We must once more reject the proposal, which might have been made, that the mere possibility of dividing experiences into instances in the form contemplated by the Canons is sufficient indication that the division is correct.

Now why does the first division into instances appear so plausible, the second so absurd? The reader will doubtless feel inclined to say that the second division is impossible, because as a matter of fact I cannot make the experiments (2) and (3). But it must be remembered that in making the second division into instances rather than the first it is not supposed that the experience is in any way altered; exactly the same things are supposed to be observed whichever method of division is adopted. There is no question of something not being observed in one case which is observed in the other. I have certainly observed that a spark passed and that the mixed gases were present in a glass vessel; in the first division I abstract the second observation from the rest of the experience and call it an instance; why should I not also abstract the first observation and call it an instance?

Or the objection may be put in rather a different way. It may be said that B alone cannot constitute an instance while D can, because the experience denoted by B is not complete. A spark cannot simply "pass"; it must pass through something and, if this something is a gas, the gas must be contained in some kind of vessel. But this objection, if accepted, would prove too much; it would prove not only that B cannot be taken as an instance, but also that it cannot be taken as a fact. For if B is inseparable from either C or D, the Canons cannot be applied at all. In place of B, (BC) or (BD) must be the facts; the instances become (1) AE, (2) AF, (3) C, (4) D, where $E = (BC)$ and $F = (BD)$. No conclusions whatever can be drawn from these instances.

Nevertheless the objections both indicate the right answer. It is that D can be selected as an instance because D is a routine and B is not. For an "instance" in the sense employed by the Canons means an experiment or some definite set of observations; an examination of the examples which are given in the discussions of the Canons shows that the term always denotes some portion of experience which can be sharply distinguished from the remainder and possesses a certain unity. It can be so distinguished and possesses this unity simply in virtue of the fact that it can be repeated independently of the repetition of any other portion of experience. We regard the observation of the presence of the gases in a glass vessel as an instance because we can observe that presence when everything else which can be altered and which is not involved in the instance is altered; we do not regard the passage of a spark (without mention of the gases through which it passes) as an instance, because we cannot repeat the observation if we alter certain things not included in the instance.

But to say this is simply to say that an instance is a routine, for portions of experience which can be repeated indefinitely are routines; that is all that a routine means (except that the relation concerned in its uniformity is dual—a matter irrelevant to the present discussion). And what is true of the instance C or D, is true of the instance ABC or ABD; these also are selected as instances because they are known to be routines.

If instances are always routines, it follows at once that the second assumption on which the use of the Canons is based is true; for if one part of the routine is included in the instance, so is the other. The considerations which have just been presented serve to indicate that the instances must be known to be routines before the Canons are applied, and that if they are not known to be routines, the Canons will not merely fail to give any result at all, but will give a result which is definitely wrong. Further they show that the knowledge that a proposed instance is a routine can be and usually is present before the application of the Canons. It remains possible (though it is certainly not actually true in the examples taken) that the instances are known to be routines through some previous application of the Canons; but if we inquire again how the instances were known to be routines for this application we must at length arrive at routines which were established by some method other than the Canons. Though it is still tenable that some.

routines can be discovered by the Canons, it is certain that all routines are not so discovered and that there must be some alternative method of discovery which is altogether more fundamental. The suspicion aroused by the discussion of the division of experience into facts, that the Canons depend essentially on some knowledge which is not explicitly stated in the usual formulation of them, is completely confirmed by the discussion of the division of the facts into instances.

And now too we can see how to define a fact. A "fact" is simply a concept; it is a portion of experience which is known to be interconnected by a relation of uniformity. A "spark" connotes the uniform association of certain electrical changes with certain luminous changes; an explosion connotes the uniform association of chemical changes with a sudden increase of pressure, and so on. It is only because we know of this uniform association that we separate out the "fact" from the remainder of experience and call it a fact. Accordingly the division of experience into facts requires the previous establishment of routines just as much as the division of facts into instances. Indeed a fact and an instance are not distinct. A portion of experience which is a fact in one application of the Canons may be an instance in another application. Both facts and instances are routines (except in so far that the U.A. involved may not always be dual); and these routines must be known before any application of the Canons can be made.

The proof of the statements just made can only follow on an examination of the various examples of the application of the Canons. There is no need here to spend time on such an examination; the reader, if he has any doubt, can readily conduct it himself. But in truth the conclusion which is urged is so obvious when it is once presented that the difficulty is rather to understand how anyone could have thought anything else. But the whole matter turns on the instinctive recognition of what is a law, and in such recognition anyone who is not thoroughly imbued with the spirit of science is sure to go wrong; for the ultimate criterion of a law is whether it has a certain scientific importance. It is here that the discussions of such people as Mill become so ludicrous. They occupy long treatises in explaining how we discover the law that sparks cause explosions in gases, but do not think the inquiry how we discover the laws that there are sparks, explosions and gases (the knowledge of which is assumed in their discussions) worth a moment's attention; and yet these laws are almost infinitely more important for science. Having no power to distinguish laws by their importance, they were driven to find some other criterion, and happened to light on the entirely irrelevant and insignificant criterion of an apparently causal relation. When they had solved to their satisfaction the problem of discovering laws which are characterised by an apparently causal relation they imagined that they had solved the whole problem of the discovery of laws. They might as well have imagined that when they had discovered how to pack watches safely for the post they had solved all the problems of the manufacture of watches.

Do the Canons prove anything? The Canons then do not provide a general method of establishing routines. Do they establish routines at all? In order to answer this question we must remember that the assumption that we have admitted so far for the purposes of this chapter, namely that all routines are dual, is not really correct. It is true that many routines can be expressed in the dual form, and even in such a way as to exhibit the causal relation, but this mode of expression is artificial and does not convey their true significance; it can often be framed only after the routine has been established. If the Canons are to have practical importance, they must be able to deal with routines which are not dual.

Now if routines are not dual, the arguments on which the Methods of Agreement and Difference are founded lose their validity. The first proves that A is not associated uniformly with C and is not associated uniformly with C'; since, according to the second assumption it must be uniformly associated with something in the same instance, this something must be B. If routines were simply dual relations between facts, we should conclude that (AB) was a complete routine. But if routines may be more complex, this conclusion does not follow; indeed it cannot follow, for we have seen that, in order to know that ABC and ABC' are instances, we must know that they are routines; (AB) is not a complete routine; though the complete routine need not include C and need not include C', it must include one of them. Thus, in our example, the occurrence of an explosion after the passage of a spark through the gases in a glass vessel is a routine, and so is the occurrence after the passage of a spark in a quartz vessel, but the occurrence after the passage of a spark through gases in no vessel at all is not a routine; the containment of the gases in some sort of "vessel" is a necessary part of the routine. If the conclusion of the Method of Agreement were that (AB) is a complete routine, the conclusion would be definitely false. What the instances prove is that the material of the vessel is unimportant; they show that we can form a new routine, including the two older routines and more general than either, by substituting for the concepts "vessel of quartz" or "vessel of glass" the concept "any kind of vessel whatever[1]." Now this information is quite important and represents a real advance in our knowledge. Such generalisations of routines play a considerable part in the development of science and they are usually effected by arguments which, if they are not always recognised as applications of the Method of Agreement, can be stated in that manner.

Similarly the Method of Difference does not prove that (AB) is a complete routine; for that conclusion would be false. What it proves is this, that if I am to form a routine including A and C as concepts, then the complete routine must also include B. In our example, if I am to form a routine including the passage of a spark through the mixed gases in a glass vessel

---

[1] Of course the proof that the vessel may be quartz or glass does not prove of itself that any kind of vessel could be used; but that conclusion would result from a sufficient number of applications of the Method of Agreement.

that routine must include an explosion. This information at first sight appears more important than that given by the Method of Agreement; for the new routine which is developed seems more distinctively novel. But it must be noted that the new routine is only developed after the routine "spark and explosion in a glass vessel" is known; all that we learn is that there is no indication that we shall arrive at a new routine by altering the concept "explosion". The Method of Agreement indicates the possibility of new routines, the Method of Difference limits the possibility. In general, therefore, it is found that arguments similar to those of the Method of Difference are of less importance in practical scientific investigation; it is perhaps because they are less often used that it is usually considered that they are less liable to error.

It is unnecessary to analyse in this manner the other Canons. The information which they provide is always of the same nature; they indicate the direction in which, having found some routines, a search for others is likely to be fruitful. Instances in which they are applied can be found if the history of various branches of science is examined, but the application is seldom recognised consciously and it is seldom quite in the form contemplated by the strict rules.

Particular causes. But the Canons are much more frequently applied for another purpose, and when they are applied for this purpose the rules are much more strictly followed. We sometimes desire to discover, not whether a law is true, but under which of several known laws a particular observation is to be grouped; or again we may know that a certain law is applicable, but may want to discover the identity of one of the terms in this particular application; in short we may want to discover a "particular cause", as distinct from a general cause. The best examples of these uses of the Canons are found in the investigation of experimental defects. Thus I may be trying to pump out a vacuum tube and find that I cannot get the pressure down low enough. I suspect either that the pump is not working properly or that gas is entering the vessel as fast as it is pumped out; and this latter alternative again may be divided into two, either that there is a leak in the walls or that gas is being generated inside. I seal off the pump and find that the pressure rises; my conclusion that the pump is not the "cause" of the trouble depends on a simple use of the Method of Agreement; the presence of A with both C and C' proves that C and C' are not the causes. I now plunge the tube in mercury; the rise of pressure ceases and the Method of Difference tells me that the cause is a leak, for, though C is always present, A does not occur unless B is present. I then cover in turn with wax each of the likely places for cracks; if the leak continues the Method of Agreement tells me that the crack is in one of the joints I have not covered; if it ceases, the Method of Difference tells me that the leak is at the place I have just covered. Such simple examples could be multiplied indefinitely.

But it must be noted that the "cause" I am seeking in these cases is not of the kind which is asserted by a law. I am not trying to discover a law, for the whole process depends on my assumption that I know all the laws in which rise of pressure is concerned. I am trying to discover the property of an individual system; in fact I am trying to find the property X (of p. 83) which is such that it turns the symmetrical relation, characteristic of the laws which I know, into the asymmetrical relation, characteristic of an individual property. The process is the exact opposite of that sometimes employed in the establishment of laws. We sometimes discover a law by finding that a number of asymmetrical relations characteristic of individual bodies can be combined in a symmetrical relation characteristic of a law; but here I am trying to convert the law into an assertion of the properties of an individual system.

It is very unfortunate that the term "cause" is used to denote such "particular causes" which are represented by the property X (or rather some group of properties which includes X). For the use of the same term to denote both the general cause and the particular cause obscures the immense difference in their significance for scientific investigation; and it is doubtless largely because that difference has not been appreciated that the idea has gained ground that the Canons are used in the establishment of laws. They are certainly useful in the elucidation of particular causes, and the recognition of their usefulness in this direction has led to the belief that they are equally useful in the elucidation of every other kind of relation to which the name "cause and effect" is given. In the popular mind the name is associated with any two terms A and B which can be related by any proposition of the form, If A, then B; and a consideration of the Canons will show that they can be applied to discover any special relation of this form, so long, of course, as the division into facts and instances can be effected rightly before the application is made. But the relation which is asserted by laws is a very special form of that asserted by, If A, then B; it is characterised by a particular form of generality which is not in the least essential to such a proposition; we could state, If A, then B, if we did not know a single other case of a similar statement. The ambiguity in the meaning of "cause" is one of the strongest reasons for eliminating it altogether from scientific propositions, to which it is not in the slightest degree essential.

How are laws discovered? If the Canons of Induction are rejected as a method of discovering laws, it is clearly necessary to consider what is the actual method of discovery. And here three questions may be distinguished: (1) What are the considerations which led to the suspicion that there may be a law of the kind that is sought? (2) What are the experiments by which the law thus suggested is sought? (3) What is the evidence for the truth of the law when the experiments have been completed and the law stated? Either of these three questions may be intended when it is asked how laws are discovered; they are not, as will appear, wholly independent, but it will be desirable to consider them separately.

The answer to the first is given more or less satisfactorily by most of those who have discussed the methods of science. It is that we are led to seek a law in virtue of some kind of analogy with other laws or of some relation already established between such laws. In a later chapter we shall consider what are the relations established by science between laws and we shall find that they are stated in propositions which will be termed theories. It is not yet certain how far the use of the term theory to denote any proposition which states a relation between laws coincides with that in current use; it does certainly not coincide exactly if the term is to be confined to those propositions which are ordinarily termed theories and denied to all which are not specifically recognised as such. The reader must not therefore dismiss as incorrect the statement that all discoveries of laws are dictated by theories because he can think of cases where laws have been discovered by an investigation which was not concerned with any proposition which he would call a theory. All that I mean by that statement for the present, is that we are always led to new laws by considerations based on the nature or relations of laws already known. In some cases, the proving or testing of a definitely recognised theory can be clearly seen to be the motive of the investigation and to determine directly the nature of the experiments undertaken; in others the suggestion of the investigation has arisen from some chance observation which has excited curiosity; but even in this case it will be found that the experiments undertaken to satisfy that curiosity are always based upon previous knowledge of laws. We may then leave any further consideration of this question until we have examined the relations between laws and the theories which state and explain those relations; we shall then be in a position to see how theories suggest further searches for laws.

The nature of experiment. The second question may seem at first to be incapable of a simple and direct answer, because the kinds of experiments which we undertake are so exceedingly various. But I think that practically every experiment of value which has been undertaken in the development of physics during the past century can be grouped in one of two classes. Both these classes are characterised by a common feature, namely that the experiment seeks to establish a uniformity between concepts and not between fundamental judgements. This feature imposes a very notable limitation on the number of possible experiments; for though the concepts employed in modern physics are very numerous, the number is definitely finite. It is difficult to estimate the actual number; but we may note that a concept is always denoted by a technical term, so that the number of concepts is roughly equal to the number of technical terms. Now the very full index to Kaye and Laby's Tables contains about 700 entries; many of these represent the same concept and the total number of distinctively physical concepts is probably not more than a few hundred. To·these must be added concepts not distinctly physical, such as those of all the substances recognised by chemistry. These amount to many thousands; but again the number, though indefinitely extensible, is always finite.

Moreover the different concepts are not used with equal frequency; some are used much more often than others. Length, weight, period, electrical current, voltage, resistance, capacity, inductance, temperature—at least one of these probably forms part of 99 per cent. of actual physical experiments. On this score alone the variety of physical experiments which is possible is much more closely limited than might appear at first sight.

Further, as was suggested in the previous chapter, the relations between concepts which experiments seek to establish are almost entirely limited to two, which characterise the two classes of experiments just mentioned. These relations are, first, uniform association, second, the "functionality" of mathematical relations. In looking through the numbers of *Science Abstracts* for a year I have not been able to find an instance which does not immediately fall into one of these two classes. The second is considerably the larger; measurement is so distinctive of physics because it is almost always the aim of the physicist to find a method of experiment which will enable him to establish a mathematical relation between two measurable concepts. But the first class is also important; it consists mainly in attempts to establish some new property of an already known "substance", the word substance being used in a very wide sense to be explained later; in fact the concepts arising from uniform association are almost all called by names suggesting a "substance".

These few vague and general considerations are not, of course, of any service in indicating the lines on which a physical research should proceed; but, equally of course, it is not my intention to elaborate instructions for research. They are included only with the object of suggesting that an "experiment" is not a term so vague that no general statements about it can be profitably made; if it is not as definite a term as was imagined by those who thought that it consisted of an application of the Canons of Induction, it is still not so indefinite that it is out of the question to give any account of the nature of the evidence provided by experiments for the laws which they establish.

Fundamental concepts. But before we proceed to discuss that evidence, which is our immediate object, one obvious question must be asked. If all modern attempts to establish laws depend on the use of concepts and these concepts depend on the validity of other laws, how were these laws in turn established? The answer is that all distinctively scientific concepts have been elaborated from concepts which were known before distinctive scientific research began. Consider the investigation which is historically the foundation of all modern physics, Galileo's research on falling bodies. His experiments were directed to establishing a mathematical relation of uniformity between the concepts of distance fallen and period of falling; as a result of them he developed a new and distinctively scientific concept, that of constant acceleration. Now the concepts of length and period date back to a time previous, not only to the earliest record of science, but to the earliest record of any human activity. Science has taken these concepts and refined them somewhat, by eliminating from them portions which were not really U.A. with the remainder and adding others which are U.A. with them; for this purpose it has employed the methods, similar to those described by the Canons of Induction, which were discussed on p. 103. But without the unrefined concepts to work with, science could not have progressed in this manner. In a later chapter we shall endeavour to analyse these concepts in some measure and to decide by what experiments they might be proved nowadays to anyone to whom they conveyed no significance; but I believe the completion of that task to be utterly impossible. The whole structure of our thought depends on their significance, and it is impossible to place ourselves in the position of those to whom they are not significant without depriving ourselves of the power of thinking at all. Our analysis of science must cease at some stage, and the point at which it seems most convenient to cease is that at which science merges into the general thought common to all mankind; to pursue it beyond that point would be to transgress the boundaries of science and to lay ourselves open to the imputations that we are so anxious to avoid. And it should be noted that when science truly merges into the general thought common to all mankind and relies on propositions the truth of which is involved in every process of thought, we have reached a stage at which universal agreement for its pronouncements can be obtained; we have therefore reached the ultimate subject matter of science.

Accordingly the only part of the process of the establishment of laws that we need consider in detail is that in which, when certain concepts are accepted as valid and the laws on which they are based as true, we can arrive at other true laws and other valid concepts. This process, it is maintained, consists in establishing relations of uniform association or uniform mathematical relations between the concepts. The next and the vitally important problem is to discover what evidence we have for the assertion that the relations thus established are really uniform.

How are laws proved? Here we return to the problem of Induction, which cannot be avoided whatever view we take of the nature of laws; for the essential feature of laws is that they state, on the basis of an examination of a small part of our experience, relations valid for other portions which have not been examined. What we observe is an association, once or in a few instances, of judgements which we know to be parts of concepts; what we conclude is that this association will be observed also in other instances. We observe once that silver dissolves in nitric acid, that a body of known weight produces a certain extension in a certain rod, or that a spark is followed by an explosion; we conclude that silver will always dissolve in the acid, that a body of the same weight will always produce that extension in the same rod, and that a spark will always be followed by an explosion.

If the view that all relations asserted by laws are causal were correct, no special proof of these conclusions would be needed. For causal relations are, by definition, invariable, so that when we have discovered a causal relation we know that it will always be found again. But of course no definition proves anything, and our expectation that causal relations when discovered will be invariable is really based on propositions used in applying the definition; these propositions are contained in the Law of Causation, stated in the form that every effect has a cause and every cause an effect. Now that we have concluded that the relations asserted by laws are not always causal, a similar expectation of the invariability and uniformity of those relations can only be based on some proposition similar to the Law of Causation.

The propositions which are to be substituted for the Law of Causation are much more vague and much more difficult to state precisely. In the first place we assert that there are relations between concepts which are uniform and that some, if not all, of these relations fall into the two classes of uniform associations connecting the properties of substances and of uniform mathematical relations. But we do not state that every concept is related to some other concept by one of these relations; indeed, as will be seen later, we assert definitely that some concepts are related in this manner to no other concept, or at least that, if they are "really" so related, the relation cannot be discovered by experiment. If asked for proof of the assertion, we can only point out that certain relations have proved uniform when applied to all past experience, but we have to admit that we can give no evidence that the same relations, or any others, will prove uniform in the future. To pretend that our past experience gives any evidence concerning our future experience in this matter would be ridiculous, for the whole point at issue is on what grounds we believe that past experience can give evidence of future experience. Nor indeed do we wish to make any such assertion, for we fully recognise that past experience is not a certain guide; there is no relation, however uniform in the past, which we cannot conceive might fail to prove uniform in the future; there is no law which we should not be prepared to abandon in the light of further experiment. While, therefore, we believe that there are uniform relations, we do not assert that any particular relation is uniform.

On the other hand, while in this manner the assertions of science are much less definite than those of studies which accept the Law of Causation, in another direction they are more definite. We cannot prove definitely that any given relation is uniform, but we can prove definitely that some relations are not uniform. It has always to be admitted ultimately by those who expound the Canons of Induction that it is impossible to prove definitely that any A is not the cause of B, although it is admitted with considerable reluctance and there is a tendency to gloss over the admission. The impossibility arises from the fact that it is necessary to accept the possibility of a Plurality of Causes and an Intermixture of Effects. In any number of given instances A may be shown not to be associated with B and therefore not to be the cause or effect of B in these instances. Since, however, B may have several causes and since the effect of A may be hidden by the presence of counteracting causes, it is impossible ever to be sure that, in some other instance, A and B may not be associated as cause and effect.

But the necessity for recognising the plurality of causes or the intermixture of effects arises from the fundamental assumption that the causal relation is dual. We do not define the relations which are stated by laws to be always, or usually, dual; though they can usually be stated in a dual form, they really relate a very large number of concepts and they can be expressed in the dual form, if at all, in a very large number of ways. Accordingly we do not recognise any intermixture of routines; if $A, B, C, \ldots$ together form a routine at all, then that routine is uniform and invariable, and a single instance which can be shown to be inconsistent with the assumption that these concepts form a routine is sufficient to prove that it is not a routine. Thus, in the example on p. 99, a single observation that the presence of the mixed gases in a glass vessel and their presence in a quartz vessel is not associated with an explosion is sufficient to prove that ADC is not a routine. Here the pronouncement of science is quite definite; if a single instance can be found in which B, C, D are not associated with A, then $ABCD$ is not a routine, though possibly the addition of more terms may make it a routine.

It is the application of this principle which actually leads to the discovery of relations which are uniform throughout our past experience. We always start from a suggestion that certain concepts may be uniformly related in a certain manner, and our experiments usually take the form of an attempt to discover conditions in which they are not related in that manner; if those attempts fail, we conclude that the suggestion is correct. Such is certainly the process we adopt in discovering the uniform relations which define substances; it is less clear that it is used in finding mathematical relations. But it must be remembered that in all these cases there is a uniformity involved which is not a mathematical relation, namely the uniform association of one particular magnitude of one kind with one particular magnitude of the other. This part of the relation is established in exactly the same manner as the uniform association defining substance. And when we find a uniform association between particular magnitudes, we always suspect that there will be a general uniform mathematical relation between all magnitudes of the same kind characterising similar systems (i.e. other systems which possess magnitudes of these kinds). The next stage is to obtain data concerning these magnitudes in other similar systems. When the data are obtained, once more a form of mathematical relation suggests itself, and once more our experiments are devoted to attempts to find instances in which it does not hold. What appears to us the most important part of the process, namely the obtaining of the data for similar systems, is only a positive part of the process of discovering a law, coming between two negative parts, that is parts in which we endeavour to find whether the law is *not* true.

Evidential value of repetition. The discovery of laws is, therefore, as we all realise, a tentative process and there is no certain road to success. The suggestion of what may be a uniform relation arises from considerations which we noticed in answering the first two questions; it may arise from the theory which suggests making the experiment at all or it may arise because the possibility of some forms of uniform relation, such for instance as define a substance, is so inherent in all our thought that we cannot think without assuming it. When it has arisen, all that is left is to discover whether we can prove the suggestion untrue. And this is the reason why the repetition of observations, if they are similar to those noted before, is held to increase the evidence for a law. Every repetition involves some alteration of the conditions and some therefore additional possibility of proving the law untrue; if we repeat often enough in sufficiently different conditions we shall feel that we have exhausted all possibilities of proving the law untrue and shall be more ready to accept it as true.

We can also explain why we feel that many more repetitions are required to establish some laws than are required to establish others. If we once observe that silver dissolves in nitric acid, we shall hardly feel that there is any need for repetition to confirm the law or that the evidence for the law will be increased by repetition. At the other extreme we feel (if for the moment an instance outside pure physics may be taken which, I believe, is actual) that a law connecting the monsoon in India with the pressure distribution in South America six months earlier requires very frequent repetition before any value can be attributed to it, and indeed that hardly any amount of repetition would render it quite certain. Between the two extremes is the law relating spark and explosion; if this were suggested for the first time, some repetition would be felt to be necessary, but quite a limited number of repetitions would make it as certain as the first law.

In all these cases we believe that it must be possible to discover some law; there must be some uniform relation between silver, the monsoon, or the explosion on the one hand and some other set of concepts on the other. The difference lies in the number of alternative laws which suggest themselves as possible. In the first case there is only one alternative. There may be many laws involving silver, but the law which we are considering here involves the concept "silver dissolving in nitric acid"; it is possible that silver may dissolve in other liquids but the laws asserting such relations do not include the one we are seeking. If there is any law of the kind we are seeking it must be the law that silver dissolves in nitric acid; either there is a uniform relation of this kind or there is not; no other alternative is important for the present purpose. Now relations of this kind, representing the properties of a substance, are expected to be uniform, if they occur at all; if there is a relation of silver dissolving in nitric acid that relation is firmly expected to be a uniform association. Accordingly when we observe it once, our purpose is attained and we consider no further inquiry necessary.

At the other extreme, though we believe that there must be a routine including the rainfall in the monsoon, we have not the remotest idea at the outset what the rest of the routine may be like and any routine which includes the monsoon, if it can be found, will serve the purpose of the inquiry. In order to be sure that the routine suggested is a routine and that the relation concerned is uniform, we have to show that all the other alternatives are not routines. But the number of these alternatives is indefinite; however many we prove to be unavailable, it is still possible that there is some other which has not yet been examined. Moreover we cannot try deliberate experiments on the monsoon; we can only wait and observe what happens; we cannot therefore set to work systematically to exhaust possible alternatives. We do not even know, when we have observed the association a given number of times, how many alternatives, and exactly what alternatives, have been exhausted; for our knowledge of the changes in the various factors which might possibly influence the monsoon is limited. Accordingly however often we observe the association, we are never sure that we have proved all alternative laws false, and are therefore never sure that we have proved this law to be true.

In the intermediate case of the explosion there are alternative laws, but the number of them is limited and fairly definite. There was not more than one routine which could include "silver dissolving in nitric acid", but there are many routines which could involve the occurrence of the explosion. On the other hand, we have some idea of what these alternative routines are and we can examine many, if not all of them, by deliberate experiment. The exclusion of alternatives is a finite process which can be completed in a finite time, leaving us quite as certain of the law as in the first case.

The conclusion which I want to draw is that the confirmation of a law by repetition is simply a process of exclusion of alternatives, and that repetition is effective in the establishment of laws only in so far as it involves such exclusion. This view is very similar to that taken by most expounders of the Canons of Induction, but I am not sure that it is universally accepted. It seems sometimes to be thought that mere repetition without any exclusion of alternatives provides confirmation of a law. But we have only to notice that repetition, if we are sure that the conditions are precisely and exactly the same in all the instances, provides no additional evidence whatever. If we observe the association of the spark and the explosion and repeat the experiment in conditions which we are sure are exactly the same, we shall obtain no additional reason for believing that there is a uniform relation between spark and explosion; it is only when the conditions are slightly different at each trial that such additional reason is obtained.

But, it may be said, one circumstance is necessarily different at each trial, namely the time at which it is made; accordingly repetition will exclude at least one alternative. But I think this alternative has been excluded already by a fundamental assumption which has not been yet specifically noted. It is that the mere time that an event happens is not part of any routine in which that event is concerned. This assumption is extremely important; in conjunction with the assumption that there are uniform relations and routines it asserts what is sometimes called the "uniformity of Nature". We cannot consider it fully until we deal with all the concepts which are connected with "time", but it may be stated in a form which is perhaps a little clearer, namely that any time relation which is uniform and is part of a routine must be a time relation between concepts which are otherwise uniformly related (e.g. by uniform association) in that routine. Accordingly all that repetition with a change of "mere time" proves is that there is no uniform relation between the explosion and any concepts of which the time relation to the explosion is different in the two instances. But if the time relation of these concepts is different their other relations will also be different; and the exclusion of the alternative routine involving those concepts will be made on the basis of relations other than those of time. The circumstances will be different and the view that mere repetition, apart from change of circumstances such as exclude possible alternatives, does not provide additional support for a law is not disproved.

It will doubtless seem that the brief discussion, in the latter part of this chapter, of the methods which are employed in the establishment of laws is a very inadequate treatment of one of the most important and fundamental problems in science. It may be felt that such very vague and general considerations cannot represent truly the whole process and that some more systematic foundation for laws ought to be stated. But it must be pointed out once more that we are only inquiring how science is actually developed, and I do not think that any of those who have been most prominent in its development would be willing or able to state in any more systematic fashion how they achieved their aims. If the discovery of laws could be reduced to a set of formal rules, anyone who learnt the rules could discover laws. But there is no broad road to progress. Herein lies the most serious objection to much that has been written on the methods of science. There is no method, and it is because there is no method which can be expounded to all the world that science is a delight to those who possess the instincts which make methods unnecessary.

But there is one matter connected with the discovery of laws which has been left out of account so far. It is generally thought that the problem of Induction is very closely connected with those of Chance and Probability, and indeed that it is considerations connected with these conceptions which lead to the attribution of a higher value to laws derived from the examination of a very large number of instances. To problems of this nature we shall have to revert. We shall not be able to understand them or several other problems left unsolved in this and the two preceding chapters until we have discussed the explanation of laws and their connection with theories. To this discussion we must now proceed.

CHAPTER V

THE EXPLANATION OF LAWS

Summary. Explanation consists in the substitution of more for less satisfactory ideas.

Ideas may be more satisfactory either because they are more familiar or because they are simpler.

Such explanation of laws as is effected by other laws is explanation of the second kind, the explaining ideas being simpler because they are more general. Generality of this kind, which is characteristic of all that part of science which is concerned with laws, is connected with the use of symmetrical rather than of asymmetrical relations.

But there is another and more important kind of explanation which is effected by theories and not by other laws.

The meaning of explanation. It is the business of science not only to discover laws but also to explain them.

Explanation is the substitution of more satisfactory for less satisfactory ideas. There are two main reasons why ideas are unsatisfactory. They may be intrinsically unsatisfactory owing to confusion or complexity; and they may be unsatisfactory merely owing to unfamiliarity. Explanation sometimes consists merely in stating the proposition to be explained in a different way and interpreting it in terms of more familiar ideas, or it may involve radical analysis and the reduction of complexity and confusion to simplicity and order.

The first kind of explanation, that which consists in the substitution of the familiar for the unfamiliar, is common whenever the layman interests himself in matters which are generally reserved for the expert. Thus, we may read one morning in the financial column of our newspaper that the Bank Rate was raised from 4 per cent. to 5 per cent., and that the Paris cheque rose 3 centimes while the New York Exchange receded a $\frac{1}{2}d$. To the bill broker or the manager of a foreign discount house that statement would require no explanation at all, but an explanation might well be demanded by anyone not habitually engaged in financial transactions. The statement does not seem satisfactory to us because we have never contemplated, or at least thought deeply about, the ideas concerned in it; the terms convey no definite meaning to our minds; they are unsatisfactory for the same reason as a statement in a language that we do not know is unsatisfactory. We shall receive part of the explanation that we desire if the technical language is replaced by that of common converse, if we are told exactly what the Bank Rate and the Paris Exchange are, and if it is pointed out to us that the very different expressions of the movement of the "Paris cheque", and the "New York Exchange", are used by an unfortunate convention to describe changes which are essentially the same. But the explanation will not be complete unless there is a substitution of ideas as well as of language and unless we are shown what the changes described would mean to anyone who wanted to borrow money in London or to pay a bill at a shop in New York.

Here it is clear that explanation consists purely in the substitution of the familiar for the unfamiliar; for the extent to which the explanation offered would really be an explanation depends on the habits of the person to whom it is addressed. A financier would probably find that the explanation which satisfied us was rather confusing than elucidating; he would prefer the technical statement because it is more familiar to him. But there is another kind of explanation which might be offered and is of a rather different character.

For the financial correspondent might suggest that the changes in the Bank Rate and in the Exchanges were connected and that one was the cause or the effect of the other. We might ask for an explanation of this connection and should be satisfied if the mechanism of international currency was explained to us and it was shown that the changes were related through the desire of the economic man to sell in the dearest market and to buy in the cheapest.

Here again the substitution of the familiar for the unfamiliar plays a part in the explanation, but a more important part is played by the substitution of the simple for the complex. The relation between the changes appears to us simpler (and not only to us but also to those most familiar with the operations concerned) if it can be analysed into a number of applications of a single general principle which is valid over a much wider range. Such general principles are usually more familiar than special applications of them, just because they are more general and because we are more likely to have encountered instances of them; but it is their generality and not their familiarity which confers on them their value in explanation, a value which would hardly be diminished if they should be less and not more familiar than the special applications which they are used to explain.

Scientific explanation. There are then two distinct types of explanation, one which consists in the substitution of the familiar for the unfamiliar, the other which consists in the substitution of the simple for the complex, often by the analysis of the complex into a number of simpler constituents. The question now arises which of these two forms of explanation is concerned in scientific explanation.

In one obvious class of cases explanation of the first type is involved, namely when we are explaining the results of science to those less completely versed in them than ourselves. Scientific ideas as well as scientific terminology are derived, as we have often noted, from the ideas and language of everyday life; and it is often possible to give the explanation that is demanded by showing the steps in the derivation. But with such explanation we are not concerned here, for we are considering science only as it is regarded by those most completely trained in all its processes. There are doubtless infelicities and ambiguities in the expression of scientific propositions the removal of which represents an advance in clearness even to the most highly-trained physicist; but the possibility and necessity of explanations of this kind arise only from the intimate and inseparable connection of words and ideas. Explanation by alteration of expression is only an indication of an elucidation and a freeing from confusion of the ideas expressed.

Moreover when explanations are offered to the layman they are often of the second kind which consists in analysis and generalisation. This kind is usually offered when we are asked to explain some process or event familiar in everyday life. Thus we might be asked to explain why white paint becomes discoloured much more rapidly in rooms lit by gas than in those lit by electricity. The explanation which we should offer would depend on certain general principles which we should lay down at the outset, namely that white paint consists often of a basic lead carbonate, that coal gas usually contains sulphides of hydrogen and hydrocarbons, and that this lead carbonate when acted upon by these sulphides produces a lead sulphide which is dark in colour. Here it is clear that there is no substitution of the familiar for the unfamiliar; the ideas on which the explanation is based are probably much less familiar to the questioner than those which they are used to explain. Of course he must have some familiarity with them. He will probably have sufficient experience of the mutual action of two colourless bodies to produce a coloured body to realise that the general propositions on which the explanation is based are not unreasonable. But in order that he should appreciate the explanation it is quite unnecessary that he should have any previous knowledge of the principles of chemistry or of the special properties of lead carbonate and hydrogen sulphide; on these matters he would be quite content to accept our statement. The account of the matter which we have given him is more satisfactory and is an explanation, not because it is based on anything he knew before, but because it reduces his experience to order, shows that a single fact is merely one instance of a general principle, and introduces the simplicity which is characteristic of general principles.

But of course explanation of this kind is not explanation of laws. Mill would probably have thought it was, but then Mill never knew a law when he saw one. It is not a law that white paint is discoloured by coal gas, for that proposition is not always true and, even if it were (if there were no other white paint than lead carbonate and no coal gas free from sulphur), it would still not have the characteristic necessity which distinguishes laws. Our explanation is simply a case of discovering a particular cause (see p. 103) and finding of what law or laws the action of the particular cause is an illustration. We are not explaining laws, but explaining facts in terms of laws.

Nevertheless this example does show some similarity to others in which there is undoubtedly an explanation of laws. Thus it is a law that a sufficiently large adiabatic expansion of a gas saturated with water vapour produces condensation. If we were asked to explain this law we might point out that adiabatic expansion produces cooling and cooling lowers the saturation pressure of the vapour, and that by the combination of these two laws the condensation by adiabatic expansion may be explained. This form of explanation depends on the fact which was noted in Chapter III that laws can sometimes be (imperfectly) expressed in the form of an assertion of a dual relation which is asymmetrical and transitive. Such a relation holds between adiabatic expansion and cooling and between cooling and supersaturation; for while adiabatic expansion always produces cooling, cooling may be produced by other changes than adiabatic expansion, and while cooling produces supersaturation, supersaturation may be produced by other changes, e.g. isothermal compression. Similar logical relations are involved in the explanation of the discoloration of white paint, for in the cases contemplated white paint always contains basic lead carbonate, while that compound may·exist in other forms, and the carbonate is always discoloured by impure coal gas, while the discoloration may be produced by other means.

What is generality? But why does the exhibition of relations of this kind constitute an explanation? The reason has already been given. The laws involved in the explanation are more general than those explained. Adiabatic expansion produces cooling even if the gas is not saturated; that is to say, this law includes associations which are not included in that which it is used to explain. Similarly, the law that cooling produces supersaturation is more general than the law that adiabatic expansion produces saturation. Further the greater generality of the explaining laws is, probably, a necessary consequence of the logical relations used in explanation. We have already seen that propositions, closely resembling laws but essentially devoid of generality, namely those about particular causes and about the properties of individual systems, are always and necessarily asymmetrical; it is only general laws which can be symmetrical. Once more we are unable to investigate the matter fully owing to the inability to analyse fully the logical structure of laws, but it seems a rule of wide application (recognised, I believe, by logicians) that particularity and asymmetry of relation, generality and symmetry of relation are closely associated. It is a special case of this rule that explanation by means of the transitiveness of asymmetrical relations is necessarily explanation by ideas of greater generality.

For it should be observed that the kind of explanation with which we are here concerned is not applicable to laws stated in the form of an assertion of a symmetrical relation. Examples of such laws can be obtained, as we have seen, in the statements of the properties of a substance, by dividing them into two groups each defining the substance; thus we may take the law that the X-ray spectrum of silver is uniformly associated with a density of 10·5, a melting point of 960°, solubility in nitric acid and so on. It will be recognised that this law cannot be explained in the same manner as the law that adiabatic expansion produces supersaturation. Such explanation as is possible can be effected only in terms of a theory of the structure of the atom. We are soon to consider the nature of theories, but even if we are not able to distinguish them clearly and definitely from laws, it is clear that the logical relations of the propositions involved in an explanation of the law of the properties of silver by means of any theory of atomic structure is perfectly different from those of the propositions in the example we have just considered. But the law to be explained here is so different in its nature from the previous example that it may be thought that the difference in the possibility of explanation by other laws arises from some difference other than that between symmetry and asymmetry of the uniformity. It may be pointed out therefore that one of the laws used in the explanation of that example, namely that cooling produces supersaturation, is very nearly symmetrical and is quite symmetrical if the qualifying conditions are so framed that isothermal compression is excluded. Now the law that cooling produces supersaturation cannot be explained in the same manner as the law that adiabatic expansion produces cooling; it cannot be resolved in the same way into a combination of two other laws one or both of which are more general than the law to be explained. However it must be remembered that all these expressions of laws as dual relations, whether symmetrical or asymmetrical, is artificial and incomplete. If the relation between adiabatic expansion and supersaturation is expressed in the dual asymmetrical uniform relation, the proposition asserting it is not universally true. If it is to be universally true, the qualifying conditions must be inserted in some manner. Now it would be found that if these qualifying conditions were fully inserted, they involved all the more general statements implied when it is said that cooling produces supersaturation, for adiabatic expansion will only produce supersaturation when it produces cooling. The law to be explained, if it is really a true law, is not less general than the laws which explain it; it is logically equivalent to those laws. The explanation does not alter in any way the content of the laws; it merely alters the expression of it so as to make it appear more general.

Are there other kinds of explanation? These considerations are presented to show that there is a form of generality in laws which is intimately connected with the apparent asymmetry of the uniformity asserted by them, and that it is this kind of generality which is attained by the kind of explanation of laws which has been discussed. We must now ask whether there is any other kind of explanation of laws which in a similar manner depends on the exhibition of a connection between the law explained and other laws. I do not think there is. Mill, whose views are often suggestive just because they are erroneous, distinguishes three kinds of explanation of laws by means of other laws. The first kind is explanation by indirect causation, the second by showing that the law to be explained is a compound of other laws, the third by exhibiting it as a special case of some more general law[1]. Now the first kind is precisely that which has just been discussed in connection with the law of adiabatic expansion and supersaturation; Mill regards the expansion as the indirect cause of the supersaturation because the expansion causes

---

[1] Mill's examples need not be given; they are all taken from obscure and unimportant parts of science and show the usual lack of appreciation of the true nature of a law.

directly cooling, while cooling causes directly supersaturation. But according to the views which have just been expressed, this kind of explanation is identical with the third; "direct causation" explains indirect only because the law stating it is more general and covers a wider range of instances. There remains therefore only the second kind. The principle involved may be stated thus. There is a law that a concept or group of concepts A is uniformly associated with another group B; it appears that A can be regarded as the compound of the terms $a, a', a'', \ldots$ and B as the compound of the terms $b, b', b'', \ldots$ and that these resolved terms of A and B are connected by laws stating uniform associations. The law connecting A and B can then be exhibited as a compound of the laws relating a and b, a' and b', a'' and b'' and so on.

It is impossible to say that an explanation of this kind is not possible, but I cannot find an example of it. That given by Mill is the explanation of the elliptic motion of the planets as the "compound" of undisturbed motion in a straight line with acceleration towards the sun. Now we shall see in the next chapter that the propositions which thus explain elliptic motion are not laws at all but theories; however even if they were laws the explanation involves the introduction of a wholly new proposition, namely that the undisturbed motion and the acceleration towards the sun are mutually independent, in other words the "law" of the independence of forces. In all the cases I have been able to find of such apparent explanation by "compound" laws, the same features are found; some proposition about independence is required in addition to the laws of which the compound is composed and, on account of the necessity for this additional proposition of independence, the explaining propositions are always theories and not laws.

The conclusion which I am concerned to draw is that whenever one law is explained by means of other laws, the explanation always consists in the expression of the law in a more general form. Explanation of this kind is generalisation; the ideas of the explanation are more satisfactory than those explained because they are more general. The removal of confusion and complexity and the reduction to simplicity takes the form of the analysis of the confused and complex group into instances of some principle of wide application. And this is, of course, the kind of simplicity that is characteristic of that part of science which consists in the establishment of laws; for laws are a means of removing complexity and attaining satisfactory ideas through generalisation.

The explanation of laws by other laws is, then, explanation of what was called in the opening paragraphs the second kind. There is however another kind of explanation characteristic of science which is more nearly explanation of the first kind; this is the explanation effected by theories.

CHAPTER VI

THEORIES

Summary. The meanings usually associated with the words Theory and Hypothesis are discussed. None of these associations will be maintained here, except in so far as they follow from the definition deliberately adopted.

A theory is defined by means of the formal nature and connection of the propositions of which it consists, namely an hypothesis, making assertions about "hypothetical ideas" characteristic of the theory, and a dictionary, relating these ideas to the concepts of the laws explained by the theory.

An example of an actual physical theory is taken, the dynamical theory of gases, and it is discussed whether it accords with the definition. The answer is, yes; but the value of the theory is derived largely, not from the formal constitution, but from an analogy displayed by the hypothesis.

This analogy is essential to and inseparable from the theory and is not merely an aid to its formulation. Herein lies the difference between a law and a theory, a difference which is of the first importance.

The development of a theory is considered in connection with the example. The distinction between changes in the hypothesis and changes in the dictionary is emphasised. The latter confirm the theory, the former throw doubt on it.

A digression is made to discuss the use, in connection with theories, of the words "molecule," "real," "cause."

The main argument is resumed. It has been shown that one physical theory accords with the definition. What others accord with it? A theory is considered often distinguished from the previous example, namely Fourier's Theory of heat conduction. It is concluded that this theory also accords with the definition, but that the nature of the analogy is somewhat different.

This conclusion does *not* lead, as might be suspected, to the result that all numerical laws are theories.

A further consideration of the way in which theories explain laws leads to some discussion of Maxwell's Theory and the Theory (usually called the Law) of Gravitation. The close connection between theories of the first and second types is exhibited.

The definition of theories is now accepted. The value of theories, and especially the relative values of those of the first and second types (often called "mechanical" and "mathematical" theories), is discussed.

What I do not mean by a theory. When laws were under discussion it was suggested that the decision whether a given proposition is or is not a law had to be left to the judgement of serious students of science. The reason for adopting this attitude was that by a law we meant simply a proposition having a certain importance for science, and that the only persons who are in a position to judge of that importance are those to whom it may be important. It is not possible to adopt the same criterion in connection with theories, for there is far more difference of opinion among scientific men concerning the importance of theories than there is concerning the importance of laws.

We are all agreed that it is the object of science to establish laws, for by them is effected that ordering of our knowledge of the external world which it is our purpose to attain; and we are all agreed as to the nature of the ordering which is desirable and possible. Indeed we were led to the view that it was part of the essential nature of a law that there should be agreement about it, and that the universal agreement in judgements of the external world which is the basis of science is simply an agreement about some very simple and elementary laws. But there is no doubt that there are propositions which are recognised on all sides as theories, but concerning the importance of which there is a great difference of opinion. Any reasonable use of the word must be such as to include these propositions.

Accordingly it will be well to start by explaining in some detail exactly what meaning I propose to attach to the term "theory". I shall not assume at the outset that my use of the word coincides with that generally adopted; indeed, since I shall urge that the general use covers propositions of widely different form and significance, I can expressly disclaim that assumption. When the meaning is defined the question will have to be put which, if any, of the propositions of science, whether generally termed theories or not, are theories according to my definition? And since the word, being adopted from common discourse, has already attached to it many connotations, it will be convenient at the outset to free it from these associations, and to state carefully what is *not* meant by the word.

In common usage "theory" is always contrasted with "practice", and the contrast is justified by etymology. Theory, in its origin, is the state of contemplation as distinct from the state of action, and it is perfectly correct to term "theoretical" discussions which can have no influence in active life. The same distinction justifies the division of treatises or examination papers into "theoretical" and "practical", so long as the latter are confined strictly to the manipulative details of laboratory experiments and the former to a consideration of all the intellectual processes and results to which such experiments may give rise. For in this original sense of the word all propositions are necessarily theoretical, since they concern thought and not action; and in this sense all science, in so far as consists of propositions, is theoretical.

A slight and obvious extension, however, leads to the use of the contrasted terms to distinguish propositions which need much thought for their establishment from those which need little. In this sense the same proposition may be theoretical or practical according to the evidence on which it is based. The statement that an unsupported stone will fall to the ground is "practical" so long as it is asserted as the result of common experience; it is theoretical if asserted as the consequence of the "law" of gravitation. Thus theory is a question of degree, and science becomes progressively more theoretical as we pass from its elementary and fundamental judgements to the various ranks of propositions derived from them.

This use of the term has certainly played some part in determining that certain propositions in actual science are termed theories; they are so termed because they are complicated. This meaning will not be attached to the word here; some of the propositions termed theories are extremely simple. On the other hand they are all removed from the fundamental propositions further than are laws, and involve another step in the development of ideas.

Another association arises directly from the use of the word "theoretical" to denote propositions which require much consideration for their establishment. All thought and all reasoning processes are liable to introduce error, and though, in one sense, a proposition is more likely to be true the greater is the consideration that has been given to it, in another sense it is more likely to be false; the longer and more complicated the process of reasoning involved in the attainment of a conclusion, the greater is the chance that error has crept in. And so it has come about that the word "theory" has become associated with a feeling of uncertainty; the view is prevalent that the more "theoretical" is a proposition, the less should be the conviction of its truth; conversely propositions are apt to be termed theories simply because their truth is not certain.

There is no need to insist on the fallacy of this opinion in its cruder forms. The desire of many half-educated persons to rely on "practical conclusions" rather than on the reasoning of the "theorist" is founded merely on ignorance and on an inability to differentiate between the kinds of thought likely to lead to truth and those which may be associated with error. It is certainly true that, if a conclusion can be obtained by a brief and simple train of reasoning, to seek to attain it by complicated argument is to court the introduction of error. But the attempt to avoid complex reasoning often results only in the concealment of it. The views of "practical men" are usually derived from assumptions and arguments no less complex than those on which theory is based; they are more and not less liable to error because they are less openly expressed. The idea that there are propositions "true in theory, but false in practice" has its foundation only in the incompetence of the uninitiated to understand theory, and in their habit of applying propositions to circumstances entirely foreign to the theory. To those who have not the power to think, theory will always be dangerous.

But the association of the word theory with a feeling of uncertainty extends to those who are quite free from such vulgar errors, and it is of the greatest importance for our present purpose to break that association at the outset. It is connected both as cause and as effect with the failure to recognise the true nature and even the distinctive characteristics of the class of propositions which we are about to consider. It is the cause of that failure, since the observation that these propositions are distinguished from others by a lesser certainty has obscured the fact that they are distinguished by other features as well; it is the effect of that failure, since the confusion in a single class of propositions essentially different in their nature has led directly to error which would have been avoided if that difference had been appreciated. It may turn out that the propositions which it is proposed to call theories can never attain to the same certainty as laws, but this result must follow on an examination of the nature of the propositions; for since laws are also not wholly free from the possibility of error, the difference can never serve to distinguish them from laws.

Closely connected with "theory" is another word, "hypothesis". In fact the two terms are often regarded, especially in the older literature, as synonymous; Laplace's Nebular Theory and Nebular Hypothesis are used indifferently. An hypothesis is, strictly speaking, a proposition which is put forward for consideration, and concerning the truth or falsity of which nothing is asserted until the consideration is completed. It is thus necessarily associated with doubt, but with doubt of a negative rather than of a positive kind, with the doubt which consists of a suspense of judgement rather than with the doubt which consists of an inclination to disbelieve. In current usage, however, the word, especially in the adjectival form, almost always connotes doubt of the second kind; to term a view hypothetical is practically equivalent to expressing dissent from it. From this connotation I want also to be free. The word will be given a special sense which is justified by its origin to this extent than an hypothesis will always be a proposition which cannot be judged to be either true or false unless there are added to it certain other propositions, although it has a distinct significance apart from these other propositions. Hypothesis and hypothetical must be taken to imply doubt of the first kind and never doubt of the second.

What I do mean by a theory. I have now stated what I do not mean by a theory and an hypothesis; it remains to state what I do mean.

A theory is a connected set of propositions which are divided into two groups. One group consists of statements about some collection of ideas which are characteristic of the theory; the other group consists of statements of the relation between these ideas and some other ideas of a different nature. The first group will be termed collectively the "hypothesis" of the theory; the second group the "dictionary". The hypothesis is so called, in accordance with the sense that has just been stated, because the propositions composing it are incapable of proof or of disproof by themselves; they must be significant, but, taken apart from the dictionary, they appear arbitrary assumptions. They, may be considered accordingly as providing a "definition by postulate" of the ideas which are characteristic of the hypothesis. The ideas which are related by means of the dictionary to the ideas of the hypothesis are, on the other hand, such that something is known about them apart from the theory. It must be possible to determine, apart from all knowledge of the theory, whether certain propositions involving these ideas are true or false. The dictionary relates some of these propositions of which the truth or falsity is known to certain propositions involving the hypothetical ideas by stating that if the first set of propositions is true then the second set is true and vice versa; this relation may be expressed by the statement that the first set implies the second.

In scientific theories (for it seems that there may be sets of propositions having exactly the same features in departments of knowledge other than science) the ideas connected by means of the dictionary to the hypothetical ideas are always concepts in the sense of Chapter II, that is collections of fundamental judgements related in laws by uniform association; and the propositions involving these ideas, of which the truth or falsity is known, are always laws. Accordingly those ideas involved in a theory which are not hypothetical ideas will be termed concepts; it must be remembered that this term is used in a very special sense; concepts depend for their validity on laws, and any proposition in which concepts are related to concepts is again a law. Whether there is any necessary limitation on the nature of the ideas which can be admitted as hypothetical ideas is a question which requires much consideration; but one limitation is obviously imposed at the outset by the proviso that propositions concerning them are arbitrary, namely that they must not be concepts. As a matter of fact the hypothetical ideas of most of the important theories of physics, but not of other sciences, are mathematical constants and variables. (Except when the distinction is important, the term "variable" will be used in this chapter to include constants.)

The theory is said to be true if propositions concerning the hypothetical ideas, deduced from the hypothesis, are found, according to the dictionary, to imply propositions concerning the concepts which are true, that is to imply laws; for all true propositions concerning concepts are laws. And the theory is said to explain certain laws if it is these laws which are implied by the propositions concerning the hypothetical ideas.

An illustration will make the matter clearer. To spare the feelings of the scientific reader and to save myself from his indignation, I will explain at the outset that the example is wholly fantastic, and that a theory of this nature would not be of the slightest importance in science. But when it has been considered we shall be in a better position to understand why it is so utterly unimportant, and in what respects it differs from valuable scientific theories.

The hypothesis consists of the following mathematical propositions:

(1) $u, v, w, \ldots$ are independent variables.

(2) a is a constant for all values of these variables.

(3) b is a constant for all values of these variables.

(4) $c = d$, where c and d are dependent variables.

The dictionary consists of the following propositions:

(1) The assertion that $(c^2 + d^2)\,a = R$, where R is a positive and rational number, implies the assertion that the resistance of some definite piece of pure metal is R.

(2) The assertion that $cd/b = T$ implies the assertion that the temperature of the same piece of pure metal is T.

From the hypothesis we deduce

$$(c^2 + d^2)\,a \left/ \frac{cd}{b} \right. = 2ab = \text{constant.}$$

Interpreting this proposition by means of the dictionary we arrive at the following law:

The ratio of the resistance of a piece of pure metal to its absolute temperature is constant.

This proposition is a true law (or for our purpose may be taken as such). The theory is therefore true and explains the law.

This example, absurd though it may seem, will serve to illustrate some of the features which are of importance in actual theories. In the first place, we may observe the nature of the propositions, involving respectively the hypothetical ideas and the concepts, which are stated by the dictionary to imply each other. When the hypothetical ideas are mathematical variables, the concepts are measurable concepts (an idea of which much will be said hereafter), and the propositions related by mutual implication connect the variables, or some function of them, to the same number as these measurable concepts. When such a relation is stated by the dictionary it will be said for brevity that the function of the hypothetical ideas "is" the measurable concept; thus, we shall say that $(c^2 + d^2)\, a$ and cd/b "are" respectively the resistance and temperature. But it must be insisted that this nomenclature is adopted only for brevity; it is not meant that in any other sense of that extremely versatile word "is" $(c^2 + d^2)\, a$ is the resistance; for there are some senses of that word in which a function of variables can no more "be" a measurable concept than a railway engine can "be" the year represented by the same number.

If an hypothetical idea is directly stated by the dictionary to be some measurable concept, that idea is completely determined and every proposition about its value can be tested by experiment. But in the example which has been taken this condition is not fulfilled. It is only functions of the hypothetical ideas which are measurable concepts. Moreover since only two functions, which involve four mathematical variables and between which one relation is stated by the hypothesis, are stated to be measurable concepts, it is impossible by a determination of those concepts to assign definitely numerical values to them. If some third function of them had been stated to be some third measurable concept, then it would have been possible to assign to all of them numerical values in an unique manner. If further some fourth function has been similarly involved in the dictionary, the question would have arisen whether the values determined from one set of three functions is consistent with those determined from another set of three.

These distinctions are important. There is obviously a great difference between a theory in which some proposition based on experiment can be asserted about each of the hypothetical ideas, and one in which nothing can be said about these ideas separately, but only about combinations of them. There is also a difference between those in which several statements about those ideas can be definitely shown to be consistent and those in which such statements are merely known not to be inconsistent. In these respects actual theories differ in almost all possible degrees; it very often happens that some of the hypothetical ideas can be directly determined by experiment while others cannot; and in such cases there is an important difference between the two classes of ideas. Those which can be directly determined are often confused with the concepts to which they are directly related, while those which cannot are recognised as distinctly theoretical. But it must be noticed that a distinction of this nature has no foundation. The ideas of the hypothesis are never actually concepts; they are related to concepts only by means of the dictionary. Whatever the nature of the dictionary, all theories have this in common that no proposition based on experimental evidence can be asserted concerning the hypothetical ideas except on the assumption that the propositions of the theory are true. This is a most important matter which must be carefully borne in mind in all our discussions.

It will be observed that in our example there are no propositions in the dictionary relating any of the independent variables of the hypothesis to measurable concepts. This feature is characteristic of such theories. The nature of the connection between the independent variables and the concepts is clear from the use made, in the deduction of the laws, of the fact that a and b are constants, not varying with the independent variables. The conclusion that the electrical resistance is proportional to the absolute temperature would not follow unless $(c^2 + d^2)\, a$ were the resistance in the same state of the system the same as that in which cd/b is the temperature; and on the other hand it would not follow if a and b were not the same constants in all the propositions of the dictionary. Accordingly the assertion that a or b is a constant must imply that it is the same so long as the state of the system to which the concepts refer is the same; the independent variables on the contrary may change without a corresponding change in the state of the system. If therefore there is to be in the dictionary a proposition introducing the independent variables, it must state that a change in the independent variables does *not* imply a change in the state of the system; the omission of these variables from the dictionary must be taken to mean a definite negative statement. On the other hand, the independent variables may bear some relation to measurable concepts, so long as these concepts are not properties of the system. Thus, in almost all theories of this type, one of the independent variables is called the "time", and the use of this name indicates that it is related in some manner to the physically measurable "time" since some agreed datum. What exactly is this relation we shall have to inquire in the third part of this volume, but it is to be noted that a relation between one of the independent variables and physically measured time is not inconsistent with the statement that a change in this variable does not imply any change in the state of the system; for it is one of the essential properties of a system that its state should be, in a certain degree and within certain limits, independent of the time.

In some theories again, there are dependent variables which are not mentioned in the dictionary. But in such cases the absence of mention is not to be taken as involving the definite assertion that there is no relation between these variables and the concepts. It must always be regarded as possible that a further development of the theory may lead to their introduction into the dictionary.

An example of physical theories. The fantastic example on which this discussion has been based was introduced in order that, in defining a theory and examining some features of its formal constitution, we might be free from associated ideas which would be sure to arise if the example were taken from any actual theory. It is easier thus to realise the difference between the hypothesis of the theory and the dictionary, and between the nature of the ideas which are characteristic of those two parts of the theory, or to recognise that numerical values can be attributed by experiment to the hypothetical ideas only in virtue of the propositions of the theory. But now we have to consider whether there are any actual scientific propositions which have this formal constitution, and, if there are, whether the application of the term theory to them accords with the usual practice; further we have to decide, if we answer these questions in the affirmative, what it is that gives them a value so very much greater than that of the absurd example which has been used so far. For this purpose an actual scientific proposition will be taken which is generally considered to have considerable value and is always called a theory; and it will be shown that it has the formal constitution which has just been explained. It will thus appear that in one instance at least our definition accords with ordinary usage.

The theory which will be selected is the dynamical theory of gases. We shall start with it in its very simplest form, in which it explains only the laws of Boyle and Gay-Lussac. For such explanation no account need be taken of collisions between the molecules, which may therefore be supposed to be of infinitely small size. Though the theory in this form is known now not to be true, it will be admitted that it is as much a theory in this form as in its more complex modern form. By starting with the simplest form we shall abbreviate our original discussion and at the same time permit the interesting process of the development of a theory to be traced. And when the development of the theory is mentioned, it should be explained that the development traced will not be that which has actually occurred but that which might have occurred; no attention is paid to merely historical considerations. One further word of warning should be given at the outset. Objections have at times been raised to this theory, and to all of similar type, by those who would admit theories of a somewhat different nature. By taking the dynamical theory of Gases as an example I am not overlooking these objections or assuming in any way that all scientific theories are essentially the same in nature as the example; we shall discuss these matters later.

Let us then attempt to express the theory in the form which has been explained. The hypothesis of the theory may be stated as follows:

(1) There is a single independent variable t.

(2) There are three constants, m, v, and l, independent of t.

(3) There are $3n$ dependent variables (x_s, y_s, z_s) $(s = 1$ to $n)$ which are continuous functions of t. They form a continuous three-dimensional series and are such that $(x_s{}^2 + y_s{}^2 + z_s{}^2)$ is invariant for all linear transformations of the type $x' = ax + by + cz$. (This last sentence is merely a way of

saying that (x, y, z) are related like rectangular coordinates; but since any definitely spatial notions might give the idea that the properties of the (x, y, z) were somehow determined by experiment, they have been avoided.)

(4) $\frac{d}{dt} (x_s, y_s, z_s)$ is constant, except when (x_s, y_s, z_s) is o or l; when it attains either of these values it changes sign.

(5) $\frac{1}{n} \sum_{1}^{n} \left(\frac{dx_s}{dt}\right)^2 = v^2$, and similar propositions for y_s and z_s.

The dictionary contains the following propositions:

(1) l is the length of the side of a cubical vessel in which a "perfect" gas is contained.

(2) nm is the mass of the gas, M.

(3) $\frac{1}{a} mv^2$ is T, the absolute temperature of the gas, where a is some number which will vary with the arbitrary choice of the degree of temperature[1].

(4) Let $\Delta m \frac{dx_s}{dt}$ be the change in $m \frac{dx_s}{dt}$ which occurs when x_s attains the value l; let $\sum_{\gamma} \Delta m \frac{dx_s}{dt}$ be the sum of all values of $\Delta m \frac{dx_s}{dt}$ for which t lies between t and $t + \gamma$; let

$$(p_a, p_b, p_c) = \operatorname{Lt}_{n \to \infty, \gamma \to \infty} \sum_{s=1}^{s=n} \frac{1}{\gamma} \sum_{\gamma} \Delta m \frac{d(x_s, y_s, z_s)}{dt},$$

then p_a, p_b, p_c are the pressures P_a, P_b, P_c on three mutually perpendicular walls of the cubical containing vessel.

From the propositions of the hypothesis it is possible to prove that

$$p_a = p_b = p_c = \frac{1}{3l^3} nmv^2.$$

But l^3 is V, the volume of the gas. If we interpret this proposition according to the dictionary we find

$$P_a = P_b = P_c = \frac{T}{V} \cdot \frac{an}{3},$$

which is the expression of Boyle's and Gay-Lussac's Laws, since $\dfrac{an}{3}$ is constant.

[1] The occurrence of a needs some remark. Is it a hypothetical idea or a measurable concept? It is neither. We shall consider its nature when we deal with temperature, but it may be stated here briefly why a number of this kind occurs in this entry in the dictionary and not in the others. The reason is this. Experiment shows that pv is proportional to T. For various reasons, which we shall discuss, we desire that the factor of proportionality shall *not* change if the unit of mass or the unit of pressure is changed; but we do not object to its changing when the degree of temperature changes. If we gave the factor a definite value once and for all, the degree of temperature would have to change when the units of mass and pressure changed; we wish to avoid this necessity and do so by changing the value of a when we change the degree. The value of a is therefore as purely arbitrary as the choice of a unit in any system of measurement.

The theory is here expressed in a form exactly similar to that of our original example, and it will now be seen that this form is not wholly artificial, but has a real significance. In explaining the laws by the theory, we do actually deduce propositions from the hypothesis and interpret them in experimental terms by means of the dictionary. Moreover the distinction between the various kinds of variable in respect of their connection with measurable concepts is apparent. l is directly connected by the dictionary to a measurable concept, and the attribution to it of a numerical value requires nothing but a knowledge of the dictionary; the hypothesis is not involved. At the other extreme, the variables or constants n, m, x_s, y_s, z_s cannot be given numerical values by experiment even with help of the hypothesis; only functions of these variables and not the variables separately can be determined. Between these two extremes lies the constant v. We have deduced from the hypothesis that $v^2 = \dfrac{3l^3 p_a}{nm}$. The right-hand side of this equation can be given by experiment a numerical value, namely $\dfrac{3VP_a}{M}$, by means of the dictionary, so that v can also be evaluated. But this evaluation depends wholly on the acceptance of the propositions of the hypothesis; apart from those propositions a statement that v has a certain numerical value does not assert anything which can be proved by experiment.

Having thus shown that the dynamical theory of gases is a theory in our sense, we must now ask what is the difference between this valuable theory and the trivial example with which we began? It lies, of course, in the fact that the propositions of the hypothesis of the dynamical theory of gases display an analogy which the corresponding propositions of the other theory do not display. The propositions of the hypothesis are very similar in form to the laws which would describe the motion of a large number of infinitely small and highly elastic bodies contained in a cubical box. If we had such a number of particles, each of mass m, occupying points in a box of side l represented by the coordinates (x_s, y_s, z_s), and initially in motion, then their momentum would change sign at each impact on the walls of the box. $l^2 (p_a, p_b, p_c)$ would be the rate of change of momentum at the walls of the box and would, accordingly, be the average force exerted upon those walls. And so on; it is unnecessary to state the analogy down to its smallest details. All these symbols, m, l, t, x, y, z, ... would denote the numerical values of actually measurable physical concepts, and it would be a law that they were related in the way described; if they were actually measured and the resulting numerical values inserted in the equations stated those equations would be satisfied.

Further the propositions of the dictionary are suggested by the analogy displayed by the propositions of the hypothesis. p is called the "pressure", and the pressure of the gas P is specially related to the variable p, because p, in the law to which the hypothesis is analogous, would be the average pressure on the walls of the box actually observed. Similar considerations suggested the establishment of the relation between nm and the total mass of the gas, and between l^3 and its volume. The basis of the relation established between T and mv^2 is rather more complex, and its full consideration must be left till we deal in detail with the theory as a part of actual physics; but again it lies in an analogy. Speaking roughly, we may say that the relation is made because, in the law of the elastic particles, mv^2 would be a magnitude which would be found to remain constant so long as the box containing the particles was isolated from all exterior interference, while in the case of the gas the temperature is found so to remain constant during complete isolation.

The importance of the analogy. We see then that the class of physical theories of which the theory of gases is a type has two characteristics. First they are of the form which has been described, consisting of an hypothesis and a dictionary; if they are to be true, they must be such that laws which are actually found to be true by observation can be deduced from the hypothesis by means of logical reasoning combined with translation through the dictionary. But in order that a theory may be valuable it must have a second characteristic; it must display an analogy. The propositions of the hypothesis must be analogous to some known laws.

This manner of expressing the formal constitution of a theory is probably not familiar to most readers, but there is nothing new in the suggestion that analogy with laws plays an important part in the development of theories. No systematic writer on the principles of science is in the least inclined to overlook the intimate connection between analogy and theories or hypotheses. Nevertheless it seems to me that most of them have seriously misunderstood the position. They speak of analogies as "aids" to the formations of hypotheses (by which they usually mean what I have termed theories) and to the general progress of science. But in the view which is urged here analogies are not "aids" to the establishment of theories; they are an utterly essential part of theories, without which theories would be completely valueless and unworthy of the name. It is often suggested that the analogy leads to the formulation of the theory, but that once the theory is formulated the analogy has served its purpose and may be removed and forgotten. Such a suggestion is absolutely false and perniciously misleading. If physical science were a purely logical science, if its object were to establish a set of propositions all true and all logically connected but characterised by no other feature, then possibly this view might be correct. Once the theory was established and shown to lead by purely logical deduction to the laws to be explained, then certainly the analogy might be abandoned as having no further significance. But, if this were true, there would never have been any need for the analogy to be introduced. Any fool can invent a logically satisfactory theory to explain any law. There is as a matter of fact no satisfactory physical theory which explains the variation of the resistance of a metal with the temperature. It took me about a quarter of an hour to elaborate the theory given on p. 123; and yet it is, I maintain, formally as satisfactory as any theory in physics. If nothing but this were required we should never lack theories to explain our

laws; a schoolboy in a day's work could solve the problems at which genera-
tions have laboured in vain by the most trivial process of trial and error. What
is wrong with the theory of p. 123, what makes it absurd and unworthy of
a single moment's consideration, is that it does not display any analogy; it is
just because an analogy has not been used in its development that it is so
completely valueless.

Analogy, so far from being a help to the establishment of theories, is the
greatest hindrance. It is never difficult to find a theory which will explain
the laws logically; what is difficult is to find one which will explain them
logically and at the same time display the requisite analogy. Nor is it true
that, once the theory is developed, the analogy becomes unimportant. If
it were found that the analogy was false it would at once lose its value; if
it were presented to someone unable to appreciate it, for him the theory
would have little value. To regard analogy as an aid to the invention of theories
is as absurd as to regard melody as an aid to the composition of sonatas.
If the satisfaction of the laws of harmony and the formal principles of
development were all that were required of music, we could all be great
composers; it is the absence of the melodic sense which prevents us all attaining musical eminence by the simple process of purchasing a text-book.

The reason why the perverse view that analogies are merely an incidental
help to the discovery of theories has ever gained credence lies, I believe, in a
false opinion as to the nature of theories. I said just now that it was a common-
place that analogies were important in the framing of hypotheses, and that
the name "hypotheses" was usually given in this connection to the propositions (or sets of propositions) which are here termed theories. This statement
is perfectly true, but it is not generally recognised by such writers that the
"hypotheses" of which they speak are a distinct class of propositions, and
especially that they are wholly different from the class of laws; there is a
tendency to regard an "hypothesis" merely as a law of which full proof is
not yet forthcoming.

If this view were correct, it might be true that the analogy was a mere
auxiliary to the discovery of laws and of little further use when the law was
discovered. For once the law had been proposed the method of ascertaining
whether or no it were true would depend in no way on the analogy; if the
"hypothesis" were a law, its truth would be tested like that of any other law
by examining whether the observations asserted to be connected by the relation of uniformity were or were not so connected. According as the test
succeeded or failed, the law would be judged true or false; the analogy would
have nothing to do with the matter. If the test succeeded, the law would
remain true, even if it subsequently appeared that the analogy which suggested
it was false; and if the test failed, it would remain untrue, however complete
and satisfactory the analogy appeared to be.

A theory is not a law. But a theory is not a law; it cannot be proved,
as a law can, by direct experiment; and the method by which it was suggested
is not unimportant. For a theory may often be accepted without the perform-

ance of any additional experiments at all; so far as it is based on experiments, those experiments are often made and known before the theory is suggested. Boyle's Law and Gay-Lussac's Law were known before the dynamical theory of gases was framed; and the theory was accepted, or partially accepted, before any other experimental laws which can be deduced from it were known. The theory was an addition to scientific knowledge which followed on no increase of experimental knowledge and on the establishment of no new laws; it cannot therefore have required for its proof new experimental knowledge. The reasons why it was accepted as providing something valuable which was not contained in Boyle's and Gay-Lussac's Laws were not experimental. The reason for which it was accepted was based directly on the analogy by which it was suggested; with a failure of the analogy, all reason for accepting it would have disappeared.

The conclusion that a theory is not a law is most obvious when it is such that there are hypothetical ideas contained in it which are not completely determined by experiment, such ideas for example as the m, n, x, y, z in the dynamical theory of gases in its simple form. For in this case the theory states something, namely propositions about these ideas separately, which cannot be either proved or disproved by experiment; it states something, that is, which cannot possibly be a law, for all laws, though they may not always be capable of being proved by experiment, are always capable of being disproved by it. It may be suggested that it is only because the theory which has been taken as an example is of this type that it has been possible to maintain that it is not a law. In the other extreme, when all the hypothetical ideas are directly stated by the dictionary to "be" measurable concepts, the conclusion is much less obvious; for then a statement can be made about each of the hypothetical ideas which, if it is not actually a law, can be proved and disproved by experiment. This condition is attained only in theories of a special, though a very important type, which will receive attention presently.

The case which demands further consideration immediately is that in which the dictionary relates functions of some, but not all, of the hypothetical ideas to measurable concepts, and yet these functions are sufficiently numerous to determine all the hypothetical ideas. In this case it is true that propositions can be stated about each of the hypothetical ideas which can be proved or disproved by experiment. Thus, in our example, if one litre of gas has a volume mass of 0·09 gm. when the pressure is a million dynes per cm.[2] then, in virtue of this experimental knowledge, it can be stated that v is $1·8 \times 10^5$ cm./sec. A definite statement can be made about the hypothetical idea v on purely experimental grounds. If the dictionary mentioned sufficient functions of the other ideas, similar definite experimental statements might be made about them. If the theory can thus be reduced to a series of definite statements on experimental grounds, ought it not to be regarded as a law, or at least as a proposition as definitely experimental as a law?

I maintain not. A proposition or set of propositions is not the same thing as another set to which they are logically equivalent and which are implied by them. They may differ in meaning. By the meaning of a proposition I mean (the repetition of the word is useful) the ideas which are called to mind when it is asserted. A theory may be logically equivalent to a set of experimental statements, but it means something perfectly different; and it is its meaning which is important rather than its logical equivalence. If logical equivalence were all that mattered, the absurd theory of p. 123 would be as important as any other; it is absurd because it means nothing, evokes no ideas, apart from the laws which it explains. A theory is valuable, and is a theory in any sense important for science, only if it evokes ideas which are not contained in the laws which it explains. The evocation of these ideas is even more valuable than the logical equivalence to the laws. Theories are often accepted and valued greatly, by part of the scientific world at least, even if it is known that they are not quite true and are not strictly equivalent to any experimental laws, simply because the ideas which they bring to mind are intrinsically valuable. It is because men differ about intrinsic values that it has been necessary to insert the proviso, "by part of the scientific world at least"; for ideas which may be intrinsically valuable to some people may not be so to others. It is here that theories differ fundamentally from laws. Laws mean nothing but what they assert. They assert that certain judgements of the external world are related by uniformity, and they mean nothing more; if it is shown that there may be a case in which these judgements are not so related, then what the law asserts is false, and, since nothing remains of the law but this false assertion, the law has no further value. We can get agreement concerning this relation and we can therefore get agreement as to the value of laws.

The development of theories. The distinction between what a theory means and what it asserts is of the utmost importance for the comprehension of all physical science. And it is in order to insist on this distinction that the case has been considered when all the hypothetical ideas can be determined by experiment, although not all of them are stated by the dictionary to "be" concepts. As a matter of fact I do not think this case ever occurs, though we cannot be certain of that conclusion until all physics has been examined in detail. There is always, or almost always, some hypothetical idea propositions concerning which cannot be proved or disproved by experiment; and a theory always asserts, as well as means, something which cannot be interpreted in terms of experiment. Nevertheless it is true that a theory is the more satisfactory the more completely the hypothetical ideas in it can be experimentally determined; those ideas may be valuable even if nothing can be stated definitely about them, but they are still more valuable, if something can be stated definitely. Thus, in our example, the theory is valuable even though we cannot determine m or n; but it will be more valuable if they can be determined. Accordingly when a theory containing such undetermined ideas is presented and appears to be true, efforts are always directed to determine as many as possible of the undetermined ideas still remaining in it.

The determination of the hypothetical ideas is effected, as we have noticed before, by the addition of new propositions to the hypothesis or to the dictionary, stating new relations of the hypothetical ideas to each other or to the concepts. The process demands some attention because it is intimately connected with a very important property of theories, namely their power to predict laws in much the same way as laws predict events. In passing it may be noted that a failure to distinguish a law from an event and a consequent confusion of two perfectly distinct kinds of prediction has also tended to obscure the difference between a theory and a law.

There is an important difference between the addition of new propositions to the hypothesis and to the dictionary. The hypothesis gives the real meaning of the theory and involves the analogy which confers on it its value; the dictionary uses the analogy, and the propositions contained in it are usually suggested by the analogy, but it adds nothing to it. Accordingly a change in the hypothesis involves to some extent a change in the essence of a theory and makes it in some degree a new theory; an addition to the dictionary does not involve such a change. If, then, a new law can be deduced by the theory by a simple addition to the dictionary, that law has been in the fullest and most complete sense predicted by the theory; for it is a result obtained by no alteration of the essence of the theory whatever. On the other hand if, in order to explain some new law or in order to predict a new one, a change in the hypothesis is necessary, it is shown that the original theory was not quite complete and satisfactory. The explanation of a new law and the determination of one more hypothetical idea by addition to the dictionary is thus a very powerful and convincing confirmation of the theory; a similar result by an addition to the hypothesis is, in general, rather evidence against its original form.

But the degree in which the necessity for an alteration in the hypothesis militates against the acceptance of the theory depends largely on the nature of the alteration. If it arises directly and immediately out of the analogy on which the hypothesis is based, it scarcely is an alteration. Thus, in the theory of gases in the form in which it has been stated so far, the only dynamical proposition (or more accurately the only proposition analogous to a dynamical law) which has been introduced is that the momentum is reversed in sign at an impact with the wall, while its magnitude is unchanged. But in dynamical systems this condition is fulfilled only if the systems are conservative; it is natural therefore to extend the hypothesis and to include in it any other propositions concerning the hypothetical ideas which are analogous to other laws[1] of a conservative system. Such an extension involves no essential alteration of the theory, but it permits the explanation of additional laws and thus provides arguments for rather than against the theory. For example, if the extension is made (the new propositions are so complex if they are stated in a full analytical form that space need not be wasted in stating them) the effect on the behaviour of the gas of the motion of the walls of the vessel

---

[1] The "laws" of a conservative system are not really laws, but for the present they may pass as such.

can be deduced and the laws of adiabatic expansion predicted. Here no addition is made to the dictionary; only the hypothesis is altered. But if the dictionary is altered, the establishment of a complete analogy between the hypothesis and the laws of a conservative system leads immediately to the view that $\frac{1}{2}nmv^2$ is the energy of the gas and to the explanation of all the laws, involving specific heats, which follow directly from Boyle's and Gay-Lussac's laws combined with the doctrine of energy and with the proposition that quantity of heat is energy. All these ideas are essentially contained in the original theory which can hardly be said to be altered by explicit statement of them. As a matter of fact they seem to have been stated in the earliest forms of the dynamical theory, although they were not necessary to explain the laws of Boyle and Gay-Lussac.

However further inquiry shows that a more important alteration is necessary. So long as we are considering only perfect gases (and it must be insisted that some gases over certain ranges are experimentally perfect) and no measurable concepts other than pressure, volume, temperature, and quantity of heat, the theory in its original form, with all its natural implications, explains all the experimental laws. The only objection to it is that the constants m, n, x, y, z remain undetermined. But if we attempt to explain the laws of viscosity or conduction of heat, we meet with new objections. The dynamical analogy leads immediately to an entry in the dictionary relating viscosity to the hypothetical ideas; for viscosity consists experimentally in the transfer of momentum from one to the other of two parallel planes in relative motion. But in the system of elastic particles there would also be such a transfer of momentum if the sides of the box in which they were contained were moving relatively to each other, and the known laws of such a system show that there is a relation between this transfer of momentum and the masses and velocities of the particles together with the distance and relative velocity of the sides; the transfer of momentum is a function of these magnitudes. Accordingly it is suggested that a similar function of the corresponding variables of the hypothesis should be related by means of the dictionary to the viscosity of the gas.

We can now deduce the relation which should exist according to the theory between the pressure, density, and temperature of the gas and its viscosity. The relation predicted does not accord with that determined experimentally; in particular it is found that the theory predicts that the coefficient of viscosity will be determined by the size and shape of the containing vessel, whereas experiment shows that it depends, in a given gas, only on the density and temperature[1]. Here the addition of an entry to the dictionary has led to a new law, but a law which is false. The theory is not true; it must be altered;

---

[1] The theory which neglects the size of the molecules leads to the familiar result

$$\eta = \frac{1}{3}\rho v \lambda,$$

but λ, the mean free path, will be the distance that the molecules travel between the walls of the vessel, and will depend on its size and shape instead of simply on the properties of the gas, as it will if the free path is between successive collisions with molecules.

and it can only be altered by changing the hypothesis. The change which is made is, of course, the introduction of a new hypothetical idea, a mathematical constant σ, and a consequent modification of the equations relating the variables and constants. The hypothesis thus modified is analogous to the laws of a system of elastic particles which are spheres of finite size, and the part which σ plays in those equations is the same as that of the diameter of the spheres in those laws. With this modification, and with such change in the dictionary as necessarily accompanies it, the relation between the coefficient of viscosity and the density and temperature predicted by the theory becomes in accordance with that experimentally determined[1]. The theory is once more satisfactory; and though in its earlier form the theory must be rejected, we do not regard the whole theory as false, because the new ideas introduced into the hypothesis are such an extremely natural extension of the old. If the analogy is based on the behaviour of elastic bodies, it is extremely natural to attribute to them finite dimensions.

Thermal conductivity is related to transfer of energy as the coefficient of viscosity is to transfer of momentum. The addition of an entry in the dictionary to introduce thermal conductivity is therefore suggested in just the same manner as the entry to introduce viscosity, for in the system of elastic particles which provides the analogy of the hypothesis energy as well as momentum would be transferred between the walls. No addition to the hypothesis is necessary to deduce the relation between thermal conductivity, density and temperature; the relation predicted turns out to accord with experiment. Here an addition to the dictionary alone has predicted a true law, and the theory is correspondingly strengthened.

But in spite of these alterations the objection still remains that n, m, x, y, z are undetermined; indeed an additional undetermined idea, σ, has been introduced. This addition does not, however, make matters worse, for in the original theory n and m were so connected that the determination of one would involve the determination of the other; whereas now n, m, σ are found to be so connected that a determination of one would determine all three. The determination is effected by the application of the theory to gases which are not perfect. The introduction of σ alters somewhat the laws predicted by the theory for the relation between pressure, volume and temperature; they are no longer exactly those of Boyle and Gay-Lussac. It is found experimentally that these laws are not actually experimentally true; by comparing the deviations found experimentally with those, involving σ, predicted by the theory a new relation between n, m, σ and experimentally

---

[1] Of course this statement is not true, so far as the temperature is concerned. Agreement between theory and experiment in respect of the variation of viscosity with temperature can be obtained, if at all, only by giving to the molecules some form more complex than spheres, and by introducing forces between the molecules when not in contact. It is not my object here to expound the dynamical theory, but only to use it as an example; that use is not affected by supposing things to turn out more simply than they actually do. The further statements which will be made presently and are equally untrue will not be specifically noticed. The instructed reader will not require the notice; the uninstructed will be merely confused by it.

determined magnitudes is established. These relations, in addition to those arising from viscosity or thermal conductivity, enable each of these three hypothetical ideas to be determined. Here we have (or should have, if the statements made were correct) the most powerful confirmation of the theory; not only is a new law predicted without addition to the hypothesis and confirmed by experiment, but undetermined ideas in the hypothesis are determined. If no further discrepancies between theory and experiment were found, when yet other propositions were introduced into the dictionary, for the completion and final establishment of the theory only the determination of x, y, z would be necessary.

But in this case, and in some others similar to it, special considerations make the determination of these variables less important than usual. In order to determine them completely it is necessary to know their values and the values of their first differential coefficients with respect to t for some value of t; their values for all other t's can then be deduced. But it can be shown that this knowledge is not required if it is required to determine only the limit to which some function of these variables tends as n tends to infinity. Whatever values of (x, y, z) and $\dfrac{d}{dt}(x, y, z)$ are associated with the value $t = t_0$, consistent with the relation between $\dfrac{d}{dt}(x, y, z)$ and v which is asserted by the hypothesis, then the value for $t = T + t_0$ of

$$\mathrm{Lt}_{n \to \infty} \sum_1^n f\left(x_s, y_s, z_s, \frac{dx_s}{dt}, \frac{dy_s}{dt}, \frac{dz_s}{dt}\right),$$

where f is any function, will tend to the same limit as T tends to infinity[1]. Or, expressing the matter in terms of the analogy, the properties of any infinite collection of the particles will be the same whatever were the positions of the particles and their velocities at a previous period infinitely distant. Now all the propositions of the dictionary which involve (x, y, z) at all, involve them in the form of the limit of some function as n tends to infinity. So long as we can imagine that the values which should be attributed to them, when experiments on the gas are made, correspond to a value t_0 such that the state of the system is unchanged for all values of t between t_0 and $t_0 - T$, where T may be greater than any assigned quantity, then the laws predicted by the theory will be the same whatever values are assumed to correspond to $t_0 - T$. For various reasons into which we need not inquire for the moment, we are prepared to make the assumption contained in the last sentence. Accordingly though we cannot determine the variables we can, by assigning any "initial" value to them that we please (i.e. values at $t_0 - T$), find values for them in the conditions of experiment which are indistinguishable by any experiment that we can perform from the values resulting from the assumption of any other initial values. That is to say, even if we could determine the variables, the deductions which could be made from the theory would be

---

[1] Certain very exceptional values of the variables and certain exceptional functions should strictly be excepted from this statement.

precisely the same as the deductions made from the theory with the assumed initial values; for if the values could be determined, these values would be associated with some initial values, and these initial values would lead to the same result as those which have been assumed.

We are therefore reconciled to the impossibility of determining these variables because we know that, if we could determine them, it would not make the slightest difference to the theory. Nevertheless, it causes us, I think, some slight mental discomfort; we feel that the theory would be even more satisfactory if they could be determined. Now the determination is impossible only so long as all the propositions in the dictionary introduce only the limits of functions when n is infinite; it would not be impossible if an entry in the dictionary could be made which introduced a function for a finite value of n. In recent years such an entry has been made in connection with the phenomenon known as Brownian motion; and the entry, without additions to the hypothesis, leads to the explanation of new laws and enables the determination of the variables to be made for certain systems. It was felt that the importance of the theory was thereby increased; and M. Perrin, on whose work the advance largely depended, wrote a book describing it entitled *Brownian motion and Molecular Reality*. He felt that his researches had made molecules real in a way that they had not been real before.

A digression on the use of certain words. This summary sketch of the manner in which the dynamical theory of gases has been, or might have been, developed has been given for two purposes. First, in order to show that the formal nature of the theory does accord with that given in the definition adopted here, that the various changes which have been introduced into it can be exhibited as changes in that formal nature, and that the importance of the changes is explicable in terms of hypothesis, dictionary and analogy. Second, the discussion has drawn attention to several features on which it will be necessary to remark at later stages in our inquiry, when we are considering in detail the actual theories of physics. But in proving that one particular physical theory satisfies the definition we have not, of course, completed our task; it must be shown further either that the class as we have defined it agrees exactly in extension with that of the propositions to which the term theory is usually attached, or that there is some good and sufficient reason for diverging from current usage.

However before we proceed to this further inquiry, it will be convenient to make a digression and to consider some matters of nomenclature intimately connected with theories.

It may have been noticed that, until the end of the discussion, care was taken not to use the term "molecule" which is so intimately associated with the dynamical theory. The reason is that the use of this word illustrates well the dangers to which reference was made on p. 53. A molecule, it may be said, is what corresponds in the analogy to an elastic particle. But strictly speaking, there is nothing said in the hypothesis or the dictionary about molecules. The analogy suggests that we should call v the "mean velocity of the molecules ", (x_s, y_s, z_s) the " position ", and $\dfrac{d}{dt}(x_s, y_s, z_s)$ the " velocity "

of the molecule s. Accordingly when we say that the velocity of the molecule s is so-and-so, or that the mean velocity of the molecules is so-and-so, we are asserting something which is asserted by the theory and has a very definite meaning according to the theory; further, since v can be determined by experiment through the dictionary, the second statement means something that can be interpreted in terms of observation and proved true or false by experiment. And if we say that the molecule s has a certain velocity, then again our statement will have a clear and definite meaning, so long as it is simply equivalent to the statement that the " velocity-of-the-molecule-s " is so-and-so. But it must be remembered that the hyphened words, though grammatically divisible, form a single indivisible idea. If we take out the grammatically separate words " molecule " and " velocity " and, in stating the proposition in the alternative form, allow ourselves to imply that there is a molecule which has a velocity and a velocity which the molecule has, then, the statement may perhaps be correct, but we are implying something entirely foreign to the theory. We may land ourselves in even greater difficulties if we say " there are molecules ", because the analogy permits the statement " there are elastic particles ", and imply that the two statements are of the same kind, supported by similar evidence. The latter statement asserts a uniform association, which is a law and defines the properties of a system. The former statement is not one of the propositions of the hypothesis; and it is very difficult to give to it any precise meaning at all. Does it state any kind of uniform

association? I cannot see what form, unless it be simply that $\dfrac{dx_s}{dt}$ is the differen-

tial coefficient of x_s and not of some other x, or that (x_s, y_s, z_s) is a single term of the 3-dimensional series. But these are not very important propositions, or, perhaps it would be more accurate to say, they are so important that they are inextricably involved in the meaning of all mathematical symbols. In either case they do not require or admit of separate expression.

I am far from urging that we should never make the statement that there are molecules. It is a very useful and compact way of calling to our minds all the assertions and implications of the dynamical theory of gases. But it has this use only because we know all about that theory and are intimately familiar with it. To anyone not familiar with the theory it would not evoke the ideas which we associate with it; and such a person, in his endeavour to find some meaning for the phrase, would be almost certain to find a perfectly wrong meaning. If there is anyone who thinks it in the least important that science should not be misunderstood by the laity, and is at all concerned to attempt the hopeless task of preserving them from egregious error, he will be careful how he uses such a phrase. But he will be very sanguine; for however careful we are in the form of our statements, the delusion concerning the relation between grammatical form and logical content, discussed in Chapter III, will probably be too strong for him.

A second word connected with theories which deserves special attention was purposely introduced at the end of the last section. It was said that researches on Brownian motion had proved the "reality" of molecules.

It is most important to observe this use of the word "real." No word has been productive of more confusion of thought and more futile controversy, but it is here used in a sense to which a very clear and definite meaning can be attached. When scientific men say that something is *real*, that something *really* happens or that the *real* truth about a matter is so-and-so, they are very often referring to a theory which has been proved to be true. The something that is *real* is an idea of the hypothesis of the true theory[1], the event *really* happens if the proposition asserting it is analogous to the assertion of some event according to the laws which provide the analogy for that hypothesis, and the *real* truth about the matter is the theory which explains it. It is difficult to prove this assertion without collecting and analysing numerous examples of the use of "real" in scientific writings. That would be a very interesting but very lengthy task. It will perhaps be a better method to use in future the term real whenever it occurs naturally, and sometimes to interrupt the argument for a moment to show that what its use implies is that which has just been stated. This procedure will be followed. But of course there is another question involved, namely why real has come to be associated with hypothetical ideas rather than with concepts. This inquiry raises very delicate considerations, but some steps in the direction of answering it will be attempted in Chapter IX.

Lastly it will be convenient to notice another ambiguous word. The word "cause" is often used to denote the connection between a theory and the laws which it explains. Thus, it might be said that the impacts of the molecules on the walls are the "cause" of the pressure on them.

This use of the word has occasioned much confusion, for among those who believe that laws assert causal relations, it has naturally led to the fallacy that what is stated by such theories is a law. It is true that the theory asserts some kind of uniformity between the impacts and the pressure, but this relation must be carefully distinguished from that discussed in the chapter on laws; the uniformity is not something observed and determined by direct judgements of the external world; it is a consequence of intellectual processes, and is something characteristic of internal judgements. The test of universal assent may be applied. Many persons have actually asserted that they do not believe in the dynamical theory of gases and do not believe in the uniform association of impacts and pressure; and those who do believe have discovered no way of converting them or of showing that they do believe, for action will always be determined by a belief in the laws which the theory explains and not in the theory which explains them.

Yet the use of "cause" in this sense is sometimes directly related to that in the sense in which causes may be asserted by laws. For, in the system of

---

[1] The statement that the "something is…" must be interpreted in the sense just discussed in connection with molecules.

material elastic particles which provide the analogy of the theory of gases, the impact of the particles would be the cause of the pressure, at least in the psychological sense of p. 63; at any rate it would be uniformly associated with it in the manner characteristic of a law, and it would be the cause if we could accept the view that laws always assert cause and effect. But in other cases the relation is not so direct, and all that is meant is that the ideas which are said to be the cause are contained in the hypothesis of the theory which explains laws in which the effect is a concept; in fact the relation of cause and effect is almost exactly that of the hypothetical ideas and the concepts in the dictionary. In yet other cases it is only meant that the concepts which are stated to be cause and effect are explained by the same theory; for instance, when it is said that the high reflecting power of silver is the effect of its high electrical conductivity, and when more is implied than that the two properties are merely associated.

It would be troublesome and superfluous to analyse all the senses in which cause and effect are occasionally used; so long as we recognise that they are used in different senses and that one of these senses implies a theoretical connection which is wholly different from the connection asserted by laws, then we are not likely to be led into error.

The main argument resumed. Another type of theory. There is a school of scientific thinkers, who owe their inspiration mainly to Mach (who again acknowledged his indebtedness to Stallo), distinctly opposed to theories of the type we have just considered. They hold that "mechanical theories", such as the dynamical theory of gases, are of little value and often positively misleading; they contrast with these theories the "mathematical theories", of which Fourier's theory of heat conduction is usually taken as the type. Our next step therefore must be to inquire whether these theories also satisfy our definition and, if so, in what respect they differ from those which have just been discussed.

Fourier's Theory may be expressed by the equation

$$\lambda \left(\frac{\partial^2 \theta}{\partial x^2} + \frac{\partial^2 \theta}{\partial y^2} + \frac{\partial^2 \theta}{\partial z^2} \right) = \rho c \frac{d\theta}{dt},$$

in which θ "is" the temperature, (x, y, z) the coordinates of a point in the body under investigation, t the time, ρ the density, c the specific heat and λ the thermal conductivity. This manner of expression immediately suggests that the theory is formally similar to the examples which we have considered before. The equation constitutes the hypothesis, certain additional propositions being implied; these are that t, x, y, z are independent variables, θ a function of these variables, λ, ρ, c constants independent of them. The dictionary is the collection of statements in the sentence beginning "in which". So far there is no difference between Fourier's Theory and the Theory of Gases; the definition of a theory which has been given covers both. The difference between the two lies in the relation between the hypothetical ideas and the concepts, and this difference is two-fold. In the first place we seem here to have an instance of a theory in which every hypothetical idea is related directly by means of the dictionary to a corresponding concept; it is the ideas themselves and not functions of them which are mentioned in the dictionary; moreover the determination of the hypothetical ideas is complete and none remain undetermined. In the second place, it does not seem clear that there is any "analogy" on which the propositions of the hypothesis are founded or by means of which the concepts to which they are to be related by the dictionary are selected[1]. If there is an analogy involved in the hypothesis, it is with the laws which the theory is intended to explain. In the usual expositions of the theory, the equation is developed from the consideration of the flow of heat through an infinite plane parallel slab. If it is the experimental laws of such flow that lead to the theory, then these laws play the same part in the theory as those of a conservative system of elastic particles play in the theory of gases. But whereas in the theory of gases, the laws which provided the analogy and led, psychologically though not logically, to the hypothesis and the dictionary are of a totally different nature from those which the theory is used to explain, in the theory of heat conduction, which explains the laws of heat conduction, the laws of the analogy are of precisely the same nature as those of the laws to be explained; both are laws of heat conduction, and the concepts involved in one set of laws are the same concepts—temperature, length, time, specific heat and so on—as those involved in the other.

These two differences between Fourier's Theory and the theory of gases are, of course, connected; and together they suggest that some revision of our view of the nature of theories is necessary. It may be that both conform to the formal definition from which we started; but if, as has been maintained, it is the analogy and not the formal structure which gives all its value to a theory, it is perhaps hardly consistent to include in an undivided class theories so markedly different in respect of the analogy. But I think a little further consideration will show that the differences are not quite so great and that the resemblances are greater than appeared at first sight.

First then let us observe that the theory is not a law, and resembles in this respect the theory which we considered previously; the observation is important because the similarity between the theory and a law is undoubtedly greater[2]; it arises from the first feature just noticed. It might be suggested that, if each of the hypothetical ideas, taken apart from the others, "is" a concept, then, since statements about concepts are laws, the hypothesis is a law. But here we must remember the very special sense in which the word

---

[1] There is, of course, a similarity between the fundamental equation of heat conduction and certain equations in hydrodynamics. If the value of the theory is considered to be at all dependent on this similarity, then it partakes of the nature of the mechanical theory considered before. But I do not think the value is so dependent, either to-day or when the theory was first proposed; Fourier's equation was, I believe, introduced into hydrodynamics after it had been formulated and discussed in connection with heat conduction.

[2] It is somewhat remarkable that, while theories of the first class have often been confused with laws, although the distinction is so obvious, the confusion has not occurred so frequently with theories of the second class in which the distinction is much less obvious. The reason will appear in the discussion.

"is" is used; it is only asserted that certain attributions of numerical values to the hypothetical ideas imply attributions of the same numbers to the concepts. Now the only numerical values which can be attributed to concepts as the result of experiment are finite values; the hypothesis on the other hand involves, by the mention of differential coefficients, the attribution of infinitesimal values to the hypothetical ideas. Such attributions do not imply corresponding attributions to the concepts, and there must consequently be a distinction between the hypothetical ideas and the concepts. Again a value can be given to the measurable concept, temperature, only for such values of (x, y, z) as correspond to points on the surface of the solid body; the hypothesis on the other hand attributes values to θ when the points lie inside the surface; these attributions again imply no corresponding attributions to the concepts. Accordingly, it is not strictly true that the hypothetical ideas are concepts even in our special sense of the word; for though the attribution to them of some numerical values implies the attribution of the same values to the concepts, there are other values that correspond to no values of the concepts. If the dictionary is amended in this sense, it becomes clear that the hypothetical ideas are not identical with the concepts, and that there are propositions concerning the hypothetical ideas which correspond to no propositions about the concepts. These propositions are not laws; and, since they are essentially involved in the hypothesis, the theory is not a law. It asserts and means something which is not expressible in terms of experiment, namely something about differential coefficients of temperature with respect to distance or time and something about temperatures in the interior of a homogeneous solid body.

And here in passing it may be noted that it is doubtful whether it is strictly true that *all* the hypothetical ideas are stated by the dictionary to "be" concepts. All actual methods for determining the thermal conductivity are usually justified by deduction from the theory, and the assumption that all these methods will give the same value to this constant is based solely on the theory. The determination actually depends on the truth of the theory quite as intimately as the determination of the velocity of the molecules depends on the truth of the theory of gases. But this dependence is not inevitable; we might define the thermal conductivity as that measured by one of the standard methods and relate this value by means of the dictionary to the hypothetical λ; if that procedure were actually adopted, λ, like all the other hypothetical ideas, would be a measurable concept.

Again, though the analogy which relates the hypothetical ideas and the concepts is rather different in nature from that characteristic of the theory of gases, Fourier's Theory resembles that theory in the fact that *some* analogy is essential to it; for it is only this analogy which distinguishes the theory from the multitude of others, similar to the absurd example of p. 123, which might also be proposed to explain the same laws[1]. But it may seem that the

---

[1] It is also distinguished *now* by the fact that it has predicted new laws which have turned out to be true, namely those involved in all the new methods of measuring thermal

analogy is less important in connection with such theories, because it is determined from the moment that the attempt to frame a theory at all is undertaken. In the theory of gases there was nothing at the outset to suggest what analogy would prove suitable; the selection of the analogy of a swarm of elastic particles was simply a brilliant idea of the inventor, dictated by no rule, and distinguishing his effort from those of others (if there were others) who tried to frame other theories to account for the same laws. On the other hand, if it is characteristic of theories of the type we are now considering that the analogy should be based on the laws which are to be explained, there is much less scope for ingenuity; it is known beforehand where the analogy must be sought, and the selection of the particular analogy which is chosen follows directly from the decision to try to frame a theory of this type at all. The analogy is not characteristic of this theory of heat conduction as against any other; it is characteristic of all theories of the type which attempt to explain heat conduction at all. It is therefore a much less important part of the theory; it is no more important from our present point of view than the acceptance of the conceptions and operations of mathematical analysis which are equally essential to theories of this type and equally free from any arbitrary choice.

Now it may be admitted freely that analogy of the kind characteristic of the theory of gases does play a very much less important part in Fourier's Theory than in the theory of gases. But there is necessarily involved in it an element which plays exactly the same part as the analogy plays in the theory of gases; it is an element just as incalculable, as free from all dictation by rule and as arbitrary; it is at the same time the element which gives the theory its value and distinguishes it from the multitude of other theories which might be proposed to account for the same facts. Let us examine the matter rather more closely.

The "proof" of the theory usually offered consists in the "generalisation" of certain experimental results, or at least of certain results which might be established by experiment; for the actual experiments which have been[*] performed are probably neither sufficiently numerous nor sufficiently accurate to establish them if there had been no reason other than experiment for believing them. First, it is established that, if the two opposite faces of a parallel slab, of which the dimensions are very large compared with the distance between them, are maintained at different temperatures, then the quantity of heat transmitted through the slab is proportional to the area of their faces, to the temperature difference and to the reciprocal of the distance between them; the constant of proportionality is determined by the material of the slab and independent of the temperature or the dimensions. Second, the rate of rise of temperature of any portion of the slab is proportional to the quantity of heat received by it in unit time and to the reciprocal of its mass, the factor being again determined only by the nature of the material. The generalisation of these results consists in the addition of two assertions:

conductivity which have been developed since Fourier's time. But it was also distinguished from absurd theories at the time it was propounded and when these new laws were not known.

(1) that these propositions would remain true to whatever extent the dimensions of the slab were reduced, (2) that they would remain true if the surfaces of the slab were not bounded, as they would be in the experiment, by some other material, such as air, but by other portions of the same material. These two assertions, as we have noticed, are not laws, because they do not state anything that could possibly be proved by experiment or even interpreted in terms of observation; they are a pure addition to the experimental facts, and the question arises why these assertions rather than any other are made. The answer which is generally given is that they are the "simplest" assertions which can be added; they are simple in themselves and they lead to simple mathematical developments.

I have no doubt that this answer is correct. But the question arises immediately why are these propositions simpler than any others or on what grounds do we judge simplicity. Any answer which is given must, I think, establish at once the conclusion which it is desired to draw, namely that the choice of these assertions rather than any others is dictated by considerations of exactly the same nature as those which dictate the selection of one analogy rather than another; and that, just as it is the analogy which gives its value to a theory of the first type, so it is the simplicity which gives its value to theories of the second. For an analogy is a function of the contemplating mind; when we say that one set of propositions is analogous to another we are saying something about its effect on our minds; whether or no it produces that effect on the minds of others, it will still have that effect on our own. But this is also true of simplicity; a proposition is simple or complex according to the effect-it produces on our minds, and that effect will be the same whatever the effect on the minds of others. An analogy is valuable, as was said before on account of the ideas which it evokes; simplicity is valuable for precisely the same reason.

. Although, therefore, it may be true that theories of the second type are not characterised by the analogy and do not derive their value from it, as do theories of the first type, they are characterised by a feature which is as personal and arbitrary as the analogy and do derive their value from it. In theories of both types there is something over and above the formal constitution, which cannot be expressed as part of the formal constitution and yet distinguishes the theory from all possible alternatives. If this conclusion is accepted, the difference between the two types is not very important for our present purpose.

Are all "numerical laws" theories? But one possible objection to the argument should be considered. It depends essentially on the conclusion that the theory is not a law[1]. Thus it was said that the extension of the ex-

---

[1] The objection which follows might also take another form. It might be said that the "simplicity" consists in the choice of mere extrapolation for the addition of propositions, that therefore a rule for the attainment of simplicity can be given, and that simplicity is not a personal and arbitrary matter. But of course there is the obvious answer that there is the choice which propositions are to be extrapolated and in what direction the extrapolation is to be made.

perimental results to slabs however small involved the introduction of propositions which are not experimental, and therefore changed the proposition from a law into something else. Now somebody may say that the process involved here is only that known as "extrapolation"; that the logical basis for extrapolation under suitable conditions is hardly different from that of interpolation, and that if we are going to refuse the name of law to every proposition derived from experimental results by interpolation and extrapolation, we shall have to deny that there are any numerical laws at all. Nobody, for example, has proved Ohm's Law for every possible value of current and potential; it has been proved for a series of values, and its truth for the remainder is assumed by interpolation. Further, there must be some greatest value of the current for which it has ever been proved; and yet we should not have the smallest hesitation in extending the law, by extrapolation, to a slightly greater value. Interpolation and extrapolation are therefore necessary parts of any numerical law.

But we are here discussing not so much the truth of the law as its meaning. When we interpolate according to Ohm's Law or extrapolate to greater values of the current, the meaning of the statements that we make is of precisely the same nature as those which are made as a direct result of experiment; we mean that one set of observations is uniformly associated with another; the meaning is precisely the same whether we assert it of observations we have made previously or of those we may not, though the strength of the evidence for the truth of that assertion may possibly be different in the two cases. But in passing from the law to the hypothesis of the theory, we are changing the meaning of the proposition. Not only *have* we never observed a temperature in the interior of a homogeneous body, but every method of measuring temperature implies that we *cannot* do so. Again, so long as the difference of temperature and the distance between two points are finite, the assertion that their ratio has a certain value is something which can be proved or disproved by experiment; however great or however small the evidence on which the assertion is made it still means the same kind of thing. But as soon as they are not finite, the assertion means something different; for a difference of temperature or a distance between two points which can be determined by experiment and yet is neither finite nor zero means nothing whatever.

In this matter what applies to Fourier's Theory applies also to any propositions in physics which involve the conceptions of the infinitesimal calculus; such propositions are all parts of the hypotheses of theories. This statement might appear startling if there were associated with the terms "hypothesis" and "theory" any connotation of uncertainty; for the use of the calculus is involved in propositions which are generally regarded as the most firmly established of any in the whole department of physics. But I have already expressly dissociated any such connotation from the terms. If these propositions are theoretical and hypothetical in the sense of the terms used here, then the conclusion is, not that they are doubtful, but that some theories and some hypotheses may be as certain as any scientific proposition can be. It does not, of course, follow that *all* theories are so certain, but the considerations just advanced are sufficient to show that assertions which are not capable of interpretation in terms of observation or of proof or disproof by experiment may be accepted universally as an essential part of physical science.

How theories explain laws. We have concluded that the two types of theory agree in two important respects, namely that they are not laws and that their value is derived from something of the nature of an analogy. We may now ask whether the types agree in their uses. Both are such that laws can be deduced from them, but does the deduction give the same kind of information in the two cases? In particular, does the second type "explain" the laws deduced?

Here we revert to our considerations of the nature of explanation. In both types there is that kind of explanation which consists in showing that the laws deducible from the theory are common consequences of a single principle. But while this generalisation is the most important feature of the explanation provided by the second type, in the first type the more important feature is usually that associated with explanation by greater familiarity. The theory of gases explains Boyle's Law, not only because it shows that it can be regarded as a consequence of the same general principle as Gay-Lussac's Law, but also because it associates both laws with the more familiar ideas of the motion of elastic particles. Indeed it might be held to provide a satisfactory explanation of that law, even if it explained no other and even if there were no generalisation at all, so long as it did not definitely fail to explain laws which, for some reason connected with the analogy, we felt ought to be explained by the same theory. If Boyle's Law were the only gaseous law known, then a theory which would explain that law, and that only, would be the only theory of gases desirable or even possible. Accordingly there is a marked difference in the explanations provided by the two types of theories, and this difference is usually recognised by not speaking of "explanation" in connection with theories of the second type; it would not be usually said that Fourier's Theory explained the laws of thermal conduction—that phrase would be reserved rather for the electronic theory, if it were successful—but only that it was a generalisation of those laws. And this habit is justified by what was said of the fundamental meaning of explanation; for in the second type of theory there is no change at all in the nature of the ideas involved; the hypothetical ideas are directly suggested by those of the laws to be explained and by no others.

But while an explanation by mere generalisation without the introduction of any new ideas at all is characteristic of the second type of theory, it is very rarely that this type is found pure. As soon as the presence of an hypothesis and dictionary renders possible the introduction of new ideas by the addition of entries to the dictionary, advantage is usually taken of the possibility; or perhaps historically it would be more correct to say that it is this ultimate possibility which has led to the framing of the theory of the second type. An excellent example is provided by Maxwell's theory of the electromagnetic field. To the reader of the first nine-tenths of Maxwell's Treatise (which were probably not the nine-tenths originally present in his mind), his theory is purely of the second type. It generalises Biot's law of the magnetic intensity at a point in the neighbourhood of a straight conductor carrying a current and Faraday's law of magnetic induction, together with laws concerning the dielectric constant and the magnetic permeability; and it generalises these laws in exactly the same way as Fourier's Theory generalises the law of heat conduction through a plane parallel slab[1]. But in the last tenth of the book an entirely new feature is introduced. It is shown that it is a consequence of the theory that, if an oscillating electric intensity is set up at one place, an electric intensity oscillating with the same frequency will appear at distant places after a finite interval of time; it is suggested that the oscillating vector in a light wave "is" such an oscillating electric intensity with its associated magnetic intensity. This suggestion is an addition to the dictionary; it proposes that the attribution of certain numerical values to the hypothetical electric and magnetic intensities should imply and be implied by the attribution of certain numerical values to measurable concepts derived from the laws of light. Now the laws of light are not of the same kind as the laws of the electric field; the concepts employed in stating one set of laws are quite different from those employed in stating the other. Accordingly by a simple addition to the dictionary the theory has been transformed from one of the second type to one of the first; the transformation has left the formal structure of the theory unaltered (except for the inclusion in the dictionary of a term involving a function of the hypothetical ideas and not the ideas themselves), for the formal structure of both types is the same; but the meaning of the theory has undergone a complete transformation. It is now regarded as valuable, not chiefly as a generalisation of the experimental laws of electric and magnetic action, but rather as an explanation (in the more limited but more fundamental sense) of the laws of the propagation of light.

It is interesting to inquire why, according to this view, the experiments of Hertz were considered to confirm the electromagnetic theory of light. For what Hertz observed was always electric intensity; the only entries in the dictionary of which he made use were those which stated that certain of the

---

[1] It is usually regarded as one of the most notable advances made by Maxwell's Theory that it introduces a new term in the current, namely the "displacement current". The introduction, which consisted in the addition of a term to the hypothesis and an alteration of an entry in the dictionary, was suggested by Faraday's theory of the electrostatic field, a theory undoubtedly of the first type. At the time that it was added no experiments were known which rendered this term necessary and accordingly the term did not appear in the dictionary at all. In this respect then, Maxwell's theory differed from Fourier's. But as soon as the experiments of Rowland, Roentgen and others had proved the "existence of this term", it had to be included in the dictionary and became of exactly the same nature as the other terms. To make Maxwell's and Fourier's theories completely similar it has only to be imagined that these experiments had preceded the theory. Unfortunately physics was not developed historically with the view of providing suitable illustrations for such a treatise as this, and we usually have to consider what might have happened and not what did happen. The point that I want to make is that Maxwell's Theory might have been developed as a theory of the second type and subsequently converted into one of the first type.

hypothetical ideas were electric intensities, entries which were characteristic of a theory of the second type. But he showed that, if the theory was to be one of the second type and to generalise adequately all the laws of electric and magnetic action, then the propositions of the hypothesis must be those stated by Maxwell and not those stated by his predecessors. It was only if the hypothesis had the form suggested by Maxwell that the entry in the dictionary relating the hypothetical ideas to optical concepts would lead to true laws of light; and it was for this reason that his experiments, though specifically bearing only on the hypothesis, were held to provide a confirmation for the entry in the dictionary. By confirming the theory as one of the second type, he confirmed it also as one of the first. This development shows how intimate is the relation between the two types of theory and how easy is the step from one type to the other, in virtue of the possibility of adding entries to a dictionary once started. For those to whom theories of the first type are of supreme importance, the importance of those of the second type consists chiefly in the prospect of their ultimate conversion to those of the first.

Another theory which should be considered briefly, because it directs attention to important features, is the Newtonian Theory of Gravitation; it states that there is between every two particles of material bodies a force proportional to the product of their masses and to the reciprocal of the square of the distance between them. It is quite obvious that, according to the definitions used here, the proposition is not, as it is so often termed, a Law; it does not state the results of experiment. The very difficult and delicate experiments that have been made on gravitational forces between bodies of which the earth is not one do not, I think, provide any evidence that the force is proportional to the product of the masses; they certainly provide no information concerning the variation of the force with the distance; and even if they did, it would be ridiculous to regard Newton's greatest achievement as a mere expression of the results of such experiments. If they had been performed with the necessary accuracy, it would perhaps be possible to regard the Newtonian proposition as a theory of the second type; it might be a generalisation of these laws, in the framing of the hypothesis of which the proposition (which could neither be proved nor disproved by experiment) had been introduced that the force was proportional to mm', even when m and m' were infinitesimal. From such a generalisation from experiments in which the dimensions of the attracting bodies were small compared with the distance between them, the results of experiments in which this condition was not fulfilled might be predicted and explained. But of course it is not in its application to terrestrial experiments but in its application to astronomical observations that the proposition is important, and it is on this application that all evidence of its truth rests.

Newton's work in this direction consisted of three distinct parts. In the first he laid down the principles of dynamics. These principles, according to what has been said already, are clearly theoretical, since they involve the use of the infinitesimal calculus. Whether they constitute a theory of the first or the second type is a difficult question which raises considerations on which general agreement appears still not to be obtained; the discussion of it is beyond the province of this volume; it is hoped that it will form the subject of the opening of the next. In the second part of his work he added to the hypothesis of this theory certain new propositions which must be asserted if it is to explain Kepler's Laws. The proposition which he added is usually stated in the form that the forces exerted by the sun on the planets must be proportional to the inverse square of the distance between them; it did not introduce any new ideas, but merely stated a new relation between those already present, namely forces and distances; the theory remained of the second type. The third part consisted of a further determination of these hypothetical ideas of the general theory of dynamics in order that it might be applied to the solar system; there was introduced into the hypothesis the proposition that the force was also proportional to the product of the masses. This addition converted the theory into one of the first type; for, in the first place, the factor of proportionality was not related, like the velocity of the molecules in the theory of gases, directly by the dictionary to any measurable concept; it could only be determined by means of theory. In the second place it introduced an analogy based on laws of systems other than the solar system, the laws, namely, of the apple which fell from the tree; it enabled the theory not only to generalise the laws of the solar system but also to explain them by connecting them with the more familiar laws of falling terrestrial bodies.

Conclusions. The value of theories. The main object of the discussion so far has been to establish that the definition of a theory given on p. 123 applies to many of the most important propositions of actual physics which are called by that name, and that the features on which it is based are among those which give to these propositions their importance. It is the formal constitution, on which the definition is based, which enables theories to be distinguished from laws; it indicates how theories may be used for what is usually regarded as their primary object, the explanation of laws; and it enables us to express clearly and simply the process of development which most theories undergo. It is true that one important proposition has just been noted which, though satisfying our definition of a theory, is not usually so called. But in this case it has been shown that the name by which it is called (a law) is clearly inapplicable and that its attribution is based on obvious error. Accordingly in the future the definition will be accepted without qualification, and the name of theory will be given or denied to any proposition according as it does or does not satisfy it.

At the same time it is recognised that it is not this formal constitution which, of itself, gives to theories their importance; it does not exhibit their true meaning and significance. If there were any propositions in ordinary use which showed the formal structure without the meaning, then the definition by formal structure would be objectionable. But I do not think there are; for the meaning, though not derived from the form, can only be expressed in that form. The meaning is derived from the fact that the theory conveys ideas which cannot be stated in a form capable of definite proof or disproof; the connection between these ideas and those which can be examined directly must be established by some form similar to our hypothesis and dictionary.

But one matter seems to require further discussion. We recognise two types of theories, and these two types can be distinguished by means of the formal constitution. In the first type the hypothetical ideas are connected to concepts through the dictionary by propositions involving only functions of those ideas; in the second type the hypothetical ideas (or the most important of them) are directly and separately related to concepts. We include them in the same class of proposition because the definition admits both forms of connection. But we have seen also that this formal difference is associated with a difference in the analogy on which the hypotheses are based; in the second type the analogy is based on laws of the same nature as those explained; in the first on laws other than those explained; further, the nature of the analogy is not the same. Hitherto an attempt has been made to show that the difference between the types arising in this manner is not sufficient to make necessary a division between them; it has been insisted that they are so intimately related as to make separation almost impossible. This opinion is certainly not universally accepted. Whether or no both types are properly termed "theories" is, of course, a question of nomenclature with which we need not trouble; we propose to call both types by that name, and so long as it is clear what is denoted by it, that is all that matters. But we must not attempt by the use of a common name to shirk questions of principle. Some people undoubtedly do distinguish very sharply between the two types[1] and attribute to one type a value very much greater than to the other. We cannot leave the subject until this view has been examined. Its examination presents great difficulties, because it is almost impossible to analyse a difference of opinion without disclosing your own; and it would be entirely contrary to the purpose of this treatise to attempt to decide any scientific questions which are still disputed. Perhaps the best way will be not to pretend to an impossible neutrality, but to warn the reader frankly that in this matter I am a belligerent.

The value of mathematical theories. Nobody denies the value of theories of the second type which are generally known as mathematical theories. The part which they play in ordering phenomena is hardly different from that played by laws. When we have discovered by experiment the law relating the magnetic intensity to the current strength and to the geometrical relation between the point considered and the current circuit, first, when the current is straight and second when it is circular, then the process of combining these two laws in a single proposition is simply an extension of the process already

---

[1] Of course I cannot feel sure that the division made here between the two types coincides with that to which reference is here made. Indeed if the considerations about to be presented are correct, the distinction would probably not have been made if the types were divided as they are here. To accept an opponent's classification is almost always to accept his conclusions. But I hope that the method of dealing with the matter adopted here will permit the issue to be clearly faced.

completed. Indeed the combination probably might be effected by a law in which no ideas were involved except measurable concepts. We prefer to effect the combination by a theory of the second kind, involving hypothetical ideas which, though directly related to concepts, are not identical with concepts; our preference is based on the great intellectual simplicity of this process and the greater ease with which new laws may be brought within the same generalisation. But the result of the framing of the theory in the matter of the ordering of phenomena is hardly different from that which would be the consequence of combination by a law.

On the other hand, to theories of the first type, which are often called mechanical theories, are attributed widely different values. One extreme of opinion holds that no theory is truly adequate unless it is mechanical; the other holds that mechanical theories are delusive and should be abandoned totally. It is interesting to observe that those who hold the first opinion are usually interested chiefly in the experimental side of the science; while those who hold the latter are mainly mathematical physicists and regard physics primarily as a source of interesting mathematical problems[1]. Now a scientific proposition may be valuable for two reasons; either because it is intrinsically interesting and provides intellectual satisfaction, or because it is a means to the end of other valuable propositions. The difference of opinion extends to both these kinds of value. Those who support mechanical theories attribute to them the highest intrinsic value; those who oppose them find them intrinsically valueless. The first school see in mechanical theories the best source of inspiration for future research and discovery; the second school regard them merely as sources of error.

The difference concerning intrinsic value is irresolvable, if it is really concerned with intrinsic value. A taste for mechanical theories can no more be forced by argument on one who does not possess it than a taste for oysters. All that we can do to convince him, in one case or the other, is to make sure that the distaste does not arise from some false association of ideas. If there is such a false association it will probably appear in a discussion of the value of such theories as means to an end, and to this we may pass immediately. But here again questions arise at the outset which cannot be discussed fully. Whether mechanical theories have actually led to error can only be decided by a history of the science. However one observation on this matter may be offered. Two kinds of error are possible; one is that of believing that something is known of a matter of which nothing is known; the other is that of preferring a false to a true proposition. I think it would be found that such error as has been associated with mechanical theories is of the first type, and in science errors of this type are almost innocuous; for they become dangerous only when they act as an obstacle to further inquiry, while some of those physical

---

[1] It is impossible to overlook the interesting fact that the difference also follows national lines. British physicists tend to mechanical theories, continental to mathematical. It almost seems that language must play a determining part, for Americans, who are so closely in touch with German science, tend in this matter to agree with us.

theories which have ultimately proved completely erroneous have at least served the purpose of stimulating research. I dissent utterly and totally from the pernicious doctrine, which is far more often stated than believed, that the main value of a theory of any kind is derived from its power of stimulating experimental inquiry, but theories have some subsidiary value of this kind, and it is probably true that a false theory is better than none.

Our inquiry thus narrows down to the question whether, by reason of their nature, theories of the first type are more liable to error than those of the second. It may be answered at once in the affirmative. The making of any additional statement is necessarily accompanied by an additional possibility of error, and theories of the first type are more liable to error than theories of the second simply because they state more. Theories of the second type can only state relations between laws of the same kind and involving the same concepts; theories of the first kind state relations between laws of different kinds involving different concepts. If we are content to abandon all attempts to relate laws of different kinds then, of course, at the same time we abandon some part of the chance that we shall be wrong. Those who find no intrinsic value in such attempts are quite right to abandon them; but those who do find it must balance that value against the chance of error. If the choice is fairly put, there will probably be little doubt which alternative will be selected; but it is often not fairly put because the division of theories into the two types is not accurately made. Thus, thermodynamical theories of the properties of "dilute" systems are often contrasted with kinetic or mechanical theories; it is implied that they are not themselves mechanical. In a later volume of this work I hope to prove that this opinion is fallacious, and that thermo-dynamical theories are just as much theories of the first kind, and even in the narrower sense mechanical theories, as are the kinetic theories; they introduce such hypothetical ideas as "intrinsic energy" which are not directly related to measurable concepts, and they are based on analogies other than those of the laws which they explain. If thermodynamical theories are to be pre-ferred to kinetic, it is certainly not because they belong to different types in the sense discussed here. And perhaps it may be suggested in passing that the selection of such ground on which to fight the battle between the theories of the two types is singularly unfavourable to the supporters of the second type; for if there is one theory in the whole realm of physics which has been more fruitful of fallacy than another, it is the theory of thermodynamics. There is none which so frequently gives rise to disputation almost theological in its intensity; and these disputations usually arise simply from a failure to recognise to which type the theory belongs.

But the basis which is usually alleged for the assertion that theories of the second type are less liable to error than those of the first is that they are, in Mach's phrase, "purely phenomenal". By this is undoubtedly implied that the establishment of the theory requires nothing that is not determined by the nature of "phenomena", or, in other words, by the judgements of the external world resulting from experiment and observation. The fallacy of this implication has been explained already; theories of both types assert equally propositions which have no meaning in terms of such judgements and cannot be either proved or disproved by experiment; neither type is purely phenomenal. But it might be urged plausibly that the first type is more nearly purely phenomenal than the second. For in the first type the analogy of the hypothesis is purely phenomenal; it is an analogy with phenomena other than those explained, and in framing the hypothesis nothing but this analogy is taken into account[1]. But in the second type more is involved than a simple analogy with the laws to be explained; the precise analogy which is chosen out of the many possible alternatives is determined largely by mathematical simplicity. About this there is nothing phenomenal at all; it is a characteristic of judgements of the internal, not of the external, world. I do not say that the framing of a theory in accordance with mathematical simplicity is any less justifiable than framing it in accordance with a mechanical analogy; but it is certainly less "purely phenomenal".

But further, even if it were true that theories of the second type were purely phenomenal and were determined wholly by judgements of the external world derived from experiment, would that make them free from all error? Is it unknown that we should err in propounding the most strictly experimental law? Of course it is not; numberless examples can be given of a law at one time believed to be true and since abandoned. Boyle believed that his law was applicable to all gases; it was long before Stefan's Law of radiation was preferred to that of Dulong and Petit; twenty years ago anyone who doubted that all lead had the same density would have been regarded as a madman. We can prove definitely by experiment that a law is not true, but no amount of experiment will ever prove that it is true. And why, from the innumerable alternatives which cannot be proved to be untrue and may therefore be true, do we select one which we assert with such confidence? Because that alternative and no other is the consequence of some theory. It is utterly false that theories are the more likely to be true the more nearly they are based on laws; but it is true that a law is less likely to be false if it is based on a theory. The test of "purely phenomenal" gives exactly the opposite result to that imagined by its proposers; the more purely phenomenal a proposition is and the less the element of theory associated with it, the less is its certainty. From phenomena and phenomena alone we can deduce only negative conclusions, never a positive; it is theory which gives us positive certainty.

For why do we call some laws "empirical" and associate with that term a slight element of distrust? Because such laws are not explained by any theory. While Stefan's Law and Dulong and Petit's were both based solely on observation, they were both empirical; there was nothing to choose between them, and great caution would have been exercised in extending either of

---

[1] Of course sometimes it is impossible on account of mathematical complexities to frame the hypothesis strictly on the analogy which we desire; but the mathematical simplification which is effected in these cases is regarded as a disadvantage, not an advantage; it decreases, not increases, our confidence in the theory.

them to conditions slightly different from that in which they had been investigated. It was only when Stefan's Law, and not its rival, was shown to be a consequence of general thermal and dynamical theory that it was held to be a better representation of the facts; it ceased to be empirical and was applied with confidence to phenomena of a much wider range than that involved in its experimental establishment. It would have been impossible to get anyone to believe that lead, really pure, from two different sources had a different density, except after the most elaborate confirmatory tests undertaken by international committees, until it was shown that the result was a natural consequence of a well-established theory. We do not believe our theories because they lead to true laws, but our laws because they are the consequence of true theories.

However, this is going too far. As an answer to assertions that propositions are certain because they are purely phenomenal it is permissible, but it must never be forgotten that the test of experiment, when it is available, is ultimate. No proposition is true if it conflicts with experiment and none has much value unless it can be shown that, in some cases at least, it does not conflict. But the test is not always available and by itself it can prove nothing definitely. It is the belief that, because the test is accepted when it is available, it is the only test which is possible or desirable that has produced chaos into statements of scientific principles and has led to so wide and so disastrous a misunderstanding of the meaning of science. In order that a law should be true, it must not conflict with experiment, but that criterion alone would never permit us to distinguish between multitudes of alternative laws each of which satisfied it equally. To decide between these alternatives another criterion, that of theory, is required. On the other hand a theory to be true must lead to laws which do not conflict with experiment, but that criterion would not permit us to distinguish between multitudes of alternative theories. Law and theory, formally distinct, are inseparable; and the method which leads to the establishment of one is inextricably entangled with that which leads to the other.

The value of mechanical theories. On such grounds I reject the view that theories of the second kind are in any manner superior in value or certainty to those of the first. But the doctrines of the other extreme school are also open to criticism. For in discussions of the matter the theories that are contrasted with those of the second type, which are often called "mathematical theories", are called "mechanical". It is implied that theories are completely satisfactory only if the analogy on which they are based is mechanical, that is to say, if the analogy is with the laws of some system obeying the laws of mechanics; indeed this view is not only implied, but sometimes expressly asserted[1]. No attempt is made to support this opinion by argument;

---

[1] Thus, Sir J. J. Thomson, *Phil. Mag.* VI. 37, 420: "If it (Bohr's fundamental assumption) is true, it *must* be the result of the action of *forces* whose existence has not been demonstrated." Similar expressions of opinion abound in William Ramsay's writings, but of course Ramsay can hardly be regarded as an expert exponent of *physical* science.

it is not urged that it is only such theories that can be true, for the truth of other theories is admitted; it is not even asserted that such theories have shown themselves especially reliable, for such an assertion would be hard to maintain in the face of the history of the corpuscular theory of light and of the elastic solid theory of "the aether". It is simply asserted that such theories alone can attain the ultimate end of science and give perfect intellectual satisfaction.

This opinion again is unassailable by direct argument; it rests directly on a fundamental judgement of intellectual value. But again if we can trace the opinion to an association of ideas it is possible that some modification of it might be produced. We may ask then whether any reason can be given why theories based on an analogy with mechanical systems appear more satisfactory than those based on an analogy (say) with electrical systems, that is to say, systems consisting of currents, charges, magnets and so on, obeying the fundamental laws of the electromagnetic field.

I think two very convincing reasons can be given. In the first place mechanics, owing to the genius of Galileo and of Newton, so far ahead of their ages, was developed highly before any other branches of physics had developed at all from the unordered collection of isolated observations and incoherent speculations to which man's knowledge of the external world was confined for thousands of years after the dawn of civilisation. The theories of mechanics were the first physical theories and their nature has determined the whole subsequent course of the science. Newton, with the superb mendacity of genius, always so blind to the true nature of its own achievement, asserted that he did not invent hypotheses; it was because he invented hypotheses and because he was the first to do so that he disputes with Aristotle the claim to the most far-reaching influence on the thought of the human race. Laplace, building on the foundations which he had laid, fresh from the triumphs of Celestial Mechanics, foresaw the time when all our daily life, the most trivial and the most magnificent, would be seen to be merely a confused and hesitating imitation of the majestic march of the heavenly spheres. What wonder then if men have thought that they could do no better than tread with reverence in the footsteps of the giants!

But I think there is another reason less obvious and yet more important. Attention has been drawn several times to a feature of the pre-scientific analysis of natural phenomena. All events and all changes in phenomena can be divided roughly into two classes, those which are produced by the voluntary agency of human beings and those which happen by themselves; it is a tendency of early speculation, which has gradually developed into the science and philosophy of to-day, to transfer phenomena from the second class to the first by introducing the conception of beings, resembling men in many respects, to whose voluntary agency many events are due, in the same way as others are due to the voluntary agency of men; in fact in mythologies which introduce God and Fate and Chance all phenomena are transferred from the second class to the first. The attempt to explain the universe is an attempt to exhibit all its changes as due to some voluntary agency. The path of science has diverged widely from the original direction. The elimination of everything voluntary is our aim. But we cannot help sometimes gazing wistfully back at the road we have left, where still the theologians wander on the broad way that leads to intellectual destruction. And such glances do no harm, so long as they remain glances; indeed in so far as they satisfy our intellectual desires they do nothing but good.

Now the laws of mechanics are much more closely related to voluntary action than those of any other branch of physics, for they state what happens when bodies move under forces. Whenever, as a result of voluntary determination, we produce any change in the external world, it is always by causing bodies to move and by exerting force, appreciated by the muscular sensations, for that purpose. All changes do not consist of motion, and the laws of all changes are not laws of motion; a change of colour, of pitch, of electric charge is not a change of motion, so far as experiment can determine. But if it is produced voluntarily it is always a result of motion produced by force; it is psychologically the effect and force psychologically the cause. And though we cannot express this relation in our laws, we have an opportunity to do so in our theories. By framing a theory in which the hypothetical ideas are concerned with motion and force, and in which the dictionary relates these ideas to colour, pitch or charge, we can establish that these changes are "really" the effects of change of motion; we can entertain ourselves with the feeling that the changes which characterise voluntary action are after all the real and fundamental thing and that other changes are merely delusive appearances of this reality.

Here I think is the true explanation of the craving for mechanical theories; this is why we feel that our task can only be completed when everything is stated in terms of motion and force. And so long as we recognise the nature of our desire, I can see no harm in attempting to satisfy it. But we should notice that the considerations which have been offered justify only the attempt to adopt some form of theory involving ideas closely related to those of force and motion; it does not justify an attempt to force all such theories into the Newtonian mould. There may be many possible alternatives to Newton's theory of dynamics. It may be that the simplest theory which will explain dynamical laws is that which relates to the concept force, the product of the hypothetical ideas, mass and acceleration, and includes in the hypothesis the proposition that the sum of this product for any number of reacting bodies is zero[1], and, consequently, that the momentum is "conserved". But from our present point of view a theory of this form should not be preferable in any way as an ultimate interpretation of laws to one which related any other function of the hypothetical ideas to the force or stated some slightly different

[1] Of course this statement involves assertions concerning the nature of dynamical principles which may not be accepted universally. In particular the view that force is a measurable concept apart from its definition as the product of mass and acceleration is directly contrary to the fashionable interpretation of dynamics derived from Mach. But these questions must be left for the present, although they are vital to the matter.

proposition about the momentum. It is the presence of some relation between a function of the hypothetical ideas and force, and the presence of some proposition about this function, not the precise nature of the relation and the proposition, which should give to the theory its intellectual value derived from the association with voluntary action. If the foundation of the demand for mechanical explanations has been rightly expressed, some of the objections urged against modern theories are unjustifiable on any grounds except pure conservatism (which, it must be remembered, is for some people a source of considerable intellectual satisfaction) and an exaggerated reverence for the memory of Newton[1].

On the other hand there are certainly other modern theories which raise difficulties for those who regard mechanical theories alone as ultimate. There is a tendency to substitute for hypothetical ideas based on mechanical analogies ideas which are not only foreign to these analogies, but positively antagonistic to them. Motion is essentially continuous in the experimental sense (see Chap. XVIII), and hypothetical ideas derived from it are essentially continuous in the mathematical sense. The introduction as fundamental hypothetical ideas of variables which are discontinuous functions of the independent variables is directly inconsistent with any analogy based on the observed laws of moving bodies. Though some of the ideas in such discontinuous theories may be related to mechanical concepts (e.g. energy), the theories as a whole cannot be mechanical and cannot give an intellectual satisfaction of the same nature as that associated with mechanical theories. As against this loss has to be set a gain. A strict mechanical analogy is not, for most men of science, the only source of intellectual satisfaction; such satisfaction can also be derived from simplicity and generality, from an explanation which is generalisation as well as from an explanation which is a reduction to more familiar notions. And it cannot be doubted that in these qualities of simplicity and generality the newer theories far surpass any of the older type that have been proposed to cover the same field. Indeed it is doubtful whether any mechanical theory could possibly possess to the same degree the quality of simplicity. It was characteristic of the earliest mechanical theories, those explaining astronomical phenomena, which have inspired all others, but in their subsequent development these theories have tended to become more and more complex. It is possible that in the future we shall have to choose between the advantages of simplicity and those of familiarity.

It is, of course, no part of our present purpose to suggest how the choice should be made. Indeed, if the past history of science is any guide, there will be no need to make the choice. There has often been a stage at which each of two rival theories explained part of the known laws, while neither explained all of them; and at that stage the choice between them, if it is made at all, has to be made often unconsciously, on such grounds as we have been considering. But of course a further stage is always reached in which one theory explains

---

[1] The reference here is, of course, to "relativity" mechanics, while in the next section it is to "quantum" theories.

the laws better than the other, or some new theory explains them better than either. Judgements of value on which all men agree replace judgements on which men differ.

But before leaving the matter it will be well to notice one misconception closely connected with errors already rejected. The principles underlying the framing of the hypotheses of the new or unmechanical theories is precisely the same as that employed in framing hypotheses of theories of the second type; it is mathematical simplicity. Accordingly some of those who believe that theories of the second type are much more valuable than those of the first are inclined to argue that this higher value should also attach to the unmechanical theories we are discussing; they are even prepared to state that these theories also are "purely phenomenal". But they overlook the obvious fact that these theories are not of the second type but of the first; the hypothetical ideas in them are not derived from analogy with the laws they explain and are not directly related by the dictionary to measurable concepts; most of the theories are still in the stage where some of the hypothetical ideas cannot be determined at all by experiment, because the dictionary does not mention a sufficient number of functions of them. Now whatever superior certainty theories of the second type may have over the first and in whatever degree they are more purely phenomenal, this feature is based on the fact that they are of the second type, that the hypothetical ideas are directly related to measurable concepts and that they are derived from analogy with the laws which they explain; the superior value is not derived from the use of mathematical simplicity rather than of any other source of intellectual satisfaction to determine the choice between possible hypotheses. Even if theories were more valuable because they are more purely phenomenal, that would be no reason whatever for preferring the unmechanical to the mechanical theory, or a theory of the first type based on mathematical simplicity to another theory of the same type based on familiarity.

CHAPTER VII

CHANCE AND PROBABILITY

Summary. Events are due to chance when they are not subject to law. But this absence of law must be objective and not subjective, if the events are to form part of science. Further, absence of law does not imply complete ignorance; our knowledge concerning the happening of chance events may vary from complete ignorance to complete knowledge. It is indicated at the outset that all ideas introduced in the study of chance will ultimately be found to be hypothetical ideas and not concepts.

Probability is a measure of our degree of knowledge concerning the happening of an event. We ask how is probability measured and why, when so measured, is it an indication of degree of knowledge?

The first part of the question leads to a discussion of the calculus of probability. The orthodox definition, founded on the enumeration of "cases", is examined. Objections are urged against it: (1) that it gives no indication why probability and degree of knowledge are associated, (2) that if it is employed in the usual manner it leads to obvious inconsistencies. A new definition must be sought.

The new definition must be such that it can be determined by experiment what is the probability of any event. It is suggested that probability is a property of large collections of similar trials. After some discussion of the difficulties which arise in framing any definition on this basis, a definition is adopted provisionally for equal probabilities; namely that events are equally probable if the frequencies of their occurrence tend to equality as they tend to infinite number. The exact meaning to be attributed to this phrase is discussed in the text. Some outstanding difficulties are left for future solution.

On the analogy of this definition, another for probabilities which are not equal can easily be given. It leads to the conclusion that probabilities which are not finite but infinitesimal have no meaning, a conclusion suggested by some mathematical paradoxes.

The meaning of the sum and the product of two probabilities is defined and discussed. The multiplication of probabilities is most important in those circumstances in which the orthodox definition of probability is completely inapplicable. The conception of independent events is introduced and some difficulties associated with it pointed out, but not entirely removed.

We return once more to the orthodox definition and point out that the inconsistencies mentioned at the beginning of the discussion are due to an application of the ideas of addition and multiplication to circumstances in which, according to that definition, they are inapplicable. The orthodox definition is now entirely rejected.

The remainder of the formal development of the calculus depends entirely on the use of the propositions involved in addition and multiplication and needs no discussion other than that found in any adequate text-book. But some special applications will be considered later in the book.

So far we have been concerned with the probability of events. There is a second branch of the subject dealing with the probability of causes. Here again the problem needs very careful statement; the problem as usually stated is one to which the calculus as usually expounded might be applied, but it is not the problem which is important and to which the calculus actually is applied.

A new definition is stated, based on the idea of degree of knowledge. Used in conjunction with certain quite arbitrary assumptions it leads to the usual Bayes' formula. The limitations of that formula due to these arbitrary assumptions are noted.

We now return to the second part of the question asked originally, namely why probability, measured according to our definition, is an indication of degree of knowledge. Answers often given, based on the effect of considerations of probability on practical life, are rejected. An attempt, not very successful, is made to base an answer on the fundamental nature of knowledge.

After more discussion an answer, which may appear fantastic but deserves attention, is offered. It is that the degree of knowledge of a proposition is measured by the (subjective) mental discomfort we should suffer if we found that it was not true, and this mental discomfort in its turn is measured by the probability that the proposition is true; for probability measures the amount of trouble we should have to take to prove that the proposition is true if once it is doubted.

This discussion has led us to consider "coincidences". It is pointed out that all the difficulties left unsolved earlier in the chapter would vanish if we could accept generally the proposition that coincidences do not occur. Support for such a proposition is sought among the ideas already introduced; some support is found but it is judged to be insufficient. It is urged that it is impossible to develop adequately the principles of probability without introducing theoretical ideas.

Our real reason for believing that coincidences do not occur is derived from a theory of chance which is now stated and discussed. The theory consists of two parts. One (sometimes called the Principle of Sufficient Reason) states that the differences between the events which apparently flow casually from the same trial are really due to differences in the trials which are rigidly connected with differences in the events. The second part states that the only distributions of trials which are really due to chance are such as are completely random and capable of analysis into series of equally probable independent events. The support for the second part is found (however great the attempts made to disguise it) in an association of randomness with the results of the operation of a free and arbitrary will. It is shown however that it is not necessary to assume that all chance events are actually due to the operation of such a will.

If this theory is accepted, the difficulties about coincidences and the independence of events vanish, and there remains nothing in the conceptions of chance which cannot be accepted without hesitation. It is also extremely doubtful whether the assumptions that underlie the calculus of probability can be stated in a definite form in which they are logically consistent But it becomes difficult to maintain that probability is a measure of degree of knowledge except in extreme cases.

Again, the theory enables us to deduce laws from "statistical" data; they could not be deduced without the theory. It is deduction of laws by this process which some writers have confused with Induction, which they falsely imagine to require for complete certainty the examination of large numbers of similar instances. Induction, if it requires large numbers of instances at all, requires them to be dissimilar; it has nothing whatever to do with the statistical method, which is highly theoretical and depends essentially on propositions which, if they can be stated at all, can certainly not be stated in terms of experiment or observation, and cannot be proved by experiment or observation. It is not suggested that, on this account, the propositions are less valuable; but rather that they are more valuable.

Chance is the absence of law. The origin of all fundamental scientific conceptions is to be traced to the general and unorganised experience of mankind. Such experience renders us familiar with the idea that the events which happen otherwise than as a direct result of our voluntary action can be divided more or less sharply into two classes. One class shows a certain regularity, so that the sequence of events can be predicted; the other shows no regularity whatever and no forecast of its sequence can be made. The first class is the domain, according to some mythologies, of Fate or, according to others, of Natural Law; the second is the domain of Chance.

These distinctions have been developed by scientific inquiry. The extent of the first class has been greatly increased and that of the second diminished; moreover the conception of the distinguishing characteristic has changed considerably; a scientific law is something very different from the Law of the exponents of Natural Theology. But the essential difference remains unchanged, and chance is still the antithesis to law. In modern science, as in ancient religion, that which is not governed by law is governed by chance[1].

However we have made one very important change in the distinction between the two classes. To the savage everything is chance which is not definitely known to be law; the second class includes everything which cannot be shown definitely to be included in the first. But in science mere ignorance of a law involving some event is not sufficient to show that it is to be attributed to chance; it is only to be so attributed if it is known definitely that the event is not involved in a law. The two classes no longer include the whole of experience; there is a third class consisting of events about which it is simply not known whether or no they are governed by laws. This addition of a third class is of fundamental importance for all the considerations which are about to be discussed. For in all discussions on chance and probability a characteristic paradox is always appearing; it is that we seem to deduce knowledge from the very fact that we have no knowledge. It is therefore of the first importance to observe and record carefully all the knowledge that we have about matters of chance; there is all the difference in the world between

---

[1] The word Chance offers a good, though not very important, example of words which cannot be defined in their scientific meaning by a proposition of the subject-predicate form (see p. 53). There is no scientific proposition of any value which begins "Chance is..."; for such a form inevitably suggests the idea that chance is an "agency" and gives rise to all the ideas associated with an anthropomorphic interpretation of the universe. We speak of events being "due to chance," but such an expression is not to be analysed into its constituents; it does not imply that there is something called "Chance" to which events are "due" or that events are "due to" anything at all. Of course we use the expression "The chance of so-and-so *is*," using "chance" simply as a shorter synonym for "probability", but the necessity for the "of" shows that this use is not identical with that of "Chance *is* a fickle goddess."

saying that an event is due to chance whenever we know nothing whatever about it and saying that it is due to chance when we possess definite and certain knowledge that there is no law, or no law of a certain kind, in which that event is involved.

But chance does not involve complete ignorance. This difference between popular and scientific conceptions of chance can also be expressed by the use of those two hardly-worked and question-begging words, subjective and objective. Popular chance is subjective; it refers to the state of mind of the particular person making a statement about it. What is the "merest chance" to one person may be no chance at all to some other better-informed. It appeared to me a short while ago as the "merest chance" that I should see in the paper one day the name of an acquaintance of whom I had not thought for years and meet him the next day in a remote village with which neither he nor I had any permanent connection. But later I discovered that there was a very direct connection between the newspaper paragraph and the train of events which led both of us to the same place. The meeting ceased to be chance when further information was available; the fortuitousness of the event depended wholly on my state of mind, and remained an "extraordinary coincidence" only so long as that state was unaltered.

On the other hand, scientific chance is objective. It depends not only on the state of mind of the person who makes a statement about it, but on the state of mind of everyone else who has considered the matter; whether or no some event is governed by chance is a question concerning which universal agreement can be obtained to the same extent as it can be obtained for any law. When it is said to be a matter of chance whether a penny tossed falls heads or tails, I do not merely mean that I do not know which way up it will fall, but that nobody knows, and that all the inquiry into the matter which has been made or, so far as can be seen, could be made, is insufficient to enable the fall to be predicted. I am quite as certain, and certain in the same manner and for the same reason, that I do not know and cannot know whether heads or tails will turn up as I am certain that the penny will fall somehow if unsupported. My certainty in one case and in the other is the result of previous observations; for I, shall only be certain that the result of the toss cannot be predicted as long as I am sure that the penny is similar to those which have been examined previously. If I have any suspicion that the penny is a "trick" coin and has heads on both sides, then my certainty will vanish and I shall no longer regard the result of the toss as governed by chance. If I have seen neither side of the penny, then, even if I suspected a trick, I may still consider it merely a matter of chance whether it turns up heads or tails, for I may have reason to believe that it is a matter of chance whether a given trick penny has both sides heads or both tails; but again such belief will be based on a knowledge of trick pennies. It is always knowledge of a special sort and not mere ignorance which leads us to attribute events to chance. There may be apparent exceptions to this rule, but on examination I believe that it will always be found that they arise from a looseness of expression. We are all apt to import into our scientific discourse expressions from our common speech based on unorganised experience and representing ideas which strict science has long dismissed as inadequate; and among these expressions and ideas are those of "subjective" chance. When we are speaking strictly and attribute some event to chance, we mean to assert, not vague ignorance, but ignorance of a peculiar and definite kind.

This ignorance need not be absolute, as it is in the case of the tossed penny, where we know no law whatever relating the turning-up of heads rather than tails to any other event; it may be only ignorance of a law of a special type. Thus we should probably admit that it is a matter of chance whether June 15 next year is a wet day; for we know definitely that it is impossible in the present state of knowledge to find any law relating rainfall to the day of the year except for a very short time in advance. On the other hand it is not a matter of chance whether it will rain at the centre of an extensive anticyclone; we know a definite law relating rainfall and some forms of distribution of pressure. Rainfall is, therefore, a matter of chance in one respect and not a matter of chance in another. Here again the scientific conception of chance differs from the popular; the realms of chance and law are not sharply divided in their extent. Events may belong to one class or the other according to the nature of the other events which are associated with them. Chance implies simply the absence of some law, not necessarily of any law.

Again, there is another sense in which the ignorance which leads to the attribution of an event to chance need not be absolute[1]. If the penny is a fair one, I am absolutely ignorant whether at a single trial it will fall heads or tails; but I am not absolutely ignorant whether it will fall heads every time in ten successive trials; and I am not ignorant at all whether it will fall heads every time in a hundred successive trials. I am quite as certain that it will not fall heads a hundred times in succession as I am certain that it will fall if thrown into the air. And yet I should attribute to chance the result of ten or a hundred successive tosses just as much as the result of one. It seems then that the ignorance of a law which is sufficient to lead to the attribution of an event to chance may vary from absolute ignorance to the absolute certainty which is the absence of all ignorance.

Now here we are approaching the fundamental paradox of chance. Absolute ignorance of a single event is compatible with absolute knowledge of a collection of events all similar to that single event. But so far the paradox is merely apparent and disappears on closer examination. For the fact of which we are ignorant is in no way the same as the fact of which we have knowledge; it is perfectly possible and familiar that we should have knowledge of a collection when we have no knowledge of its constituent parts; we may easily know the weight of a bag of shot without knowing the weight of each individual shot. Of course there may be some essential fallacy in this

---

[1] The statements made in this and the next paragraph are subject to later revision. But they seem to represent the ordinary view of the matter.

analogy, which is not sufficient without further consideration to remove the difficulty, but it is sufficient to show that the paradox is not necessarily insoluble. However, the feature which is immediately concerned here, namely that the degree of ignorance which constitutes chance may vary greatly, can be illustrated by examples which do not suggest the paradox. Thus, if I draw a card from a pack, I shall be absolutely ignorant whether the card will be red or black; but I shall not be absolutely ignorant whether or no it will be the ace of spades, for I have a strong suspicion that it will not be that card. On the other hand, though my ignorance of the matter is not absolute, I still regard the card which I draw as being dictated by chance, because I know that no law can be discovered which will predict which card I shall draw.

Before we proceed to consider the matter further it may be noted that none of the examples which have been given have been drawn from subjects which are definitely physical or even scientific; it may seem that they should be so drawn if it   scientific conception of chance that is under consideration. But it is . .possible to give examples out of the true subject matter of science of events, determined by observation, which are regarded as due to chance, for there are no such events. Observations do not become part of science until they are ordered, and this ordering involves the discovery of laws; any observations which have not been, to some extent, ordered in laws do not form part of science; what distinguishes the subject matter of science from that which is not subject matter is the fact that the former matter, but not the latter, is ordered in laws. On the other hand, because there are and can be no observations which at the same time form part of the province of science and are known not to be ordered in laws, it must not be concluded that the conception of chance plays no part in science. For there is a part of science which does not consist of laws, namely the part which consists of theories. The conclusion at which we shall arrive ultimately is that in science chance is always a theoretical conception; and the analogy on which, like all theoretical conceptions, it is based is with such events as the tossing of a penny or the drawing of cards, which constitute our examples. These observations are not themselves part of science, and cannot be part of science so long as they are regarded as due to chance; on the other hand they do suggest the analogy on which is based the theoretical conception of chance which is used, not to describe observations, but to explain them; they do therefore represent the scientific conceptions of chance. The matter will become clearer as we proceed, but it is well to notice it here for fear of misunderstanding. After this digression let us return to the main argument.

Probability. The orthodox definition. It appears then that though two events may both be equally dictated by chance, and though it may be known in each case that there is no law asserting that they will happen at a particular trial, yet our knowledge or our ignorance concerning them may differ widely. It is this fact which gives rise to the conception of Probability as a property of an event which can be measured and thus distinguished from the corresponding property of another event. The number which represents the probability of an event measures in some manner the degree of knowledge which we possess about its happening; it is such that we are equally ignorant and equally certain about the happening of two events which are presented by the same number and such that we are more certain that the event which is represented by the larger number will happen than we are that the event which is represented by the smaller number will happen.

Such is apparently the fundamental meaning of the concept of probability. In connection with it two questions immediately arise. First is how the probability of an event is determined; second why probability, determined in this manner, is a measure of degree of knowledge, how knowledge can have various degrees and what exactly we mean by degrees of knowledge. The two problems are really inseparable, for the use to which the knowledge of probability is to be put, when once it has been obtained, must influence considerably the processes employed in obtaining it, but for the purposes of discussion it is possible to separate them completely.

The first problem leads directly to a discussion of the whole very elaborate mathematical theory of probability. Of course there is no need, in order to study the second problem (which is that with which we are directly concerned here), to trace out its complete development; all that we require to know are the fundamental principles on which probability is determined. On the other hand if none of the formal developments were considered here much of what is said would have to be repeated when they were considered. Accordingly, although we shall be thereby led to the discussion of matters which are of no importance for our immediate purpose, it will be convenient to trace the mathematical theory from its first principles up to the point where no further question concerning those principles can arise.

A very common definition of probability in the standard treatises on the subject is this: "The probability of the happening of an event is the ratio of the number of cases favourable to that event to the total number of possible cases." The discussion based on this definition always speedily leads to the conclusion that some further proviso is necessary, which is usually stated in the form that all the possible cases must be "equally probable". It is therefore necessary to add to this definition at the outset some definition of equal probability, and it is here that the difficulty arises. It is usually concluded that no such definition can be given which can be applied with the full rigour of a mathematical demonstration, and that, in all uses of the theory of probability, assertions that cases are of equal probability are of the nature of assumptions from which the calculation starts and which have to be regarded as ultimate and beyond question. But it is precisely these assumptions which are of importance for our present purposes; we cannot know what we mean by probability until we know what we mean by equal probability, and our first efforts must be directed towards finding that meaning.

It will appear that, when we have succeeded in defining equal probability, a definition of probability in general immediately follows. And since this definition differs widely from that which has been quoted and leads to the almost complete abandonment of the "orthodox" exposition of the theory of probability, it will be convenient at the outset to notice reasons for believing that this exposition is not satisfactory, even if we accept the view of the determination of equal probability that is generally associated with it.

A very simple example seems to prove that it is deficient, so simple indeed that it is extraordinary that so acute a writer as Poincaré, who uses the definition and considers the example, has not even thought the objection worth noting. It is the example of drawing a card from either of two packs, one a whist pack of 52 cards and the other a picquet pack of 32 cards, lying side by side on the table. At first sight we are inclined to say that, according to the definition, the probability of drawing a given card, say the ace of spades, is 2/84, for there are two favourable cases (namely two aces of spades) and 84 total possible cases (namely 84 cards, each of which might be drawn). But this conclusion, according to the orthodox exposition, is wrong. The right answer is that the probability is 21/832, which is rather greater than 2/84. It is unnecessary for the moment to inquire how this "right answer" is obtained; it is necessary only to inquire what it means when it is obtained. According to the definition it must mean that there are 832 possible cases, or events which may happen, all equally probable, and that of these 21 consist in drawing the ace of spades (or, of course, some multiples of 832 and 21). Now is this statement true? I maintain that it is not, and challenge anyone who believes it is true to say what are the 832 equally probable events and what are the 21 which form the special group. To this question I believe that no satisfactory answer can be given, but if it cannot be given there must be clearly something very wrong with the theory on which it is based. It is not disputed that the estimation of the probability as 21/832 is "right"; all that is asserted is that the answer is inconsistent with the fundamental assumptions of the theory. The theory asserts that the probability is the ratio of numbers of cases and one of its results is to state a probability which is clearly not a ratio of numbers of cases.

Probability is experimental. Attention is drawn to this example not only because it suggests doubts of the definitions on which it is based and helps to justify our departure from them, but also because it indicates the direction in which we are to seek for a more satisfactory theory. For it may be asked pertinently why and on what grounds the conclusion that the probability is 2/84 is rejected as wrong and the alternative conclusion accepted as right. What kind of evidence are we to accept of rightness and wrongness? Is a conclusion right merely if it is deduced by some correct purely logical process or is there some other kind of evidence or reasoning required?

If we trace out the argument we find, of course, that the decision depends on what events are taken as equally probable. The first estimation of the probability of drawing the ace from the two packs was said to be wrong, because cases had been taken as equally probable which were not really so; the estimation would have been right if the two packs had been shuffled together, but it is not right if they are lying separately side by side on the table. If they were shuffled it would be equally probable that any card in the two packs would be drawn; but if they are separated the analysis into equally probable cases must be made differently. First, the choice must be divided into a choice either of the whist pack or of the picquet pack; either of these choices is equally probable; the choice of the whist pack must then be divided into equally probable choices of each of the cards in it, and a similar division made of the choice of the picquet pack. Thus we are led directly to the question on what evidence judgements of the equality of probability are made; and a consideration of this instance suggests the only answer which is possible.

For an indefinite series of arrangements of the two packs can be made which are intermediate between that of being shuffled and that of lying side by side on the table. Suppose I start with the last arrangement and the packs lying in two neat heaps; I then spread each pack out, taking care that the boundary of one does not overlap the boundary of the other; then I make the boundaries less distinct by making part of each nearly surround a part of the other—and so on till I have shuffled the two packs inextricably on the table. At what stage in this process does the "right" analysis into equal probabilities change from that characteristic of the separated packs to that characteristic of the shuffled packs? Are there intermediate "right" methods of analyses corresponding to the intermediate arrangements? What kind of argument or investigation is necessary and sufficient to answer these questions?

The answer that I want to obtain is that the necessary investigation must be to some extent experimental. The features in which the various distributions of the packs differ are accessible to observation only; when I say that the packs are shuffled or that they are separated or that they are in any intermediate condition, I am asserting something which is and can only be the result of observation. And if there is to be associated with these differences in distribution a difference in the analysis into cases of equal probability, the association can only be based on such investigation as generally leads to the discovery of associations in which the results of observation are concerned, that is to say, experimental investigation. If we judge one of the proposed estimations of the probability of drawing a given card to be right and judge another to be wrong, it can surely only be on the grounds of some experimental investigation; the decision on a matter of this kind in which observations and judgements of the external world are so intimately concerned cannot be made on a basis of *a priori* thought or purely internal judgements. And that is why the definition of equal probability and the decision what cases are equally probable must always lie outside the province of the mathematical theory of probability.

If then we are to find a satisfactory definition of equal probabilities it must be such that the judgement whether or no probabilities are equal can be made by experiment and observation essentially similar to that by which laws are established. It must also be such that mathematical calculation can be applied to such judgements; and finally it must fulfil the condition that it expresses adequately what we mean by probability, a condition which is not fulfilled by that which we have considered already. With these considerations to guide us let us attempt to find a satisfactory definition.

We must be guided at the outset by the last condition. The meaning of probability is intimately connected with that of chance, and is strictly applicable only to events which, in some respect, are dictated by chance. The idea of probability arises only when we are considering events associated with some special circumstance, which may generally be called a "trial". It is in respect of this trial that the event to which probability is to be assigned must be dictated by chance; it must be known that there is no law associating the event with the trial, so that it is unknown whether or no that event will happen as the result of the trial[1].

On the other hand when we assert that the event has a certain probability we are certainly asserting some relation between the trial and the result, and this relation would seem to be invariable. The apparent paradox that, while expressly denying that there is any law associating the trial and the result, we assert an invariable relation between them is, of course, solved by the considerations which have already been suggested. The invariable relation which we assert is not between *a* trial and *a* result, but between a collection of trials and a collection of results. It is therefore in the properties of collections of events which are dictated by chance that we must seek for the means of defining probability in a satisfactory manner; and in seeking in this direction we are only following the implications of the meaning of probability; for it need not be insisted that this idea is inseparably connected in our minds with the properties of collections and, especially, of very large collections of similar events.

Definition of equal probability. The real meaning of probability would perhaps be conveyed by the definition that events are of equal probability if they happen the same number of times in a very large number of trials. But such a definition is open to obvious objections. In the first place it does not permit of an experimental determination whether events are equally probable, unless the "very large number" is fixed definitely; for if the events happen equally frequently in some one very large number of trials, the next trial must obviously make the number of happenings unequal, since only one event can happen at that trial. Accordingly we shall not know whether to base our judgement on the set of trials in which the events have happened equally frequently, or on that in which they have happened unequal numbers of times, and shall have no reason for preferring the judgement that the probabilities are equal to the judgement that they are unequal. If, on the

[1] It is worth while to remark that the conditions in which the conception of probability is applicable are necessarily those which give rise to the idea of "psychological" cause and effect (see p. 63). For the circumstance which constitutes the trial is necessarily prior in our minds to the event which is its "result". But examination of some of the instances given below will show that this relation is only the "psychological" cause and effect, and that there is no necessary time-relation between the trial and the event which is its result.

other hand, we fix definitely the large number of trials and say that the events are equally probable if they happen equally frequently in a number of trials N (N being a multiple of n, the number of the events which are equally probable), then we shall arrive at a contradiction if we repeat the series of observations. For, suppose we have made one set of N trials and have found that the n events happen equally frequently; then we conclude that the events are equally probable. Now we repeat the series. When we have made $N - 1$ trials one of two things must have happened; either $n - 1$ of the events has each happened N/n times and the nth has happened $(N/n - 1)$ times, or there has been some other distribution of the happenings. If the first alternative has happened, then, since the n events are equally probable, the definition shows that the Nth event must be that which has happened only $(N/n - 1)$ times; we shall know definitely which event must happen next. But the conclusion that we know which event happens next is inconsistent with the assumption, under-lying every consideration of probability, that the events are dictated by chance; for that assumption means that we know no law which will predict at any given trial which event will happen. If the second alternative happens, then it is impossible that in the N trials each of the events should happen N/n times and accordingly the new series of trials will prove that the events are not equally probable, and will contradict the first conclusion. The defini-tion which attributes to the "very large number" a definite value leads inevitably to contradictions.

We might propose to amend our definition in two ways. First we may propose to say that the events are equally probable if they happen *nearly* the same number of times in *any* assigned large number of trials. We thereby imply that, if the events are equally probable, some number of trials N can be found such that the happenings of the different events are nearly equally numerous in any number of trials greater than N; this implication is not objectionable, for if it turns out not to be true in any particular instance, it is only proved that the events are not equally probable. If it turns out to be true, the first objection urged against the previous definition vanishes, for it will not matter on which set of trials our judgement is based, so long as the number of them is greater than N. The second objection also vanishes, for the latitude allowed by "nearly" prevents our drawing any conclusion as to the happening in one particular trial. Nevertheless obvious difficulties are apparent. We must assign some meaning to "nearly" unless we are to conclude that all events are equally probable. If we assign a definite meaning to "nearly" we encounter precisely the same difficulty as was met when we assigned definitely the value of N. Suppose we say that the events are equally probable if, when N trials or more have been made, the difference between the number of times that one event has happened and the number of times any other event has happened is less than some assigned number q[1]. Then,

---

[1] It would be better to say that the ratio of the number of times one event has happened to the number some other event has happened must not differ from 1 by more than some assigned fraction q. But this definition also is open to the objection in the text.

as before, if by one series of observations it had been decided that the events were equally probable, and if, in a second series, a stage was reached in which one event had happened $q - 1$ times oftener than some other, then we should know that the first event could not happen at the next trial, or else that the events were not equally probable. In either case there is a contradiction. If again we attempt to avoid the contradiction by denying that the case contemplated could arise if the events were equally probable, we are in effect substituting $q - 1$ for q in the definition, and a repetition of the argument will lead once more to the contradiction. The conclusion is unavoidable that if we fix definitely what is to happen in any series of trials in order that the events may be judged equally probable, then circumstances must arise in which we are forced to conclude either that events which have been judged to be equally probable are not equally probable, or that we know beforehand the result of some particular trial; and this last conclusion is essentially inconsistent with the assumption that the events are regulated by chance.

Another possibility is to amend the definition so that it states that events are equally probable if they happen exactly equally frequently in *some* very large number of trials. Such a definition obviously leads to the conclusion that no events can be judged definitely to be not equally probable; for however many trials we have made without reaching a stage at which the events have happened equally frequently, the possibility can never be excluded that a continuation of the trials might lead to such a stage; unless again we make the assumption, inconsistent with the view that the events are dictated by chance, that at certain trials one of the events cannot happen. However, this objection is not very serious and we shall see that it is probably unavoidable by any definition. What is more serious is that the definition would doubtless lead to the judgement that events were equally probable when an ideal definition would show that they were not; for it is possible that events which are not equally probable may occur "by chance" in equal numbers at some stage in a very long series of trials. To exclude such events it is necessary that the events be not judged equally probable unless the numbers in which they happen are not only equal at some stage in the trials, but remain equal, or nearly equal, at all subsequent stages. But here again we introduce the word "nearly" and encounter the same difficulties as before.

Nevertheless the definition which has been suggested is on the right lines and with a little further elaboration will give the result which we are seeking. For after all what we really want to say and what we really do assume in the mathematical development of the science of probability is that equally probable events are those which happen equally often in an infinite series of trials. And our difficulty arises only from our attempts to state the definition in such a way that it is applicable to experiment.

But if we remember the Newtonian definition of the infinitesimal, on which all modern mathematical conceptions of the infinitely great and the infinitely small are based, we may obtain a useful hint. An infinitesimal quantity, according to Newton, is one which can be made less than any assigned quantity; and an infinite quantity is one which can be made greater than any assigned quantity. Let us therefore examine the following definition which is suggested by these ideas: Events are equally probable if, by increasing sufficiently the number of trials, a stage can be reached at which the ratio of the number of times one event has happened to the number of times another event has happened differs from unity by less than any assigned quantity, and after which the difference of this ratio from unity remains less than any assigned quantity during a number of trials which is greater than any assigned quantity. That is to say, if p_1 and p_2 are the number of times two of the events have happened, these events are equally probable if, and only if, a value of N can be found such that, during the n trials following the Nth trial, $(p_1/p_2 - 1)$ remains between $+ e$ and $- e$, where n is greater than any number which may be assigned and e is less than any fraction which may be assigned.

It is necessary, as has been noted, that the number n should be included, specifying that the condition must be fulfilled over a certain range of trials, for we should not judge the events to be equally probable if the ratio of the numbers of their happenings were found at some stage of the experiment to be unity, but diverged from unity at a later stage. But we can alter the definition so that the explicit mention of n is avoided. For if N is increased sufficiently, then, even if the next n trials should all result in the happening of the same event, the increment of the ratio p_1/p_2 during these n trials (p_1 referring to the event which happens every time) can be reduced below any assigned limit, however great the value assigned to n. Accordingly if it is possible to reduce the quantity $(p_1/p_2 - 1)$ below any assigned limit after some number of trials which exceeds any assigned limit, then it will also be possible to make that quantity remain below its assigned limit over any assigned number of trials. In place of the specification concerning the number of trials during which the condition must remain fulfilled, we may put the specification that the condition must be fulfilled after some number of trials N, greater than any assigned number. The definition now becomes that the events are equally probable if a number of trials N can be found, greater than any assigned limit, such that when N trials have been made the ratio of the numbers of happenings of those events differs from unity by less than any assigned fraction.

These two definitions appear to be equivalent and merely to express the same ideas in rather different ways. There is a third way which is also equivalent and is more immediately applicable in some important instances. We may say that the events are equally probable if some number of trials N can be found such that, for all numbers of trials greater than N, the ratio of the frequency of the events differs from unity by less than any assigned magnitude. This definition is equivalent to the first if by "all trials" we mean a number of trials greater than any assigned magnitude; but it draws attention to features essential for future developments more clearly than the first definition. In what follows we shall regard the three modes of expression as interchangeable and shall also use as equivalent to any of them the statement that the ratio of the frequencies tend to unity as the number of trials tends to infinity; but it must be remembered what this expression means.

Some difficulties. This definition in its alternative forms seems to satisfy the necessary condition that it shall convey the true meaning of probability. It is also, as we shall see, applicable to mathematical calculation. But it has still to be considered how far it makes the determination of equal probability a matter of experiment and whether it is consistent with the fundamental assumption that the events are dictated by chance.

The definition will certainly permit an experimental demonstration that events are equally probable if the observations turn out in a special way. For when once the devil's advocate (who is a necessary participator in a research depending on a definition of this kind) has fixed his assigned lower limit for N and his assigned fraction e, it is quite possible that a value of N might be found, greater than this assigned limit, at which the ratio of the frequencies of the two events differed from unity by less than e. Further, no repetition of the investigation could lead to a result inconsistent with that already established. Nothing whatever is asserted about the result of one particular trial, for it is not necessary that the value of N at which the desired ratio of the frequencies is obtained in one experiment should be the same as that at which it is obtained in another; all that is necessary is that there should be some value of N at which it is obtained. Consequently the definition is not inconsistent with the assumption that the events are dictated by chance. Nor can any repetition of the experiment prove that the events are not equally probable and prove in this manner inconsistent with the first series, for, even if the desired ratio of the frequencies has not been obtained at the same stage as in the first trial, there is always the possibility that a continuation of the series will lead to it.

Moreover there is one way in which an inconsistency of subsequent series with the conclusion based on the first can be avoided with certainty. We can, by making N in the first set sufficiently large, ensure that, whatever happens in the second set, the ratio of the happenings of the equally probable events remains as near unity as we please. That is to say, if we make the series of observations which establishes the equal probability of the events so long that any subsequent addition to it that we want to make will be only an inappreciable fraction of it, then we may make sure from the outset that no future observations will upset the conclusions reached. And in fact, a process of this kind is actually adopted. The best proof of the equality of the probability of heads and tails in the tossing of a penny is derived from the immensely long series of observations which some laborious people have undertaken; any casual observations on the matter which we make now are so few compared with those in these series that, whatever their result, they cannot alter the fact already established.

On the other hand it must be observed that the impossibility of inconsistency arising from the application of the definition is necessarily associated with the impossibility of proving that any alternative events whatever are *not* equally probable. Whatever observations may have been made, it is always possible to suppose that future trials will give the results necessary to establish the equal probability of the events; for any limitation on the possible results of future trials would necessarily lead to a contradiction with the assumption that the events are dictated by chance. In this respect a judgement concerning the probability of an event (for, as we shall see, these considerations apply also to judgements of probability other than those of equality) is exactly contrary to the judgement that an event is associated with another in a law. No amount of observation can prove that a law is true, although observation can easily prove that it is not true; while observation can prove that the probability of an event has a certain value, though none can prove that it is not that value. A consideration of the part played by conceptions of probability in the determination of laws (to which this discussion is intended to lead) will show that each of these conclusions is a necessary consequence of the other.

The impossibility of proving by experiment that any proposition about probability is not true is inevitably associated with the meaning of chance and probability. For if the events are dictated by chance it is always possible that at any trial any of the alternative events may occur whatever their probability; accordingly whatever value is attributed to the probability any sequence of results of trials is possible, including any sequence which would establish that the probability had some value other than that which is attributed to it. How far this feature robs the conception of probability of all value depends simply on what the results of sequences of trials are actually found to be. If it were found that different series of trials did not as a matter of fact lead to the same conclusion concerning the probability of an event, then, although the definition given would be formally satisfactory, it would be practically useless. That it is not useless, but very useful, depends on the fact that such discrepant series of trials are not actually found. Though we believe that the probability of a penny falling heads is equal to the probability of a penny falling tails, and therefore that the frequencies of the two events should tend to equality as the number of trials tends to infinity, it must always be recognised as possible that any number of consecutive trials should occur in which the penny falls heads every time and never falls tails; to deny that possibility would be to deny that the falling is determined by chance. But as a matter of fact sequences of this kind are not observed; all the sequences which are observed are such as prove definitely that heads and tails are equally probable.

We have here one more illustration of the fact that the definitions of science are framed to give an account of facts as they are. It is never asserted that facts might not be different from what they are, but if they were very different our concepts and their definitions would be changed. It is no objection to the definition of probability that circumstances might occur in which it would be useless, for that objection would apply equally to any other scientific definition. The only difference between the definition of probability and that of some concept connoting a law is that in the former the possibility of the definition being useless owing to the occurrence of special observations is a direct consequence of the ideas on which the definition is founded, whereas in the latter it is not a direct consequence.

The usefulness of the definition, then, though not its formal validity, depends on the fact that there are events which, according to the definition, are of equal probability. And here it should be noted that if the definition had been altered slightly there would have been no such events. Thus if, instead of saying that the ratio p_1/p_2 must remain between $1 + e$ and $1 - e$ as N is increased indefinitely, where e is less than any assignable magnitude, we had said that $p_1 - p_2$ must remain less than ϵ, where ϵ is any integer however small, it would still have been conceivable that the conditions contemplated by the definition should occur and the definition would have been formally satisfactory. But as a matter of fact we should never have been able to find any equally probable events; though the conditions might occur, they do not actually occur when the events are dictated by chance. Accordingly the choice of the ratio p_1/p_2, rather than the difference $p_1 - p_2$, as the function which is to determine probability is not simply arbitrary; it is founded on an examination of what actually occurs. It is essentially similar in this matter to the concept founded on a law. And just as we feel that in defining a concept we are defining something real, because the conditions contemplated by the definition actually occur, so also we feel that in defining probability by means of the ratio of the frequencies of the events rather than by their differences we are defining some "real" property of the sequences of trials.

Probability in general. We have now decided what is meant by equal probability. We have next to decide what we mean by probabilities which are not equal and how we are to allot numbers to represent the different probabilities. In making this decision we are so far bound only by the necessity of allotting the same number to represent the probabilities of events which are equally probable; so long as this condition is fulfilled, and so long as the definition is such that it can be applied to determine probabilities by experiment, any definition may be adopted. That which is actually adopted is based on the consideration of those cases in which all the alternative events which may happen as the result of any trial are equally probable. If there are n such equally probable alternative events, then it is easy to deduce from the definition of equal probability that, for each of these events, p', the number of times that it happens in N trials, tends to N/n as N tends to infinity. For if p_r' and p_s' refer to any two of these events, we have

$$p_r'/p_s' \text{ lies between } 1 + e \text{ and } 1 - e.$$

Therefore

$$(\Sigma p_r')/p_s' \text{ lies between } n + ne \text{ and } n - ne.$$

But $\Sigma p_r' = N$; so that

$$1/p_s' \text{ lies between } n/N (1 + e) \text{ and } n/N (1 - e)$$

and $$p_s'/N \text{ lies between } 1/n (1 - e + e^2 - \dots) \text{ and } 1/n (1 + e - e^2 + \dots).$$

Now e can be made less than any assignable fraction, so that the expressions in brackets can also be made less than any assignable fraction. Consequently as p_r'/p_s' tends to 1, p_s'/N must tend to $1/n$.

p_s'/N, therefore (or rather the value to which it tends as N tends to infinity), is a quantity which is independent of N, the number of trials, and dependent only on the nature of the event P_s (which determines whether it will be equally probable with the alternative events) and the number of the alternative events; it is a quantity characteristic of the events under consideration and not of the number of trials; and it is the same for all equally probable alternative events. It is therefore a quantity which may be used suitably to distinguish the event in respect of the features which are under consideration at present, and to be called the probability of the event. But there is nothing in the ratio p_s'/N to indicate that it is assumed that all the events alternative to P_s are equally probable with it, and the definition may be extended by a natural process of analogy to events which form part of a collection of alternative events which are not all equally probable. Accordingly the following general definition of the probability of an event is adopted: The probability of an event P is p, if, in a series of trials at each of which the event may happen but at none of which it must happen, a stage can be found after which, however greatly the number of trials made is increased, the ratio p'/N, where p' is the number of times P has occurred, differs from p by less than any assigned magnitude. This condition may be expressed again by saying that p'/N tends to p as N tends to infinity. It should be observed that there is something completely arbitrary in the definition, even if the fundamental ideas on which it is based are accepted. Even if we agree that the probability of an event means something to do with the relative frequency with which it happens, so that the probability must be determined by the ratio p_s'/N, the choice of this ratio simply, rather than of some other single-valued function of this ratio, is completely arbitrary.

It follows from this definition and that of equal probability that if P and all the alternative events, the total number of which is n, are all equally probable, then the probability of P and of any of the other alternative events is $1/n$; and that the probability of an event which happens at every trial is unity. These results follow of course also from the definition mentioned on p. 165. But it should be observed that our definition, unlike the orthodox definition, assigns a definite value to the probability of an event which forms part of a collection of alternative events which are *not* all equally probable; the older definition will only give a value to the probability of an event if it can be shown to be involved in a set of alternative events which are all equally probable.

And another important feature should be remarked which distinguishes our definition from that which depends merely on the ratio of numbers of equally probable cases. The latter does not suggest that any special consideration need be given to examples in which the number of cases is infinite; for infinite numbers have a ratio as well as finite numbers[1]. But the former

---

[1] I am not sure if this statement is true.

shows at once that it must be impossible to determine by experiment any probability which is not finite. For if p is infinitesimal, then, whatever the value of p may be, the ratio p'/N must tend to o. Now it may be possible to show experimentally that p is infinitesimal and that by increasing N sufficiently the ratio p'/N can be made less than any assignable magnitude; but it is quite impossible to distinguish between one infinitesimal probability and another. If n, the number of alternative events is infinite, then it is impossible to decide by our definition whether these events are or are not all equally probable; if some of them are of finite probability, while of others the probability is infinitesimal, this distinction can be demonstrated; but it is impossible to distinguish between two events both having infinitesimal probabilities. This consideration is important, because it is well known that discrepancies and inconsistencies occur when infinitesimal probabilities are introduced. For example, the usual theory of probability leads to many inconsistent values for the probability of a chord of a circle being less than the side of the inscribed square; each of these values is deduced from a different assumption as to what chords are equally probable. Now since the probability of any given length is infinitesimal, our definition shows that it is impossible to distinguish between the different assumptions and to decide which is right and which is wrong. Discrepancies arise simply because in this case the definition of equal probability is inapplicable.

Addition of probabilities. The further development of the theory of probability depends upon two and only two definitions or propositions, which assign meanings to the sum and to the product of two or more probabilities. The probability of an event is the sum of the probabilities, p and q, when the event consists either in the happening of P (of probability p) or in the happening of Q (of probability q). The probability of an event is the product of two probabilities p and q, when the event consists in the happening of both P and Q. The addition and multiplication of probabilities depends therefore on the conception of an event which consists, in some sense, of other events. We must examine this conception more carefully and consider its application both to the definition of probability which has been rejected and to that which has been substituted.

The conception involved in the addition of probabilities is quite simple. We are still considering a series of trials in which any one of a number of alternative events may happen, while at any particular trial no particular one of them must happen. When we are estimating the probabilities which are to be added, we regard each of these events as distinct; when we add them, we are considering some of those events $P_1, P_2, \ldots$, of which the probabilities are added, as identical and indistinguishable, and all of them as constituting equally the same event Q, which has the probability which results from the addition. The proposition that the probability of Q is the sum of those of $P_1, P_2, \ldots$ follows immediately from our definition. For the N trials are all trials in which Q may happen; if $P_1, P_2, \ldots$ have happened $p_1', p_2', \ldots$ times, then Q has happened $(p_1' + p_2' + \ldots)$ times; and if the differences of $p_1'/N \ldots$

from p_1 ... can all be made less than any assignable magnitude by increasing N sufficiently, then, so long as the number of the events P_1 is finite, the difference between $(p_1' + p_2' + ...)/N$ and $(p_1 + p_2 + ...)$ can be made less than any assignable magnitude. Consequently the probability of Q is $p_1 + p_2 + ...$

It will be seen that in this argument it is necessary to use the definition of probability in its third form. (Of course to each of the forms of the definition of equal probability corresponds a form of the definition of probability which assigns numerical values.) For if the argument is valid it is necessary that there should be some one value of N which makes the difference between p'/N and p less than any assignable magnitude, for all the events P which are added. This condition will only be fulfilled if, after the difference has been made less than the assigned magnitude for one of the events P_1, it remains less while N is increased until the difference is also made less for $P_2, P_3, ...$; it is on these grounds that the specification must be inserted that the difference remains less than the assigned magnitude for all values of N greater than some value.

Again, it should be noted that the conclusion would not follow if the number of the P's were infinite; for then, though each of the ratios p'/N could be made less than any assigned magnitude, the sum of all of them might always remain greater. But since we have already concluded that the concept of probability as here defined is not applicable to an infinite number of alternative events, this limitation is of no importance.

The proposition concerning the addition of probabilities follows equally from the definition which depends on the enumeration of "cases", so long as these cases are all equally probable. For then the number of cases of which Q consists is the number of cases which, when the probabilities are added, are considered as forming a single case. The ratio of the probability of Q to that of each individual case will be simply the number of the individual cases included in Q. On the other hand that definition does not prove that the probability of an event consisting of either of two alternative events which are not of equal probability is the sum of the probabilities of those events; it will only prove that proposition, if each of these unequally probable alternative events can be shown to consist of a number of equally probable alternative events, so that the unequal probabilities arise from the summation of unequal numbers of equal probable cases. We shall notice presently a consequence of this limitation.

Multiplication of probabilities. The conceptions involved in the multiplication of probabilities are rather more complex. For multiplication here is not simply repeated addition. The general relation between the addition and the multiplication of such measurable quantities as are employed in science will be considered in Chapter XII[1]. We shall find that the multi-

---

[1] When that chapter is reached the question may occur to the reader in what class of measurable quantities is probability to be placed. The answer is that it is a defined magnitude and depends for its measurement entirely on the measurement of the fundamental magnitude, number.

plication of a measurable quantity, such as probability, by a number is a
mere process of repeated addition and depends for its meaning entirely on
the conception of addition; but multiplication of any one measurable magnitude by any other (except a number) is a process which has nothing whatever
to do with addition, and derives its meaning from entirely different conceptions.
Thus, there is a sense in which the multiplication of probability is a repeated
addition; for instance $a \times p$ is the probability that the event will happen
which consists of any one of a events, each of which, if it is considered as a
separate and distinct event, has the probability p. But here a is a number
and the product $a \times p$ is the result of multiplying a probability by a number;
a is not the probability of anything, and the product is not the result of
multiplying a probability by a probability[1]. The meaning of that process
involves ideas which are quite distinct from those of the addition of probabilities.

The idea of the multiplication of probabilities arises in such circumstances
as these. There are m sets of alternative events, each set consisting of events
dictated by chance, so that, as a result of the trial characteristic of that set,
one of the events in that set must happen, though it is not known which will
happen. The probabilities of the events in each set are known; let them be
$p_1, p_2, \ldots$ for the first set; $q_1, q_2, \ldots$ for the second, and so on. The p's, q's,
r's and so on are quantities of different kinds, and the P's, Q's, R's of which
they are the probabilities are not alternative events in any trial. The p's refer
to what happens when the kind of trial which is characteristic of the first
set is made; the q's refer to what happens when the kind of trial characteristic
of the second set is made. Thus the P's may be the drawings of specified
cards out of some pack; the Q's the falling of a raindrop on specified areas
on the ground. On the other hand, though they may be as completely different
as this, the P's and Q's may be so similar that they can hardly be distinguished;
but, whether in their nature they are similar or dissimilar, they are always
differentiated by the feature which is of importance in connection with
multiplication, namely, that they are unconnected in the sense that, while
one P is alternative to another P, no P is alternative to any Q.

Now suppose that we make one trial in each of the sets of alternative
events, and ask what is the probability that in each of the sets one particular
event occurs, say the event P_a in the first set, Q_b in the second, R_c in the third,
and so on. The answer is, of course, that the probability of this form of
composite event is $p_a \times q_b \times r_c$.

We have now to show that this answer is a consequence of the definition

[1] It should be observed that it is multiplication of this kind which is really involved in
the process of addition according to the definition of probability by means of equally probable "cases". Even when only two cases are added, it would probably be more correct to
regard the process as a multiplication of the probability of either of them by the number
of them, than as the addition of two distinct probabilities. However, this is rather a subtle
question which is quite irrelevant to our present purpose; but the consideration draws
attention to the difference in the processes which are sometimes included under the single
name of multiplication.

of probability and of the defined conditions of the trial. The proof is simple. Let N trials be made each consisting of one trial of each of the sets $P, Q, R, \dots$. Then P_a will have happened $(p_a + e) N$ times $= N_1$ times (say); by increasing N, e can be made less than any assignable magnitude and, so long as p_a is finite, N_1 greater than any assignable magnitude. Now consider the N_1 trials in which P_a happens; since N_1 can be made greater than any assignable magnitude, then (subject to a condition to be considered presently), in these N_1 trials, Q will have happened $(q_b + f) N_1 = N_2$ (say) times; if q_b is finite, N_2 may again be made greater than any assignable magnitude by increasing sufficiently N_1 or N. Similarly in the N_2 trials, R_c will have happened $(r_c + g) N_2$ times—and so on. Consequently the number of trials in which P_a, Q_b, R_c happen in their respective sets is $(p_a + e) (q_b + f) (r_c + g) N$. If m is the number of times in which the composite event happens, consisting of the happening of $P_a, Q_b, R_c, \dots$ at the same trial, then

$$m/N = (p_a + e) (q_b + f) (r_c + g) \dots,$$

which, since $e, f, g, \dots$ can all be made less than any assignable magnitude, can be made to differ from $p_a q_b r_c \dots$ by less than any assignable magnitude. It follows that the probability of the composite event is $p_a q_b r_c \dots$.

But, as was indicated in a parenthesis, one important assumption has been made in the argument. It is that the N_1 trials in which P_a happens are a suitable set of trials for estimating the probability of Q_b, and that the probability of Q_b estimated from these trials will be the "true" probability. Now there is one case in which this assumption is obviously true; it is the case when Q_b never happens except when P_a happens; for in that case the only trials available for estimating q_b are trials similar to the N_1; and, if Q_b has a probability at all, it must be the probability estimated by such trials.

If Q_b never happens except when P_a happens, it must be for one of two reasons. First P_a and Q_b may be related by a law or rather by a series of laws. If there were only a single law relating them, then Q_b would necessarily happen whenever P_a happened and the probability of Q_b would always be unity; this case is not interesting, for from the point of view of probability P_a and Q_b would constitute a single event. But there may be several laws including P_a of which only one includes Q_b and the remainder include the other alternative Q's; we have seen that such cases may arise owing to the fact that the expression of the law by a dual relation is inadequate. Thus the property of dissolving in nitric acid is associated with the other properties of both silver and lead; the properties of silver cannot occur unless the body will dissolve in nitric acid, but the converse proposition is not true, for lead will also dissolve. It is possible therefore for Q_b to be connected with P_a by a law in such a way that Q_b cannot occur without P_a, although when P_a occurs other Q's can also occur. On the other hand, it is not clear that, if P_a and Q_b are connected in this manner, the events can be considered as dictated by chance or that Q_b can have a probability. We will leave this question on one side for the moment, noticing only that if in such cases Q_b has a probability as well as P_a, then the conditions will be such that the conception of multiplication can be applied, and the probability that Q_b will happen at the trial which results in the happening of one of the P's and one of the Q's will be the product of the probability of P_a and the probability of Q_b.

Another instance in which Q_b cannot happen unless P_a happens occurs when P_a is a composite event, in the sense employed in the addition of probabilities, and Q_b is one of the constituent events which compose P_a; then by the definition of P_a, the happening of Q_b means the happening of P_a. Circumstances may occur in which we know the probability that conditions will be such that one of the events constituting P_a must occur rather than that they will be such that P_b occurs; and we may know the probability that, if such conditions occur, the result will be Q_b rather than any other Q. The probability that Q_b will actually occur is then the product $p_a q_b$; for the probability of Q_b, in connection with this series of trials at any rate, is necessarily its probability in the series of trials in which P_a, rather than any other P, occurs. It may be observed that Q_b cannot legitimately be a constituent of two composite events P, for, if it were, those events would not be alternative and the conditions necessary for the application of probability would not be present.

There is a second type of case in which the assumption made in deducing the rule of multiplication will be justified, and the probability in the selected N_1 trials will be the true probability of Q_b. This occurs when it is definitely known that Q_b may happen whether or no P_a happens, and yet it is also known that the probability of Q_b is the same in a series of trials in which P_a happens as in a series in which any of the other alternative P's happen. P_a and Q_b are then said to be independent, and the fact of independence can, of course, be established by experiment. This second type of case is in a sense the opposite extreme to the first case; in the first there was (or might be) a law relating P_a and Q_b, in the second it is definitely known that there is no law. But more must be known than that there is no law; for conditions may occur in which no prediction of the occurrence of Q_b can be made, whether or no P_a has occurred, and yet the probability of Q_b differs according to whether P_a has or has not occurred. Thus, whether or no it has rained on June 14, it is unknown whether it will rain on June 15, so long as the event is considered a long time before those dates; but the probability that it will rain on June 15 is known to be greater if it has rained on the previous day than if it has not. The probabilities of rain on two consecutive days are not independent, although there is a definite probability of rain on either day; on the other hand the probabilities of rain on two days a year apart are independent. For intermediate periods, dependence merges into independence by a gradual approximation of the probability of rain after rain on an earlier day to the probability of rain without rain on that earlier day.

Accordingly in these two extreme types of cases the rule for the multiplication of probabilities holds, if q_b is the "true" probability of Q_b, that is the probability in *all* trials made in the conditions considered. However, it should be observed that the rule will hold in other cases as well, when it is known neither that Q_b can only happen when P_a happens nor that Q_b and P_a are independent, if, but only if, q_b is always taken to be the probability of Q_b, given the fact that P_a has already happened. The rule is really perfectly general; it is only in the value to be attributed to q_b that a distinction must be made between various cases. q_b is always the probability of Q_b in those trials in which P_a has occurred; in some cases this is the same as the probability of Q_b in all trials; in other cases it is not the same as this probability.

A further apparent difference should be noted between the two types of cases in which q_b is the probability in all trials. In the second type, when P_a and Q_b are independent, it makes no difference to the proof of the formula of multiplication if we begin by selecting the trials in which Q_b happens instead of those in which P_a happens. But in the first type of case, Q_b never happens at all unless P_a happens, and P_a always happens if Q_b happens. If therefore we select first the cases in which Q_b happens, the value of p_a must necessarily be 1, for in the N_1 selected cases it will happen every time. It might seem therefore that the value of the product $p_a q_b r_c \ldots$ must depend on the order in which the events are considered, and that we ought to distinguish between $p_a q_b r_c \ldots$ and $q_b p_a r_c$. But it must be remembered that by selecting first the cases in which Q_b happens we have changed the value of q_b. If we select first the trials in which P_a happens, q_b is determined by the frequency with which Q_b happens in a series of trials in which P_a always happens; if we select first the trials in which Q_b happens, q_b is determined by the frequency with which Q_b happens in a series of trials in which P_a may or may not happen. In the first method the events alternative to Q_b consist of the remainder of the set which, taken together, constitute P_a; in the second method they include other events which are not included in the set which constitutes P_a; and we have seen that in order to specify the probability of an event a statement of the alternative events must be included. Accordingly the variation of p_a with the method of selection is accompanied by a variation of q_b; and it is easy to see (there is no need to give the proof) that the concomitant variations are such that, whichever mode of selecting the trials is adopted, the product $p_a q_b$ always remains constant, if P_a and Q_b are related in the manner which we have supposed. In both types of cases we may take the product of the probabilities of the constituent events to represent the probability of the event composed of them in the manner characteristic of multiplication.

Independent events. And here we must notice an instance of the first importance of events which are independent in the sense that we have discussed. The events which constitute the series which is examined when the probability of an event is determined must be independent. For if P_r, one of the alternative events, is not independent of some other event P_s, the probability of P_r's happening will be different according as P_s has or has not happened before it; accordingly the probability of the event will be constantly changing throughout the series of N trials, and that series will not determine *the* probability of that event, but some number intermediate between its probability when the other event has happened and the probability that it has happened.

However, it should be remembered that the probability of an event must depend in any case on the exact nature of the trials by which it is determined, and that we have defined that probability by means of the frequency with which the event happens. Even if it were true that P_r and P_s are not independent in the series of trials, and that P_r occurred more frequently in trials when P_s had happened than in trials when it had not, still the probability of P_r would be that determined by the frequency with which it happened both when P_s had happened and when it had not. If the conditions were slightly altered, so that P_r and P_s became independent, a repetition of the trials would give a different value for p_r; but this is in no way inconsistent with our ideas of probability, for they admit that the probability varies with the condition of trial. It is not therefore strictly necessary for the application of the calculus of probability that the alternative events of which the probability is determined in a series of trials should be independent.

On the other hand, in practice it is always assumed that they are independent, and trials for the determination of probability are not undertaken except in conditions such that the alternative events are independent. Indeed if they are not independent, we should be inclined to say that the events were not dictated by chance and that the conceptions of probability were not applicable. There is a tendency, which we shall examine later, to attribute to chance, not all events which are such that it is known that there is no law associating them uniformly with the other events under consideration, but only those of which the probability is independent of the occurrence of those other events, and it is possible that the definition of probability should be amended by the insertion of a proviso that all the events are independent.

But here a difficulty arises. If we are to determine probability only in series in which the events are known to be independent, we must have some method of ascertaining that they are so. Such a method is provided by the rule of multiplication. If the events are independent, then the probability that P_r and P_s occur in some fixed relation (say P_r at the trial subsequent to P_s or at the second trial after P_s) is $p_r p_s$; and this relation holds even if P_r and P_s are the same event. Accordingly we must examine the series, and see if the frequency of P_r-and-P_s-in-the-given-relation tends to $p_r p_s N$ as N tends to infinity. But the considerations which lead us to demand that P_r and P_s shall be independent lead us also to further demands, namely that the composite event P_r-and-P_s-in-the-given-relation shall be independent of any other event in the series, e.g. P_t. Accordingly again we shall have to examine whether the frequency of some event involving P_r, P_s, P_t tends to $p_r p_s p_t N$ as N tends to infinity, and here again P_t may be the same event as P_r or P_s or the composite event made of them. If we continue to push these demands, we shall find ourselves eventually demanding that the frequency of some event tends to $p_r p_s p_t \ldots N$ as N tends to infinity where the number of terms in that product is infinite, or greater than any assigned magnitude; for even if the number of the alternative events P is finite, since in the product p_r and p_s may be the same, an infinite product may be made out of these probabilities. (For instance the event may be simply the happening of P, m times in succession, where m may be greater than any assigned magnitude; the probability of this event is $(p_r)^m$, and we shall demand that the frequency of the event tends to $(p_r)^m N$ as N tends to infinity.) But since p_r etc. are all proper fractions, an infinite product of them must be infinitesimal; we shall thus be led by our demands for independence of the events to a demand for the determination of an infinitesimal probability, which we have decided to be impossible.

Our conclusion is that if, in the determination of probability, the events must be independent, and if by independence we mean, not merely the independence of any two of the alternative events, but also the independence of any sequence of these events, then it is impossible to decide experimentally whether the events are so independent, and impossible therefore to determine a probability experimentally. And I can find no reason why, if we demand any independence, we should not demand this full independence. If the falling of a penny is not determined by chance unless the probability of its falling heads is independent of the result of the previous trial, then surely it is not determined by chance unless it is also independent of the result of the previous two trials—and of the previous three trials—and so on indefinitely. A very grave difficulty is thereby raised. For if on the other hand we cease to demand independence at all, we seem led to the conclusion that the conception of probability is applicable to events which are not dictated by chance and are associated by laws; and that, even if it were known that a penny always fell heads and tails alternately, we should still regard the falling of heads or tails at any trial as equally probable, because it would still be true that the frequency of heads and tails would tend to equality as the number of trials tended to infinity. And yet, if this were so, the degree of knowledge concerning the falling of either heads or tails would certainly not be equal because we should know definitely which would fall. There seems to be presented to us the dilemma that we must either admit the applicability of the conception of probability to events which are not dictated by chance and so completely divorce probability and degree of knowledge, or else admit that we have no means of determining a probability experimentally. We shall return later and inquire whether there is any means of avoiding the dilemma; for the present we shall overlook it entirely and resume the main argument.

Criticism of orthodox definition. The definition of probability which depends on the enumeration of equally probable cases is much less satisfactory than that which we are adopting in dealing with the multiplication of probabilities. It deduces the rule from a consideration of the number of different cases which arise from the combination of one of the events from each of the sets P, Q, R. If there are n_p, n_q, n_r equally probable alternative events in the respective sets, then the probability of any P, Q, or R is $1/n_p$, $1/n_q$, $1/n_r$. On the other hand the number of different cases obtained by combination is

$n_p n_q n_r$. If it is assumed that all these different cases are equally probable, then the probability of any one of them is $1/n_p n_q n_r$, and the rule of multiplication follows. Since all judgements of equal probability are regarded as lying outside the theory, there can be no objection to the introduction of this assumption, but, though it is vital, it is seldom explicitly stated; it involves, though it is not identical with, the assumption that the events of the different sets P, Q, R are independent.

If they are so independent, the rule follows from the definition; but the rule does not follow in the other case to which it is often applied, namely that in which Q_b is such that it cannot happen unless P_a happens. In this case the combination of events P_b and Q_b is impossible; the number of possible cases obtained by combination of the P's and Q's will not be $n_p n_q$, but simply n_q; and the rule ought to lead to the conclusion that the probability of any Q happening is $1/n_q$. The rejection of this conclusion and the use of the ordinary rule of multiplication in these cases is absolutely inconsistent with the idea of probability contained in the definition. The recognition that there is something essentially similar in the relation between the P's and Q's, both when they are independent and when the P's are necessarily associated with the Q's, and that the same rule of multiplication can be applied to both types of relation, depends, I think, simply on the unconscious substitution of a definition of probability similar to that which we have been considering.

Accordingly the ordinary definition of probability seems gravely defective both in connection with the addition and with the multiplication of probabilities. It leads to no rule for the addition of unequal probabilities and it cannot deal with the most important cases of the multiplication of probabilities. It is for this reason that the discrepancy arises in the example given on p. 166; for here both of the defects are most noticeable. The argument by which the result which is judged "right" is reached is of this nature. The trials of the drawing of the card may be divided into two sets in the manner contemplated by multiplication. One of these sets, P, is the choice of either the whist pack or the picquet pack; these choices are equally probable, so that both the p's are $\frac{1}{2}$. The other set, Q, is the choice of a card from the pack chosen; one of the q's is $1/32$, the other $1/52$. Accordingly it is concluded, first, that the probability of the choice of a card from the picquet pack, since it consists of P_a and Q_b, is $p_a q_b$ or $\frac{1}{2} \times 1/32$; the probability of a given card from the whist pack is similarly $\frac{1}{2} \times 1/52$. Again the choice of a given card from either of the packs is the event which consists, according to the idea of addition, of the choice from the picquet pack or the choice from the whist pack; consequently the probability is $\frac{1}{2} \times 1/32 + \frac{1}{2} \times 1/52 = 21/832$. But none of these conclusions follow from the definition. The case to which multiplication is applied is not one in which the events are independent; it is one of our second type. The definition is not applicable to this type at all; if an attempt is made to apply it, the only conclusion can be that the total number of cases is $32 + 52$, that the favourable cases are 2, and that the probability is $2/84$. Again, the probabilities which are added are not equal, and the rule gives no reason for supposing that the probability of the composite event is the sum of the probabilities of the components. There are therefore involved in the conclusion assumptions which are inconsistent with the ideas on which the definition is based, and it is not surprising that the final result cannot be stated in terms of those ideas.

Here we may stop our consideration of the probability of events. All further developments of the calculus depend on applications of the principles which have been discussed. But before we pass to another branch of probability, there is one question which should be raised. So far we have spoken only of the probability of alternative events and have regarded the numerical probability as stating something about the happening of one such alternative event rather than another. But is there any relation between the probabilities of events which are not alternative? The probability that I shall draw a red card rather than a black is $\frac{1}{2}$, and so is the probability that a penny will fall heads rather than tails; but the drawing of a red card is not alternative to the falling of a penny heads. Is there any meaning in the statement that the probabilities of these two events are equal? I think there is. I think there is significance in the statement that our degree of knowledge is equal concerning the drawing of a red card and the falling of a penny heads. But the association of degree of knowledge and probability is to be discussed presently; the matter is raised here only because it becomes of importance in connection with the second branch of the calculus of probability, namely that of the probability of causes.

Probability of causes. The problem. Problems of the probability of causes are often regarded as the converse of problems of the probability of events, such as we have been considering. In the latter, it is said, we ask what is the probability that a given event happens as a consequence of a known cause; in the former we ask what is the probability that a given cause has produced a known event. And there are circumstances in which this view of the matter is correct, although these circumstances are not those in which the most important problems of probability of causes arise.

The problem of the probability of causes is the converse of that of the probability of events only in the first class of cases to which the idea of the multiplication of probabilities is applicable. We know that as the result of the trial some one of certain alternative events P will happen; as a result of each of the P's certain other alternative events Q will happen, either because P simply consists of the happening of one of these Q's or because P and Q are connected by a set of laws. Among these Q's (or "effects") there are two or more, each the result of a different P (or "cause"), which, for some purpose which we are considering, can be regarded as the same event (although they must not be so considered when we are estimating probabilities). We make a trial and find that one of these events Q happens; we ask the probability that it has happened as a result of one of the possible P's rather than as the result of another. Thus, in the example which has been taken, the trial is the drawing of a card from one of the two packs lying on the table; the event which happens is the drawing of the ace of spades. This card may have been drawn from the whist pack or from the picquet pack; we ask the probability that the "cause" of the drawing of this card is a drawing from the whist pack or that it is a drawing from the picquet pack.

It is to be noted that the word "cause" in this connection is used in the sense mentioned on p. 104, which is far more general than that employed in the law of causation. All that is asserted when it is said that the P's are causes of the Q's is that, if a P happens, then one of the corresponding Q's happen, and that, if a Q happens, one of the P's must have happened. The relation of cause and effect concerned is more general even than that asserted by laws; not only need it not be a temporal relation, but it need not even be uniform in the sense of Chapter III; it may obtain only in the very special circumstances of the trial. On the other hand, the scientific relation of uniform association which is expressed by laws is a special case of this generalised relation of cause and effect, so long as the law involving it is expressed in the asymmetrical form which permits more than one "effect" to be associated with a single "cause". Thus the relation between dissolving in nitric acid (as "effect") and that of a density of 10·5 (as "cause") is an example of such a relation, for the solubility may be the "effect" of other "causes", e.g. a density of 11·4. Accordingly it is conceivable that the question which is raised by the probability of causes might have a scientific importance, for a relation may be involved in it which plays a large part in scientific inquiry.

Before the question can be answered the probability of a cause must be defined. The definition which has been put forward for the probability of an event suggests another for the probability of a cause. It is that the probability of the cause P_r for the event Q_s is w, if the ratio of the number of times that Q_s happens as the result of P_r to the total number of times Q_s happens tends to w as the number of trials tends to infinity.

In the circumstances we are considering this definition can be used experimentally to determine the probability of a given cause of a given event, and it can be shown that there is a relation between w on the one hand and the probabilities of P_r and of Q_s on the other For let p_r be the probability that P_r, rather than one of the alternative P's, is the result of the trial; let q_{rs} be the probability that, as the result of the "cause" P_r, the event Q_s happens rather than any of the other Q's which may happen as the "effect" of that cause[1]. Then the argument on which the rule of multiplication is based

---

[1] It is just worth while to note that it is now necessary to denote the q's by a double suffix. In deducing the rule of multiplication it was necessary to suppose that all the Q's are different and that none could happen as the result of more than one P; for if that had not been true, the P's would not have been alternative events; two of them might have happened at the same trial. But now we are supposing that two of the Q's are, for the immediate purpose, indistinguishable, and that the same Q may happen as the result of two different P's. This change of attitude involves no uncertainty in the argument as will be seen readily by examining special examples.

shows that the number of times that Q_s will happen as the result of P_r tends to $p_r q_{rs} N$ as N tends to infinity. The number of times Q_s happens at all will tend to $\Sigma p_r q_{rs} N$ as N tends to infinity, where the summation is to be taken over all the values of r corresponding to the different P's. (If Q_s is never associated with P_n, the value of q_{ns} is to be taken as o.) Consequently it follows that the ratio of the number of times Q_s happens as the result of P_r to the total number of times that Q_s happens tends to $p_r q_{rs} N / \Sigma p_r q_{rs} N$ as N tends to infinity; or, according to our definition, $w = p_r q_{rs} / \Sigma p_r q_{rs}$.

This well-known result, usually called Bayes' formula, follows in this case directly from the proposed definitions of probability. (It also follows more or less directly from the definition based on the enumeration of cases, but we need not consider that definition any further.) But this case is of little interest to science. Its essential feature is that we can conduct experiments in which we observe that Q_s is sometimes the effect of P_r and sometimes the effect of another P, P_t. When questions important to science about the probability of causes are asked it is always known certainly that Q_s, if it occurs at all, is always the result of the same P; it is conceivable that Q_s might result from more than one P, but as a matter of fact it is known that, in the condition of the trial, it results from one P and one P only; what we want to know is of which of the P's which might conceivably be the cause it is actually the effect. The chief application which we shall have to make of the probability of causes is to errors of measurement. Here we know that the measurements, i.e. observations, which we make are all the "effects" of some definite "real magnitude" (see Chapter XVII) of the system we are measuring; however many measurements we make, that real magnitude is always the same and all our observations must be the effect of that single real magnitude. On the other hand we believe that this real magnitude might be any one of several possible alternatives; whichever of these conceivable alternatives is the "cause" it is always the cause; but we do not know which of the conceivable alternatives is always the cause. It is in our endeavour to answer this question that we raise inquiries concerning the probability of causes. Another possible application which we shall have to consider, not differing essentially from the last, is to the truth of some law. Here again we know that our observations are all effects of one and the same law; but we know also that they might all be the effects of several alternative laws. We inquire of which of these alternatives are they all the effects.

Now in both these cases the conditions are absent which are necessary for the application of the definition of the probability of causes which has been suggested. No amount of experimenting can ever display Q_s as the result of more than one cause, for the fundamental assumption underlying our question is that it is always the effect of the same cause. At each trial the cause is the same; there is only one P; $p_r = 1$ and all other p's are o; so that the probability of p_r being the cause, according to the definition, is always 1. But even this conclusion is trivial, for we can never even observe Q_s as the effect of P_r; if we could ever make a single experiment in which the cause of

Q_s was known, we should not make the inquiry at all. The proposed definition does not convey what we mean by the probability of a cause in the only cases which are of importance to science.

Nor is any definition based on the enumeration of cases more applicable; for such a definition will again make the assumption, totally inconsistent with the ideas underlying the question, that in the same series of comparable trials, Q_s can be the result of more than one cause. As a matter of fact, most attempts that I have seen to state what is meant by the probability of a cause are based simply upon Bayes' formula; they simply define the probability of a cause as the function of the probability of events given in that formula. It is possible that the statement is true and that the probability of a cause is given by that formula; but the statement does not convey in the least what is meant by the idea, and it obviously requires proof.

Probability of causes. Definition. In order to realise what is meant by the probability of causes in such applications, when it is known that only one cause can be acting, we must return to the standpoint from which our discussion of probability started. Our first idea was that probability was a measure of degree of knowledge, and the main object of our inquiry was to discover how such a measure was to be obtained. When we decided that the real meaning of probability was connected with the frequencies with which events happen in very long series of trials, we were not rejecting the view that the real meaning was also a measure of degree of knowledge, but only that both these meanings are equally real and fundamental; presently we shall inquire what is the connection between them in virtue of which they are equally real. Now it is clear that the real meaning of the probability of causes is also a measure of degree of knowledge; the greater the probability of a cause, the more certain is our knowledge that this is the cause of the event in question. It is just this knowledge which we are seeking when we inquire into the probability of causes, and the results of that inquiry will be important only in so far as it provides a basis for belief. On the other hand the probability of causes has not, like the probability of events, a second meaning connected with the properties of a very long series of trials; when we ask about the probability of a cause we are not asking something about a very long series of events or causes, but something about one particular event and one particular cause. It is the absence of this second real meaning that has made it impossible to give an adequate definition of the probability of a cause. Can we find any other meaning which, while being a real meaning of the conception, will enable us to determine the probability of a cause experimentally and thus lead to a measure of the degree of knowledge?

I do not think we can. The probability of a cause, in the sense important for science, means a degree of knowledge and nothing else. But if we accept the fact that the probability of an event is a measure of the degree of knowledge of its future happening (leaving for future consideration the reason), we can establish some connection, such as is given by Bayes' formula, between the probability of a cause and the probability of events.

For the only kind of evidence that can give us any basis whatever for a belief that one cause rather than another is the cause of a particular event is that on which the measure of the probability of that event is based. If I know that the event Q may be the effect of one of several causes P, that knowledge must be derived from experiments in which the P's have been put into action and Q has been observed to follow; and these experiments are also those by which I determine the probability of the event Q happening as a result of the P's. Further, if I have any reason for believing that Q in a given case is the effect of one of the P's rather than the effect of another, it can only be because my experiments on the connection between Q and the P's have shown that Q is related to this P in a way different from that in which it is related to others. But a difference between the relation of the Q to one P and its relation to the others means a difference between the probability that Q will happen as a result of that P and as a result of the others, for the only relation which can be different is in respect of experiments which determine that probability. If then the probabilities of the different causes differ, it can only be because the probabilities differ of the event happening as a result of those causes. That conclusion is not sufficient of itself to prove that the probability of the cause does differ with the probability of the event happening as a result of that cause; but it does show that if we do not base our judgements of the probability of causes on the probabilities of events, we can have no experimental reason for believing at all that the probabilities of different causes are different or for introducing the conception of the probability of a cause. The fact that we have such reason and that we do introduce the conception is doubtless connected with the fact that the probability of an event is also a measure of degree of knowledge.

It follows then that w_r, the probability that the event Q is in the given conditions caused by the cause P_r, must be a function of $q_1, q_2, ..., q_r, ...$, the probabilities that the event Q will happen as a result of the causes $P_1, P_2, ..., P_r, ...$, if these causes are known to be in operation; and further that the function must be such that, if $q_r = q_s$, then $w_r = w_s$. Let us now introduce three arbitrary definitions, based on analogy with the corresponding definitions of the probability of events: (1) that the least possible value of w is 0; (2) that the probability of a cause is 1 if it is certain that it is the cause of Q; (3) that the probability that either P_r or P_s is the cause of Q is $w_r + w_s$. The first and second of these definitions are absolutely arbitrary; the third is not entirely so, for it seems implied by the every meaning of knowledge that it cannot be less certain that either one or the other of two propositions should be true than that only one of them should be true; accordingly the function of w_r and w_s which represents the probability that either P_r or P_s is the cause must be such that it is not less than either w_r or w_s. This condition is satisfied by the definition chosen, since by (1) w cannot be negative, but of course it would be fulfilled by many others.

We can now deduce certain other propositions about the relation between w and the q's. Since there can never be less reason for believing that P_r is the cause of Q than when Q has never been observed to be the result of P_r, we must have $w_r = 0$, if $q_r = 0$. On the other hand Σw_r must be equal to 1, since it is certain that Q is the result of one of the alternative causes. These and the other propositions relating w and the q's would be true if $w_r = aq_r$, where a is a constant; and, if so, since $\Sigma w_r = 1$, a must be equal to $1/\Sigma q_r$. But they would be true equally if w_r is of the form $\Sigma_n a_n q_r{}^n$, where n may have any finite positive value; and unless further arbitrary assumptions are introduced there is no reason, except mathematical simplicity, for preferring the relation $w_r = aq_r$ to any other. If we adopt that form, as we shall, it must be remembered that it is largely arbitrary, and that while it is in accordance with the definition of the probability of a cause as a measure of the degree of knowledge that the event is the result of that cause, many other alternative formulae are equally in accordance with that definition. We are not able, as we were when considering the probability of an event, to find a single mathematical formula which represents our ideas uniquely.

We propose then to assume that w_r the probability that P_r is the cause of the event Q is given by $w_r = q_r/\Sigma q_r$, where q_r is the probability of Q in trials in which P_r is known to be in operation. This result does not accord entirely with Bayes' formula, except when the p's in that formula are all equal. If, as we have assumed so far, our belief that P_r is the cause of Q is determined entirely by observations on the frequency with which Q happens as a result of the various P's, then there is no room in our conclusions for quantities of the nature of the p's. But in certain circumstances we have reasons, based on considerations other than these, for believing that P_r rather than any other P is the cause; or, as it is usually expressed, the probabilities *a priori* of the various P's are not equal. When Bayes' formula is applied to such questions as concern us now and not merely to the condition discussed on p. 187, then the p's in that formula are called the probabilities *a priori* that the various P's are in operation.

The reasons that we may have for believing that some of the P's are more probable than others, apart from observations of the q's, are of two kinds. In the first place we may know that the conditions in which the trial is made are more likely to put some P's into operation than others. Thus, if we alter our usual example a little, we may be drawing a card from a single pack which is known to be either a whist pack or a picquet pack, though it is not known which. Now suppose this pack was selected "by chance" from a collection of packs in which whist packs and picquet packs were mixed in a known proportion; then we shall have reason to attribute a probability *a priori* to the pack being of one kind rather than another. In the second place, we may have reason for believing that one cause rather than another is in operation, because we have already observed the happening of some events from the same cause. Thus, we may already have drawn an ace of spades from the pack from which we now propose to draw another; the fact that we have done so may have given us some reason for believing that the pack is of one kind rather than another.

In either of these cases, where there is a probability *a priori*, it is easy to show that we must alter our formula so that it becomes identical with that of Bayes. Thus in the first case, let p_r be the probability of the cause P_r being set into operation by the conditions in which the trial is conducted. Then since q_r is the probability that Q will happen if this cause is in operation, the rule of multiplication shows that the probability that Q will happen in the conditions of the trial as the result of P_r is $p_r q_r$; that is to say, as N tends to infinity, the number of times Q happens as the result of P_r will tend to $p_r q_r N$. Accordingly in the argument which was used previously $p_r q_r$ is precisely equivalent to q_r in determining our reason for believing that Q is the result of P_r; and that argument, with the same limitations and the same degree of arbitrariness, leads to the conclusion that $w_r = p_r q_r / \Sigma p_r q_r$, which is Bayes' formula.

In the second case, let the result of the first trial be Q' which may or may not be the same as Q. Then, as a result of that trial, $w_r = q_r'/\Sigma q_r'$, and this is the probability *a priori* or p_r. Now a second trial is made and Q results. If P_r is the operating cause in both cases, and if the two trials are independent in the sense of p. 180, then the probability that Q' will happen in the first trial and Q in the second is $q_r' q_r$. This product again plays the same part in the argument as q_r did previously, so that $w_r = q_r' q_r / \Sigma q_r' q_r$. Now

$$q_r' q_r / \Sigma q_r' q_r = \frac{q_r' q_r}{\Sigma q_r'} \bigg/ \frac{\Sigma q_r' q_r}{\Sigma q_r'};$$

and since $\Sigma q_r'$ is not a function of r, we may write

$$\frac{\Sigma q_r' q_r}{\Sigma q_r'} = \Sigma \frac{q_r' q_r}{\Sigma q_r'} = \Sigma \left(\frac{q_r'}{\Sigma q_r'} \cdot q_r \right).$$

But $q_r'/\Sigma q_r' = p_r$. Hence $w_r = p_r q_r / \Sigma p_r q_r$.

Such are the arguments on which can be based the use of Bayes' formula for the probability of a cause which is a measure only of degree of knowledge. It must be insisted again that they involve many entirely arbitrary assumptions, and that the formula does not follow from the definition of probability in the same direct manner as the rules of addition and multiplication follow from the definition which was adopted for the probability of an event. We must expect therefore to find, when we apply the formula, that the results obtained from it are somewhat indefinite and that in the interpretation of them there will always be an element of arbitrariness. The presence of such an element is recognised in all treatises on probability; it is only its source which is not always fully explained.

This arbitrariness has one rather important consequence. In every application of the probability of cause a new assumption has to be made; and though it is in a sense always the same assumption, its effect upon the final result varies with the nature of the case. Hence the probability of causes which are not alternative and represent different assumptions are not comparable. The number which represents the probability of a cause is comparable with that which represents the probability of an alternative cause, but not with that which represents a cause which is not alternative. It does not follow that we are more certain that A is the cause of B than that A' is the cause of B' because the probability of A is greater than that of A'; we are only more certain that A rather than A' is the cause, if they are both alternative causes of the same event B and if the probability of A is the greater. This remark is important when the theory of errors of measurement is considered.

Probability and knowledge. We have now completed our survey of the ideas and of the chief propositions on which the calculus of probability is based; we have seen how far they are concerned with matters and state facts that can be established by experiment, and how far they are completely arbitrary and dictated by no judgements of the external world. Most of the rest of the development of the calculus consists of a series of logical deductions from these propositions and raises no further questions which concern us here. In some special applications additional assumptions that may be questioned are introduced, but it will be more convenient to deal with these in considering the applications. We shall now revert to the inquiry from which we started. If probability is defined in the manner which we have investigated, and if the propositions about it which have been elaborated are true, why is it that the probability of an event or the probability of a cause is a measure of the degree of knowledge that the event will happen or that the cause is in operation?

We have seen that the answer to the second part of the question follows immediately if we can give an answer to the first. If the probability of an event is a measure of degree of knowledge, then the probability of a cause, defined by Bayes' formula, is also such a measure. Our question therefore resolves itself into this. Why does a knowledge of the frequency with which an event happens in an infinite series of trials give us any reason for believing that it will or will not happen at a single particular trial?

One answer which is sometimes given to this question is, *Solvitur ambulando*; the probability of an event does not give us any knowledge of its happening in a particular trial; we are as ignorant whether a penny will turn up heads 100 times in succession as we are ignorant whether it will turn up heads next time. The only objection that can be urged against this answer is simply that it is not true. Degree of knowledge is, at least as far as science is concerned, a fundamental notion. I cannot explain to anyone else who professes ignorance what I mean when I say that I am more certain of one event than of another, any more than I can explain to them what I mean when I say that I believe one proposition and that I do not believe another; and if anyone asserts that they do not feel any difference in belief or certainty or knowledge corresponding to extreme differences in probability I cannot prove that they do feel it. I can only assert to the contrary that I do feel it.

But wait, can I really not prove it? Let us remember the conclusions we reached in Chapter I concerning the basis of our knowledge of what other people feel and believe. We concluded that the basis of such knowledge was observation of their actions. If it turns out that people, whatever they may assert regarding degree of knowledge, do act differently in respect of any event which has a very small probability and in respect of one which has a very great probability, then we shall have just that ground for asserting that they experience the same difference as ourselves in degree of knowledge which is of any importance to science. By this test we can soon refute their answer. If anyone asserts that they have no greater degree of knowledge in the prediction of a highly probable than of a highly improbable event, we need only ask them if they will agree to give us £100 if the penny turns up heads next time, if we agree to give them £100 if it turns up heads each of the next hundred times.

A man must be either a madman or a millionaire (if indeed the alternatives are distinguishable) to accept the offer. But is it quite certain that the test is a fair one? We can only be perfectly certain if it is quite clear that the offer is made for one occasion only and that, in making our decision whether to accept it, we are quite free from any idea of a repetition of it. For if we are considering at all the result of a long series of such offers, all accepted, then it would indeed be madness to accept; for what we assert in saying that one event is less probable than another is that in a sufficiently long series it will occur less frequently. Now it is extremely difficult to avoid such considerations when we are deciding whether to accept, because in practical life our actions are (or ought to be) always decided by a consideration of the effect of a long series of similar actions. Everyone may not admit as a universal principle Kant's ethical maxim, Act as though your action were to be made a general rule, but everyone applies it very widely. We often have to decide how to act in circumstances which we know will recur, and then, of course, we take into account the probable effect of our repeated action; we seldom know definitely that the circumstances will not recur, and if even we do know it, we have to act somehow; accordingly we act as we would if we knew that they would recur.

I think therefore that if it is urged that our feeling of a different degree of knowledge about the happening of events of different probability is really a delusion, and that, when we think we have different knowledge about the happening of the particular event we are confusing such knowledge with knowledge of the result of a long series of similar events—if such an argument is urged, it cannot be dismissed summarily. There is little doubt that degree of knowledge, as it affects practical action in everyday life, is largely if not entirely knowledge of the result of many similar actions. I am less willing to act as if a less probable event were about to occur because, if I always acted in that manner, I should suffer more severely than if I acted as if a more probable event were about to occur. If two events are equally probable, I am quite indifferent which I shall assume to be about to happen, not because my "degree of knowledge" about the two is the same, but because I have the very definite knowledge—knowledge as certain as any knowledge and admitting of no degree—that whichever assumption I make the ultimate result will be the same in a long series of similar actions; this knowledge is certain because it is precisely what is asserted when I say that the events are equally probable. In the same way I choose to assume the more probable of two unequally probable events, not because there is a difference in degree of knowledge, but because there is the definite knowledge derived from the definition of probability that this assumption is the wiser to adopt if I am to be faced repeatedly with the same choice.

It seems then that the difference in our practical action in respect of more and less probable events does not prove that we have any difference of degree of knowledge about any one particular event, but only knowledge concerning collections of such events. The usual method of ascertaining the opinions of others is therefore unavailable in this instance, and it has to be admitted that if anyone denies a difference in the degree of his knowledge it is impossible to prove him mistaken. The admission may lead us to examine our own position rather more carefully. There are certainly branches of science in which we seem to associate very closely the probability of single events or single causes with a degree of knowledge about them; for instance, in statistical mechanics and in the Gaussian theory of error. But without denying the legitimacy of such applications of the calculus of probability it is possible to inquire what exactly is the association; whether it is really an association of definite probabilities with definite degrees of knowledge; and, if so, what adequate basis can we find for such an association.

It will be well to take the last question first, for our judgement of what our views are and of what we are really prepared to maintain is sure to be influenced by the evidence that we can adduce for our views. We may note, then, that some kind of association between probability and degree of knowledge seems to follow directly from the very nature of knowledge. Thus we may assert confidently that our degree of knowledge about the happening of any event is the same as that about the happening of any equally probable alternative event. For if we knew nothing about the events, except that they are alternative and that one of them may happen as the result of a trial, we have no reason for distinguishing between those events. Whatever we know about one—whether it is much or little— we know about the other. Now when the additional knowledge is added that the events are equally probable, since the addition affects both events similarly, there is still nothing to distinguish them; and still whatever degree of knowledge we have about one we have also about the other.

From this result we may proceed another step. If A and B are any alternative events, it can scarcely be denied—if degree of knowledge is a significant conception at all—that our degree of knowledge that either A or B will happen is greater (or at least not less) than our degree of knowledge that A will happen or our degree of knowledge that B will happen. Accordingly it seems legitimate to conclude that when probabilities are increased by the addition of the probabilities of alternative events, greater degree of knowledge is associated rightly with the greater probability. Similarly it could be argued that when probabilities are decreased by the multiplication of probabilities of alternative events, a lesser degree of knowledge is rightly associated with the lesser probability; our degree of knowledge of "A-and-B" cannot be greater than our degree of knowledge of A or our degree of knowledge of B. Now if, as the orthodox calculus of probability asserts implicitly, all unequal probabilities of alternative events arise from the addition or multiplication of equal probabilities of some other alternative events, this argument would seem to show in general that, among alternative events, a greater degree of knowledge is rightly associated with a greater probability. We have been led to deny that fundamental assumption; if it leads to any conclusions at all those conclusions would seem to be contradictory; and accordingly we cannot accept this defence of the association. But the argument is probably used unconsciously to support the general association, and it is important to notice that in this form it is erroneous.

It would be acceptable only if greater degree of knowledge could be shown to be associated with greater probability even when the events (or causes) are not alternative; for it has not been denied, and later it will be urged, that events of unequal probability may be regarded in a sense as compounded by addition or multiplication of equally probable events which are not alternative. And perhaps some proof in this direction may be given. Suppose the event P, which is certain to happen, is composed by addition of n equally probable alternatives p, and that Q, also certain to happen, is composed of m equally probable alternatives q. Our degree of knowledge about P is the same as our degree of knowledge about Q. But the argument of the preceding paragraph indicates that, if n is greater than m and the probability of a p less than that of a q, the degree of knowledge of a p happening relatively to that of P happening is less than the degree of knowledge of a q happening relatively to that of Q happening; for in the first case there is a larger number of alternative events. Since then our knowledge of P and Q is the same, our degree of knowledge of p is less than our degree of knowledge of q. This appears to be the only way of justifying a comparison of degree of knowledge of events that are not alternative, but I do not feel personally that the argument is very convincing. For it assumes that degree of knowledge is something that is measurable, and this is one of the chief points at issue. If it is measurable, then it is easy to accept the conclusion that probability is a measure of it; but the point concerning which we have really to inquire is whether there is such a thing as a degree of knowledge, intermediate between complete knowledge and complete ignorance (or absence of knowledge), and such that it is capable of having any "value" between these two extremes, the "value" being something which is capable of processes closely analogous to numerical addition. This doctrine appears to me far from certain.

Let us therefore try another line of argument. In place of describing our attitude towards the happening of events in terms of "degree of knowledge," let us describe it in terms of surprise, a state of mental discomfort which is closely associated with degree of knowledge. When we say that we have a considerable degree of knowledge that an event will happen we mean that we shall be in a state of considerable mental discomfort if it does not happen. This state will occur only if an improbable event happens; it will not occur if either a very probable event happens or if one of a number of equally probable alternative events happens. Accordingly we shall be able to establish a connection between degree of knowledge and probability, if we can find a reason why in the first case, but not in the others, a state of mental discomfort is natural and proper.

Such a reason, I think, can be found. Suppose that there are only two alternative events P_1 and P_2, of which P_1 is very much more probable than P_2, so that p_1 is nearly 1 and p_2 nearly 0. Now suppose that P_2 actually happens at the trial that we make. The question immediately arises whether we were right in asserting that p_2 is very nearly 0. Once any doubt on the subject arises we must undertake more experiments to remove it, and the number of experiments we shall have to undertake in order to re-establish the truth of our assertion concerning P_2 will be greater the less is p_2. For in saying that the probability of P_2 is p_2 we mean that, by sufficiently increasing N, we can make the number of times P_2 occurs as near p_2N as we please; if P_2 has occurred once, then, even if it never occurs again, we must perform at least $1/p_2$ further trials before we have reached the stage at which there is any evidence that the probability is as small as p_2. On the other hand, if P_1 occurs as a result of the trial, then no further experiments at all will be absolutely necessary to prove that the probability of P_1 is at least as great as p_1, for we have already found a value of N consistent with that statement. Of course many more experiments would be required to establish for the first time that the probability is p_1, but, if P_1 occurs at the trial, no further experiments are necessary to prove that the result of this trial is consistent with the conclusion already reached.

Now the prospect of having to perform a very large number of further experiments, in order to prove that the result of the trial just made is consistent with a statement made beforehand, is also a source of natural and proper mental discomfort. And the discomfort becomes extreme if the number of experiments which would have to be performed in order to show that the result of the trial is consistent with the assertion of probability is so large that it could not possibly be performed in any imaginable future. Thus, if we tossed a penny a hundred times, and it turned up heads every time, no possible number of experiments which could be made in the probable lifetime of the human race could show that this result is consistent with the assertion that heads and tails are equally probable. If such a result occurred we should be in the uncomfortable position of having made an assertion which we could not possibly ever prove to be true.

For this reason the mental discomfort which we call surprise is legitimately associated with the occurrence of a very improbable event, but not with the occurrence of a very probable event. If the two events are equally probable, then the same argument will show that, whichever of them occurs, the same number of experiments would be necessary to show that the assertion of probability was consistent with the result of the trial; and this number need not necessarily exceed two. The mental discomfort is therefore small whichever way the trial results, and the associated surprise should also be small.

This argument may appear rather fantastic, but I believe that it does represent an important reason for believing that a very improbable event will not occur, and that it enables us to trace a relation between probability, as we have defined it, and the mental attitude, called degree of knowledge, which is associated with probability. We believe that very improbable events will not occur because, if they did occur, we should find it impossible to prove them very improbable; our degree of knowledge of the happening of the more probable event is greater and our mental uncertainty or discomfort less, because we should be put to greater trouble to prove that the event is the more probable if it did not happen at the next trial.

However two objections may be raised. The first is suggested by the consideration of those cases in which there are a very large number of alternative events all of which have a very small probability. Thus, if I toss a penny 100 times, then there are 2^{100} possible alternative results of the trial; each of them has a probability of only 2^{-100}, and, whichever of them actually occurs, I should have to perform 2^{100} more experiments before I could prove that the probability of that event was what I have asserted it to be. The argument that has been given ought then to prove that my mental discomfort will be extreme whichever of the events happen, my surprise enormously great, and my degree of knowledge extraordinarily small. But as a matter of fact, I shall not usually experience any mental discomfort as a result of the trial and shall not be surprised; on the other hand, my degree of knowledge of the happening of any one of the events is extraordinarily small. It might seem then that in this case the relation between surprise and degree of knowledge was different from that in the previous example and that the argument would not explain the facts.

But the apparent difference may arise only from the fact that it is quite impossible to contemplate equally a large number of possible alternatives. When I am faced with such an enormous number of alternatives, I cannot avoid dividing them subconsciously into groups; the alternatives of which I am thinking before the trial occurs are these groups and not the individual results of the trials. What I am prepared to assert in such cases is that, if I name beforehand any one of the alternative events, that event will not occur as a result of a trial. The mere fact that I have thought of it distinguishes it in my mind from the rest; the alternatives that I am considering are, on the one hand, this particular event and, on the other, the group consisting of all the remainder. This group, taken as a whole, has a very great probability and if this highly probable event occurs, I shall experience no surprise; but my surprise will be very great indeed if the specially distinguished event occurs. And my knowledge of the highly probable event is not small, but so great as to amount to certainty; it is only my knowledge of the individual events which make up the highly probable event which is small. Absence of surprise if an event occurs appears to be associated with very small knowledge that it will occur, only because the surprise and the knowledge are not about the same thing; the surprise is about a vast collection of events, the knowledge about the individual events. If we are sure that surprise and knowledge are about the same thing, they are associated as they were before, and both surprise and knowledge are fully justified by the argument which has been given.

The second objection is this. It may be argued that degree of knowledge and surprise cannot be related so simply, because degree of knowledge is before the event, surprise is after it. It is quite true that the surprise after the event is associated with and justified by the mental discomfort arising from the difficulty of proving the assertion made; but this mental discomfort does not justify and is not necessarily associated with any mental attitude before the trial. Why should we assume, as we seem to do, that the result of the trial will be such as to spare us surprise and mental discomfort?

This is a very profound question, to which we shall have to revert; and I do not think that any answer to it which will satisfy everyone can be given. The question really is how we are enabled to study science at all. We study science in order to satisfy our intellectual desires, or in order to obtain mental comfort. If the results of our experiments were such that they did not give us mental comfort and intellectual satisfaction we should cease to make them. The fact that we do make them and that we are able to study science proves that they are of such a nature as to give the intellectual satisfaction which we desire. It is possible that this fact is an indication of some fundamental property of the universe—whatever that may mean; it is also possible that it only indicates that we refuse to notice any observations which are not of the kind we like. But for the moment we must content ourselves with noticing that the fact is a fact, that the assumption that "the universe is rational" and that observations can be ordered in a manner which is intellectually satisfactory underlies not only that branch of science which is concerned with probability but the roots of the whole structure.

It should be observed also that this second objection does not arise in connection with the probability of causes, and it is in this connection that the association of degree of knowledge with probability is most important. The degree of knowledge here concerns the cause to which a given event which has occurred is to be attributed; the surprise, if any, felt at its attribution to that cause is simultaneous with and not consecutive to the knowledge. In fact the argument which has been given justifies degrees of knowledge of causes more directly than degrees of knowledge of events about to happen. For if we propose to attribute an event to a cause of which it would be a very improbable result, then, in order to make our assumption that it is the result of this cause consistent with the very small probability that it should result from this cause, we shall have to make a large number of experiments in all of which the cause is in operation and the event does not result from it. The probability of a cause, as given by the formula developed on p. 187, is an inverse measure of the number of experiments which would have to be made in order to show that the attribution of the event to that cause is consistent with the statement we have made of the probability of the event resulting from that cause. It is therefore an inverse measure of the mental discomfort arising from the attribution, or the surprise which it excites; and is therefore a direct measure of the degree of knowledge which we feel about the matter.

Coincidences. I have argued as well as I can for the general association of probability and knowledge; but considerations are already forcing themselves on our attention which seem to me to undermine all such arguments, because they make it necessary to introduce new ideas into the treatment of probability. The proposition which we have been trying to explain and justify, namely that the probability of an event is a measure of the degree of knowledge that it will happen, may be roughly expressed, in the extreme case when the knowledge amounts to certainty, by the statement that "coincidences do not happen"; for by a "coincidence" we mean an event of which the probability is very small.

So far we have discussed only the justification for the proposition applied to one particular trial which is under immediate consideration, but of course if we intend to apply it in turn to all such trials we are in effect asserting it generally. And it seems necessary to the whole theory of probability that we should assert it generally, and declare from the outset that coincidences never happen. For the argument of p. 172 shows that without such an assertion we could never ascertain experimentally what is the probability of any event. Any sequence of alternative events is consistent with any assertion of the probability of those events, and all that experiment can show is that the sequence which we have observed is consistent with the values of the probability which we propose to attribute, not that it is inconsistent with other values. We can only rule out certain values by using the assumptions that extreme coincidences do not happen. There has been offered what appears to be a sufficient justification of this assumption in particular cases; but if it is applied generally or asserted as a general principle it immediately leads to contradiction.

For if by a coincidence we mean nothing but a very improbable event, the principle would mean that no very improbable event can happen, while it is an immediate consequence of the fundamental ideas of probability that some very improbable events must happen. For any sufficiently long sequence of any independent events, however probable is each, is as improbable as we please, and yet such a sequence must happen; any sequence of 100 tosses of a penny is almost infinitely improbable, and yet we can certainly toss a penny 100 times and note the successive falls. We must therefore admit some coincidences, and the assumption that underlies all applications of probability will be reasonable only if we confine it to certain coincidences and assert only that these coincidences cannot happen. But on what grounds is the distinction to be made between coincidences which are to be excluded from possible happenings and those which are included? Actually in the tosses of the penny we shall incline to exclude the sequence which consists of 100 heads or that which consists of 100 tails, but to include all "irregular" sequences. But the calculus of probability cannot offer the smallest ground for such a distinction. If it is equally probable that a penny falls heads and tails, and if the probability of its falling heads (say) is the same whether or no the penny has already fallen any given number of times in succession, then the calculus most certainly shows that whatever sequence actually occurs when the experiment is tried is not a whit more probable than the sequence of 100 heads. We must deny either the principles of the calculus, or render the calculus perfectly useless by admitting all coincidences as possible, unless we can give some reason independent of all experimental estimates of probability for distinguishing between those coincidences which never happen and those which, though they are no more probable, may and must happen.

This argument only expresses a familiar paradox which is mentioned in all discussions of probability and is constantly occurring in the correspondence columns of card journals. I am quite sure that I shall not be dealt 13 trumps, although any hand that I may be dealt is just as improbable as 13 trumps. The solution usually given is this. I am not really sure that I shall not be dealt 13 trumps, but only that I am sure that I shall not get that hand so long as somebody has not been arranging the cards. If I did get 13 trumps, I should simply conclude that somebody had arranged the cards, and that the conditions which I was contemplating, when I said that I was sure I should not get that hand, had not occurred. I deny that the hand could result from those conditions, because if it did happen I should conclude that it had not resulted from those conditions. In fact, the problem is really one of the probability of causes; the cause of the event may either be "mere chance" or deliberate arrangement of the cards; and though the *a priori* probability of the deliberate arrangement may be very small, it will always be great enough to justify, by Bayes' formula, the conclusion that the cards have been deliberately arranged.

According to this view coincidences are not merely improbable events but improbable events for which the probability *a priori* of some cause other than that contemplated at the time of the trial is finite and considerable. Any event may be a coincidence in suitable circumstances. A very regular hand, like that which consists of 13 trumps, will always be a coincidence, but a wholly irregular hand may also be one. When I have dealt myself a normal hand I do not usually regard it as a coincidence; but suppose that, before I had dealt myself that very hand, I had mentioned or thought of the possibility that I might have that hand, then the dealing of it would be one of those "coincidences which never happen". For though I might not have the slightest idea how the cards might have been manipulated in order to produce that hand, simply because I had thought of it or mentioned it, a cause, consisting of some intentional relation between my mention of the hand and the arrangement of the cards so as to produce it, would have a finite probability *a priori* large enough to lead to the conclusion that this cause, and not mere chance, was in operation.

The theory of chance. Events and trials. But to this explanation of the matter, there is one fatal objection. The distinction between coincidences which never happen (the word will be confined to this sense in future) and events which, though very improbable, may happen—this distinction underlies the whole calculus of probability. It must be made before any estimates of probability are undertaken. But the argument that has been given depends on the results of the calculus and, especially on the estimates of the probability of causes, which form the most advanced and most obscure part of the calculus. The argument is undeniably circular. Moreover there are other difficulties connected with the calculus of probability, which seem closely related to the problem of coincidences, which are still unexplained; there is, for instance, the dilemma mentioned on p. 182; we can never prove completely the independence of events and yet assume in all our calculations that the events are independent. And yet there is something in the argument; it forces us to recognise that there is a theory, as well as laws, of chance. Let us return to some of the fundamental characteristics of chance, from which we started.

The question is often asked in discussions of chance how we reconcile the existence of events dictated by chance with the assumption of the universal "reign of law". We can avoid this question, as some others who have discussed chance cannot, by denying that the reign is universal. We have recognised from the first that it is only part of our whole experience which can be ordered in scientific laws; we admit that there is another large part which can never be so ordered. Accordingly there is nothing to prevent us from selecting from this part another portion which, while still unregulated by law, has the kind of regularity that is characteristic of "objective" or scientific chance. But though no inconsistency is involved in such procedure, it is not very convenient. For the events which are regulated by chance are often very closely similar to those which are regulated by law; they appear at first sight of exactly the same nature and it is only the closest examination which forces us to exclude them from the domain of law. And it is precisely such events that are of the greatest importance for science, because they are so similar to those regulated by law. An obvious example of such events are those concerned in measurement; events which are capable of measurement would seem to be distinctively scientific and peculiarly characteristic of the domain of law; and yet, as is well known, some part of these events have to be relegated to the domain of chance. It is almost intolerable to have to admit that there are involved in measurement two classes of events which differ in their nature fundamentally, and that one is to be included in and the other excluded from the region of strict science. Such classes would differ as greatly as those, for instance, which depend respectively on time or space judgements and on judgements of good or of beauty.

It would be much more convenient if we could imagine that after all events which appear to be regulated by chance are really regulated by law; and there is no doubt that we can and do so imagine. The idea is made possible by observing that in some events a very small difference in the cause makes a very great difference in the effect. If we are caught by a shower on the main watershed of the Engadine, we shall probably be amused by reflecting (if our discomfort permits) that the water which drips from one arm will find its way to the North Sea, and that which drips from the other to the Black Sea. A difference of a few feet in the "cause" may cause a difference of thousands of miles in the "effect". By abstraction we readily arrive at the idea that a difference in cause which is inappreciable to the most careful and accurate observation may produce a very appreciable difference in the effect; and once we have that idea the "explanation" of chance is easy. We have only to suppose that the members of the series of trials, which are all apparently identical and yet lead to different events, are not really identical, but merely differ so slightly that we cannot appreciate the difference. We may then associate with every different event some difference in the trial which leads to it, and suppose that each event follows from the corresponding trial by a perfectly regular law. The appearance of irregularity is merely due to a failure to distinguish between similar laws all of which are perfectly regular.

This account of how and why we attribute events to chance is due to Poincaré. He points out that an event is due to chance when it is such that a very slight difference in the "cause" will produce a very large difference in the "effect". Thus we attribute to chance the result of a throw at roulette, because a difference in the manner in which the wheel is spun or the ball thrown, though it may be much too small to be appreciated by the marker or the players, will cause a great change in the division in which the ball ultimately comes to rest. Again we might say that the 7th figure in the characteristic of a logarithm is due to chance, while the first figure is regular; for, if we picked out from the tables a succession of numbers and took the 7th figure of their characteristics, we should not be able to trace any connection between the numbers and the 7th figures, unless we knew beforehand that the numbers were taken from a book of logarithms; on the other hand there would be an obvious connection between the numbers and the first figures of their characteristics. The difference in this respect between the first and the 7th figure lies in this, that a very small change in the number will produce a very big change in the 7th figure of the logarithm, but not a very big change in the first figure. A third example may be taken from the dynamical theory of gases. We say that the distribution of the molecules at any instant is dictated by chance and is independent of the distribution at some previous moment, because a very slight change in the distribution at that previous moment will cause a very great change in the distribution after a large number of collisions have taken place[1]. In these cases and in all others of events

[1] There will, of course, be a very great change only if we are considering the positions of the individual molecules, regarded as separately identifiable. If we suppose that the molecules are not identifiable, so that all distributions are the same in which the same number of molecules is present in the same volume, then there is no change of distribution with time. But this consideration is not relevant to our present purpose. When we say that the distribution of the molecules is dictated by chance we are thinking of the molecules as identifiable. The possibility of regarding certain large collections as identical although the elements

which are dictated by chance, we can trace the same feature that a very small change in the cause produces a very large change in the effect.

This then is how we can reconcile, if we will, the existence of a class of events due to chance with the assumption that all such events are really due to the operation of law. I am not certain that we make full use of the opportunity and regard *all* events, apparently casual, as really regulated in this manner by law, but we certainly do make use of it in connection with all apparently casual events which are important for science; we always do assume that the apparently similar trials which give rise to different results are not really similar, but differ in some respect which is too small to appreciate. It is of the first importance to recognise what is the exact nature of the assumption which makes the "reconciliation" possible. It consists, of course, of a theory, as is indicated by the lavish use that has been made throughout this paragraph of the word "really", a use which, I believe, will be found to be perfectly natural. The propositions which establish a connection between differences in the results and differences in the trials form a theory; they state something of which the meaning cannot be expressed by assertions concerning experiments. All experiments prove that there is no general connection between the results and the trials; trials, which are precisely the same so far as experiment can determine, produce results which are different. If we say that there is "really" a difference between the trials corresponding to the difference between the results, as is usual when we employ the word "really", we are asserting a theory. The hypothetical ideas, which are without meaning apart from the theory, are the differences in the trials imperceptible to observation. The hypothesis of the theory is simply the statement that the trials do differ; the dictionary states that differences in the trials mean differences in the observed results[1].

Random distributions. But the theory in this form does not wholly remove our difficulties; it has merely pushed them a stage further back. To every different kind of event—so says the theory—corresponds a different kind of trial; the relation between the trial and event is one of strict law, or, more

---

of which they are composed are different and distinguishable gives rise to the study of statistics. There is a close connection between statistics and probability, but the use of statistics may be quite independent of the conceptions of chance which we are examining now.

[1] The theory in this simple form is sometimes called the Principle of Sufficient Reason. This principle is often regarded as fundamental to all scientific investigation, but I have preferred to make little reference to it, because it is so difficult to state in any precise form. Its apparent importance is probably largely due to its vagueness; it can be used to prove anything because it can mean anything. Sometimes it seems to be given a sense almost identical with the Law of Causation, sometimes it is equivalent to the statement that the "universe is rational". It is sometimes interpreted to mean that two states of the universe cannot differ only in a single particular, and it is of this meaning that the theory of chance can be regarded as a special application. But here again the whole significance depends upon what is to be regarded as a "single particular"; is the event a single particular or is the combination of trial and event a single particular? It seems better, therefore, not to regard the theory as a special instance of any more general proposition, but as separate and independent.

accurately, it is stated by a hypothetical proposition which, according to the analogy, corresponds to a strict law. It follows that the distribution of the events which leads us to attribute them to chance must be reproduced among the trials; they also must be distributed in the manner characteristic of chance. Thus, when I am tossing a penny, the tosses which give heads are distinguished in some manner from those which give tails; they seem to be identical only because the distinction between them is so small that I cannot appreciate it. But if we admit this distinction, it becomes relevant to ask why the two kinds of trial are distributed in the manner which is observed, why the frequencies of their occurrences tend to equality as they tend to infinity, and why the occurrences are "independent". The theory does not explain how events come to be distributed in the manner characteristic of chance; it merely transfers the chance from the observed events to the hypothetical trials. Fortunam *expellas furca, tamen usque recurret*. All that we have gained towards an explanation so far is the substitution of the hypothetical ideas of the different trials for the concepts of the different events; this substitution is a gain because any proposition which we assert about the events can be tested directly by experiment, while a proposition about the trials can only be tested indirectly through the deductions made from it; we have greater latitude in our choice of propositions.

In order to complete our explanation of the phenomena that we attribute to chance, we must introduce into the hypothesis a proposition stating the distribution of the different kinds of trials; and this proposition, in accordance with the principles of Chapter VI, must be in some way analogous to a law, or at least have that familiarity which is generally given to theories by analogy with laws. The analogy which is used is derived from those series of events which are always taken as examples when the calculus of probability is expounded, the tossing of a penny, the drawing of a card, the choice of a number from a book of logarithms. Such events are said to be perfectly random. Every theory which explains phenomena that are attributable to chance involves essentially this conception of "random".

This conclusion may appear trifling, but let us analyse somewhat further the meaning of random. In all these series of events which are regarded as perfectly random and as typical of the action of chance, a person endowed with volition plays an essential part; the fact that the events are due to chance arises from the part played by this person. If we eliminated him and substituted some regular mechanism, the result of the trials would no longer be perfectly random. Perhaps this last statement is not entirely true. A machine for tossing pennies would probably give results as random as tossing by hand; and again it is possible to get results in other experiments which are perfectly random without the intervention of a personal agent; thus the distribution of drops on a sheet of paper held out in a shower of rain is perfectly random. But such exceptions to the rule that random events are produced by arbitrary volition does not alter the fact that randomness and arbitrary volition are very closely associated in our minds, and that the most typical and characteristic series of random events are those produced by an agent acting according to the arbitrary dictates of his will.

For, even if random distributions are produced by causes other than arbitrary volition, it is certain that volition which is consciously arbitrary must produce a random distribution. For random means "without perceptible order or reason", and "arbitrary" volition is volition which we feel to be dictated by no reason and regulated in no order. It is such events that the person determining the trials will produce if he feels that he is acting arbitrarily. It is true that if he were drawing cards from a pack, he might feel that he is acting arbitrarily and yet the results of his drawings might not be random; but that is because when he determines what his action is to be he does not know what the result of it will be; he says, I will draw that card, but he does not know what the card is. But if he is selecting numbers by deliberate choice from a table (and we shall see that this is the case we want to consider), he cannot be unaware of what his choice will be; he cannot produce order in his results without knowing it, and as soon as he realises he is producing order he will cease to produce it. Everyone must know the feeling who has been asked to select numbers at random; he begins (say) 47, 53, 29—then realises that he is selecting primes and goes on 36, 24—realises that all his numbers are between 20 and 60 and goes on 13, 98—and so on. There is no need to insist further; it is obvious (and it is important in this connection just because it is obvious) that random distributions are such as are produced by persons acting arbitrarily and that arbitrary volition will produce random distributions.

Now I think—and it is on this that I want to insist particularly—that it is because random distributions are associated so intimately with arbitrary volition that a theory of chance of which the hypothesis asserts that the trials are distributed at random provides an explanation, and an ultimate explanation, of chance events. It provides an explanation because arbitrary volition is familiar, and the explanation is ultimate because for science arbitrary volition is an ultimate fact which admits of no inquiry. Science cannot and will not explain why free will acts as it does; the very fact that it is free will and different for different persons excludes it from the domain of science; we simply accept as ultimate the fact that free will acts in a manner entirely opposite to that characteristic of law. When therefore we find that events are not regulated by laws, but are due to chance, the suggestion occurs immediately that they may be due to free will; and if we find that they can be regarded as due to free will, we have said everything about them that can be said; there is nothing more to explain.

On the other hand if we stated explicitly in the hypothesis of our theory that the trials were distributed at random because they were determined by the free will of some personal agent, we should introduce an intolerably anthropomorphic element into our theory. Such theories are tolerable only if these distributions are exactly like those produced by free will and yet are not actually so produced. In order to see how such distributions arise we must remember that the randomness that is characteristic of the operation of free will is subjective and relative. By this I mean that randomness does not consist in the absence of all order (if indeed such a thing is possible), but only in the absence of some particular kind of order; and that it refers to the state of mind of the perceiver rather than to the state of the thing perceived; a thing appears random when we cannot perceive any order in it, although some other person better informed may be able to detect order. Thus—to take a simple example—the distribution of a number of points on a sheet of paper may appear perfectly random to anyone who does not know how they were placed; but the person who placed them may know that they were placed by some regular geometrical construction consisting of related circles and straight lines, and with that knowledge he may be able to see the pattern in a distribution which to others appears wholly without order. Again the randomness in this example is relative, because the absence of order only extends to relations of the points in the plane of the paper; if we are considering positions out of that plane, it is clear that the distribution is by no means random but regulated by a very simple order, namely that all the points are in the same plane. A distribution is said to be random if and only if it might have been produced by the voluntary action of some person whose mind was undetermined by any considerations of some special sort; and if it is so produced it is random only relative to such considerations.

The example of the dots on the sheet of paper indicates how a random distribution may be produced by a mechanism acting according to fixed laws, so long as that mechanism is sufficiently complicated. We may be unconscious of order, because the order is so complex that the mind refuses to grasp it. It is because a random distribution may arise in this way, as well as from the arbitrary action of a free agent, that we do not feel that the acceptance of theories involving random distributions conflicts with our determination to exclude from science everything associated with personality. Nevertheless it seems also undeniable that we accept randomness as fundamental and feel no need for further inquiry or explanation, because it is so closely associated in our experience with that arbitrary action of voluntary agents concerning which we regard inquiry as impossible and explanation as unnecessary.

And here a matter should be noted in which Poincaré's statement of the theory of chance seems defective. Poincaré seems to think that, because chance events are such as arise from the actions of causes in which small differences produce great differences in effects, it follows immediately that chance effects must be random. A chain of regular mechanism, he argues, which produces great differences of effects from small differences in causes, must necessarily be extremely complicated; and therefore it must produce random distributions. This last conclusion appears unjustified. To return to the example of the watershed; if the distribution of the rain drops were regular, their ultimate destination would also be regular; but still a very slight change in that distribution would produce a very great difference in the ultimate destination. The randomness of the ultimate destination is due to the randomness of minute differences in the cause, not to randomness of the action of the mechanism which produces from these small and inappreciable differences a great and appreciable difference.

On the other hand, in other examples, the randomness does seem to lie in the action of that mechanism. The roulette board is a case in point. Even if we eliminated the human element and introduced an automatic mechanism which, after each throw, picked up the ball, spun the wheel, and threw the ball on it, we should still expect to find the results random. We might explain this randomness by pointing out that there are many factors which influence the final resting-place of the ball; that the interaction of these many factors, even if it were perfectly regular, would produce an immensely complicated order of sequence of the results; and that it is this immensely complicated order that we mistake for a random distribution. We *might* so explain the results; but, even in this case, I do not think that we *do* so explain it; we regard the random distribution of the results, not as an ordered distribution too complex to grasp, but as really random and produced by a random, not regular, action and interaction of the factors which make up the complicated mechanism. Even when we have a complicated mechanism which might enable us to explain randomness we do not explain it, but merely introduce it into the working of the mechanism.

This is the conclusion I want to enforce through this tangled and difficult discussion. It is impossible to expound our ideas on the matter clearly because those ideas are necessarily obscure. I urge that we must accept the conception of a random distribution as fundamental to all the study of chance and probability; we are prepared to accept the statement that some distribution is random as an ultimate statement and as one that requires no explanation. All chance events are to be explained in terms of random distributions and when we have so explained them there is nothing more to be said. Our real reason for accepting random distributions as ultimate and inexplicable is that they are such as result from arbitrary volition; it is this association of ideas which gives its meaning to the analogy involved in the explanation. But this fundamental meaning is satisfactory only so long as we carefully conceal it from ourselves and do not recognise it explicitly. For, first, the random distributions with which we meet in scientific observations (such as the distribution of rain drops and many other meteorological phenomena) are not caused, in the experimental sense, by the arbitrary volition of any personal agent. Second, the mere idea that we are using conceptions so foreign to science, if we are conscious of it, is distasteful. The first difficulty is met by referring the random distributions actually observed to hypothetical random distributions, the members of which, though differing inappreciably, cause (in the theoretical sense) appreciable differences. The second is met by remembering that random distributions, though usually produced by arbitrary volition, might be produced by a regular but complicated mechanism producing an order which is subjectively random because it is too complex to be grasped as a whole.

Consequences of the theory. Such is the best account that I can give of the ideas which seem to underlie all treatment of chance phenomena. We must now consider how they account for the difficulties which we have encountered.

First, we may inquire what are the characteristics of a random distribution expressed in terms of the technical conception of probability. The answer is obvious. The typically random distribution is that of equally probable independent events. The distribution of equally probable independent events (such as the results of tossing a penny) is a random distribution precisely because it has no reason and no order; in the course of its development we may think that we have discovered order, but further progress always destroys the idea. At some stage in the trials we see that an event A has happened much more often than B; we think that we have discovered order; we make more trials and B happens more often than A until the happenings are equal and B begins to outstrip A. We see, at some stage, that A has happened more often after B than after C; we think again that we have discovered regularity and dependence; we go on again and our imagined dependence vanishes. It is only if the events are distributed in the way which we have decided is characteristic of independent equally probable events that we are unable to discover any order; any other arrangement would show some signs of order[1].

Here is the foundation of the orthodox definition of probability which has been discussed. It is based on the idea that all events due to chance are composed ultimately of equally probable independent events. If in that statement it is implied that the ultimate equally probable events are events actually observed and experimentally distinguishable, the statement is untrue. But if it means only that, in the theory which explains the observed distribution, the conception of chance is introduced by means of such events, then it is certainly true; it merely states that such theories always involve a random distribution. It is because theories of this nature are always available that the orthodox definition is always applicable; but if we attempt to interpret its results directly in terms of experiment we necessarily arrive at contradictions.

Second, we can resolve our difficulties about coincidences and explain why we assert, in our special sense, that coincidences do not occur, while we admit the occurrence of events no less improbable (in the technical sense) than such coincidences. An examination of any actual instance will show that a coincidence among the events involves a coincidence in the fundamental trials which are, according to the theory, to be distributed at random and in

---

[1] This statement may not be true. On p. 174 it was noted that it might have been possible to define equal probability by the statement that $p_1 - p_2$ tends to 0 instead of that p_1/p_2 tends to 1. So far as I can see, if events did occur in that way and were independent (independence being defined as before), they would appear perfectly random. If this view is correct, we must say that of all the ways in which events actually occur, it is only that characteristic of equal probability as defined which gives a random distribution. But I cannot help thinking that a better logician might prove the view to be mistaken.

the manner characteristic of arbitrary action. Now a coincidence in the trials, if they are of such a nature, is impossible, for the very reason that it would be impossible for a person, asked to select 10 numbers at random, to choose 1, 2, 3, 4, 5, 6, 7, 8, 9, 10; if he began to make such a choice, he would immediately realise that he was not choosing arbitrarily, that he was allowing one choice to be influenced by its predecessor and, generally, that a reason could be given for his choice; he would break off the series and choose another. If the fundamental trials are to be random, like the choice of a person acting voluntarily, coincidences of this nature are excluded; and it will always appear that the coincidences which we wish to exclude are of this nature. I do not say that we really believe that such coincidences are excluded because the trials do actually represent the choice of some person; all that I say is that we can reconcile ourselves to the exclusion of such coincidences without feeling that we are abandoning anything implied by our theory of probability; indeed we should feel that we should be abandoning something essential to the theory if we did not exclude them.

But what effect has this explanation of the nature of coincidences on our view of the association of probability and degree of knowledge? We have found a reason for asserting that certain extreme coincidences do not occur, but the reason also forces us to admit that other equally improbable events will and must occur. Is not this admission fatal to any general association of probability and degree of knowledge? Personally I think it is; it seems to me that it makes it very doubtful if there is any justification for basing any degree of knowledge of an event on its probability, unless it is such as to be, in the technical sense, a coincidence. I believe that, apart from the assertion that coincidences do not occur, we have no reason whatever to pretend to any knowledge at all about events regulated by chance. However I hardly hope to convince others on this point. The feeling that the less probable event (in the technical sense) is less likely to occur (in the psychological sense) is so deeply rooted that I can hardly hope to destroy it. But I can find no justification for it, except in the very difficult arguments of p. 196.

In the same way we can clear up the difficulty about independence. We noticed that it is impossible to prove that any events are independent. But we do not require to show that the equally probable events are independent; we only require to be unable to discover that they are not independent. As long as any relation, inconsistent with independence, which we may think that we have discovered between the occurrences of the events, turns out on further investigation not to exist, the events will appear random and such as might be produced by a person who recognised no relation between the events. The number of relations which will suggest themselves to us is finite and they are all comparatively simple; so long as we can exclude these, the proof that we have not excluded some which have never suggested themselves to us is not required. For a relation so complex that it does not occur to us when we are investigating the series would not occur to the supposed agent acting arbitrarily who produced the random distribution, or at any rate would be too complex for him to follow in making the distribution. If we show that he has adopted none of the possible orders which are intelligible, we are confident that he has adopted no order at all.

Applications of the theory. Laws. It is such considerations as these, I think, that enable us to escape from the paradoxes of probability. We do not actually resolve the paradoxes and show definitely that the supposed inconsistencies do not occur; we only show that the supposition that they do not occur is quite consistent and in harmony with the fundamental ideas on which the calculus of probability is founded. And we should not be able to show this unless these ideas were theoretical ideas involved in propositions which are not directly provable by experiment. But the theory has a yet more important application than that of ridding us of the mental discomfort which arises from the simultaneous acceptance of logically inconsistent notions. Like all other theories that are of value, it leads to the discovery of new laws.

We have decided that all chance distributions in any theory of chance are to be random distributions. How then are we to explain chance distributions that are not random? For chance is concerned whenever events are such that it cannot be predicted which of several alternatives will occur and yet each of these alternatives has a definite probability. Events which satisfy these conditions are not always equally probable. Thus, suppose that a stream of black and white balls is issuing from the end of a tube and I am examining their succession. I can find no law which will enable me to predict whether a white or a black ball will come next; on the other hand black and white balls are not equally probable, for on the whole black preponderate and the ratio of their numbers tends, as the numbers tend to infinity, not to 1 but to 2. Here is a phenomenon in which chance is clearly concerned and yet is not characterised by a perfectly random distribution; the distribution is not such as would be produced by a voluntary agent selecting balls arbitrarily, or without any reference to their colour.

Two explanations are possible and consistent with our general ideas of probability. First, the chance events which are not equally probable may be composed, in the sense of multiplication or addition, of more elementary events; they may consist either in the joint happening of several of such elementary events or in the happening of either one or another of them. It is difficult to apply such an explanation to the distribution of the black and white balls, for there is no easy method of analysing the issuing of a black ball into one collection of elementary events and the issuing of a white ball into another collection of the same events. Nevertheless we shall see presently that analysis of this nature is effected in some instances. Second, the chance events may not be wholly due to chance; they may be due to the superposition of some constant and regular law upon the results of a random distribution. And such would doubtless be the explanation that would be adopted here. We should probably suppose that the balls were being selected at random from a collection of balls, as they might be by an agent drawing them blindfold from a bag. The regularity of the result, the deviation of the numbers of black and white balls form a purely random distribution, is due to a regularity in the collection from which the balls are drawn at random; there are twice as many black balls as white balls in it.

This resolution of a distribution of unequally probable events into a random distribution of probable events and a law is familiar, but none the less extremely important. For it leads to the discovery of laws. If we did not believe that, if chance is involved at all, it must be involved in the form of a random distribution, we should have no reason for undertaking any analysis at all, and therefore no reason for believing that any regular law was involved in the matter. The procedure is so important that it will be well to take another example less remote from the actual problems of science.

I take several sheets of paper; some I place out in a shower of rain; others I place behind a target marked with a bull's-eye while a marksman shoots at it. I examine the points thus marked on the sheets; and in both cases I cannot discover from the examination of some of the sheets any law which will enable me to predict where the points are on the others of the same series. The positions of the points are due to chance, whether they are marked by the rain or by the bullets. But there is a difference between the two series which is obvious to mere inspection; the rain marks are distributed at random over the sheets, the bullet marks are not random, but form what I shall immediately recognise as a pattern. I then try to analyse the marks so that I may describe the difference more accurately, and for this purpose introduce the generalised conception of "events" following "trials". I discover that if I divide up the sheets into regions of equal area in any manner and regard the placing of a point in one of these regions as a "trial", then, when the rain marks are examined, all the "events" are equally probable; on the other hand, when the bullet marks are examined, the events are not equally probable. It is more probable that a mark will fall into a region in one part of the paper than into a region of equal area in another. If I want the bullet marks to represent events of equal probability, I must mark out the regions which characterise the trials so that their areas are greater in some parts of the paper than in others.

Now why do I begin the analysis by a division of the paper into equal areas? and why do I judge that the distribution is not random because, though I can divide it into independent events of equal probability, these equal probabilities do not correspond to equal areas? Only one answer is, I think, possible. It is that if I place marks on a sheet of paper with the feeling that I am acting completely arbitrarily I find, as a matter of fact, that it is equally probable that I shall place a mark in any region of equal area. If in any actual distribution I find that equal areas correspond to equal prob-abilities, then the distribution will be random and similar to that produced by arbitrary action; according to the theory, it is then and only then that the distribution is to be attributed merely to chance and no further inquiry made concerning its origin. For this reason, when we have dis-covered that among the rain marks equal probabilities correspond to equal areas, we feel that we have analysed the distribution completely; we have shown that it is due to pure chance and that there is nothing more to say about the matter.

On the other hand, the theory, if it is correct, indicates that it must be possible to analyse the circumstances of the trials which give rise to the bullet marks, distributed by chance but not at random, in some manner which will show that the distribution, in so far as it is determined by chance, is purely random. This analysis is effected by supposing that the trial consists of two stages (not necessarily separated in time); in the first stage in all the trials, the mark is aimed at the same spot on the paper; in the second stage it is deflected at random from this spot. But on examination I find that, however the spot from which deflections are measured is chosen, the deflections are not random; deflections within a range of given extent are more probable the less are the deflections. Such a distribution of deflections is not random because it is not the distribution I should make if I were acting arbitrarily. To remove this difficulty recourse is made to the first possible explanation of chance events that are not equally probable. The unequally probable events are conceived to be compounded in different manners of elementary equally probable events. It is supposed that any observed deflection is made up of many elementary deflections, all of them of the same magnitude, but distributed at random as regards direction, so that the probability of an elementary deflection occurring in one direction is equally probable with that in any other direction. It can then be shown that if the actual deflections are so composed of such elementary deflections the distribution of them would be that which is actually observed.

This explanation is clearly theoretical; the equal elementary deflections are hypothetical ideas, and the theory is such that they are purely hypothetical and cannot be directly connected through the dictionary with the concepts of any law. Nevertheless, the theory does predict a law, namely that the point from which the deflections are supposed to be measured is specially distinguished in the aiming of the marksman. And I can show experimentally that the law is true. If I make a similar sheet under such conditions that I know how it is produced, I shall find that the trials do all involve a constant element, namely the aiming of the bullets at a mark; and that this mark is the point on the paper from which I had to measure deflections in order to reduce them by the method adopted to random events[1]. The theory has predicted a true law; and its value is therefore greatly increased.

But it is well to insist that the theory is involved essentially in this discovery of a law. It might be thought that, from the moment when it was apparent to the eye that the distribution of the bullet marks is not random, it must be obvious that there is some law involving a special relation between the trials and one particular point on the paper. Certainly there must be a

---

[1] Probably the mark will not coincide with the point; but I shall find laws relating the divergence to the state of the wind, to the position of the sight and so on. The relation between the mark and the point is fixed by laws—that is the important conclusion.

relation, but, apart from the theory, there is no reason why the relation should be a law, or, more particularly, why it should be a law of such a form that the remaining factor determining the trials can be regarded as a random distribution. It is distinctly conceivable that we might have to recognise determinations of trials which were neither regular laws nor random distributions, but something intermediate between them. But as long as the theory is true there is no necessity for such recognition. The theory asserts that anything in which the trials differ must be reducible to a random distribution; anything in which they agree must be a strict law, rigidly applicable to all trials alike.

The matter is of great importance, since the discovery of laws in this manner provides a large part of the material of science. And here we come back to the considerations which suggested our whole investigation of probability. It has been held that laws are discovered and confirmed by large numbers of repetitions of the same experiment. I have dissented strongly from this view if it is to be applied to most laws, especially to most laws of the highly developed and characteristically experimental science of physics. In such sciences repetition provides new knowledge only in so far as it is definitely known that in the successive repetitions the conditions of the experiment are not the same and it is known what the differences are; repetition is only useful to exclude possible alternatives already suggested. But these repetitions designed to exclude alternatives are only possible when the experimental conditions can be controlled; they are not possible in a science that is necessarily observational, like meteorology. Here we cannot control our experiments at all. Our first assumption in coordinating the observed results is that all the conditions of the observations or "trials" are the same as far as observation can tell; the resulting differences are due to chance. But often it appears that they are not due to pure chance because they are not distributed at random; the theory of chance then suggests that there may be a law concerned in the matter and states that, if there is a law it must be such as to leave the remainder of the differences in a truly random distribution which alone can be produced by pure chance.

This, I believe, is the process involved in the deriving of laws by the statistical examination of large numbers of observations. It is certainly a very important part of some sciences, but it seems often to have been thought that it is in some way essential to the whole process of induction. That view is false. So far as induction is a process at all, it is complete after a very limited number of experiments. The finding of laws from a large number of experiments has nothing whatever to do with what is usually regarded as induction; it is a process depending essentially upon deduction from a definite theory, which states and depends wholly on ideas and propositions inaccessible to experiment. These ideas may be ineradicable from our minds and the propositions may be indubitable; they are doubtless based upon analogy with experiments and derive from those experiments their meaning; but no experiments can give them certain truth or validity.

I fear that this chapter will be found unpalatable to most readers. Much of it is so trite that it differs little from the exposition of quite elementary text-books. The remainder is so vague and elusive as to be almost unintelligible. But I do not think the fault lies wholly with the exposition; ideas about probability are chaotic. Everyone knows the witty saying of Poincaré that nobody understands probability because mathematicians think its foundations are experimental, and experimenters think its foundations are mathematical. It is quite true. No treatise that I know gives any reason for believing that probability has any application whatever to experimental science; and accordingly when it is so applied the process of its application is seldom understood. When people have been using ideas for a long time without ever stopping to sort them out, they are sure to be in a tangle; and since all that I am trying to do is to express what the ideas of men of science are, extreme lucidity can hardly be expected.

But though it has been very difficult to state exactly what the Theory of Chance is, I hope I have convinced the reader that there is a theory; until that fact is realised the removal of confusion of thought is impossible. Let us cease to talk about the Laws of Chance; there is only one law; the law that there are no laws. Let us talk about the Theory of Chance; then we may realise how we overcome the fundamental difficulty of the subject that we appear to produce knowledge from the very fact of ignorance.

CHAPTER VIII

THE MEANING OF SCIENCE

Summary. Two criteria for the value of scientific propositions have been recognised, universal assent and intellectual satisfaction. A summary of the conclusions reached already is undertaken in order to show exactly how and where the two criteria are applied.

The value which a scientific proposition derives from the first criterion is called its truth, that which it derives from the second its meaning. Meaning is more important in theories than in laws, but it is insisted that laws have also meaning as well as truth.

The reasons why there has been a danger that the meaning of science will be overlooked are mainly historical. The chief changes that have taken place in the attitude towards scientific knowledge are briefly sketched, and special attention paid to the very important views of Mach. Much of those views is accepted, but it is maintained that the object of science is not "economy of thought".

The neglect of the meaning of science has led to the stifling of the scientific imagination in education and wherever else science is brought to the notice of the laity. It is maintained that science should be regarded as an art.

Two criteria in science. Throughout our discussion when we have had to determine why a scientific proposition has value and what degree of value it has we have referred to one of two principles. First, a proposition is valuable if truly universal assent can be obtained for it; second it is valuable if its contemplation causes intellectual satisfaction to students of science. These two principles are to some extent contrary and, if the test provided by each of them is applied to the same proposition, one might sometimes determine that the proposition is valuable and the other that it is not. For a student of science is a student of science in virtue of some difference between his intellectual constitution and that of the rest of mankind; if he finds intellectual satisfaction in a proposition it is almost certain that persons with different training and different interests can be found to whom it will give none; and on the other hand the mere fact that a proposition is approved by everyone, however different their modes of thought, will deprive it for him, not of course of all its value, but of that very special value which is the basis of the second principle. It is necessary therefore to examine the two principles rather more nearly and to determine exactly what part each of them plays in the establishment of scientific propositions.

The general nature of the solution of the apparent inconsistency is sufficiently obvious. Every scientific proposition must satisfy in some manner the first principle. Unless in some manner and to some extent universal agreement can be obtained concerning it, then it is scientifically valueless;

and again if there is anything about it which directly conflicts with any proposition for which universal assent can be obtained, then it is not worthy of a moment's consideration. But many propositions can sometimes be found, all of which satisfy equally the principle of universal assent in some measure and, indeed, in the same measure, and which are yet mutually inconsistent. Among such sets of propositions some, but not all, satisfy the second principle. These propositions which satisfy the second principle are then preferred to those which do not. But if it should ever appear that one of these propositions, satisfying the second principle, does not really satisfy the first, then without any hesitation it is to be rejected.

Let us then recapitulate our previous discussion in order to see exactly at what stages in the development of scientific propositions the two principles are applied. We start with the selection of material for study, and in this task we rely wholly on the principle of universal agreement. There is a certain class of judgements concerning which universal agreement can be obtained as it can be obtained about no other class. These judgements are those about the association of sensations; not about the occurrence of sensations, for I cannot be certain that anyone else has the same sensations as I have (whatever that may mean), but about their uniform association which determines action. These judgements if they were expressible explicitly at all would be expressed as laws, but since the ideas involved in them are more fundamental than any language they are not so expressible. These ideas, which are related to the laws as concepts are to the more complex laws, are so involved in the very structure of our thought that the bare conception of their invalidity is impossible to most people. There can be here no application of the second principle because no alternative to the acceptance of these ideas could possibly be intellectually satisfactory.

The study of these fundamental concepts leads us to the formulation of more complex laws into which the fundamental concepts enter as terms between which the relation of uniformity is asserted. In the formulation of these laws we are not under the compelling necessity which excluded before the consideration of any alternative. In the first place we have more liberty of choice of the judgements that we shall consider. Most of us could not live our daily life or think at all unless we accepted all the concepts which form the basis of our conception of a material and external world; but when we turn our attention to the relations between constituent parts of the material world, though our comfort may be greatly advanced by studying some of those relations rather than others, there is nothing that makes it impossible for us to neglect intellectually any portions that we please. And as a matter of fact we do pick and choose. We deliberately exclude from the subject matter of science, out of which its propositions are developed (although not necessarily from the matter which can be "explained" by those propositions once they are established), all those judgements of the material world which are individual and personal and concerning which universal agreement is not obtainable; we include only definite "experiments" which can be repeated and can be shown to other observers. Here again we apply the first principle in determining the value of a proposition for scientific purposes, but, as was suggested on p. 36, it is not certain that we do not also apply the second. It is not certain that, even if there were no other observers available whom we could use to apply the first principle, we should not be able to select the matter which is actually selected by means of the second; for the laws which we can base on this matter are "simpler" and intellectually more satisfactory than those which could be based on matter that included judgements rejected by the test of universal agreement. This is possibly the first application of the second principle, but there is no need to decide whether it is actually employed, for actually other observers are available and actually there does not appear to be any conflict between the results of the two principles.

But in the establishment of laws we employ the second principle in a much more definite and more important way. We use it to determine, not what judgements we shall try to arrange in laws, but in what laws we shall arrange them. It is characteristic of a law that it asserts something more general than the evidence on which it is based; for that is what we mean when we say that a law predicts and that is what gives rise to the central problem of induction. We observe that, in certain circumstances, a certain potential difference at the ends of a wire is associated with a certain current through it; we assert that the same potential difference will be associated with the same current in other circumstances, differing from those in which it has been observed by the position of the earth with reference to the stars, for instance. We observe that the magnitudes of the potential difference and the magnitudes of the current which are thus associated are related by mathematical relations of which simple proportionality is one; we assert that the magnitudes of the potential differences and the currents which we have not observed will be related by the relation of proportionality, and not by one of the indefinite class of other mathematical relations which would equally well represent the relations of those which we have observed. It has been maintained, and indeed it is generally recognised, that in choosing, among the indefinite number of alternative propositions which would represent equally well the observations concerning which universal agreement can be obtained, that proposition which will be asserted and which will be expected to cover the observations which have not yet been made, our choice is determined by an application of the second principle. The simplest law is chosen; and simplicity here, however it is analysed, always reduces to some form of intellectual satisfactoriness. Moreover the satisfactoriness is not one which is necessarily apparent to all mankind or for which it is certain that universal agreement could be obtained. If it were, no reason could be given why all men should not be equal in discovering laws, given equal training in the previous results of science. It is true that judgements in this matter do not usually differ greatly; it would usually happen that all men to whom the observed facts were presented would concur in selecting a law to represent them; but they clearly might differ, and if they did it would be found that the judgement of some persons was more satisfactory than that of others. For it must be always remembered that, though there is no certain method of telling *a priori* which of the possible laws is the more satisfactory, there is a certain method of telling *a posteriori*; when new observations are made, universal assent will be obtainable for the assertion that they accord with some of the alternative laws and do not accord with others. A law is satisfactory if it thus accords with universal agreement concerning judgements made after it is enunciated, or, in other words, if it predicts truly. While therefore laws are enunciated in the first instance by the second principle of value, they are always liable to revision by the first; it is only because and so long as the indications of the first are ambiguous that the second may be admitted at all.

From laws we proceed to theories; we attempt to find propositions from which laws may be deduced. And here again we are met with ambiguity. Even if it were true—and, as we have just seen, it is not wholly true—that laws were determined entirely by the principle of universal agreement, there would still be an indefinite number of propositions from all of which the same laws might be deduced. Universal agreement will not enable us to decide between them; we must have recourse to the second principle. A theory must not only "explain" the law in the sense that the law can be deduced from it; it must also give intellectual satisfaction. And now it is much more obvious that this intellectual satisfaction is not a matter of universal agreement, for many cases occur immediately to memory in which there has been an obvious and notorious failure to agree; and again it is more obvious that certain persons are much more likely than others to produce a satisfactory theory by an application of the second principle, and that difference in the power to do so is something which does not depend merely upon training and knowledge. A satisfactory theory is one which predicts new laws which are true, just as a satisfactory law is one which predicts observations which occur; theories, like laws, can be distinguished *a posteriori*, though not *a priori*, by the first principle of value. Just as in the establishment of laws, so in the establishment of theories, the second principle is admissible only because and in so far as the indications of the first are ambiguous.

Truth and meaning. It is important to observe that both the principle of universal agreement and that of the intellectual satisfaction of a minority are used in the establishment of laws as well as of theories and in the determination of the value of scientific propositions of all kinds. In virtue of this use of both principles, such propositions always have values of two distinct kinds which will be called (the implications of the terms must be considered further) their truth and their meaning. The truth of a scientific proposition, in this sense, is its value determined by the first principle, its meaning that determined by the second; a proposition is true in so far as it states something for which the universal assent of all mankind can be obtained; it has meaning in so far as it gives rise to ideas which cause intellectual satisfaction. Truth is here used to mean a quality which has the same significance for others as

for ourselves; it is something of which we can convince others and of which
we shall not be sure unless we do convince others. Meaning on the other
hand is something individual and personal; it is something which depends
on the qualities of my mind and is present in my mind whether or no it is
present in the minds of others; a proposition may have meaning for me even
if it has meaning for nobody else; and it is not certain ever that its meaning
for me is the same as its meaning for anyone else.

But though all scientific propositions are valuable only if they have both
truth and meaning, the relative importance of the two features may seem to
vary widely. The value of a law lies chiefly in its truth, that of a theory
chiefly in its meaning. It is unnecessary to insist that a theory must have truth
as well as meaning, but it may be well once more to insist that a law must
have meaning as well as truth. There is something about a law which gives
it value and yet is not determined wholly by universal agreement. This
something consists partly in its form and is of the nature of "simplicity",
but it consists also in what the law asserts. A law asserts that certain observations will be made, not only in this instance and in that, but in *all* instances;
it asserts that there is something necessary about the sequence which it predicts; and though men actually agree about the necessity asserted by actual
laws, it is plainly possible that they should differ, and that, even if they did
differ, laws would not necessarily lose their value.

The meaning of a law (as distinct from its truth) is less obvious than that
of a theory because the application of the second principle is less obvious in
the establishment of laws. We are conscious of much less scope in the choice
of what law shall be used to describe given observations than in the choice
what theory shall be used to explain given laws. Moreover men differ far less
in their power of discovering laws than in their power of discovering theories;
a great deal of valuable scientific work is done and many important laws
discovered by persons who bring to their task little more than the facility
in handling apparatus acquired by suitable training. But the absence of
choice in recording his results which is usually felt by the experimenter is
very often due to the fact that the choice has already been made by considerations derived from some theory; a theory indicates that there must be some
constant relation between two measurable magnitudes and only leaves to the
decision of experiment precisely what is that relation; it may even indicate
what the relation is and leave only the decision whether a theory which gives
such an indication is true. Even when a merely empirical law is sought and
no guidance is derived from theory, experiments usually consist in the search
for a permanent uniform relation between two or more of a quite limited
class of concepts, the use of which necessarily decides many of the questions
which might arise concerning which of the attendant conditions will influence
the observations; we no longer think it necessary to inquire whether our
experiments will be influenced by the position of the satellites of Jupiter or
the progress of the latest revolution in Central America; the concepts we
employ in stating our results preclude such influence. But it must be remem-

bered that the simplicity of this sort which we now habitually assume is precarious and that events might always occur to make us investigate much more deeply and thoroughly the extent to which laws can be made to fall in with our usual conceptions of simplicity. Again in so far as the simplicity which is selected is that of a mathematical relation the choice is again determined by something that is not strictly characteristic of the law. Functions are simple according as they are amenable to mathematical analysis; there does not seem to be anything intrinsically simple about a sine or a logarithm which would be apparent to anyone unfamiliar with analytical operations. The judgement of scientific simplicity which is made is that physical laws can usually be represented by mathematically tractable functions; and this judgement, like those just mentioned, is so habitual and familiar that we have lost the consciousness of making it. The distinction between mathematically tractable and intractable functions is not made on the basis of either of the two principles of scientific value. It is doubtless something concerning which universal agreement can actually be obtained, but it is a judgement of the internal and not of the external world; and though there is concerned in it a judgement of simplicity, it is of mathematical and not of physical simplicity; between these there appears to be a difference, for the instincts of the pure mathematician and of the physicist are by no means always associated.

On this account the application of the second principle to the determination of laws is apt to be overlooked; but it is essential, and without it the problem of induction would be insoluble. Moreover the circumstances which enable us to dispense with conscious judgements of intellectual satisfaction in the establishment of laws also sometimes make them unnecessary in the formulation of theories. Here again, habit based on long experience often suggests that a theory must be of a given form and gives little scope for selection within the limits of that form; it enables those who are endowed with but little of the true scientific insight to frame theories which are found to be satisfactory[1]. But here again habit is a dangerous guide, as is shown, in the opinion of many, by the history of dynamical theories of atomic and molecular constitution. The difference in this matter between laws and theories is one of degree rather than of kind.

Some historical considerations. Perhaps in all this discussion I have been insisting on the obvious. Everybody recognises to-day that what I have called truth is an essential element of a scientific proposition and few, if any, will deny explicitly that what I have called meaning is also important. But it does not seem to me that facts which are universally admitted openly, or their implications, are always remembered when the most general and fundamental questions concerning science are raised. In such discussions attention is apt to be concentrated on the truth and the meaning is apt to be left out of sight.

The tendency is natural. The great advance or, more accurately, the first beginnings of scientific knowledge which took place in the 16th and 17th

---

[1] Lest I should cause offence by an appearance of superiority I would add that I include myself in this category.

centuries was a consequence of the recognition of the possibility of scientific truth. To say that science must be based on experiment and observation is simply to say that it must satisfy the first principle of value, for it is only concerning the results of such experiment and observation that universal agreement of the kind which is characteristic of science can be obtained. It is the neglect of truth, the failure to test evidence according to the canons of modern science, the acceptance of well-attested fact, vague rumour, and the product of riotous imagination as equally valuable—it is the attitude of mind to which such things were possible which raises an insurmountable barrier between ourselves and the most enlightened of the ancients. That science should have meaning, they would have agreed readily; it was the doctrine that it should have truth which was strange to them. The ghost of Greek learning still stalks ruins not yet abandoned; it still disturbs timid minds and has still to be exorcised; the weapon of Galileo cannot be allowed to rust in its sheath, and while it has still to be used other dangers may be neglected.

However there is a more cogent reason why truth rather than meaning receives emphasis whenever any question is raised of the value of science or of its relation to other studies. Truth, it has been said, is a quality of which we may hope to convince others; it is a valuable quality because it is appreciated by everyone. And there is actually no doubt that scientific propositions have the kind of truth that is here attributed to them and that this truth has some value. Nobody disputes that truth, if they once agree to use that word in our sense; what they may dispute is whether or no it is misleading to call this quality truth and what is its value in comparison with that of other qualities. When therefore there has been any discussion of the value of science as a whole, its supporters have tended naturally, but, as I think, mistakenly, to insist on that element of science which everyone agrees is valuable and to attempt almost to conceal other elements concerning the value of which a difference of opinion is possible. They have tried to maintain that science is nothing but truth and indeed that it differs from other systems of thought in consisting of nothing but truth. Such were the motives which led, for instance, to Huxley's famous definition of science as "organised common sense", a phrase admirably suited for polemics and the obscuring of clear thinking. The word "organised" begs the question completely. It is not disputed that science, like all other forms of knowledge[1], has its basis in common sense, the agreed judgements of mankind, among which are those (relating to the external world) which have the truth characteristic of science. But the problem is how and by whom this common sense is to be organised, and whether the organisation adopted by science introduces anything which does not share the truth of the things organised.

[1] Perhaps this statement is not quite true. The system of thought against which Huxley was specially concerned to defend science was theology, and some theological systems rest, not on common sense, but on immediate and fundamental judgements or revelations which are definitely stated to be confined to the elect. Such systems have not the truth characteristic of science. The value of their propositions is determined wholly by principles analogous to the second and not at all by those analogous to the first.

The confusion introduced by this method of meeting attacks was all the more serious because those attacks were mainly directed against theories. The doctrines in dispute, those for example concerning the structure of the solar system or the origin of species, were theories and not laws. Though it is necessary to recognise that laws have meaning as well as truth if we are to understand how they are formulated, it is not so necessary to insist on that meaning if we merely wish to show that they are valuable; to the unscientific mass of mankind a law is almost as useful if it is applicable to each of any assigned collection of instances as if it has the necessity which is implied by its application to all instances. But the main value of theories consists in their meaning; to conceal their meaning is to render them worthless and unintelligible. The attempt to show that science was all truth led directly to an attempt to show that all valuable scientific propositions were laws. The controversialists succeeded well in bamboozling their opponents; they made them talk glibly about the "law" of gravitation and even the "law" of evolution; they succeeded in convincing a pious gentleman that there was "natural law in the spiritual world", the laws which he discovered being almost exclusively theories. But unfortunately, as so often happens, they succeeded equally well in bamboozling themselves, their supporters and their colleagues; for a generation "theory" was almost abolished from the scientific vocabulary or, when used, had always a connotation of distrust.

The writings of Mach, and perhaps even more of Poincaré, led to a saner view. Mach, in his doctrine that science sought the "simplest" interpretation of observations, recognised the meaning of scientific propositions and the application of the second principle; Poincaré, though often using the same word, allows to simplicity a much more generous scope. But even Mach, I venture to think, failed to reach the core of the matter. He justified the adoption of the "simplest" view on the ground that it is the object of science to attain "economy of thought". That doctrine, if the words are to be interpreted in any natural sense, is to me utterly intolerable. The best way to attain economy of thought, a way only too successfully followed by the vast majority of mankind, is not to think at all. Science is a branch of pure learning; thought is its object. To engage in science in order not to think would be as sensible as to engage in commerce in order not to make money. Even Mach himself in one passage suggests that his remarks may be valuable if they suggest ideas which have not previously occurred to the reader.

But of course it will be said that I misjudge Mach, and that he did not mean that the object of science was to render all thought unnecessary, but only special kinds of tiresome thought that have no intrinsic value. However, though that idea may have been in his mind, I think that its explicit recognition and statement deprives his theory of science of all foundation. He may have meant merely what Professor Whitehead said lately in a phrase that has already become classical, that operations of thought are like cavalry charges, to be reserved for critical occasions. That view, I can readily believe, is perfectly applicable to the pure mathematics of which Professor Whitehead was speaking;

the formalities of mathematics, its elaborate symbolism and all the rest of it, do enable thought to be reserved and attention concentrated for vital efforts. But I do not think that it is applicable to physics; there seems to be here an example of the dangers which arise when men whose interests are primarily mathematical expound the principles of physical and experimental science. For what is there in science which corresponds at all accurately to the formal rules of addition or differentiation which enable complicated operations to be performed mechanically? I can think of nothing. The only forms of scientific thought which seem to me disagreeable, and to be avoided whenever possible, are the efforts of memory required to retain numerical constants; and these forms we avoid, not by the establishment of any scientifically valuable propositions, but simply by the mechanical device of printed tables. There is no economy or avoidance of physical thought (though there may be of mathematical thought) in stating the relation between current and resistance by the function of proportionality rather than by a more complex function; there is simply substitution of a more agreeable for a less agreeable form of thought. It is only in the applications of science that true economy is achieved by science. In practical life we may be forced to consider certain observations or possible observations, and the ordering of these observations may save time and trouble in the consideration. But in pure science we are not forced to consider any observations at all if we do not care to do so, and we can economise thought in a manner far more successful than any provided by science by simply not thinking at all.

Again, even if we admit that the process which consists of the preference of a simpler for a more complicated relation in the statement of laws is an economy of thought, what are we to say of theories? A theory is almost a pure addition to thought. Can anyone pretend that we are saved any thought about Boyle's and Gay-Lussac's laws by a knowledge that they can be explained by the dynamical theory of gases? Surely not; for those persons who are truly concerned to save thought, because they are interested only in the applications, are inclined to be utterly contemptuous of theories. If explanation were of the first kind of Chapter V and consisted in the substitution of the more general for the less general idea, then theories might achieve the same kind of "economy" as laws. But it is not this kind of explanation that is characteristic of theories; it is the second kind which substitutes the more for the less familiar, often or usually at the expense of greater complication. Only those who, like Mach, rate the value of theories very lowly and desire that they should be excluded as far as possible from science (or at least should be confined to mathematical theories which may economise in the same manner as laws), only such persons could entertain for a moment the idea that it is the object of science to economise thought.

Moreover the phrase "economy of thought" by suggesting one very definite and precise reason for selecting one of the many possible alternative laws rather than another tends to conceal the fact that there is another and much more important reason. We cannot select any law that may happen best to economise thought; we have (if we are to be successful) to select one and one only; it may and indeed does happen that this law is also one which economises thought, but those which do not economise thought are not all equally objectionable. Suppose, for example, that we have observed the relation between the current and the potential difference for a long series of integral values of the former. Then we can describe our results (1) by the function of proportionality, (2) by some function much more complicated than proportionality, but differing from it so little over the range of any observations we are likely to make, that even for fractional values of the current its values are experimentally indistinguishable from those of proportionality, (3) by a function agreeing with proportionality at integral values but differing from it very widely at fractional values. Now on the ground of economy of thought there may well be no reason for preferring a function (2) to a function (3); either may be equally complicated and much less simple than (1). But, even if there were no economy of thought, (2) would always be preferable to (3), because it will remain satisfactory when fractional values are investigated. Even if it is true that we actually select laws by the principle of economy of thought (and it is admitted that we select them by some principle not very different) there still remains the very important fact that what we achieve by our selection is not mere economy, but a truth of the law which is determined by the first principle of value and not by the second.

Science and imagination. But the fundamental reason why the meaning of science has been unduly neglected lies in the unwillingness of men of science themselves to recognise it. Their training in the methods necessary to attain truth has impressed on them so firmly that, in this part of their work, everything that can possibly be a matter of personal opinion must be excluded, that they are afraid to admit that anything can properly form part of their study which involves deliberate, though often unconscious, choice. In the early days both of the individual and of the study such caution is both desirable and necessary; there is an undoubted temptation to relax the criterion which must be applied before truth can be firmly established. But when the individual and the study have come to full maturity the danger has passed away; there is now no need to insist at every turn that science must have a firm experimental basis. The time has come to face the facts boldly. The search for truth alone never has and never will lead to any science of value. The spirit which must be so carefully curbed in the search for truth must be given free rein when truth is attained. Our passionate desire that truth will be found in one form rather than in another must never be allowed to influence our decision in what form it actually appears; but once that matter is settled, we not only may but must choose in accordance with our desire in which of the innumerable alternative forms that truth must be expressed; the more freely we choose the more likely it is that a renewed search for truth will confirm our choice.

The attempt to conceal from ourselves that choice is necessary may stifle the imagination on which the choice depends; and therefore I make no apology for insisting, even at the risk of irrelevance, on the necessity of pro-claiming openly the imaginative element in science. Our view of the meaning of science must influence our methods of teaching and training ourselves and our pupils; 19th century philosophy, with its anxiety to conceal the essential part played by imagination in scientific discovery, is largely respon-sible for the ineptitude of modern scientific education. The very man who laughs to scorn the doctrine that a love of literature or an imaginative appre-ciation of its value is to be obtained by the grinding out of Latin hexameters will proceed gravely to assert that science is to be taught only by the deter-mination of the nodal points of lens systems. Of course for the student who means to take science seriously and hopes in his turn to take his share in its advancement, a thorough training in the experimental art is as essential as is a complete understanding of the intricacies of metre and construction to the classical scholar. But neither the scholar nor the man of science will have a living grasp of his study if he buries himself in these pedantries. The scientific imagination can be developed by tedious laboratory practice no more than the artistic imagination by the laborious study of Greek particles, by the day-long practice of a musical instrument or by unceasing copying in the galleries. It must come from direct and intimate contact over the widest possible range with the great original works which represent its noblest expression. It is doubtless difficult to introduce a student to the latest modern theories of solid structure, of atomic constitution, or of relative motion, before he has an entire understanding of what are commonly regarded as the elements of physics; but it is no more difficult than to teach a boy to read the Odyssey before he can parse and interpret any word; and the failure to overcome the difficulty is equally disastrous.

Doubtless "there is nothing like leather", but I cannot refrain from suggesting that it would have been better if chemistry had not come to be regarded as the standard and natural "elementary" science. For chemistry, so rich in laws (though not often explicitly named as such) and so powerful in the ordering of facts, is poor in theory. And since it is in theory that the highest meaning of science is expressed, chemists are more apt than the students of other sciences to overlook its vital importance. The absurdities of the "heuristic" school, fortunately short-lived, could hardly have taken root at all in any other soil; no physicist could imagine that there was any similarity between the "discovery" of a law by the elementary pupil under the eye of his teacher and the true discovery of that law when it was unknown. Chemistry has but one noteworthy theory and but one set of hypothetical ideas, the theory of the combination of atoms into molecules with its funda-mental idea of valency. It is a most beautiful theory, surpassed by none other in the intellectual satisfaction it affords, but unfortunately it is not easily or certainly applicable to the compounds on which the attention of the ele-mentary student is concentrated; we know far less about the constitution of water than about that of some organic compound with a name a yard long—long simply because the theory is so strictly applicable to it. If chemistry is to be the vehicle of elementary instruction in science, we should begin with stereo-isomers and proceed (if we have time) to the simple compounds of oxygen, hydrogen, and nitrogen.

Nor should we think only of the effect of our repression on those who are serious students of science. The opinion of our fellows, even if they are not our colleagues, cannot fail to react, directly or indirectly, on our own studies. If scientific education to-day is unsuited for those who are to make science their life work, it is even less suited for those to whom it is merely to be part of a general education. Men of science complain of the lack of a wide appreciation of scientific knowledge; what else can they expect if they offer to the world only the dry bones of knowledge from which the breath has departed? Nothing could be better adapted than the ordinary school course, with its tedious insistence on bare and uninspiring facts, to kill any rising enthusiasm. It is important certainly to impress the student with the nature of scientific truth and with the possibility of definite positive knowledge concerning the material world. No doubt it is the failure to realise that there is such knowledge, the mistaken notion that everything is a matter of opinion on which two sides should be heard, that produces, so ludicrous if it were not so lamentable, the familiar chaos in the administration of the affairs of state and industry by the half-educated persons who pride themselves on their ignorance of science. But to insist on the truth of science and to neglect its meaning is to aggravate the evil which we seek to cure; those who are endowed with any measure of creative imagination can never hold in anything but contempt a study from which such imagination appears to be wholly banished.

Such attempts as are made to exhibit the imaginative element in science are almost more disastrous than the attempts to conceal it. The "romance of science" is usually associated with childish books and popular lectures on speculative geology and "spherical" astronomy[1]. Now both geology and astronomy are magnificent sciences, offering superb examples of the highest meaning of science; but they also contain elements, of no importance to their earnest students, which possess a specious and flashy interest which makes a passing appeal to shallow minds. An audience of children of all ages gapes amazedly while the lecturer discourses glibly of times reckoned in millions of years and distances in thousands of millions of miles. But science has something better to offer than sensational journalism; nothing could be less characteristic of its spirit. The mere fact that the interest of the uninitiated can thus be easily stimulated with serious training suggests doubts of the value of the stimulus; nothing worth having in this world is to be had without effort.

Science and art. When we so often hide what is best in science and display only its less admirable features, it is not surprising that in the outside world there is suspicion of its ultimate intellectual value. There has been in recent years a great improvement in the general appreciation of the

---

[1] I have heard this term used wickedly to denote the form of science which, at the end of the 19th century, was closely associated with the name of Sir Robert *Ball*.

meaning of science; but open antagonism has been in part replaced by an armed neutrality which indicates no better understanding, but merely greater caution. Many will still be found to deny that science can satisfy our imaginative needs to the same extent as art and literature, and the denial does not arise only from conservatism and ignorance. Science, it is said, is impersonal; the highest good must be intimately connected with personality. It is overlooked that the impersonal truth of science is inseparable from its personal meaning. Science, it is said, is mechanical; the accusation at once displays the misunderstanding. A mechanism is certainly something which will produce desired results independent of the attention or volition of a skilled operator, but it is also something which is and must be the individual product of a human mind. A mechanism implies an inventor; it is a means by which one exceptionally endowed man makes his endowments available for the common good; it is something characteristic, not of dead matter, but of the highest spirit of man; it is something that theologians and savages do not understand. If the term is rightly understood science is truly mechanical; for science, like mechanism, is the expression of genius in a form which the dullest can appreciate.

It is curious how even to-day the laity seem unaware of the part played by the genius of great men in the development of science. They recognise perhaps that the often quoted examples of the greatest achievements of science, the discovery of Neptune or of Hertzian waves, represent something not easily attained by the common mass of mankind; they are willing to admit that Newton or Leverrier, Maxwell or Hertz, must have had some qualities to distinguish them from lesser folk. But they have no knowledge of what these qualities are; they have no idea that their work was an expression of their personality just as surely as the work of Giotto, of Shakespeare, or of Bach. They still tend to contract the cold-blooded rationalism of the man of science with the passionate dreamings of the artist. But science too has its dreamers, and their dreams come true; they dream, and messages flash across the empty ocean; they dream again, and a new world springs into being and starts upon the course that they have ordained. Nor does the quest of knowledge inspire less passion than the quest of beauty. It is not sickly sentimentality but honest emotion that makes us cry

> Car c'est chose divine
> D'aimer, lorsqu'on devine,
> Rêve, invente, imagine
>   À peine...,
> Le seul rêve intéresse;
> Vivre sans rêve, qu'est-ce?
> Et moi, j'aime la princesse
> Lointaine[1].

Nothing could be more absurd than the attempt to distinguish between science and art. Science is the noblest of the arts and men of science the

---

[1] Rostand, *La Princesse Lointaine.*

most artistic of all artists. For science, like art, seeks to attain aesthetic satisfaction through the perceptions of the senses; and science, like art, is limited
by the impositions of the material world on which it works. The lesser art
accepts those limitations; it is content to imitate or to describe Nature and to
follow where she leads. The greater refuses to be bound; it imposes itself
upon Nature and forces her to submit to its power. The apostle of Art in a
previous generation can make no higher claim for the greatest art than this:

CYRIL. But you don't mean to say that you seriously believe that Life imitates
art, that Life in fact is the mirror, and Art the reality?

VIVIAN. Certainly I do. Paradox though it may seem—and paradoxes are
always dangerous things—it is none the less true that Life imitates art, far more
than Art imitates life. We have all seen in our own day in England how a certain
curious and fascinating type of beauty, invented and emphasised by two imaginative
painters, has so influenced Life, that, whenever one goes to a private view or to
an artistic salon one sees, here the mystic eyes of Rossetti's dream......there the
sweet maidenhood of the "Golden Stair," the blossom-like mouth and weary loveli-
ness of the "Laus Amoris."......And it has always been so. A great artist invents a
type, and Life tries to copy it, to reproduce it in a popular form, like an enterprising
publisher.......Literature always anticipates life. It does not copy it, but moulds it
to its purpose. The nineteenth century, as we know it, is largely an invention of
Balzac[1].

But if to lead the way and to bid life follow is the distinctive character
of the greatest art, what art can be so great as science? A Newton, a Faraday,
or a Maxwell conceives a theory and Life adapts itself for all time to the laws
which it predicts; by the force of his imagination he creates no passing fashion,
but the permanent structure of the world. He is no puny creature closely
bound by the laws of time and sense; he is the creator who lays down those
laws; verily the winds and the waves obey him.

Of course such powers are not given to all who pursue science. There are
degrees of scientific as of artistic imagination. But the least of us can share
in some small measure these achievements. A man need not abandon all
pretensions to the proud title of artist because he could not design the
Parthenon or write the Fifth Symphony. Most of us who have attempted to
advance science have had our all too brief and passing moments of inspiration;
we have added a single brick to the mighty structure or finished some corner
which the master in his impetuosity has overlooked. And though our tiny
efforts rightly pass almost unnoticed by the rest of mankind, they have a value
for ourselves beyond what we can tell; one instant we have stood with the great
ones of the earth and shared their glory. Even if nothing as yet has stirred in
us the creator's joy, we can yet appreciate the success of others. Nobody who
has any portion of the scientific spirit can fail to remember times when he has
thrilled to a new discovery as if it were his own. He has greeted a new theory
with the passionate exclamation, It must be true! He has felt that its eternal
value is beyond all reasoning, that it is to be defended, if need be, not by the

---

[1] Wilde, *The Decay of Lying.*

cold-blooded methods of the laboratory or the soulless processes of formal logic, but, like the honour of a friend, by simple affirmation and eloquent appeal. The mood will and should pass; the impersonal inquiry must be made before the new ideas can be admitted to our complete confidence. But in that one moment we have known the real meaning of science, we have experienced its highest value; unless such knowledge and such experience were possible, science would be without meaning and therefore without truth.

CHAPTER IX

SCIENCE AND PHILOSOPHY

Summary. The fact that science has both meaning and truth shows that the material world must be in some sense in harmony with our desires. An explanation of this harmony can reasonably be demanded. It cannot be given by science, as that study has been defined hitherto; the problem is distinctively philosophical. But as it undoubtedly interests· men of science some attention is paid to it.

It is first asked what kind of explanation is required. In answer three conceivable explanations are quoted, none of which are actually true, but all of which will be admitted to be of the right kind.

Analysis of the three explanations shows that they are very similar to those offered by theories, and that the propositions on which they depend can be expressed as hypothesis and dictionary. This method of expression suggests an inquiry which was omitted in Chapter V, namely whether the logical form in which theories were expressed there conveys their true significance. It is maintained that it does and that any feeling to the contrary is due to a failure to observe the very close connection between logical deduction and the generalised causal relation. We ask why the three suggested explanations are to be rejected and find that the reasons are the same as those for which physical theories might be rejected. They do not explain other things which we feel that they ought to explain. We are thus led to a brief review of the part of experience which is excluded from science.

But if any of the three explanations were satisfactory as theories, would the explanations which they offer be ultimate or require yet further explanation? It is maintained as a personal opinion that they would be ultimate.

In the absence of any explanation which fulfils the necessary conditions, further discussion of the matter is impossible. But since metaphysicians pretend they have or may shortly have adequate explanations, it is worth while inquiring whether their explanations could give us what we require.

Any mention of metaphysics leads at once to the introduction of the words, reality, existence, and truth in very special senses. An inquiry is set on foot to discover what men of science mean by reality. It is suggested that the fundamental sense is derived from the form of the law which defines the concepts of material objects, and that the only things which they are prepared to maintain finally as real are material objects, hypothetical ideas corresponding through the analogy with material objects, and other persons. But the words "real" and "really" are also used in another sense in which they are contrasted with "apparent" and "apparently". It is the use of the words in a sense similar to this but not identical with it that led us to the conclusion in Chapter VI that hypothetical ideas were more real than concepts. This sense of real is subsidiary and not, like the other, fundamental.

A similar inquiry (necessarily very superficial) into what metaphysicians mean by reality shows that their sense resembles the subsidiary rather than the fundamental scientific sense; but no attempt is made to discover exactly what their sense is. The conclusion is sufficient that it is quite different from the scientific sense.

An inquiry, again similar, is conducted concerning the meaning of truth in science. It is maintained that truth in science, as in practical life, is always determined by belief by some person or persons. In both there are two kinds of truth, absolute truth deriving its meaning and value from universal assent, and relative truth, valid only to the individual and having no meaning for others. Truth which is at first relative may become absolute; in practical life such a change happens only in connection with propositions and beliefs which affect action; but in science it happens with all the propositions valuable to that study.

Metaphysical truth does not seem to be the same as either the absolute or relative truth of science. As before the attempt to determine what it is is carried only far enough to show that it is quite different from any concept important to science.

It is concluded therefore that metaphysics and science can never agree; not because one believes to be true what the other believes to be false, but because they concern entirely incompatible ideas; the kind of truth which is applicable to one is not applicable to the other.

The conclusion that ultimately we must agree to differ and regard some parts of our truth as merely relative (although they may be relative to all men of science and not only ourselves) may seem objectionable. Accordingly three reasons are given for believing that relative truth is necessarily more ultimate, and therefore in a sense more valuable, than absolute truth.

How is science possible? I have tried to insist, in case it should be doubted, that science has meaning as well as truth; that it is only in virtue of their meaning that scientific propositions all of which are equally true can be distinguished; and therefore that it is only the meaning of those propositions, especially their meaning for great men highly endowed with scientific imagination, which enables them to predict and to preserve their truth for the rest of mankind. But it may fairly be asked why meaning and truth are thus associated, why a theory or a law turns out to be true because it is intellectually satisfactory, why Nature thus proves herself complacent to our intellectual desires or, as Professor Lamb expressed it, why she honours our cheques? And since it is only because Nature is so complacent that we can study science, our question really is, How is science possible?

Students of science undoubtedly do ask such questions, and it is probably because no satisfactory answer to them can be furnished that they often hesitate to admit the fact which they cannot explain. And of course I am no better able to answer the question than anybody else and have not the smallest intention of attempting to answer it. However it does not follow that there is no use in considering the question; for though we cannot answer it, it may be well to inquire what kind of answer we require. For on this matter opinion seems to be somewhat confused. It does not seem as clear as it ought to be that the kind of answer that should be or could be given to this question is utterly different from that which can be given to a question concerning some proposition of science. The criteria of value which must be applied to any answer that may be offered are quite different from those which are applicable to the value of a scientific proposition. For what we are asking is why the criteria of value of a scientific proposition are adequate; and no answer to that inquiry can depend on an application of those very criteria the applicability of which is in question.

The question why the material world accords with our intellectual needs is a metaphysical not a scientific question. And when I say it is metaphysical, I mean only that it is the kind of question that those who accept the designation of metaphysician attempt to answer, and that an answer might be given in terms of the ideas which such persons employ. I do not mean in the least that any answer which those persons have actually given is adequate or that any validity is to be attached to the ideas which they actually employ. I do not even mean that it is necessary to pay any attention to those answers or those ideas; in fact in most of what follows I propose to neglect them almost entirely. Here, as elsewhere, I am addressing myself to serious students of science, and the only ideas which concern me at all are those which appeal to such students. It is an undoubted fact that, to the vast majority of them (a majority in which I am included), the ideas which metaphysicians handle so readily, and which to them are the most fundamental and elementary in the whole range of thought, are productive of nothing but intense mental confusion and discomfort. Whatever answer is to be given to our question it is clearly not one in which such ideas are involved, and we need only consider these ideas in so far as it is necessary to distinguish them from our own and to decide why we find them so supremely unsatisfactory.

Possible explanations of science. The inquiry which I wish to conduct will be best introduced by quoting some examples of answers which might be given to our question. I hope it is hardly necessary to state explicitly at the outset that I do not recommend any of these answers or accept any of them myself. But they are, I think, the kind of answer that we want; what is wrong with them is merely that they are not true. If I asked what is the relation between the pressure and the volume of a gas at constant temperature, I should get the kind of answer which I want if I were told that the pressure is proportional to the square of the volume; my sole objection to the answer would be that it is false. This simple example may explain my attitude towards the answers which will be taken as the basis of our discussion.

First, then, we might be offered a theological answer. We might be told that the material world and our intellectual desires were in accord because both are under the control of, and have been set and maintained in action by, a God who, under the instigation of nothing but his own volition, preferred to produce a world in which they were in accord rather than one in which they are in conflict.

Second, we might be offered an evolutionary answer. We might be told that men's intellectual desires differ so greatly and over so wide a range that, even if there were no necessary connection, mere chance would be enough to ensure that there should be some men whose desires were such as the material world could satisfy. The fact that such men are in the immense majority (at least so far as the laws, but probably not the theories, of science are concerned) is due to the elimination of the remainder in conflict with hostile Nature; they have survived and propagated their kind in virtue of the very quality which is in question.

Third, we might be given a psychological answer. We might be told that, even in waking life and still more in dreams, our sensations are determined by our desires. If I desire a law shall be of a certain form, I find actually that it is of that form, for a reason strictly analogous to that which makes Arctic explorers dream almost exclusively of the consumption of dumplings.

I hope it will be agreed that any one of these answers might prove the answer we require, that it is the right kind of answer, and that, if we reject it, it is wholly on the ground that it is not true.

These answers are theories. The feature which is common to all these answers and that on which I want to insist is that the "explanations" offered are very closely similar to those which theories offer of laws.

Theories, as we saw, "explain" propositions by deducing them from other propositions; the ideas of the second set of propositions are of a nature different from those of the first (at least in the "mechanical theories"), and are connected with them by relations which are suggested by some analogy based on the nature of the ideas of the second set; nothing can be asserted about them apart from the theory. This analogy is essential to the theory and gives it its meaning. Now I think it is clear that it is possible to express any of the three "explanations" which have just been offered in this form. The theological theory introduces the new idea of a God, based on the analogy of human personality. From propositions about the nature of God, e.g. that he is benevolent, based on analogy with propositions about the natures of men, we are led to assert propositions of the hypothesis concerning what God would wish to do. From other propositions about his nature we are led to the dictionary connecting the things we observe with statements about what God would do as the result of his wishes. And from these propositions we deduce the facts which are actually observed. Apart from the theory and the facts which it is used to explain we know nothing about God[1]; we should have no idea whether he was benevolent or malevolent, powerful or impotent.

Similarly the evolutionary theory introduces hypothetical ideas based on analogy, or supposed analogy, with the observed development of species; the fundamental idea is a development of species in the past similar to that which is proceeding in the present. The psychological theory uses the analogy of a dream in which desires and apparent perceptions are observed to be regularly connected. It is unnecessary to work out the formal analysis in detail for it will probably not be doubted that the explanations can be expressed in the manner suggested.

---

[1] It is assumed, of course, that the theology is purely "natural"; if the conception of revelation is introduced, things are known about God which are not deduced from the properties of the material world.

On the other hand it may well be doubted whether they should be so expressed, and these doubts, though they were not mentioned at the time, may equally well occur in connection with the physical theories which were discussed in Chapter VI. It may be thought that, though so much insistence has been placed on the meaning of theories, an important element in that meaning has been totally neglected, and that the exhibition of a theory as hypothesis and dictionary obscures its true significance. It may be urged that the relation between the nature of God and the nature of the material world, or (in the example that has served so often) between the impacts of the molecules and the pressure on the walls of the vessel, is something much more vital and intimate than that of bare logical implication. The relation between the impacts of the molecules and the pressure is just as vital, as physical, as real, as that between the impacts of actually visible highly elastic balls and the pressure that they produce. The protest against the use of the word "cause" to denote the relation in one case as in the other is mistaken; the two relations are essentially the same.

Such a feeling is probably general among students of science, but this is one of the few matters in which I cannot accept such a consensus. I am not prepared to dispute that the relation "really is" the same in the two cases, for I simply do not know what such a statement means; attempts to analyse it reduce me to a confusion which soon passes into imbecility. And I am certainly not prepared to dispute, but most strongly to maintain, that the assertion which is actually made concerning the relation in the two cases is as definitely and strictly true in one as in the other. What I wish to insist is that the evidence on which the assertion is made, though equally convincing, is of a totally different kind in the two cases. When I say that the impact of visible balls on solid surfaces produces a pressure, I am asserting an experimental fact, something that I actually observe; the evidence for that fact is the universal assent of mankind which is the basis of the kind of truth that is characteristic of science. But when I say that the impact of the molecules produces a pressure I am not asserting something that I observe, or that I conceive it possible that I or anyone else ever should observe in the same way as they observe the impact of the visible balls; whatever evidence there may be for the assertion, it is not the evidence of the universal assent of mankind ascertainable from their actions. And the simple proof of that fact is that people have actually dissented from the dynamical theory of gases without differing in any way from the rest of mankind concerning any matter on which they are universally agreed. I do not know (and do not greatly care) whether it is generally held that two relations can "really be" the same when the evidence for the assertion of one is totally and inevitably different from the evidence for the assertion of the other; but it must surely be admitted that this difference of evidence is in some way important, and it is merely this difference of evidence to which I want to draw attention.

And exactly the same difference of evidence exists between that for the hypotheses of the three explanations and that for the analogies on which they are based. Our evidence for believing that species have originated in a certain manner in the unobserved and unobservable past is quite different from that for believing that they are originating in this manner at the present time under observation. The evidence for the view that life is all a dream is different in nature from the evidence for my having had a nightmare last night. And we do not know that God made the world on evidence of the same nature as that which would prove to us that a man made a watch; the best evidence for the last statement would be that somebody saw him make it, but the most anthropomorphical theologies do not imagine that anybody saw God make the world. It is more difficult in these cases to say exactly what the difference of evidence is because the nature of the evidence which proves the analogy has been (and perhaps can be) less perfectly analysed; but it cannot be doubted that there is a difference in the relation asserted by the theory and that asserted by the observed analogy on which it is based, if the nature of a relation is determined by the nature of the evidence which proves its existence.

The meaning of theories. But what is the difference and why is there any tendency to overlook it? I think that some rather obvious considerations may help us in this matter, if we return to the physical theory. The relation between the impacts of the visible balls and the pressure they exert is uniform association; it is the relation of which one special form is the causal relation; and though it has been maintained that in this instance the relation is not actually causal, in the narrower sense that has come to be attributed to that term, we shall fall into no error and shall simplify the discussion if, for the moment, we regard it as causal. We shall say then that the impact of the visible balls causes the pressure, meaning that if we can observe the impacts, then always and necessarily we shall be able to observe the pressure. On the other hand the relation between the impacts of the molecules and the pressure is one of logical deduction[1]; from propositions about the impacts we deduce propositions about the pressure. Now the causal relation is connected closely with logical deduction. Historically and psychologically the latter is developed from the former; a sufficient proof of that statement is that we use such terms as "consequently" or "it follows" in tracing a logical deduction; such terms are obviously based on the causal relation where the effect follows and is consequent to the event. I do not think it would be difficult to show (perhaps the fact is familiar to logicians) that all forms of the syllogism and of the simpler standard forms of deduction are derived from analogy with corresponding variations of the causal relation[2]. The causal relation is that which is primarily

---

[1] Of course logical deduction is not all the relation; there is also the part arising from the satisfactoriness of the analogy; but this part merely enables us to distinguish between many alternative logical deductions.

[2] Let me explain what I mean by an example, that of the familiar syllogism, All men are mortal; Socrates is a man; therefore Socrates is mortal. This argument is closely similar in form to one which involves relations characteristic of scientific laws—or at least relations out of which those characteristic of such laws have been developed. By experiment and observation I find that the possession of certain bodily and mental properties (themselves uniformly associated and giving rise to the concept, man) are uniformly associated with the property of mortality; I state a law that they are uniformly associated. I now find a man,

and fundamentally true; from familiarity with it mankind arrived at the very notion of truth. The discovery that there was another source (or another kind) of truth arising from logical deduction is altogether later; primarily logical deduction led to truth exactly in so far as it resembled induction through the causal relation. And in this matter, as in so many others, the history of the individual repeats the history of the race. All educationalists are aware that very few children have any faith in or recognise any cogency in logical deduction; they all recognise and appreciate the causal relation. It is only quite exceptional children who believe a geometrical proposition in virtue of the formal demonstration; the vast majority believe it, if at all, because they have drawn the figure and found experimentally that it is true. And this feeling persists in later life. Even among persons of education and some intelligence a real appreciation of the processes of logical deduction is rare; it is characteristic, of course, of mathematicians, but of few others. I am doubtful myself whether I believe things because they are logically demonstrated in the same perfectly confident manner as I do if they are proved by experiment.

Now we are perfectly confident of the truth of theories—not perhaps all of us in the truth of the same theory, for opinions differ; but there is for each of us some theory of which we are as perfectly sure as we are about any law. This confidence makes us unwilling to recognise that there is involved in theories a process of thought, logical deduction, in which we do not feel instinctive confidence. And we can more easily conceal from ourselves the presence of this process because of its great similarity to that in which we have implicit trust; the deductions of laws from a theory can often (so long as the purely mathematical part is left out of account) be exhibited in a form in which every step of the deduction is precisely analogous to some step involving the causal relation. But we must not deceive ourselves; we must recognise that logical and not causal relations connect the hypothetical ideas to the concepts. The conclusion which we should draw from our confidence in theories is not that logical deduction is not concerned in them, but that logical deduction, which in some of its applications we cannot accept with the fullest conviction, may be so accepted when it is supported and confirmed by the intellectual satisfaction in the result which gives to theories their meaning.

defined by the associated properties, whom I had not encountered before; he is an individual object, and there is something associated asymmetrically with those properties distinguishing him from all other men. I conclude from my law that mortality will again be associated with those properties; the conclusion is necessarily involved in the very meaning of a law.

When I am asked to assent to the syllogism, I always find myself contemplating an argument of this kind. When I realise that the syllogism is to be applied to things which, from their very nature, are not determined in any way by experiment or observation, and that I must utterly banish an argument of this kind from my mind, then I find that it is extremely doubtful whether I have any confidence in the syllogism at all. Logical deduction loses its conviction for me as soon as it is completely divorced from "Induction".

Here is, I think, the fundamental reason where attempts by mathematicians to expound the philosophy of science are apt to be unconvincing. The source of truth which they rate more highly, we rate less highly, and *vice versa*.

I find myself, and I hope others will find too, that if this point of view is carefully considered and the mind accustomed to it, it is possible to realise that the relation between the impacts of the molecules and the pressure is not the causal relation, and that it is essentially different from the relation between the impact of visible balls and the pressure, without any sacrifice of the full certainty of the theory or the introduction of any doubts that one relation is as important and as real as the other.

If this view is accepted, it will probably also be granted that the doctrines which might explain the harmony between the material world and our intellectual desires are essentially theories, and differ from physical theories only in the nature of the propositions to be explained. The form in which the explanation provided by a theory has been exhibited is applicable to these doctrines as much as to physical theories; and the considerations which have just been advanced tend to show that this form is really and fundamentally characteristic of theories, and is not a mere artificial device which obscures their true significance. If it is once concluded that the explanation or the answers to metaphysical questions which are required by students of science (once again I suggest nothing of what may be required by others) are those given by theories, the consideration of some further matters is rendered possible.

Why are the theories unacceptable? Thus we may ask why all three explanations are so unsatisfactory and expect in reply to be given reasons similar to those which lead us to reject (or at least fail to accept—for there is a distinction between these mental attitudes) physical theories. The chief of such reasons are the following:

1. The analogy is unsatisfactory; (a) because it is not the kind of analogy which gives intellectual satisfaction; (b) because the analogy, though of the right kind, is actually false, e.g. if the analogy is with a law which is known not to be true, such as the law that the pressure of a gas is proportional to the volume; (c) because the analogy, though it might be used satisfactorily to explain some things, is not satisfactory as an explanation of this thing. What I mean here is that a very complicated theory, though it would be acceptable as an explanation of laws even more complicated, is not acceptable as an explanation of something quite simple; we feel that the complexity of the apparatus of explanation is altogether disproportionate to the purpose for which it is used.

2. The deduction is unsatisfactory; (a) because the proposition to be explained cannot be rightly deduced from the theory; (b) because, though the proposition immediately to be explained can be so deduced, other propositions which are not true can also be deduced from it by extensions of the dictionary which are inseparable from the nature of the hypothetical ideas; (c) because propositions which ought to be deducible from the theory, because they are closely allied to those which are deduced, cannot be deduced.

If anyone will consider why he fails to accept any actual physical theory, he will, I think, be able to place his reasons under one or other or several of these heads. And the reason why I, at least, reject the three explanations of p. 232, can be similarly placed; others may reject them for different reasons or even accept them; but they will appreciate that the reasons are of the right kind. The psychological explanation I reject chiefly under 1 (a), but 1 (b) and 2 (b) are also applicable. The evolutionary explanation I reject chiefly under 1 (b); it is very doubtful whether evolution by natural selection is a fact; but 2 (b) applies also. The theological theory I reject under 1 (c) and 2 (b). And to all three 2 (c) seems equally applicable; they may explain science, but they do not explain anything else.

But here reference is made to propositions, other than that which is the main object of our inquiry, which are or ought to be explicable by the same theory. What are these propositions? They are those which arise in one manner or another from immediate judgements which are excluded from the province of science. It must be remembered that we have definitely decided that the whole field of our experience is not the domain of science, but only a very limited portion of it. The parts which are excluded can be divided into two main regions; first those which, according to the common-sense view, are concerned with perceptions of the material world, and second those which are concerned only with the internal world. The first region includes all our personal experiences, all the events of history, everything that happens and is important just because it is unique; concerning such matters there can be no universal agreement and they can form no part of science; yet, for reasons into which it is not necessary to inquire in detail, they are regarded as part of the material world. According to the view of early 19th century enthusiasts all such matters might and, in time, would be brought within the range of science; when all the laws of Nature had been fully elucidated, it would be possible to predict from any state of the material world at one instant its state at any other time. But, as was frequently pointed out, it is still possible and necessary to inquire why the state at the first time was what it was and no other; questions can always be pushed until the "first cause" is reached, and such questions science, by her very nature and most intimate structure, must always refuse to answer. On the other hand, these questions, like that of the reason for the harmony between our intellectual desires and the events which do form part of science, bear directly on the relation between the material world and all our various joys and sorrows; they are all part of one great question, why we find life interesting to some degree and why we do not find it all equally interesting and satisfactory. Accordingly if our explanation is to answer one part of this question, we expect it to answer another, and any theory must be rejected which predicts rightly one part of our experience in this matter and wrongly another.

The second region which is excluded from science is that of our inner judgements which are not directly concerned with the material world at all, even if that phrase is interpreted in the laxer sense. For of course we make such judgements, which are as immediate and as indisputable as those concerning the material world, judgements of good and evil, beauty and ugliness, love and disgust. It is difficult to compare these judgements with those on which science is based, because they are so utterly contrary in their nature; what gives value to one deprives the other of all value. Our judgements of the material world are valuable because they are shared with others, our inner judgements are valuable because they are personal; we feel almost distressed when anyone appears to share exactly our sense of beauty unless his personality is almost merged in ours by the strongest attachments of love; we feel that to share our favourite works of art is almost to profane them. But though these judgements are so different from those of science, they at least have this resemblance to the judgement to which we have been led by a consideration of science, that they are rooted in the deepest recesses of the human mind. Again we feel that an explanation which accounts for one source of aesthetic satisfaction ought in some way to account for all.

It is in respect of these portions of experience which lie outside the region of science that the explanations suggested fail so completely. The psychological theory (which of course does not resemble anything that anybody has taken in the least seriously) explains nothing but the bare fact to which it was directed. The evolutionary theory, if it explains anything, may explain every experience in which our desires are clearly in accordance with the impositions of the material world, but it is quite incapable of explaining the equally noteworthy experience in which the material world conflicts with our desires and hampers all our aspirations. The theological theory can only be made to explain the whole realm of experience by attributing to God qualities so contradictory that the analogy with human beings is completely lost; He must be sometimes benevolent, sometimes malevolent, powerful and impotent, wise and childishly silly. A theory involving such a being could explain anything; from it could be deduced, not only the actual state of the world, but any other state, however different. It is because the explanations fail as theories, and fail as any physical theory might fail, that they are rejected; they are rejected simply because they are untrue in the scientific sense and not because, if they were true, they would have no meaning or not the right kind of meaning.

Could such answers be ultimate? Nevertheless it is worth while to ask one further question about them. Suppose that they were true and provided a sufficient explanation of all experience; would that explanation be ultimate or should we in turn require to explain the explanation? The question is important; for if we should have to answer it in the negative, we should either have to admit that no ultimate explanation of the universe was conceivable, an admission from which most minds will rebel, or have to seek some other kind of explanation.

The answer to the question must again be personal; I can only give my own view, recognising that others may differ from it. But my answer is that one, and perhaps two, of the explanations, if they were satisfactory at all, would be ultimate, and that no further explanation would be required. To justify such an answer we must notice that we have not used a theory to explain a similar theory; if we once entered on such a course, there would be no obvious point at which to stop and we should be led to an endless regress. But though we have used a theory to explain science which consists largely of theories, the theories that are explained are not of the same nature as the theory that explains them. A physical theory, the dynamical theory of gases for example, enables laws, involving ideas which are concepts, to be deduced from hypotheses, involving ideas which are not concepts. No one physical theory explains another; where it is sometimes loosely said to do so all that is meant is that the hypothetical ideas of one theory form part of those of the other. Thus, it might be said that the electronic theory explains the theory of electrolytic conduction, because the idea of an indivisible charge characteristic of all elements alike, which is fundamental in the latter theory, forms an important part of the hypothesis of the former; but even here the expression would not often be used. Explanation in the scientific sense always involves the deduction of propositions concerning one set of ideas from propositions concerning another set. This feature is characteristic of the theories which we are considering as much as of any others[1]. And while this feature persists there is clearly no reason why we should regress endlessly in our explanations; that we have regressed from ideas A to ideas B, and from ideas B to ideas C, is no reason why we should go further and introduce ideas D. We shall stop —and this is the point I want to make—when the ideas which we have reached in our explanation are so satisfactory that no further development could produce more satisfactory ideas.

But are there such ideas? For myself, and probably for others, there are. It has been urged that the reasoning process which is involved in the explanation of theories is acceptable because it is somewhat similar to that which depends on the various forms of the causal relation; it does not really involve that relation at all, but it is because the relation of the hypothetical ideas to the ideas explained is similar to the causal relation that we regard it as the possible basis of an explanation. But the similarity to the causal relation is possible only so long as the ideas to be explained are such that they might

---

[1] This statement would not perhaps be true if the evolutionary explanation were applied to "explain" biology which included the theory of evolution. We might then be introducing in a later stage of the explanation ideas which had already been explained in an earlier. Objections of this kind can often be raised against attempts to explain science in terms of ideas which are characteristically scientific and present difficulties, additional to those mentioned further on, to "materialistic" theories of the universe. But it should be noted that it is not certain that the objection is valid. The fact of which we are at present mainly concerned to consider the explanation is not that any particular scientific theory (e.g. the theory of evolution) is true, but only the fact that we can by a certain mental process arrive at scientific theories which are true. To use one of these theories to provide the analogy to explain the fact does not seem certainly objectionable. On the other hand, if we attempted to use the evolutionary theory to explain matters connected with the "first cause", or the reason why certain scientific theories rather than others are actually true, then, if among these theories is the theory of evolution, the process is certainly objectionable. But I do not think anyone has attempted to use evolution to explain why evolution occurs; those who have believed some form of evolutionary theory of the universe have regarded the fact of evolution as ultimate and unexplainable.

have causes; for if they are not such, then no hypothetical ideas could stand to them in any relation resembling the causal relation sufficiently to make the explanation acceptable. When, therefore, in our process of successive explanation we arrive at ideas (if there are such) which we regard as essentially causeless, then explanation can proceed no further and we have reached an ultimate explanation.

Now there are such ideas. Processes which are initiated by volition are essentially causeless[1]. It has been pointed out many times that, throughout the development of science, the idea persists that events which depend upon volition are essentially contrasted with those which can be ordered in laws by means of the causal relation; just because science tries everywhere to order some events by means of the causal relation (or, more accurately, the relation of uniform association of which the causal relation is a special form) it refuses to attempt to order others which depend upon volition; a failure to be consistent in this matter would reduce science to chaos. Accordingly, if at any stage of our explanations, we introduce hypothetical ideas based on an analogy which is inseparable from the idea of volition, then—so it seems to me—the explanation can proceed no further; these hypothetical ideas cannot be explained by any relation resembling the causal relation, for such explanation would involve the denial that they were really volitional. Now one of the suggested theories does involve hypothetical ideas which are essentially volitional, namely the theological theory. And my own feeling is that, if that theory were true, it would be satisfactory and would provide an ultimate explanation. If I could regard all the events of the world as expressions of the uncaused will of God, then for me they would be perfectly explained; it would never occur to me to ask why God wished what he did wish and not something else. I might think it very foolish or wicked of him to wish what he did, but I should not ask why he wished it. And this feeling is undoubtedly widely shared, for those people who can accept a theological interpretation of the universe (and they are to be found even amongst the most distinguished students of science) seem perfectly satisfied with it and do not crave any further explanation. Moreover the feeling extends to any theory, which, though not definitely theological, introduces as hypothetical ideas beings

---

[1] I hope nobody will think that by this statement I am committing myself to one side or the other in the time-honoured controversy between free-will and determinism. But as students of science are not always familiar with the bickerings of theologians, I would define my attitude a little more definitely. It is a fact, of which I and I alone must be the judge, that I feel, as an immediate judgement, that my acts of volition are uncaused, that is to say, that they are not related by uniform association (which, it must be remembered, is characterised by necessity) to any other events whatever; I feel that whatever those events have been, I can act as I will. This fact is not in the least inconsistent with quite another judgement, namely, that the acts of other people which, from analogy with my own, I judge to be the effects of volition, are uniformly associated with certain events in their lives. It is not even inconsistent with the possibility that, by reflection and guidance derived from the experience of the acts of others, I may come to judge that my own volitional acts are uniformly associated with events in my life. But what is important here, when we are considering methods of attaining intellectual satisfaction, is the immediate judgement of free will, not the derivative judgement of determination.

analogous to human beings, beings who are in any way endowed with personality and· the possibility of volition; it extends, that is, to all "idealistic" interpretations of the universe. I feel that such explanations, if they were true, would be ultimate and would leave me with no further questions to ask; my only objection to this is that they are not true[1]. Idealistic philosophies have a perpetual attraction for mankind because others show the same general feeling but differ, as scientific men differ from each other, on the question of the actual truth of such philosophies.

Diametrically opposed to idealistic theories are materialistic theories which are also accepted by some persons as providing ultimate explanations. I cannot explain adequately the motives which lead to their acceptance, for I do not share them myself, but they are probably also connected with a feeling of causelessness. In such theories the fundamental idea that replaces the freely acting personality, which is the main characteristic of idealistic theories, is a mechanism. A mechanism when in full operation is, in a certain sense, causeless; the products of its operations are not uniformly associated with anything that is not part of the mechanism; the mechanism, like a personality, is a self-contained whole. Some such feeling as this probably determines the attraction for materialistic explanations for some minds; for myself I cannot dissociate the idea of a mechanism from that of the inventor who designed it and the worker who set it in operation. Even if the universe could be completely explained by hypothetical ideas analogous to some mechanism working on fixed and determined principles, I should still want to ask and to be told who designed the mechanism in that particular fashion and why it was set in operation in this particular manner and in no other. On the other hand I am quite prepared to recognise that one view has as much and as little foundation as the other; I know that the conviction of those who disagree with me is impossible and I have no wish to attempt their conversion. Perhaps it may be noted that it is at first sight strange that idealistic theories should, on the whole, attract those who are not trained in science and materialistic theories those who are. For it is the former and not the latter who, being unfamiliar with the design of mechanism, might be expected more readily to regard a mechanism as causeless and to be able to overlook the necessity for an inventor; whereas the latter, being used to inventing mechanisms themselves, might be expected to feel more deeply the need for associating with every mechanism a designer and an operator. The paradox, if paradox it be, is solved when we remember that systems operating according to the fixed laws

---

[1] Since there are people who delight in misunderstanding any statements of this sort, or at least pretending to misunderstand them, I would add an example by way of analogy. My sole objection to idealistic theories is that none so far proposed are true; but it is not the less a serious objection. If somebody told me that the paper on which I am writing is blue, I should similarly object to this statement simply on the ground that it is not true; I should be quite prepared to admit that it might have been true and that, if it were true, it might be important and relevant. But that does not mean that I am the less certain that it is not true, or that I have the smallest hesitation in rejecting it. I am as certain as I can be certain of anything that it is not true. That is my position towards theological and other idealistic philosophies.

of mechanisms play a much larger part in the intellectual life of scientific men. They are so accustomed to regarding the elucidation of such laws as a necessary and integral part of any intellectual operations which are to lead to results of value that they are tempted to believe that no intellectual operations can be of value which do not consist entirely of the elaboration of such laws. They would not, of course, maintain that view explicitly, but we are dealing here with mental processes which are beyond the reach of criticism or of explicit statement; we are considering what is felt rather than what is expressed, asserted, or defended.

Science and Metaphysics. In what has just been said, as throughout this volume, it has been my object, not to instil any new ideas or to combat any old ones, but simply to bring to the mind of the reader ideas which he will recognise as familiar; it is possible that if these ideas are presented in novel order and relationship, he will be enabled to judge more definitely of their value. And if there were nobody in the world but those whose intellectual interests are predominantly scientific, there would be little more to say on these matters. For if an adequate theory of the nature that we have been discussing could be given, explaining the relation between our aesthetic or intellectual desires and the material world, then we should feel that all the questions which we are inclined to ask had been answered. No further philosophical difficulties would trouble us and we should find no interest whatever in any further metaphysical problems. And again, while an adequate theory is still wanting, we feel interest in those problems only because it is suggested to us that they may lead to such a theory.

But the questions which we have been discussing appear to concern others whose primary interests are different and who are inclined to give totally different answers to them. It would probably be wise for us to ignore altogether those with whom we can never agree, but in such a matter it is not easy always to be wise. Many people, who have no tastes for professional metaphysics, seem to be sometimes perturbed by what professional metaphysicians may say. Accordingly it may be well to consider as briefly as possible some of the views which are found to be perturbing. In doing so I shall not have the slightest expectation, or even desire, that I may convert any metaphysician from his doctrines; I am merely concerned to render them innocuous to others.

The three most fundamental ideas of metaphysics appear to be reality, existence and truth. Of these reality and existence are closely connected; reality (so far as I can ascertain) is simply what exists, and existence is what all reality does, though reality may do other things than exist. Reality and existence again are connected with truth; it seems that the purest and highest truth, the only thing that can properly be called truth, is something applicable only to reality and perhaps only to the conception of the existence of reality. It is not of course the case that all propositions about reality are true or that no propositions are true unless they are about reality, but there seems to be some connection, which I do not profess to understand completely, between reality and truth.

Now the words reality, existence and truth are also used in science (or their grammatical transformations, real, exist, true, and so on); what I want to consider is whether this community in the use of words (which is undoubtedly the source of the trouble which we are trying to remove) indicates that the metaphysical ideas have any connection with the scientific ideas and whether scientific propositions throw any light upon metaphysical propositions. At first sight it appears that there is no connection. Metaphysicians are prepared to assert that molecules are not real, that silver does not exist, and that science is not true; not all metaphysicians assert these things, but even those who do not are prepared to admit that the assertions are significant and might be true; the most convinced "realist" is prepared at least to argue about such assertions and thus to show that he thinks them conceivable. But to the man of science such assertions are not conceivable; it is not simply that they are false[1], but that they are simply unthinkable. A man who asserts that silver does not exist or that science is not true is not in such a state of mind that it is any use to argue with him. If we are silly, we shall be rude to him; if we are wise, we shall shrug our shoulders and pass on; but we shall not stop to argue.

However it is just possible that we may be able to make argument possible by removing linguistic difficulties. It may be that he is not using words in the same sense as we are; that the difference between us is only that which divides an Englishman and an American in the use of such a word as "sick"; and that a little patience on both sides will remove the obstacle to intercourse. It will be well therefore to consider rather carefully what we mean by the words, and when we are quite clear on the point approach him once more. I do not believe personally that by such methods we shall actually come nearer to agreement than before; but the attempt is worth making, if only out of politeness. It will in any case serve the useful purpose that if we still differ we shall know that the difference is irremovable and shall not waste further time in trying to remove it.

Scientific reality. What then do we believe to be real and believe to exist; for in science at least those two phrases appear to be synonymous? Firstly material objects and substances. These, it has been decided, are concepts, dependent for their meaning on the truth of certain laws[2]; those laws are expressed by the statement that the material object or the substance exists. Accordingly some part of scientific reality consists of concepts, but it is important to notice that not all concepts are real. Pressure, volume, density, temperature, force are all concepts, but they are not real. We may

---

[1] Of course there are, or have been, men of science who did not believe that molecules were real, but they believed in the reality of some other hypothetical ideas which metaphysicians would deny to be real.

[2] We decided (p. 81) that the proposition which gives rise to the concept of an individual material object is not a law, because it is not characterised by necessity But all that is important for our present purpose is that it involves the relation of uniform association and differs from the law which defines a substance only in the presence of a special element of asymmetry.

occasionally speak of a real pressure or say that a force between two bodies exists, but we shall recognise that in so speaking we are not using the terms in quite the same sense as when we apply them to material objects, and we shall be willing to abandon that use when it appears to cause confusion in others. The words in such connection only express that there is some special element of truth in the statements we make; we have, of course, still to consider the very difficult problem of what we mean by truth, but it will not be doubted that we do make true statements about things which are not regarded as real. "Really" is often a mere synonym for "truly".

In former chapters an effort was made to exhibit the similarity between those laws which lead to concepts which are real and those which lead to concepts which are not real, and I have no intention of modifying what was said. For strictly scientific purposes it seems to me much more important to appreciate the similarity than to appreciate the distinction, if only because hitherto it has been more often overlooked. But of course the fact that one kind of law leads to real concepts and the other to unreal does indicate an important distinction. If we had been able fully to analyse laws and to display their relational structure completely, it would be possible to say precisely what this distinction is. Some distinctive features have been described; thus, in laws defining substances, all the concepts which are uniformly associated appear to be involved in the same way, and the law can be adequately expressed as a symmetrical relation, while in other laws a distinction usually has to be made between the concepts which are uniformly associated and the conditions of uniform association. Further, the concepts of substances or material objects are always involved (usually among the conditions) in the laws defining concepts of other kind; pressure, volume and so on, are the pressure and volume of an object or substance; force acts on an object. It is probably this last feature which leads us to regard pressure and so on as the properties of a substance or object; but it must be noted that the class of substances and objects and the class of their properties do not exhaust the class of concepts; the example of force shows that there are concepts which are neither objects, substances nor properties. However neither feature indicates the true root of the matter; there is some characteristic of the laws defining substances and objects which leads us to regard the concepts which they define as real; but as I have not been able to make up my mind exactly what this characteristic is, I prefer to leave the matter entirely open rather than to offer suggestions which are known to be incomplete. All that appears certain is that our decision whether a concept is real is determined in some way by the form of the law which defines it.

The second class of things which we judge to be real are hypothetical ideas, molecules or electrons for example. Here again it is not all hypothetical ideas which are judged to be real, but the distinction between those which are and those which are not so judged is immediately clear. A hypothetical idea is judged to be real if, according to the analogy on which the hypothesis is based, it corresponds to a concept which would be judged to be real

Molecules are real because they correspond to small elastic bodies, electrons because they correspond to small charged bodies. Indeed the confidence with which we judge molecules and electrons to be real is probably based largely on a failure to distinguish such hypothetical ideas from the concepts to which they correspond. It is a familiar saying that a molecule is as real as a table, and I have not the least wish to dispute that statement; but though one is as real as the other, there is between them the important distinction which was discussed earlier in this chapter. The recognition of this distinction need not at all alter the judgement of reality; personally I am quite clear about the distinction, quite clear that a molecule is not a material object in the same sense as is a table; none the less I am quite clear and definite in my assertion that molecules are real.

The third and last class of real things is that of "other persons". The idea of other persons is not employed explicitly in science, or at least in physical science, but the discussion of Chapter I shows that it is necessarily involved implicitly. We select the judgements which science is to study by means of the opinions of other persons concerning them. This use of the idea would not make us inevitably assert that other persons are real, because we undoubtedly make great use of and place great reliance on ideas of things which are not real; but as a matter of fact we do judge them to be real. Again no pretence can be made of giving our reason for the judgement; but it may be suggested that it is essentially the same as that for attributing reality to material objects. Persons are doubtless very unlike material objects, but they differ in their properties rather than in the relation between their properties. We judge material objects to be real because the law defining them and relating their properties has a certain form. It is even more impossible to state with any precision what is the "law" defining other persons than to state what is the law defining material objects; but if the considerations advanced in Chapter I are accepted, it will be agreed that there is some proposition of the nature of a law defining them. We speak of other persons because we observe certain uniform associations. It is, I believe, because the relations involved in these uniform associations (though not the terms related) are almost the same in the laws defining material objects and in those defining other persons that we attribute reality alike to both.

It will be observed that I have spoken of "other persons". Do we also attribute reality to ourselves? At first sight most people will probably be inclined to answer, yes. For systems of philosophy have been based on the assumption, supposed indubitable, that everybody believes in his own existence; and, so far as I can make out, the objections raised against such systems have not involved the denial of this fundamental assumption. But, for myself, I am inclined to deny it most strongly. I am not aware of my own existence, and I simply cannot conceive any state of mind in which I could be aware of it. On the other hand, I am equally indisposed to admit that I do not exist; I simply do not believe that the conception of existence is applicable to myself at all.

This attitude may appear to some people paradoxical; indeed I have always found the greatest difficulty in explaining it to those with whom I have discussed it. Accordingly, although it is a mere personal opinion, it may be well once more to try to state it clearly.

The point at issue is essentially the same as that which occurred in our discussion whether hypothetical ideas "really are" concepts; can two propositions mean the same kind of thing when the evidence for them is essentially different? My evidence for the existence of other people consists of certain external judgements; that for my own existence (if there is such evidence) in internal judgements which are of an utterly different nature. I cannot explain what the difference in nature is, but anyone who needs explanation can hold no converse with me. The external judgements lead to the indirect judgement that there are other people only in virtue of analogies which involve the internal judgements. The very meaning of the term "myself" and "other persons" involves the conclusion that I cannot make about other people those internal judgements which lead (if anything leads) to the judgement that I exist; and on the other hand, external judgements could only lead to the conclusion that I exist if for the moment I am able to regard myself as another person. Accordingly the evidence for the assertion that other people exist can never lead to the judgement that I exist; and the evidence for my own existence can never lead to the belief in the existence of others; the two kinds of evidence are essentially different and mutually exclusive. It is for this reason and with this intention that I say that, if I use the phrase "I exist" at all, I do not mean by it the same kind of thing as I mean when I say that other persons exist.

If I make the statement at all that I exist, it is only in protest against the assertion (expressed or implied) of some other person that I do not exist. I certainly want other people to be as certain that I exist as I am certain that they exist. But I should never make it for my own benefit but only for the benefit of others. Somehow—I cannot explain how—the statement that other people exist seems to me worth making to myself and for my own benefit[1]; the statement that I exist is not. Again, the statement that other people (or that particular other people) do not exist has a perfectly definite meaning to me; that my stepmother does not exist, never has existed, and never will, is to me a perfectly intelligible statement which might be important in some circumstances; it is definitely capable of proof or disproof. The statement that I do not exist is not intelligible; if I try to consider what it means I merely lose my temper.

Such discussions lead us into very deep water, and the attempt to remove one source of obscurity generally leads to the introduction of several others. If the reader has not appreciated my meaning already, he will never do so. I draw attention to the question of the meaning of the phrase "I exist", spoken

---

[1] The reason probably is connected with the possibility of proving the statement to somebody else. If I can conceive of proving it to somebody else, I can also conceive proving it to myself.

by any speaker, not because I wish to press a personal opinion in the matter, but because if we once could admit that "existence" in that phrase has a wholly different meaning from that in the phrase "other people exist", we should remove a difficulty in the way of deciding what we, scientific people, mean by existence and reality. For the sense of existence, and the associated term reality, in every other phrase but that which asserts our own existence, can be traced clearly to one fundamental sense, namely that in which material objects are said to exist. If we once agree to abandon the assertion, "I exist", then we can say that things are real and exist when they are concepts defined by laws involving that special form of uniform association which is character- istic of material bodies, or when they are hypothetical ideas analogous to such concepts. We shall also recognise that things need not be unimportant or unessential to the progress of knowledge simply because they do not exist; some non-existent things are quite as important as any existent things. Some people will perhaps think such a definition of our words is to explain the less by the more obscure; but others, I believe, will find it intelligible and not wholly useless.

It may be noted that among the things which it has been decided that we call real there is not included one thing which is sometimes thought to be characteristically real—so real that the assumption of its reality is fundamental to science. This thing is "matter". It is sometimes stated, even by those conversant with science, that science is not possible unless it is assumed that matter is real. I dissent from this view; I do not think that science makes any use whatever of the proposition that matter is real or that it would ever occur to any student of science to assert it, if (and this is the important point) the word, matter, is given the sense which it usually has in that state- ment. When we speak, if we do speak, about matter, we mean by matter simply the collection of all material objects and use it simply in place of the enumeration of a vast number of objects, chairs and tables, blocks of lead and vessels of water, the bodies of other persons and animals, and so on; in logical terms, matter, as used by science, is the name of a class defined by extension. On the other hand, when it is said by others that matter is real, matter is the common characteristic of a class defined by intension; its signi- ficance depends wholly on the belief that there is something common to the whole class of material objects; it is this thing that is common, and not the material objects to which it is common, that is said to be real. In the view of physics the only thing that is common to all material objects is the ultimate particles of which they consist; we have already discovered one kind of particle, electrons, common to all material objects, and we are well on the way to the discovery of others; even if we have not discovered them, we believe, and always have believed, that their discovery is possible, and that in the end we should be able to analyse material objects into different collec- tions of the same ultimate particles. Now these ultimate particles are all hypothetical ideas and we certainly assert that they are real; but I do not think that anyone would regard the assertion that matter is real as simply equivalent to the assertion that electrons, helium nuclei, and similar things which have yet to be discovered, are real. If the term, matter, means something common to material objects which is not electrons or helium nuclei or so on, then it is something of which science denies the validity; and we certainly do not assert, but very strongly deny, that it is real. For this reason I think that the assertion that matter is real, if interpreted in the sense in which it is employed by persons other than physicists, is certainly not fundamental to physics and indeed is regarded by physicists as false and not as true[1].

It should also be pointed out again, as in the Introduction, that "space" and "time" are not included among the things which we call real. These concepts will be discussed in Part III.

Reality is usually theoretical. The conclusion which has just been reached may appear inconsistent with that to which we were led in Chapter VI. It was noticed there that the words "real" and "really" are often used to denote hypothetical ideas and propositions in distinction to concepts and laws; it seemed to be indicated that the only things which we thought real were such hypothetical ideas, molecules, electrons and so on, and that we directly contrasted the reality of these ideas with the unreality of concepts. Such a conclusion would seem directly contrary to the view that it is concepts, or certain kinds of concepts, that are characteristically and fundamentally real, and that reality is attributed to other things only in so far as they resemble these concepts.

It might be possible to remove the inconsistency if it could be admitted that one thing could be more real than another, that reality was capable of degree. For what has just been said is only that the idea of the reality of hypothetical ideas is based on that of concepts, and this conclusion would not be inconsistent with the view that the reality, though so based, was greater than that on which it is based. But such an admission cannot be made; a thing is either real or it is not; there is no third alternative. If hypothetical ideas are more real than concepts, concepts cannot be real at all. However the difficulty may be removed if we ask why we call things real and what we mean by reality; for so far we have only asked what it is that we call real. The inquiry is very difficult, for the notion of reality is probably ultimate, but some considerations which are important intrinsically can be put forward

When we say that a hypothetical idea is real, do we mean anything other than that the theory in which it is involved is true? I believe we do; I believe we are thinking of the meaning of the theory rather than of its truth; in support

---

[1] When people believed in the "aether", the position was rather different, for they believed the aether to be real and often included it with material objects in the class matter; and yet it was not held to consist of the same ultimate particles as material objects. However I think it was generally felt that some day it would be shown that these ultimate particles were made of aether or that aether and the ultimate particles were made of the same thing. But the statement that matter was real, even if it included the aether, did not mean the same thing as the statement that this thing was real, out of which aether and material objects were made.

of that belief I would point out that it is mechanical rather than mathematical theories of which the hypothetical ideas are real; and it is the former rather than the latter which have meaning. It is quite possible for a theory to be true and yet to have little or no meaning (the absurd theory of p. 123 provides an example); and if it is true and yet meaningless, its hypothetical ideas are not judged to be real. Many people would regard in this manner some theories actually under discussion in modern physics, the quantum theory and the theory of relativity, for example. They admit that they are true and predict laws rightly, but they say that they have no meaning and consequently would not be prepared to say that the hypothetical ideas in them (such as an indivisible unit of energy) were real. Reality, therefore, seems confined to those hypothetical ideas which, being similar to concepts, confer on a theory its meaning.

Now laws, which give rise to concepts, have meaning as well as truth, and I would suggest that when we say a concept has reality we are thinking of the meaning rather than the truth of the law which defines it. The meaning of a law, we have decided, is contained in the statement that the uniform association is necessary and will always be found, as distinct from the statement that it will be found in this example and in that. When we assert that a concept is real, I think it is this element of necessity in the law which is prominent in our minds; so long as we have the slightest doubt that the law, though true in every experiment we have tried and likely to be true in every further trial that we can make, is always and necessarily true, we shall be disinclined to attribute reality to the concept which it defines. I cannot think of an entirely suitable example, for laws to which this element of necessity does not attach are rare, and among them I can find none which defines the concept of a material object; but if the reader will think of Bode's law, concerning the distances of the planets from the sun, and try to imagine that it defines a concept of a material body, then I think he will feel that he would be doubtful about calling that concept real, because he is doubtful about the necessity of Bode's law, though not about its actual truth.

Now if reality depends on the meaning of scientific propositions rather than on their truth, the reason why we say that hypothetical ideas are more real than concepts is immediately clear. For meaning is a much more important element in theories than in laws, and all that we shall mean by the statement is that reality is a much more important quality of hypothetical ideas than of concepts. I hope it will be agreed that reality is connected with meaning in the manner suggested and that, if there were no other reason for asserting that hypothetical ideas are more real than concepts, this would provide one. For, if it is true, it is clearly most important to recognise that reality is due to meaning rather than to truth, and that it is essentially based on theories, or on what is most characteristic of theories, rather than on laws, or on what is most characteristic of laws. On the other hand, I do not think that we have yet found the chief reason why we speak of hypothetical ideas as the more real.

Reality and appearance. There is one reason that is undoubtedly valid in some instances but need not detain us long, because it is not general. There is sometimes in the explanation afforded by a theory an actual substitution of real hypothetical ideas for unreal concepts. In the example taken of a physical theory, one of the concepts to be "explained" was pressure. Now pressure is not real, it is not even the property of a real object in quite the same sense as temperature is such a property. In the course of the explanation we substitute, by means of the dictionary, for the unreal concept pressure the hypothetical ideas of the mass and velocity of real objects. These are, as we shall note later, properties which are very closely connected with the reality of the objects of which they are the properties; they might almost be said to confer on those objects their reality. The ideas of the explanation are truly more real in this sense than the ideas explained.

But a much more important reason may be based on the frequent opposition of "real" to "apparent". Here "reality" is used to contrast what appears as a result of a more complete examination with the "appearance" that results from a less complete.

> I thought I saw a banker's clerk
> A-riding on a bus;
> I looked again and saw it was
> A hippopotamus.

That is to say, the thing which was *apparently* a banker's clerk was *really* a hippopotamus. But no assertion is made about the reality of the clerk; it is not said that clerks are not real, or even that any particular clerk was not real, for the essence of the statement is that there was no clerk concerned in the matter at all. I simply made a mistake, which was corrected by further observation, and that is all there is to be said. For "really" it would be better to put "truly"; an untrue proposition is contrasted with a true; but neither untrue nor true propositions are, in any sense of the word true, necessarily about either unreality or reality.

Another example of the contrast between apparent and real occurs in connection with "illusions". There is a well-known method of "feathering" lines drawn on a sheet of paper, so that, though they are *really* parallel, they *appear* convergent. What we mean here by saying that the lines are *really* parallel is that if we make certain measurements they will turn out in the way characteristic of parallel lines[1]. Again reality is what we arrive at as the result of an examination more complete than that which leads to a statement about appearance. And again "really" means "truly". For the judgement about the lines based on measurement is true in a sense in which the judge-

---

[1] We might also mean that the lines before they were feathered appeared parallel, and that we have every reason to believe that the feathering does not change their parallelism. But the other meaning is more fundamental. Further, when it is said below that universal agreement about the parallelism of the lines judged by eye cannot be obtained, it is not meant merely that there are not people who would not be taken in by the illusion (though this is probably true), but that our general experience of judging the parallelism of lines by eye shows that it is a matter on which opinion may easily differ.

ment based on simple inspection is not; it is scientifically true. For universal agreement about the results of the measurements is possible, whereas universal agreement in the judgement of the unaided eye is not possible. We substitute the measurement for the direct guess for precisely the same reason and in exactly the same way as we substitute measurements of wave-length for judgements of colour, in which colour-blind persons may differ from the rest of mankind.

Now it is important to insist that this contrast between appearance and reality is not that which we assert when we say that the hypothetical ideas of a theory are more real than the concepts of a law. In explaining the laws by the theory we are not substituting in any sense the true for the untrue, for the laws are quite as true as the theory—indeed, if we distinguish between truth and meaning they are more true. Nevertheless this use of "really" to mean "truly" is connected with that which we are considering. A close analogy to the explanation of laws by theories can be found in the discovery of the working of a mechanism. I hold in my hand a closed box which seems to resist my efforts to turn it about, as if it were alive; I open the box and find that it contains a rapidly rotating fly-wheel. The change in my knowledge about the box is very similar to that which follows the formulation of a true theory, and I may say that I have discovered the real constitution of the box. But if, as is probable, I said at the outset that the box behaved like a live thing and not that it was a live thing, my discovery has not in any way substituted truth for error; it has merely added one truth to another. And the change is similar to that involved in the two previous examples, first because the change of attitude is the result of further and more minute inquiry, second because the new statement, though not more true than the old, is intellectually more satisfactory. Our entire view of science is based on the doctrine that propositions can be satisfactory on grounds other than their truth, if by truth we mean scientific truth or that cruder common-sense conception out of which scientific truth has been elaborated.

Accordingly I believe that what we mean to assert when we say that the hypothetical ideas of a theory are more real than the concepts related to them through a dictionary is that the hypothetical ideas are the more satisfactory and that they have been attained by a more elaborate intellectual process. We are simply saying that the theory explains the laws, for explanation is the substitution of more for less satisfactory ideas by further investigation. "Real" and "really" in such statements are very closely allied to the same words when they are used in the sense of "true" and "truly", and in contrast to "apparent" and "apparently". But though they are closely allied they are not the same; the theory is not more true than the laws in the sense in which truth is used in science; and the laws are no more "apparent" than the theory. Moreover this sense of "real" is not the same as that which we discussed earlier. In that sense—and it is the more fundamental sense and the one more difficult to express in any other manner—hypothetical ideas and concepts are equally real, and reality is not something which is capable of degree.

In that sense reality may be a more important feature of one thing than another, but one thing cannot possess more of it than another.

This double use of the word real is undoubtedly unfortunate. It has been argued in Chapter II that complete consistency in the use of terms is not in the least necessary to science, and that the detection of verbal inconsistency is not always a proof that there is any confusion of thought. But inconsistency is undesirable where care is not taken to analyse the meanings of the words used; there would be no danger in our using "real" in as many senses as we pleased, if only we took care to distinguish them in our minds. That condition is not fulfilled. Indeed the state of the case is much worse than has been indicated; I have only examined the uses of the word in more or less strict scientific statements; if we examined its uses in common discourse we should find innumerable other senses, none of which are usually distinguished carefully. The word is always slipping into our language, and I am quite certain that I have used it many times in this book in ways which I could not defend. On the first revision of this chapter I struck out 33 "real's" and "really's" in order to avoid confusion when the stricter sense of the words was under discussion; in most cases they could go without anything being substituted in their place. It cannot surprise us to find that a word so abused is a source of confusion when students of different branches of learning address each other.

Metaphysical reality. In the last few pages I have been trying to set down the circumstances under which men of science use the term real. I do not pretend, of course, to have explained the full meaning of the word, for I believe it to be inexplicable, but I have tried to examine that meaning sufficiently to make distinctions which are necessary for our immediate purpose. The conclusion which I want to draw is that, if we use the words "real" and "reality" in a sense which we are not prepared to abandon under pressure, then we are asserting that the thing has a certain resemblance to material objects and substances, which are concepts defined by laws of a special form. But we do use the words in another sense, in which they are nearly but not quite equivalent to "true" and "truly" and are contrasted with "apparent" and "apparently". This sense is not identical with the special and essential sense. Further, propositions may be strictly and entirely true even when they are not about things which, in that sense, we judge to be real.

And now, having reached that conclusion, let us go back to our metaphysician and see if we can come to any better agreement with him. I am perfectly sure that we shall not. I cannot of course explain what the metaphysician means by the terms, for I have not the remotest idea; but we may be able to catch enough of his meaning to be sure that it is different from ours. Thus, from the outset it seems perfectly certain that the meaning he attaches to the term is analogous in some way to our subsidiary sense rather than to our fundamental sense. He cannot possibly use it in our fundamental sense, for, if he did, he could not conceive that material objects, which provide the basis of that sense, are not real; the fact that his use is analogous to our subsidiary sense is indicated by his persistent use of the term in contradistinction to "apparent". "Appearance and reality" is a phrase which seems to form the theme of most metaphysical treatises.

When our metaphysician tells us that science is not (or may not be) true, and that its ideas are not real, he is perfectly certain to bring as a support to his statement something about "illusions". We shall hear much about optical illusions, about colour-blind and tone-deaf people, about people looking through a stained glass window and all the rest of it. The senses, he will say, are clearly liable to error; how can you found on them any system of truth? The formal answer is so ridiculously simple that it is hardly worth while to give it once more. It is perfectly true that the senses are liable to "error", but it is precisely the business of science and its characteristic function to detect and exclude such error. Indeed if it were not for scientific activity we should not be aware of the existence or possibility of the error. We say that the judgements of the colour-blind person are in error and those of the "normal" person true only because the latter and not the former pass the test of scientific criticism; the latter agree with judgements concerning which universal agreement can be obtained, the former do not. That, and that only, is the reason why we recognise illusions and error. To say that science must be liable to error because there are such things as illusions is as sensible as to say that the average height of an army which has an especially high standard in passing recruits must be very small because some of the population from which it is drawn are dwarfs. Science may possibly be liable to error of some kind, but the one kind of error from which it is most certainly free is that which is associated with the "illusions" which it devotes so much labour and care to excluding from its subject matter.

This, I say, is so obvious and trite that it is hardly worth saying again. Our metaphysician will probably admit it as readily as we do. To suggest that he failed to recognise it would be to accuse him of imbecility, and we know that some metaphysicians are extremely sensible people. But his use of an analogy which seems to us so fallacious makes it very difficult to understand him. If the difference between appearance and reality is at all analogous to that between illusion and scientific truth, surely science, which first recognised that difference and has elaborated with enormous care complicated apparatus for detecting it, is the proper study to decide what is appearance and what reality. When he fails to draw this conclusion, we feel that the very nearness of our thoughts at some points makes their approximation more difficult where at present they diverge.

Another indication of what metaphysicians mean by reality is given by the statement (less usual among the moderns than among their predecessors) that it is something independent of perception. Here again their view comes very close to ours; for of course scientific reality must be independent of perception in a certain degree. It must be independent of the perceiver. This is what we mean when we say that there must be universal agreement concerning the laws which define reality. (But of course, according to science, not all that is independent of the perceiver is real, and mere independence will not establish that kind of reality which attaches to theories.) If a thing is "independent of perception" when it is true that, whoever goes to observe it and whenever he goes, the perception will be the same, then so far scientific and metaphysical reality agree; and it would seem that science, which has made it its business to investigate things which are so independent of perception, might claim at least equal right with any other study to decide about reality. Or again, if "independence of perception" means that reality is not changed by being observed, we shall agree that our reality has this property; we certainly assume that the things we observe are not changed by our observing them. But by this assumption I think we mean nothing more than that we can make many observations and make them in different ways and that yet the observations will continue to agree; for strictly I cannot see what we mean by the state of reality when it is not observed. All information about scientific reality comes from observing it, and there can, by the very nature of the case, be no evidence about it when it is not observed. Personally I find it very difficult to attribute any meaning to a proposition about which there cannot possibly be any evidence[1].

And there is yet another view of metaphysical reality which may help us to understand its meaning. Berkeley maintained *Esse est percipi*, and based on this doctrine the conclusion that, since reality undoubtedly continued to exist while no human being observed it, there must be some non-human being observing it in the intervals. (He does not explain how he knew it existed when no human being observed it.) Nobody agrees with Berkeley to-day, but the objections urged against his system are not usually that he did not know what reality meant. Now his view of reality seems exactly contrary to that we have just considered; reality, so far from being independent of perception, consists of nothing else than its being perceived. To me, and I believe to most men of science, the idea is unintelligible; I can conceive of something being altered by being looked at, though such a thing could not possibly be scientifically real; I can just conceive something so vain that it would not perform (and existence may be some kind of performance) unless it was looked at. But neither of these ideas seem to represent the meaning that is concerned here.

[1] This statement must be interpreted strictly. I can easily attribute meaning to a proposition concerning which there actually is no evidence, e.g. that John took the jam when nobody was looking. But that is because I can conceive of evidence of another kind than seeing the jam taken, such as that derived from the effects on John's digestive organs. If the only evidence possible were that somebody saw him take it, then I should not attribute any meaning to the statement that he took it when nobody was looking. Any difficulty which is felt in accepting that view arises, I believe, from the difficulty of imagining that it should be absolutely impossible that there should be other evidence.

This observation may be important in connection with past events. We cannot have the same kind of evidence of past events as of present, but we have evidence. The evidence is almost always of the nature of a theory; we find that, accepting the theory that effect always followed cause as it does to-day, certain effects to-day can only have been caused by certain events in the past. It need not be insisted that the assumption made is theoretical.

These simple considerations should show that scientific and metaphysical reality are different. I shall doubtless be told—if anyone takes the trouble to tell me—that I have misrepresented the views of metaphysicians; but if I have, my error proves my contention. For I have not erred for lack of good will, but simply because their views are such as my mind cannot grasp; I am in the position of one blind man trying to explain to another the meaning and significance of colour. The very fact that in some respects metaphysical and scientific reality are not very different makes the comprehension of the difference all the more difficult. If the two ideas had been developed from completely different originals, there might have been some hope of understanding; but they are developed undoubtedly from the same original, from the same fundamental common-sense conceptions. Two roads which start from the same point and diverge are much less likely to cross again than roads which start from different points; and it is just because we have developed the common-sense ideas which we share in such divergent ways that it is certain that the very structure of our minds is different and no ultimate agreement possible. On these matters students of science and of metaphysics cannot usefully converse; an attempt at conversation will merely lead to heat and they had better agree to differ.

Truth and belief. But the metaphysician cannot agree to differ; it is impossible for him to acquiesce, as others might be prepared to do, in the maintenance by different persons of contrary, if not contradictory, propositions. He cannot admit that, in any sense, both the opposing views should be right and both the propositions true. For he seems always to believe in absolute truth, and to regard nothing as true at all unless it is equally true for all persons, all places and all times. How far can we recognise such truth? The question leads us to investigate what we mean by truth just as before we were led to inquire what we meant by reality. And it is high time for this inquiry. The reader will doubtless have noticed that in this chapter I have apparently been very lax in the use of the term. In the earlier chapters I tried to avoid as far as possible using the term truth; in Chapter VIII I gave it a definite sense and contrasted the truth of a scientific proposition with its meaning; but later I have used it both in this narrower scientific sense and in a wider sense of which no explanation has been necessary. I make no apology from this procedure; it will aid us rather than hinder us in our discussion. For I think it will be found that all the uses of the term have been "natural"; that the word has only occurred where it is to be expected; if it has been used in various senses it can only be because it is habitually used in various senses, and an examination of these senses may give an answer to some of the questions that are about to be asked.

One of the most fundamental questions about the nature of truth is how it is connected with belief. Is a proposition true because it is believed, and, if so, by whom must a proposition be believed in order to be true? If a proposition is not necessarily true because it is believed by some person or persons, if truth is independent of belief, then what meaning or criterion of truth can we give? Personally I am quite clear that, in some cases at least, truth and belief are inseparable; these cases occur either when everybody believes, has believed and will believe it, or when nobody believes, has believed or will believe it[1]. If a proposition receives universal assent it is true; if it is universally rejected it is false. *Securus judicat orbis terrarum*. The adage is acceptable if interpreted strictly. If everybody believes something, the very suggestion that it is not true is almost impossible, for that suggestion will probably be made only by somebody who does not believe it. I simply cannot conceive of any state of affairs in which everybody (including my interlocutor and myself) believes a proposition and knows that everyone else believes it, and yet the question is raised whether it is true. I cannot conceive what is meant by a proposition being true (or untrue) when nobody thinks that it is true (or untrue). I do not mean that I can attach no meaning to the phrase that all the world is and always has been in error about something, for I can mean by it that at some future time the opinion of all or part of the world will change; but if I carefully exclude from my mind this possibility (it is not easy to exclude it; a distinct and sustained effort of thought is required), and if I also exclude the possibility that there are beings, whose opinion on the matter is ascertainable and yet are not included in "the world"—if these conditions are fulfilled, then the conception of a proposition universally believed but untrue, or universally disbelieved and true, is empty of all significance. The doctrine that universal assent is sufficient to establish truth is doubted probably only because it has been misapplied by theologians to crush the doubts of a minority; but of course if there is a minority, there is not universal assent and the criterion is inapplicable. Between a minority and a majority, the minority is far more likely to be right.

Now it is characteristic of science that it recognises that there are propositions for which universal assent can be obtained; and while those propositions receive such assent they would seem to represent what men of science mean by absolute truth. It has to be admitted that in the future propositions which now receive universal assent may fail to do so; and if they fail they will cease to be true. But we cannot conceive that, even if propositions which are now absolutely true cease to be true, they will not be succeeded by others which are true. If no propositions could be found for which universal assent could be obtained, then all scientific knowledge would be impossible; the entire structure of our thought as constituted at present would collapse, and it is impossible to say what, if anything, would take its place. Absolute truth in this sense is an integral part of science and the foundation on which it rests.

But such propositions do not form the whole of our thought or even the whole of science. Even scientific propositions, though they always state something which is absolutely true, also always state something concerning

---

[1] Difficulties always occur when the conceptions of the past or the future are introduced into such fundamental discussions. An attempt to consider some of them will be made in Part III, but they are not serious here, and any objection raised to these considerations will probably not be connected with them.

which it is recognised that difference of opinion is possible. And outside the range of science there are no propositions which receive certain and universal assent[1]. This class of propositions, which is excluded from science, includes a great many judgements of the material world which are extremely important in daily life, in the study of history, and in many other branches of intellectual activity. We cannot obtain for these judgements universal assent, often for the reason that it is only a small minority of mankind who have had or can have the experience on which such judgements could be based; but we can get the universal assent of everyone who seems to us to matter. Either everyone who can make the judgement at all makes the same judgement, or for some reason or other we think the judgement of those who dissent of little importance. The assent that we can obtain is, for the purpose which we have in view when we consider the matter at all, as good as universal assent; and our feeling of the truth of the propositions has almost the same basis as if universal assent could be obtained. Here again a proposition is true when it receives the assent of everyone to whom we are prepared to listen. It may be noted that if mathematical propositions are not to be included in the first class they are to be included here.

At the opposite extreme to this class of propositions, which are usually said to express "facts", is the class of propositions that expresses our "opinions" and our tastes, such statements for example as that Tolstoi is a greater novelist than Balzac, or that coffee is nicer than tea for breakfast. Concerning such statements we have no expectation of obtaining universal agreement and no desire to obtain it; we recognise that they are personal to ourselves and are often distressed rather than pleased when we find that the crowd shares our view. If such statements are in any sense "true", they are not

---

[1] Some people will probably want an exception made in favour of mathematical and fundamental logical propositions. Personally I am not prepared to make that admission. I think the universal assent for mathematical propositions, if it exists, is to be distinguished from that for scientific propositions on the grounds discussed in Chapter I, namely that it would be impossible to prove whether a doubter "really" doubted. Moreover, I think there is an appearance of universal assent only because people do not understand to what they are asked to agree and because they confuse mathematical and scientific propositions. Thus, if I am asked to agree to the proposition (one which is taken as fundamental in Russell and Whitehead's *Principia Mathematica*) that, if q is true, then p or q is true, I cannot help immediately thinking of such a statement as that which is given as an example, namely, that, if to-day is Tuesday, then to-day is either Tuesday or Wednesday. Now this example is, for me at least, something that can be interpreted in terms of observations; it is essentially of the nature of a scientific proposition. When I am told that, if I am to assent rightly, I must assent to the proposition when it involves ideas to which all perception of the external world is entirely foreign, then I am far more doubtful. Concerning such ideas, I do not think that I either believe or disbelieve the proposition; I am equally willing to accept it or its contrary. I will accept either for the purposes of what seems to me a very pleasant intellectual game, but I don't mind which I accept. An objector might accept this attitude so far; but he would then go on to ask whether I do not believe that, if I accept this proposition and certain others, then certain consequences follow—and that it is *true* that these consequences follow. But I think I should take up the same attitude towards this and any further propositions of the kind; I am simply prepared to accept them, or their contraries, for the sake of argument so long as they lead to an interesting argument. I certainly do not believe either as I believe scientific propositions.

true in the same sense as statements of fact, but again truth is associated with belief. They are not true if nobody believes them and if it is inconceivable that anybody should believe them, and on the other hand, if they are true at all, they are true if and because we believe them. We do not admit the possibility that we should be wrong in the matter. My opinions may change and probably will change throughout my life both in artistic and gastronomic matters; but this change is expressed rather as a change in the "I" who hold the opinions than in the truth of the opinions themselves. When my opinions change I say that I have changed, owing to advancing years or more perfect experience. My judgement of yesterday was true for the "I" who made it then, and my judgement of to-day is true for the "I" who makes it now; they are judgements made by two different people who existed at different times and yet are connected in the intimate manner which characterises the evolution of a single individual; they are no more inconsistent than judgements made by two different people existing simultaneously. In such matters belief is again the one and only criterion of truth; the difference is merely in the persons whose belief is relevant.

But intermediate between these two extreme classes comes another which raises grave difficulties. There are statements, of opinions rather than of facts, concerning which there is not universal assent and yet are such that the judgements of others than ourselves, differing directly from ourselves, are distinctly relevant. The most obvious judgements of this class are political judgements, the proposition that Protection is a better economic policy than Free Trade, or that Ireland should have Home Rule. That there is difference of opinion on these matters is only too clear, and equally clear is the fact that we do not consider our own opinion alone, but regard the opinions of others as important and as definitely right or wrong, true or false, according as it agrees or disagrees with our own. If truth is here to be associated with and determined by belief, it is neither the universal belief of mankind nor our own belief, for, though we may not be prepared to admit it to others, we are prepared to admit to ourselves that we may be wrong. What can we mean by such an admission? What criterion of truth other than the belief of ourselves or of all mankind can we apply?

When I say that I may be wrong, what I seem to mean is that I can distinctly conceive circumstances in which I should make the contrary judgement. The change in my opinions may be due to one of two causes; it may be due to a mere change in myself, such as produces a change in my tastes; or it may be due to a change in the evidence on which the judgement is made; facts which are not available now may be available in the future, so that I, even if I had not changed in the interval, would make a different judgement about them. But why should I say that my future judgement, if it differs from that I make at present, is any more right or true? The reason is partly the delusion, from which the most enlightened people can scarcely free themselves, that the opinions of youth are less reliable than those of age; but it is more that we believe that, if additional evidence occurs which will change my opinions, it will change also the opinion of others, and that, in the course of time, something approaching unanimity will be obtained on matters concerning which there is now the fiercest and most irreconcilable difference of opinion. We have seen such things happen in the past. Nobody of the smallest importance maintains now that the policy which led to the separation of the American colonies was right or that the passing of the Reform Bill was wrong; on these subjects, once the source of passions no less heated than those of the politics of our own day, an agreement, as complete as that which can be obtained for "facts", now prevails. Even in the realm of opinions, we hold once more that, if universal assent can be obtained, then it is a sure and ultimate criterion of truth.

It is interesting, though perhaps hardly relevant, to consider how these opinions, concerning which we think that universal agreement may be, and indeed should be obtained, differ from the purely personal tastes which were considered before. The difference lies in their relation to action. I am not prevented from enjoying a work of art because other people think it worthless, and I can get coffee for breakfast although other people prefer tea[1]; but I cannot give full expression to my political desires unless the majority of my countrymen agree with me. Here of course is the reason why I refuse to agree to differ about such things, but it is not always noticed that here is also the reason why there is hope that ultimate agreement will be obtained. For agreement is not reached by the conversion of those who differ from us; changes of fundamental political opinion are comparatively rare[2]. But men die, and are succeeded by others. If we can make our views prevail for the time being, they must influence the atmosphere in which the new generation is reared; and since men are profoundly affected by that atmosphere, ideas may be commonplaces to the new generation which were intolerable to the old. If we cannot make our views prevail, it is possible that our failure to translate them into action is due to their inherent weakness; they will not change the world of affairs and they will die with us. It is only because men and not their opinions change that progress is possible or tolerable in face of the innate conservatism of the vast majority of mankind; it is for this reason that the minority can be usually right.

To sum up then, in these practical affairs truth appears always to be a function of belief and to be determined wholly by belief. If a proposition is such that it is possible or conceivable that universal assent (or what counts

---

[1] Unless "other people" includes my wife. But then the opinion is apt to be transferred to the other class, namely that concerning which a difference may be a source of conflict.

[2] When I was a boy, an older man said to me that everyone, by the time they reached 30, ought to have attained fixed opinions on politics, religion and art. The saying disgusted me at the time, but now I have passed that critical age, I think there is a great deal of truth in it. Of course there are notable cases in which men have changed in mature age their whole outlook on life, and the change has shown nothing but the greatness of their spirit; but such a change much more often shows some moral or intellectual weakness. It is no defence against "ratting", which is usually rightly condemned, to reply that if people did not change their opinions there would be no progress. Progress consists in the conversion of our successors, not of our contemporaries.

for practical purposes as universal assent) can be obtained for it, then the proposition is true if, and only if, that assent is actually attained. If it is such that it is certain that opinions concerning it will always differ or, at least, if there is no reason for thinking that universal agreement concerning it is obtainable, then we hardly judge it to be true at all; we say that it is true for ourselves who believe it, and regard as without meaning the question whether it is true for others.

The concepts of science are always based ultimately on those of practical life; and it is doubtless in such considerations as have just been noticed that the distinction between the truth (in the stricter sense) and the meaning of a scientific proposition is based. The truth is concerned with propositions of the nature of facts, the meaning with propositions of the nature of opinions. But fortunately these are not mere opinions; they belong to the class concerning which universal assent is ultimately obtainable. To-day, when the theory is discovered, we believe it because we believe it, and for no other reason; we are undeterred by the disbelief of others. But we do so in the full confidence that ultimately everyone else will believe it too. They may be led to change their beliefs by additional evidence (or, of course, we may be led to change ours), but no amount of additional evidence, no amount of established scientific truth, can force them to believe. The change, when it comes, will much more probably come by the rise of a new generation, free from the prejudices of the old, and accustomed from the first to the ideas which we press on them. Lord Kelvin almost to the last adhered to the elastic solid theory of light propagation and never really accepted the modern electromagnetic theory; to-day our veterans find it impossible to abandon "the aether" or to grasp theories of which the fundamental ideas are discontinuous. They will die as he has died; and we shall be able to reverence their memory, thinking only of the great works they have done and not at all of their errors. It is not in science that the evil that men do lives after them. *Magna est veritas atque prevalebit.*

Absolute and relative truth. This discussion has been directed to show that the two kinds of "truth" which are recognised by science are but developments of "truth" as it is known in the world of common sense and practical affairs. In that world two kinds of truth are recognised, that which is applicable to statements of facts and that which is applicable to statements of opinion; of the former the criterion is the universal assent of all persons whose opinion we think (as a matter of opinion) worth considering; of the latter there is no criterion. Statements of opinion are true if the person making them believes them; since in these matters there is no way of discovering what anyone believes if we once begin to have doubts on the matter, there is no possible criterion which one man can apply to the truth of statements of opinion by another, while we have no need of a "criterion" to judge of the truth of our own statements. Truth in matters of opinion is wholly relative to the person making the statement; truth in matters of fact is absolute and is related in the same way to every person. What was called in Chapter VIII "scientific truth", or simply "truth", is the conception developed from the common sense idea of absolute truth; meaning, on the other hand, is the development of personal and relative truth. Absolute and relative truth are connected both in science and in practical affairs by the fact that relative truth often becomes absolute truth; and it is usually held that we attach value to relative truth in these departments of activity only because of this fact. In other departments, when we make judgements of taste (which are one form of judgements of opinion) there is not this connection; neither experience nor a priori expectation indicates that in these matters relative truth is likely to become absolute.

And now what of the absolute truth of metaphysics? This is clearly not our absolute truth derived from universal assent; metaphysicians do not, so far as I can understand, think that their doctrines are valuable because they have received or are likely to receive universal assent, though perhaps they might say that they ought to receive such assent. This last conception of something which "ought to be believed" appears to be derived from the class of opinions of which political opinions are typical. When I say that something ought to be believed I mean to assert very firmly that it has relative truth for me and that I see some prospect of its having some day absolute truth; if it does not seem to me possible that it should have absolute truth, I should not use the phrase; I should not say that everybody ought to think coffee nicer than tea[1]. Unless therefore the statement that metaphysical propositions ought to be universally believed means that there is some prospect of their being universally believed, and unless the absolute truth of metaphysics is thereby assimilated to the absolute truth of practical life, I am unable to understand what it does mean.

But although metaphysicians do not value their doctrines because they are absolutely true in our sense, it might turn out that they were absolutely true in that sense and that they were valuable to us for reasons other than those which confer the value for their authors. However they do not appear to be so absolutely true. Experience does not indicate that universal assent for them can be obtained[2], nor are they of such a nature that we expect that

[1] Of course "ought" often has a moral flavour. But morality, as I understand it, applies only to actions and to opinions which may influence action. If metaphysical doctrines were in the class of opinions which influence action and if, therefore, the moral "ought" were applicable to them, then there would be some prospect of attaining universal assent for them.

[2] Many writers have recently defended philosophy from the charge of making no progress towards universal assent; but the defence has always been either that certain views have been shown definitely to be false, or that new questions have been raised and solved in a manner commanding universal assent. No progress has been made in connection with the questions which interest us, namely to what extent, and why, the material world is in harmony with our desires. I doubt even whether in this connection any views have been rejected with universal assent; an appearance of universal assent has been obtained in some measure merely by the withdrawal of some of the combatants from the action. We are no longer all professional metaphysicians. Those of us who find no satisfaction in the metaphysical fashion of the moment leave metaphysical discussion alone, not because we are not interested in the questions or hold no views on them, but because we do not think that such discussion leads to any advance.

universal assent could be obtained. For they are not opinions which influence action. We cannot judge what a man's metaphysical opinions are from his actions even to the extent that we can judge his political opinions; he may even go to church or be a professional minister without accepting any of the doctrines which his church pronounces to be fundamental; in fact the best way at present to secure advancement in the Church is to profess the opinions of its sternest opponents. The absolute truth of metaphysics and religion has none of the characteristics of the absolute truth of science or of practical life.

The conclusion which I would draw is that there is no common intellectual ground between metaphysicians and students of science. They entertain ideas which to us are not merely false, but incomprehensible; and the converse is doubtless also true; their reality is not our reality, neither their truth our truth. The conclusion is so familiar that it would hardly have been worth while to write this chapter to arrive at it, had there not seemed some chance of arriving at a clearer idea of exactly where the fundamental difference lies.

And here before we leave the matter a final remark may be offered. The admission that the most fundamental truth of all is relative and not absolute, and that ultimately we must always agree to differ, will be very distressing to some people. I would therefore conclude with three considerations which may do something to relieve their distress, and to show that the acceptance of relative truth as fundamental is unavoidable.

First, then, I would point out once more that in science itself relative truth ranks higher than absolute. In the formulation of a law or of a theory it is relative truth which arbitrates between conflicting absolute truths. The propositions of science are absolutely true, but so also are many other propositions which science rejects; and their rejection is on the ground of relative truth, on the ground of their truth for me and not for you, or their truth for you and not for me. But it may be replied that this admission of relative truth into science is possible only because relative truth will ultimately become absolute truth; it provides the best test we can apply while we wait for absolute truth. Personally I deny that doctrine entirely; it is relative truth and not absolute truth that gives science its value for me; it is pleasant when others agree with me, but it is no more, and I am not quite sure that a theory does not lose some of its value for me when it gets into text-books, just as my favourite books are profaned when they appear in popular editions. Others may feel differently, and I pass to other arguments.

Second, it is relative truth that gives its value to absolute truth. Absolute truth is that on which all men agree, and we attribute value to it because all men agree about it. But we should not attach so much value to this universal agreement unless there were also irreconcilable differences. It is just the fact that men who differ from me entirely in every taste, in every opinion, in every experience, will agree with me that two events are simultaneous or that two collections have the same number—it is just this agreement, emerging from a sea of disagreement, that gives the matters on which we agree such peculiar importance. If everyone agreed with me about everything I should attach no special importance to the opinion of other people; indeed I probably should not form the conception of other people; I should regard them as other bodies animated, like my own, by my own mind; I should be in the position of the man on the desert island who was discussed in Chapter I. If there were no relative truth, there would be no absolute truth; relative truth is necessarily the more fundamental.

Third, there is of course another sense in which relative truth is the more fundamental. The judgement that there is absolute truth in any proposition must ultimately depend on a judgement which has only relative truth. For after all, it is I who judge that other people agree with me; or, if it is held that there is universal agreement that there is universal agreement, it is still I who judge that there is this universal agreement. Ultimately the conclusion cannot be avoided that other persons (if anyone cares to express it so) are merely inventions of my own mind, and that their judgements are my judgements. My bitterest opponent is as much a creation of my own imagination as my most faithful disciple. Of course these statements sound absurd when they are so expressed, but that is because language is incompetent to express what I mean without distortion. Language is built on the assumption that I am only one of other people; it could not be built on any other assumption, for it is only on that assumption that it can be used; I do not need language to express my thoughts to myself. Nearly all my active life is based on the assumption that I am one of others, but times must come when I retire into myself and force myself to recognise that the assumption is not true. And this truth is of course relative truth; it cannot possibly be expressed or comprehended by anyone else—if there were anyone else to comprehend it. To attempt to express the truth immediately leads to an inextricable tangle of inconsistencies. But if I am charged with them, I reply to myself, These inconsistencies are part of me; how can I be inconsistent with myself? Or in a wiser mood I hold my peace.

PART II

MEASUREMENT

CHAPTER X

FUNDAMENTAL MEASUREMENT

Summary. Measurement is the assignment of numerals to represent properties. Why is the process important and why is it applicable to some properties (e.g. weight) and not to others (e.g. colour)?

The answer must lie in some relation between numerals and measurable properties which does not apply to non-measurable properties. This relation is found in the common possession of order. The conception of order is analysed, as well as the relation between numerals and numbers. All measurable properties are capable of being placed in a natural order by means of definite physical laws which are true of them.

But the possession of order alone will not enable a property to be measured, except possibly by the use of previously established systems of measurement for other properties. In order that a property should be measured as a fundamental magnitude, involving the measurement of no other property, it is necessary that a physical process of addition should be found for it. By a physical process of addition is meant an operation which is similar in a certain manner to the mathematical operation of addition.

This similarity is analysed, the property of weight being taken as an example. It is shown that, if there is to be a satisfactory process of physical addition, two laws, the first and second laws of addition, must be fulfilled. Both these are definite physical laws, so that it is experiment and experiment only that can determine whether a property is fundamentally measurable. The two laws, though closely connected, are independent and one of them may be true without the other.

The difference between properties that are and those that are not capable of satisfactory addition is roughly that between quantities and qualities.

If a fundamental process of measurement can be found at all, the assignment of numerals to represent properties is perfectly definite, except for one arbitrary element, the unit.

It was suggested in Chapter I that physics could be distinguished from other sciences by the part played in it by measurement. Other sciences measure some of the properties which they investigate but it is generally recognised that when they make such measurements they are always depending, directly or indirectly, on the results of physics. All fundamental measurements belong to physics, which might almost be described as the science of measurement. Accordingly before we can enter upon any discussion of the actual results of physics we must have a clear idea of what measurement is and what are the conditions necessary for its application; to this inquiry, and questions arising directly out of it, this part of the volume will be directed.

Measurement is the assignment of numbers. Measurement is the process of assigning numbers to represent qualities; the object of measurement is to enable the powerful weapon of mathematical analysis to be applied to the subject matter of science. The questions that have to be answered are What is the nature of the process, and How does it serve to attain that object? The answers to both of them may seem very obvious, and this obviousness itself may seem the chief reason for the difficulty which I believe that some people will find in giving a perfectly clear and unambiguous answer to them. It will therefore be well to base our discussion on the consideration of a question which will probably appear more capable of a definite answer, Why can and do we measure some properties of bodies while we do not measure others?

I have before me on the table a tray containing several similar crystals. These crystals possess many properties among which may be included the following: Number, weight, density, hardness, colour, beauty. The first three of these qualities are undoubtedly capable of measurement—unless it be judged that number is to be excluded as being more fundamental than any measurement; concerning hardness it is difficult to say whether or no it can be measured, for though various systems of measuring hardness are in common use it is generally felt that none of them are wholly satisfactory. Colour cannot be measured as the others can, that is to say it is impossible to denote the colour of an object by a single number which can be determined with the same freedom from arbitrariness which characterises the assigning of a number to represent weight or density[1]. The last property, beauty, can certainly not be measured, unless we accept the view which is so widely current that beauty is determined by the market value. What is the difference between the properties which determine the possibility or impossibility of measuring them?

We can dispose very easily of the case of "beauty", which it was perhaps rather fantastic to introduce. Beauty is not a property with which science can have anything to do, because no agreement can be obtained for judgements concerning it; it could only become a matter for scientific investigation if a relation can be established between it and some property, such as price, concerning which agreement could be obtained.

The other properties, however, are all such that agreement concerning them can be obtained (for we will suppose that colour is to be judged only by normal persons—see p. 26), and the reason for the difference must be sought further afield. Since measurement is the process of assigning numbers to represent properties, it is obvious to inquire whether that difference may not be due to some greater resemblance between number and measurable properties than between numbers and immeasurable properties. Let us ask therefore what are the properties of numbers.

Numerals and Numbers. At the outset we must note that "number" is often used to denote two (or perhaps three) entirely different things; when I say that the number of my room in a hotel is 187 I am not speaking of the

---

[1] Of course it might be possible to measure colour by means of the wave-lengths and amplitudes of the components of the reflected light. But the discussion below will show that such a method is irrelevant to our present purpose.

same kind of thing as when I say that two and two are four; or when I say that I have five fingers. The fact that my room is 187 and yours is 58 does not mean that either or both of us have any nearer relation to the occupant of room 245 than to any other person; nor does it imply necessarily that there are 187 rooms in the hotel. "Number" in the first sentence should be replaced by "numeral"; all that I mean by the statement is that there is on the door of my room a piece of brass cut in the shape which is conventionally used to represent the number 187 on a printed page; the proper name for anything which thus represents a number is a "numeral" and it will be used throughout what follows. A numeral is a material or quasi-material symbol, a black mark on a piece of paper or certain sounds which I utter. The numeral 2 is thus clearly distinguished from the number which is involved in the statement that two and two make four, a pure arithmetical proposition; according to Mr Russell this number two is a class of classes, but we do not need to know for our purposes what it is; we only want to distinguish it from a numeral and, later, to know some of its properties. What is the exact meaning of number in the last sense (when I say I have five fingers) and whether it is identical with numeral or mathematical number is one of the problems we have to solve. But in case we have cause later to make a distinction I shall henceforth always write the mathematical concept, the class of classes, with a capital letter, Number.

Numerals and Order. The fact that numerals are used to represent Numbers shows that there must be some close relation between them; part at least of this relation is that they have a common property; this property is the possession of a definite order. Numerals are usually and normally found always in the same order; and I shall be seriously annoyed if I find that my room in the hotel is not between Nos. 186 and 188—though I may pardon the landlord if it lies between 185 and 189, the even numerals being on the opposite side of the passage. Now things may come to possess a definite order in one of two ways; the order may either be assigned arbitrarily as the result of a mere convention which everyone accepts, or it may arise from special relations between the things which possess the order. It is order of the first kind which is possessed by numerals. If we forget for the moment the relation between numerals and Numbers, there is no more reason why we should write 1, 2, 3, 4, 5, 6, 7, 8, 9 rather than 2, 6, 3, 8, 1, 4, 7, 9, 5; the usual order of the numerals arises from pure convention; it is as conventional as the order of the letters of the alphabet or the order of ranks in the Lord Chamberlain's table of precedence; it is merely something that civilised people have agreed to accept and which might be entirely changed if we began civilisation over again. But the convention which establishes the order of the numerals has a great advantage over that which establishes the order of the alphabet or of ranks, an advantage so great that the ingenuity which suggested the convention has often been described as one of the most remarkable achievements of the human mind. The advantages are (1) that the convention enables the order to be remembered very easily; we have only to carry in our minds an arbitrary order of 10 symbols and a few very simple rules for the order of their combinations; (2) that the list of things ordered can be indefinitely extended and yet the order of them remains perfectly definite; (3) that interpolation to any desired extent can be effected without changing the order already established. Thus, if we have already arranged five symbols in the order 1, 2, 3, 4, 5 and we want to add a sixth which is to come between 2 and 3, we can leave the five symbols as they are and add a new symbol 2·1 which is known by the convention to come between 2 and 3; if we find later we want a symbol between 2·1 and 2, we can use 2·11 and so on. It is these advantages which lead to the wide-spread use of numerals, rather than any other arbitrarily ordered symbols, to denote objects of which the order is important, such as houses in a street[1]. It is only very foolish people who put their friends to the trouble of remembering that Chatsworth comes between Seaview and Chez Nous instead of that 16 comes between 15 and 17; and it is almost equally foolish and even more common to call 32 a instead of 32·1 the house which has been built between 32 and 33.

The relation generating order. But order may also arise, not from an arbitrary convention, but from real properties of the things ordered; and it is of course the existence of this real order which has led to the invention of arbitrary orders to denote the things characterised by it. Such real order is possessed by the houses in a street and by Numbers, and by many of the other objects which are usually denoted by numerals. Now this real order, as pure mathematicians inform us, arises from certain relations obtaining between the things which are ordered, namely, such relations as are technically called "transitive and asymmetrical". A transitive relation is one such that if A has it to B and B has it to C, then A has it to C; a symmetrical relation is one such that if A has it to B then B has it to A. Thus, in a family, the relation of father to son is intransitive and asymmetrical; the relation of children of the same parents to each other is symmetrical and intransitive, but would be transitive if we regard a person as bearing that relation to himself; the relation of ancestor to descendant is transitive and asymmetrical. Similarly, of the relations used in science, "of the same colour as" is transitive and symmetrical, "different in colour from" is symmetrical, but may be intransitive (i.e. if C is of the same colour as A), "heavier than" is transitive and asymmetrical, "one gramme heavier than" is intransitive and asymmetrical. Now a number of terms will form a series and will have a real order if there is a transitive asymmetrical relation such that every term has either this relation or its converse to every other term. (By the converse of a relation R is

---

[1] It is perhaps worth while to note that objects which possess no natural order are often denoted by numerals, for instance soldiers or telephones. The advantage of numerals over any other kind of name for such purposes arises only from the possibility of indefinite extension; however many objects there are we can never run short of names for them if we use numerals, for there are definite rules according to which new names can always be invented. Here again few people have the sense to be consistent and use only numerals; in England (but not in France) we still call our telephone exchanges by pet names, as if they were dogs.

meant the relation which B has to A when A has the relation R to B; for example, "lighter than" is the converse of the relation "heavier than".) The condition that such a relation exists is sufficient to establish a definite order and to place the terms in a series[1].

Measurement of hardness. We are now in a position to decide why measurement is applicable to "hardness" in a way that it is not applicable to colour. In respect of hardness all bodies to which the concept applies at all are related by a transitive asymmetrical relation "harder than" or its converse "softer than"; every body the hardness of which we want to measure at all is either harder than or softer than every other body in that class. (For the moment we omit the possibility that two bodies are equally hard, and shall return to the consideration of it later.) Now "harder than" is a transitive asymmetrical relation. We will leave out of account modern methods of measuring hardness (the Brinell test, the impact test and so on) and suppose that by hardness we mean the property which led to the establishment of Mohs' scale used by mineralogists. Then one body is harder than another if it will scratch it. "Harder than" is transitive because, if A will scratch B, and B will scratch C, then A will scratch C; it is asymmetrical because if A will not scratch B, B will not scratch A[2]. Accordingly since every body with which we are concerned (omitting again those of equal hardness) will either scratch or be scratched by every other, the condition for the formation of a series is fulfilled and it is possible to arrange all these bodies in a series having a definite order of hardness, such that each body is harder (or softer) than the body which follows it and softer (or harder) than that which precedes it in the series.

When we have arranged the bodies in this series, they are suitable for denotation by numerals. We call the softest (or hardest) of them 1, the next in the series 2 and so on. This is precisely the procedure adopted by Mohs in his scale of hardness; it depends simply and solely on the fact that hardness is a transitive and asymmetrical relation. If it had turned out that the relation was symmetrical and that, while A would scratch B, B would also scratch A, there would have been no reason for putting A before B or B before A in the series; if on the other hand it had turned out that the relation was intransitive and that, though A would scratch B and B scratch C, yet A would not scratch C, but C would scratch A, then we should not have known whether to place C after B or before A.

Now we must introduce the bodies which are such that they will neither

---

[1] For a discussion how far the condition is necessary as well as sufficient and for the consideration of certain complications connected with "closed series", which will not concern us, reference should be made to Russell and Whitehead's *Principia Mathematica*. Of course no proof has been offered here that a transitive asymmetrical relation can generate order; perhaps such a proof can hardly be given, for what is "order" except something generated by such a relation?

[2] Neither of these propositions is strictly true. See Winkelman's *Handbuch*, 2nd ed., *Allgemeine Phys.*, II. p. 860; but Mohs' scale is based on the assumption that they are true —as is pointed out by Auerbach in the passage referred to.

scratch nor be scratched by some body in the series. Their introduction into
the scheme, in spite of the fact that the condition of a series is not fulfilled,
is possible for this reason. We find that a body B which will not scratch A
or be scratched by A behaves towards other bodies exactly as A behaves;
that is to say, it will scratch all the bodies which A scratches and be scratched
by all which scratch A[1]. It is this fact, which could not have been foretold
a priori, which makes us call B of the "same hardness as A"; if B, though
neither scratching nor being scratched by A, had not behaved in the same
way as A towards any other body C, we should not have known where to
put it in the series; but as it behaves exactly like A, we put it in the same
place as A and denote it by the same numeral. It will then still be true that
any body denoted by a larger numeral will scratch any body denoted by a
smaller numeral; we have only to introduce a new idea to deal with bodies
denoted by the same numeral (a feature not contemplated in the original
formation of the series), namely that bodies denoted by the same numeral
will neither scratch nor be scratched by each other.

Colour cannot be measured. We cannot apply the same process to
colour because we cannot find a similar transitive and asymmetrical relation
which expresses differences of colour and covers the whole range of coloured
bodies. "Different in colour" is, as we have noted, symmetrical but not
always intransitive; "redder than", "darker than" are intransitive and symmetrical relations, but they do not cover the whole field. Some colours are
neither redder nor less red than others, two shades of the same blue, for
example; and yet they are not "equal in colour", as the two bodies which
would neither scratch nor be scratched by each other were equal in hardness.
For they are not similarly related to all other coloured bodies; one may be
darker and the other lighter than some third colour. Accordingly we cannot
range them in a single series characterised by a definite order, even if we have
recourse to the device of allowing the same place in the series to be occupied
by several terms. There is no natural order of the colours which enables
us to denote them by the series of numerals except by the most arbitrary
convention[2]. Dyers often issue patterns of wool marked with numerals,
but the assignment of the numerals to the colours is as purely arbitrary as
the assignment of numerals to soldiers; it is dictated simply by the fact that

[1] Again this proposition is untrue, but again the assumption that it is true is essential
to the scale.

[2] It may be noted that if the three-colour theory of vision is true it would be possible
to represent colours by numerals in just the same way as minerals are represented in respect
of hardness. For then it would be true that every colour is either redder or less red than
any other, while at the same time it is either bluer or less blue and greener or less green.
Accordingly we might have three scales of redness, blueness, and greenness and denote a
colour by three numerals, such as 4, 7, 11, representing respectively its position in the three
scales. Colours which were neither redder nor less red, neither bluer nor less blue, neither
greener nor less green than some other colour B could then be given the place the same as
B because it would differ from all other colour C in the same manner as B differs from C.
The kind of series which would be generated in this manner would be a three-dimensional
series, concerning which we shall have more to say in Part III.

numerals are numerous and not by their possession of an order. The assignment of numerals to colours is arbitrary, because it is not dictated by experiment, that is by the results of judgements which form part of the subject matter of science and for which universal and impersonal assent can be obtained. Once we have decided on the scheme of our scale of hardness, the numeral which we are to allot to any body in respect of hardness is fixed by experiment; it is experiment which determines whether A will scratch B or be scratched by it and, therefore, whether A is to be represented by a greater or a less numeral than B[1]. On the other hand, in allotting numerals, as the dyer does, to represent colours, the particular numeral which is to be allotted to a particular colour is not determined by experiment; no experimental information is conveyed by representing it by one numeral rather than by another. The representation of hardness by numerals does convey certain experimental information; the representation of colours by numerals does not; and that is why we say that hardness is a measurable property in a sense in which colour is not.

The first conditions for measurement. This then is our first conclusion. In order that a property shall be measurable at all and in order that its representation by numerals shall convey any information of importance to science, it is necessary that systems which differ in respect of that property shall be related by some transitive asymmetrical relation, R. When we say that A differs from B in respect of this property (and the statement that A "has" a property means nothing else than that it differs in some respect from other bodies), we must mean that it can be shown by experiment that A and B are related by such a relation.

Further, the class of systems which includes all systems A and B such that A is related to B by this relation R (i.e. the class of systems "having the property" in question) must possess the following features. (This class is called "the field" of R.) If X is any system in the class, X must bear either the relation R or the converse relation R' to every other system in the class; or, if there is in the class some other system X' to which X bears neither of these relations, then X must bear the same relation as X' to every other member of the class; that is to say, if X' bears to any other member Y the relation R, the relation R' or neither of them, then X must also bear to Y in each case the same relation. Systems which are related as X to X' are said to have the same property or to be equal in respect of it; while if X_1 bears to X_2 the characteristic relation R, it will be said generally to be "greater than" R. It should be observed that equality is a transitive symmetrical relation; for if X has the same relation to Y as X', then X' has the same relation to Y as X, and if X has the same relation to Y as X' and X' has the same relation to Y as X'', then X has the same relation to Y as X''; that is a necessary consequence of the meaning of the word "same". Equality in

---

[1] Numerals are not really greater or less; strictly I mean a numeral which comes earlier or later in the arbitrary order and is used conventionally to represent a greater or less Number.

respect of a property is the transitive symmetrical relation which is thus developed out of the transitive asymmetrical relation which is characteristic of the property; we usually regard it as the limit which is reached when the differences expressed by the relation R and its converse are reduced (e.g. bodies of equal density are regarded as being reached by reducing indefinitely the relations of "just denser than" and "just less dense than"); but the definition given here is capable of being stated more briefly and precisely. Systems which are equal in respect of a property are assigned the same numeral.

But such measurement is not satisfactory. This condition is fulfilled by the other three examples which were given of measurable properties, number, weight and density. "More numerous than", "heavier than", "denser than" are all transitive asymmetrical relations; and the further condition is fulfilled that (e.g.), if a body B is neither heavier nor lighter than A, then B is heavier than C if A is heavier than C, and lighter than C if A is lighter than C. These three properties are therefore measurable. Indeed it is obvious that they are not only measurable, but measurable in some higher and more important sense than is hardness (according to Mohs' scale); there is still an arbitrariness about the assignment of numerals on Mohs' scale which is absent from the assignment of numerals to represent weight or density. The unsatisfactoriness of the scale of hardness was thus expressed recently in an engineering journal: "According to Mohs' scale, the hardness of diamond is represented by 10, of ruby by 9 ..., of talc by 1. But these figures are not proportional; and it is probable that the difference in hardness between diamond and ruby is at least as great as between ruby and talc". Nobody would make a similar statement about the scale of weight. What precisely is the distinction between the two scales?

We have seen that, in the scale of hardness, experiment determines uniquely and certainly the order in which bodies are to be placed, and it imposes certain limitations if numerals are to be used at all to represent hardness. Thus, if A is harder than B, the numeral which represents the hardness of A must be greater than that which represents the hardness of B (according to Mohs' convention, which might equally well have been reversed); if A is 8, B cannot be 7. On the other hand there is nothing whatever to determine how much larger the numeral of B must be; for all experiment can show, B might be equally well represented by 9, or 50, or a billion; whichever we chose we could still find numerals to represent hardness intermediate between that of A and B, and no difficulty or contradiction would arise. In fact experiment, while determining the order of the numerals, leaves the difference between them (or, more accurately, the difference between the Numbers conventionally represented by the numerals) quite undetermined; the choice of the difference is as arbitrary as the dyer's choice of numerals to represent his colours, and the engineer is perfectly right in implying that the differences between the assigned numerals have no physical significance whatever; it does not represent the physical difference[1]. On

[1] Of course the engineer's statement is somewhat confused. He had in his mind

the other hand, when we represent one weight by 8 and another by 3, we feel that the difference in the properties of the two weights is in some manner represented by the difference between the Numbers 8 and 3 which are represented by the same numerals.

Here we encounter entirely new ideas. So far we have been concerned with numerals only as representing order and possessing a quality not essentially different from that of the letters of the alphabet. Instead of representing hardness by numerals 1–10, we should have lost little if we had represented it by letters A–J or by ranks, dukes, marquises, earls ...; the only difference would have been that we should have had to have invented some new convention of order when we wanted to interpolate. But when the idea of difference is introduced the distinction between the methods of notation immediately appears; there is a significance in the difference between 1 and 10 which there is not in the difference between A and J, and this significance is connected, not with the actual symbols used as numerals, but with the Numbers which they are always used to represent. It seems indicated now that measurement is a process of establishing a relation not between properties and numerals, but properties and Numbers. Further these new ideas are associated with a more definite determination of the numerals which are to represent properties; those properties for which the difference between the representative numerals is significant are also those for which these numerals are definitely fixed. When the scale of hardness was found, the choice of a numeral to represent the hardness of one body did not limit the choice of numerals to represent any other body to one and one only; but in our scale of weight, when we have fixed the numeral which is to represent one weight we are not longer left with any arbitrary choice of the remainder; we are forced to represent every other weight by one numeral and one only.

Density. Derived magnitudes. Before we proceed to consider what is the distinction between those properties for which numerals are thus fixed, and for which differences are significant, and those which resemble hardness in this matter, we ought to decide to which class those properties which have been enumerated as examples belong. At first sight it will doubtless appear that all the three remaining, number, weight and density, belong to the first class, but a little consideration will show that they are not entirely similar. It is true that the numeral which has to be assigned to represent the density of any substance is fixed quite as definitely as that which represents its weight, but on the other hand the significance of differences of density is not quite the same as that of differences of weight. It will be recognised that the relation between a pair of substances of density 1 and 2 and another pair of density

a definition of hardness by some property other than simple scratching, namely the amount of material of a given kind which can be worn away in given conditions with the use of the substance as an abrasive. This amount can be measured; and what he really meant to assert is that the amount worn away is not proportional to the Number indicated by Mohs' scale. That is to say, he is assuming that a satisfactory method of measuring hardness as a derived quantity (see later) has been found, and stating that Mohs' scale does not agree with the result of that method.

2 and 3 is not so simple as that between the pair of weights 1 and 2 and the pair 2 and 3; we can think at once of a very simple experiment to show that the difference between the weights of one pair is equal to the difference between the weights of the other pair, but there is no experiment of equal simplicity which shows that the difference in density of the two pairs is the same.

Further, if we inquire how we are able to fix with perfect definiteness the numeral to be assigned to represent density, we realise at once that the method employed involves the measurement of other properties; the definite measurement is possible only because we identify density with the ratio of mass to volume and because we can measure mass and volume. It is rather difficult to say whether, in the present stage of development of physics, we actually mean by density this ratio, or whether we merely employ that ratio as an indication of some other property, which is what we really mean by the term; but at any rate we can describe the property which we call density without any reference to mass or volume. Thus we may say that A is denser than B if a liquid can be found such that B will float in it and A sink[1]. This definition is not, of course, applicable to all substances which have density, but it would not be difficult to elaborate it so that it would cover the whole range. Now since we are inquiring how properties are measured, it is obviously no answer to our questions to describe a process which involves the measurement ·of other properties, unless the process by which those properties are measured has already been determined. It has not yet been determined in the case of mass and volume, and hence it is of no use for our present purpose to refer to the measurement of density as a "derived magnitude"; our question is whether density would be measurable if it were defined without any reference to other measurable properties.

The property of sinking in a liquid in which another property will float can be shown by experiment to be transitive and asymmetrical, and to cover the whole range with the exception of bodies which fulfil the condition for equality. Hence density, defined without reference to mass or volume, is at least as measurable as hardness; but is it more so? No; a little inquiry will show that if we define density by means of this property we can proceed exactly as far as and no further than we could with hardness. We can arrange bodies in order of density and assign a series of numerals to represent their density; but the fixing of the numeral to represent the density of one body places no limitation on that to be assigned to any other except that it must be larger or smaller. The only difference between hardness and density is that

[1] I am inclined to think that this is historically the ultimate meaning of density, that to Archimedes, for example, density was simply the property in virtue of which some bodies floated while others sank, and that the discovery that this property was represented by the ratio of the mass (or rather weight) to the volume was a later and independent discovery. It is questions of this kind which ought to be, and never are, discussed in histories of science.

It is worth while here to ask exactly what is meant when it is said that the ratio "represents" the density. It simply means that the order in which bodies are placed in respect of density, or the order generated by the transitive asymmetrical relation "denser than", is the same as the order of the Numbers of the ratios mass/volume.

in the latter and not in the former the generating relation really is transitive and asymmetrical, so that the most minute inquiry would not disclose any discrepancies in our series. The difference which appears to exist between the power of measuring density and the power of measuring hardness arises only from the fact that we can define density adequately as a derived magnitude (see Chapter XIII) and that we cannot at present so define hardness. If the researches that have been undertaken in recent years to define hardness as a derived magnitude, e.g. by the area of the impression caused by the blow of a definite weight falling through a definite distance, are successful, hardness will be measurable in exactly the same degree as density. But the process involved presupposes the measurement of area, just as the measurement of density presupposes the measurement of mass or volume; neither process is a fundamental process of measurement and it is only such processes which interest us for the moment.

Significance of addition. Density, therefore, must be classed with hardness, and the break in the series of properties which has been enumerated occurs between density and weight. For weight undoubtedly is a property which is definitely measurable; the fixing of the weight of one body fixes uniquely the weight of all others, and yet the process of measuring weight does not involve the measurement of any other magnitude[1]. For this reason we shall term weight a "fundamental magnitude" in distinction to density which is a derived magnitude. Now the distinction between density and weight in this factor is, it has been suggested, connected with the physical significance of the difference between the Numbers represented by the numerals which represent also the property; in the matter of weight the difference between the weights 2 and 3 is equal to the difference between the weights 3 and 4 in some way in which the difference between the densities 2 and 3 is not equal to the difference between the densities 3 and 4. It is indicated that in the measurement of weight we make use in some manner of the conceptions of addition and subtraction, conceptions which are applicable to Numbers but not to numerals. In the measurement of density or hardness we make use of a similarity between these properties and numerals; in the measurement of weight, we make use of a similarity between that property and Numbers.

And of course it is obvious how we make use of addition to fix definitely the numeral to be assigned to represent weight. We choose some body to which we assign some numeral, say 2; we take another body which has the same weight; we combine them in a manner which we call addition, and so obtain a body of which the weight is definitely and uniquely fixed to be 4. That is to say, the definite fixing of the numeral to be assigned is associated with the finding of some clear physical significance for the process of addition.

The difference between those properties which can be measured perfectly definitely, like weight, and those which cannot arises then from the possibility or impossibility of finding in connection with these properties a physical

---

[1] With the possible exception of number—a matter to be discussed presently.

significance for the process of addition. Our next inquiry, then, must be what is the process of addition and how physical significance can be attributed to it.

Nature of addition. Addition is a process which is peculiarly characteristic of Numbers. What precisely the addition of Numbers is and what are the special properties of Numbers which make addition so particularly applicable to them, these are questions which lie far outside our province; they are discussed in such treatises as that of Russell and Whitehead, and if I attempted to summarise their conclusions I should probably blunder. But there are certain propositions about addition which are undoubtedly true, although the exact nature of their foundation may be doubtful; moreover they are the propositions on which the application of the conception of addition to the further development of arithmetic is based. These propositions are known by the names of the associative and distributive laws; they may be stated thus: If by $a + b$ we mean the Number which results from the process of addition applied to the Numbers a and b, and by $(a + b) + c$ the Number which results from the addition of c to the Number which results from the addition of a and b, then

$$a + b = b + a,$$

and
$$(a + b) + c = a + (b + c).$$

There is a third proposition which is not so often stated and may possibly have a rather different foundation, though it is not less certainly true, namely, that, if a is any Number, $(a + 1)$ is greater than a, and more particularly that $(1 + 1)$ is greater than 1. These three propositions contain, I believe, all that is necessary to the development of that part of arithmetic which is concerned only with addition, and not with multiplication or division or any other operation. It should be insisted again that it is not necessary for us to decide whether these statements are mere definitions or significant propositions; it is possible that all are propositions or all definitions, or that some are one and some the other; all that matters to us is that they truly represent certain properties of Numbers and of the process of addition.

It will be observed that the propositions involve, beside the symbol of addition $+$, the symbol of equality $=$. To state fully the significance of this symbol and to use it properly in developing arithmetic from the propositions, some further knowledge about it is required. We require to know that it represents a transitive symmetrical relation, so that if $a = b$, $b = a$, and if $a = b$ and $b = c$, then $c = a$ or $a = c$.

Further, we need for the development of arithmetic certain propositions about individual Numbers and not merely about general relations between them. We need for example to know that $2 = 1 + 1$, $3 = 2 + 1$, $4 = 3 + 1$ and so on. Again, we need not decide whether these are definitions of the Numbers or propositions about them derived from other propositions; but it is in virtue of such propositions, together with the distributive law, that we arrive at such propositions as that $4 + 3 = 7 = 5 + 2$.

Lastly, since our discussion arose from the consideration of the meaning of "difference" it will be convenient, though not strictly necessary, to state the meaning of this term and the associated process of subtraction. For our purpose subtraction may be regarded simply as the inverse of addition; if adding b to a is the process which turns a into c, then subtraction of b is the process which turns c back to a. And difference will be sufficiently defined for our purpose by stating that, if c is the sum of a and b, then b is the difference between c and a, a the difference between c and b; alternatively we may say that the difference of p and q is what results by performing on p the process of subtraction of q. These definitions are actually equivalent in many, if not all, cases; but it is quite unnecessary for us to inquire why or when they are equivalent.

Physical addition. So much for the properties of Numbers in virtue of which addition and subtraction are applicable to them. What is the similarity between these properties and the properties of bodies in respect of weight which enable us to apply to weight the process of addition? The similarity is between the relation denoted by the sign of addition and a relation which can be established experimentally between bodies in virtue of the fact that they have weight; the propositions which are true of one relation are true of the other.

The example of weight will make the meaning clear. We measure weight by means of a balance. We state that the weights of two bodies A and B are "equal" when, if A is placed in one pan of the balance and B in the other, the final position of the pointer of the balance is unchanged. We say that the body C is "added to" the body A, when A and C are placed in the same pan of the balance; and that it is "subtracted from" the body composed of A and C in the same pan by removing C from the pan. When we have thus defined "equal" and "added to" in the use of the balance, we can state, corresponding to arithmetical propositions which involve addition and equality, propositions about what will happen to the balance when we place bodies in the pans. Thus suppose that the symbols a, b, c are taken to represent the bodies A, B, C (a, b, c are not numerals necessarily; "a" means simply that we are referring to A rather than to B or C); then the statement that $a + b = c$ will simply mean that A and B in the same pan balance C. Now let us state in this manner propositions corresponding to the laws of addition. Then, corresponding to the arithmetical proposition that, if $a = b$ and $b = c$, then $a = c$, we shall state that, if a certain body A balances another body B and if B balances another body C, then A must balance C; corresponding to the distributive law, $a + (b + c) = (a + b) + c$, we shall state that if P is a body which balances B and C on the same pan and Q a body which balances A and B on the same pan, then A and P on the same pan must balance C and Q on the same plan; and so on for the other laws.

Now these statements concern experimental facts; they assert that, in certain circumstances, we shall observe something. The statements may be true or false; and, as with all statements of experimental fact, experiment only can determine whether they are true or false. If they are true, there will be a certain similarity between the arithmetical process of addition and the arithmetical relation of equality on the one hand and the physical process of addition and the physical relation of equality on the other; if they are false, there will not be this similarity. It is similarity of this sort which was meant at the opening of this section.

The principle of measurement. If these experimental propositions, corresponding to the laws of addition, are true (and in the case of weight they are) we can proceed at once to measurement. We know that the Number 2 is that which results from the addition of the Number 1 to the Number 1; that the Number 3 results from the addition of the Number 2 to the Number 1, and so on for all other Numbers. Accordingly if we can find a body corresponding to the Number 1 we can discover in a unique and perfectly determinate fashion what bodies will correspond to other Numbers; and if we agree that the weights of bodies are to be represented by the numerals which represent also the Numbers to which they correspond we can assign numerals to represent their weights. For the present we shall not inquire on what principle we choose the body which corresponds to the Number 1, but suppose it is selected by an act of purely arbitrary choice. Having selected it we proceed thus. We have first to introduce again a definition used in establishing order, namely that, if two bodies are equal in weight they correspond to the same Number and are to be represented by the same numeral. We then find another body equal in weight to the body 1 (and therefore also corresponding to 1) and place it on the same pan with that body; the weight of this composite body is then 2. We find another body balancing, and so equal in weight to, the composite body, place it on the pan with the body 1 and so obtain a composite body 3; and so on. So long as we can always find a body (single or composite) equal in weight to the composite body produced by "adding" the body 1 to the previous composite body, we can continue finding new bodies corresponding to the successive Numbers 1, 2, 3, 4, 5, 6, ... the weight of which is to be represented by the corresponding numerals. By this process we assign numerals in a perfectly determinate manner to an indefinitely long series of bodies which form what we shall call the standard series.

Having obtained our standard series we can also determine uniquely the weight of any body which is equal in weight to any one of the standard series, in virtue of the definition that bodies equal in weight are to be represented by the same numeral.

The criteria of addition. The First Law. Of course nobody who is likely to read this book requires to be told what the actual process of weighing is; if mere description had been the object there would have been no need for the long account which has just been given[1]. But we are inquiring why

---

[1] It may be doubted even whether the long account is accurate. We do not actually establish a standard series of quite the nature or in quite the way which has been described. We do not actually include in our standard series all the terms 1, 2, 3, 4, 5, 6, 7, 8, 9, but

such a process exists for the measurement of weight and not for the measurement of density. The answer to this question is not so familiar. I have never seen it given adequately; the omission may be due to the fact that it is too trite to be worth stating, but I have to confess that I only found it out for myself after long thought. There are many things which appear obvious when they are once stated but are not so easy to state precisely for the first time.

The answer which our recent discussion indicates is this. In respect of weighing a process of addition and a relation of equality can be found which are similar, in the sense that has been explained, to the arithmetical process of addition and the arithmetical relation of equality; but a process of addition and a relation of equality which are thus similar to the arithmetical process and relation cannot be found in respect of determinations of density. But the matter will not be completely cleared up until it is known exactly in what respect the similarity which holds in one case fails in the other.

It would seem at the outset that the difference between weight and density cannot lie in the relation of equality. For we have seen that the characteristic relation which generates order leads directly, both for weight and for density, to a relation of equality which is so far similar to the arithmetic relation that it is transitive and symmetrical, and these properties are all that are explicitly asserted for arithmetical equality. Such a relation must exist for any property which can be ordered and measured to the same extent that hardness can be measured. It may seem therefore that it is only the process of addition which is lacking. But the two are really inseparable, because the laws of addition to which the physical laws have to be similar involve the symbol of equality as well as that of addition. A process of addition which might correspond adequately to the arithmetical process with one relation of equality might not correspond adequately if another relation of equality were chosen. The possibility must be borne in mind that we could find two or more characteristic relations, each of which would represent properly the meaning of density and give rise to a transitive symmetrical relation of equality; and yet that if one of these were adopted, but not if another were adopted, a satisfactory process of addition could be found. (A proposed process of addition will be termed "satisfactory" if it is found to be similar, in the sense described, to the arithmetical relation.) The decision whether the possibility ever becomes actual must be left until we have examined further the process of addition.

Again, the characteristic relation which generates order and lies at the basis of all measurement, complete or incomplete, gives at once some indication of what processes of addition will prove satisfactory. For the process of

only 1, 2, 2, 5, ... or even 1, 2, 4, 8, ..., and we do not make the 5 by five successive steps from 1, but by making it equal to 1 + 2 + 2. But this method involves the proposition, which we have not yet discussed, that 1 + 2 + 2 = 5. Further we sometimes get rid of the necessity for some of these steps by placing weights on the other pan; if we do this we only need a still more restricted series; but in that case we need the proposition that, if $x + p = q$ and p and q are known, x is known. If we only knew what we suppose that we know at present, the method given would be necessary.

addition must be such that the system which is produced by adding one body possessing the property in question to another must be greater than either of the bodies added[1]. It is this proposition which corresponds to the arithmetical proposition, included in the laws of addition, which states that $a + 1$ is greater than a. This proposition will be called the First Law of addition. (Since any body can be taken as 1 no really greater generality would be obtained by stating that $a + b$ must not be equal to a.) Now "greater than" is an expression which has meaning quite apart from any measurement or assignment of numerals; "greater than" is the characteristic relation which underlies the very beginning of measurement; and accordingly, before we have begun to assign numerals at all, we are able to apply one test to discover whether any process of addition is satisfactory. It is true that we might be forced, in order to find a satisfactory process of addition, to change the meaning originally attributed to "equal"; but since "equal to" must always be associated in the manner discussed with "greater than" and "less than", a change in the meaning of equality will not abolish the need for a characteristic relation, "greater than", and the test can always be applied.

Moreover the law of addition, $a + 1$ is greater than a, is not only the first law which can be tested; it is also the first law which is necessarily applied in the process of measurement. For in our description of the process of establishing a standard series of weights it was implied that the system resulting from the addition of 1 to 1 was different from 1. If this assumption had not been true, the standard series would have consisted of bodies all of which were equal, and we should not have been able to assign a numeral to any body except to that arbitrarily selected as 1; the whole proposed system of measurement would have broken down from the outset.

This, then, is the reason why the first law of addition, in the form $1 + 1$ is greater than 1, must be fulfilled if the process of addition is to be satisfactory. And this is also the reason why it is possible to find a satisfactory process of addition for weight and not for density. We can find a process of combining two bodies of equal weight, which gives a body of a weight greater than either; but we cannot find a process of combining two bodies of equal density which gives a body of density greater than either[2]. However we combine two bodies of equal density we always obtain a body of the same density; however we define addition for density, we always find that $1 + 1 = 1$, and that the first law of addition is untrue.

[1] In view of the possibility of negative magnitudes, which are discussed later, it would be more accurate to say "greater or less". But at present we know nothing of sign, and the more limited expression will serve.

[2] By "bodies of equal density" is meant here bodies of really equal density, composed of the same substance. I say that bodies are not *really* of the same density unless they are composed of the same substance, because unless that condition is fulfilled they are not related entirely in the same way to any third body. A solution of potash and a solution of sulphuric acid may have the same density and fulfil the condition for equality in respect of the relation which characterises the property density; but if equal quantities of the two solutions are mixed with the same quantity of some third solution, say another solution of potash, the density of the resulting mixture will be different in the two cases.

Qualities and quantities. It will be recognised, I think, that this difference between weight and density is the true root of the matter; the criterion which is here applied to distinguish the two properties depends on their real meaning. For it is just because the proposition $1 + 1 = 1$ is true for density and not true for weight that these two properties are important for physics and important in different ways. The distinction between the two properties corresponds to the distinction, which everyone recognises, though few analyse it, between a substance and its properties. We feel that the amount of substance in a body is something which is increased by combining two bodies, while the properties of the substance are something which are not changed at all by any combination of two similar bodies; accordingly we feel that properties for which a process of addition can be found which satisfies the first law of addition represent the amount of some kind of substance, while those for which the law is always false represent the qualities of a substance. In general we desire to be able to place a property in one or other of these two classes, either the class of amounts or quantities of substance, or the class of qualities of substance. When we discuss the matter fully in a much later chapter we shall find that no property can be regarded as a quantity of substance unless it is fully measurable and a process of addition which fulfils all the laws can be found for it. Accordingly, if we find a property such that no process of addition can be found which fulfils all those laws, so that the property is excluded from one class, we always try so to define the property so that it falls into the other class, inclusion in which implies that $1 + 1 = 1$. It is not mere accident that there is a large class of physical properties of which this proposition is true; besides density, there are viscosity, solubility, dielectric constant and a host of others; they are all the result of deliberate intention; they have been deliberately defined so that they are the same for any combination of similar bodies as for the component bodies. It is because they are so defined that they are important in physics and their values are tabulated in our works of reference.

We recognise then that there is a large class of properties of the greatest importance for physics which are such that no complete system of measurement, such as is available for weight, is applicable to them. Except in so far as they are "derived magnitudes", and numerals can be assigned to them which are based on the measurement of other magnitudes, they are not capable of measurement, except in the limited and incomplete way in which hardness is measured on Mohs' scale. This class of properties will be termed "qualities". The class of properties which obey the first law of addition will for the present be called "quantities", though the meaning of that term will be limited later. All fundamental magnitudes must be quantities in this sense; but the converse proposition need not be true.

The criteria of addition. The Second Law. So far only one of the laws of addition has been considered. We must now inquire into the other laws and ask whether, if the first law is true, the others are necessarily true;

or, if not, in what circumstances they are true and what kind of evidence of their truth is possible and sufficient.

For this purpose it will be convenient to express the laws in a manner slightly different but logically equivalent. In place of the commutative and distributive laws we shall substitute the following Second Law of addition: The magnitude of a system produced by the addition of bodies $A, B, C, \ldots$ depends only on the magnitude of those bodies and not on the order or method of their addition; it is the same so long as the magnitude of the bodies combined is the same and so long as the order and method of combination satisfies the condition laid down in the definition of the process of addition. (Note that the definition of the *same* magnitude does not require any measurement depending on addition.) A special case of this law is that if A_1 is equal to A_2 and B_1 to B_1 then the system produced by adding A_1 and B_1 is equal to that produced by the adding of A_2 and B_2.

It will be found that the physical laws corresponding to the commutative and distributive laws as ordinarily stated are precisely the same as that corresponding to this Second Law. This is obviously true in the case of the commutative law. In the case of the distributive law, we have $(b + c) = b + c$ by definition; hence $a + (b + c) = a + b + c$ by second law; but $(a + b) = a + b$, and $(a + b) + c = a + b + c$. Therefore $a + (b + c) = (a + b) + c$.

Further, for some of our later discussions, it will be necessary to consider what form the laws of addition take when "greater than" or "less than" is substituted for "equal to". In the arithmetical propositions, we have, first, the statement that the relations greater than and less than are transitive and asymmetrical, and, second, corresponding to the commutative and distributive laws, the following:

If $a + b \gtreqless c$; then $b + a \gtreqless c$.

If $(b + c) \gtreqless d$; then $a + (b + c) \gtreqless a + d$.

To the first of these corresponds again the Second Law stated above. Corresponding to the second we have that the addition of equal magnitudes does not alter the order of magnitude of the bodies to which they are added. This law also must be true if the process of addition is to be satisfactory when we are considering inequalities as well as equalities.

The question is then whether these laws are necessarily true, if the first law of addition is true; it is best examined in the example of weight. We define the addition of bodies in respect of weight as the placing of them in the same pan. The second law of addition will be true if the system which will balance a given combination of bodies in a pan is the same however those bodies are placed in the pan and if, when we add to each of the previously balanced pans one of a pair of bodies of equal weight, the pans will remain balanced. Now whether these conditions are fulfilled depends entirely on what we mean by a balance. If we mean the most carefully constructed instrument made by the maker of the highest reputation, we shall probably find that they are fulfilled; but if we mean anything that a second-hand dealer in cheap apparatus would call a balance, we shall find that they are not always fulfilled. This, of course, is obvious, but it is not an answer to the question which is being asked; for we are supposing that the process of measurement has proved satisfactory up to this point, and that supposition excludes many of the most imperfect balances. The first law of addition does not, it is true, exclude many imperfections; so long as the beam is free to swing at all the addition of some body to one pan will always make that pan sink; but the condition that the relations of greater than and equal to have the necessary properties does exclude many common imperfections. Thus, if the balance had unequal arms, the second law of addition would not be true, for interchanging the bodies on the pans (which is not excluded by the definition) would alter our judgement of equality; but it would also make the relation of greater than not always transitive and asymmetrical and the relation of equality not always transitive and symmetrical. Such an imperfection is already excluded in the process of establishing merely an order of weight. But there are imperfections which might not be discovered in establishing that order which would make the second law of addition untrue. For example, if the pans were improperly hung and their knife edges not parallel to the main knife edge, the weight of a body (as we should say now) would depend on its position in the pan. In balancing single bodies against each other we might put them always in the same place and so arrive at perfectly consistent judgements of equality; but if we are to add bodies and place two in a pan at the same time, they cannot both occupy the same position as they did when they were balanced singly; pairs of bodies which, weighed singly, were equal may not give equal sums. Or a discrepancy might appear if the nature of the bodies weighed was unsuitable, even if the balance was perfect when other bodies were used. Suppose that one body was a magnet and the other a piece of soft iron; if the piece of soft iron was placed in the same pan very near the magnet it would change the force on it due to the earth's field and would (as we should say) alter its apparent weight; if the magnet were balanced against a nonmagnetic body and we placed in each pan a piece of soft iron of equal weight the balance would be disturbed.

It is such defects as these which we are considering when we speak of a "perfect balance", or say that certain conditions are necessary for accurate weighing. The experiments which are described in any adequate text-book of physics as the tests which must be made on a balance before its indications can be accepted as accurate will be found on analysis to consist almost entirely of examinations whether the second law of addition is fulfilled in all cases; and the warnings issued against the neglect of certain precautions (such as that the bodies weighed must be at the same temperature as the balance) are directed against conditions in which that law is known to be false. The only other matter which is taken into account is whether the indications of the balance are likely to be consistent if the observation is repeated. This is a subject we shall examine presently.

Our conclusion is then that the truth of the second law does not necessarily follow from that of the first; that the second law of addition is a true and independent experimental law; and that experiment only can show if, and in what conditions, it is true[1]. Until we have examined carefully the property which we propose to measure we cannot be sure that measurement is possible, and the doubt may be concerned with the second law of addition as well as with the first law or with the nature of the proposed characteristic relation generating order. The possibility of measurement at every stage depends entirely upon the assumption of certain experimental laws.

But still there is a difference in this matter between the first and second laws of addition. The truth or falsity of the first law seems involved in the very nature of the property which we are proposing to measure. If the first law were not true for weight or if it were true for density, the significance of the properties of weight and density would be quite different from what it actually is. The second law in a sense seems much less important; any difficulty which is experienced in defining addition so that it is true is connected rather with experimental details rather than with fundamental principles. It will be admitted that, even if the first law is true, there are circumstances in which the second law is false; but it may yet be questioned whether it is really possible that, if the first law is true and the property concerned is so defined as to be a "quantity", it should be impossible to find any conditions in which the second law is true.

Questions which involve the hypothesis that our observations might be other than they are can never be answered definitely. But I do not think it can be judged inconceivable that we might be unable to measure a property because we could not fulfil the second law. There is no doubt whatever that we find very great difficulty in fulfilling the second law in some cases, and that in some which have occurred in the more recent developments of science the difficulties are not yet overcome. There are some properties which obey the first law and are therefore regarded as representing the quantity of some substance, but for which a really satisfactory system of measurement has not been worked out. An instance is provided by the "intensity of X-rays". We regard that property as representing the quantity of a "substance" (namely, energy) carried by the rays; but neither the method of ionisation, nor of chemical action, nor even of heat development is really satisfactory for measuring and comparing the amount carried by rays of different hardness. And if we inquire why none of the methods are completely successful we should find in each case that it was doubtful whether the second law of addition was fulfilled, that is, whether rays equal in intensity added to rays equal in intensity always produce sums equal in intensity, or whether a process of addition

---

[1] It may be thought that the conditions necessary for a perfect balance and accurate weighing could be deduced, without actual experiment, by deduction from known principles, such as the laws of statics. But investigation would show that our belief in the truth of these laws is based directly on our knowledge that measurement of weight (and other forces) is possible, and thus assumes that the second law of addition is true in certain circumstances. Indeed the experiments on which the laws of statics might be based would certainly include those which show that there is such a thing as a perfect balance.

can be defined such that the intensity of the added beams depended only on the intensity of the beams added.

In this case, however, we feel that the progress of knowledge may enable the difficulties to be overcome. But I think there is one case which has been so completely studied that it will be felt unlikely that any further research will remove the obstacles which still exist. This instance is "quantity of heat". The full consideration of the matter is impossible until the complete discussion of the science of heat is undertaken, but enough can be said to indicate the position, if no attempt is made to examine all the complications or to prove all the statements made.

In order to define the characteristic relation of order in this instance we may say that the quantity of heat contained in a body[1] A is greater than that contained in B, if A when dropped into a certain volume of water raises its temperature more than B dropped into the same volume. This relation under suitable conditions proves suitable as a characteristic relation. Quantities of heat are now defined to be added when the bodies containing them are dropped into the same liquid. The first law of addition is fulfilled, for dropping a hotter body into a colder liquid always produces a rise of temperature. But addition of equals does not always produce equals. A and A' may produce the same rise when dropped in the same volume of water, and so may B and B', while A and B dropped together in the same volume will not produce always the same rise as A' and B'. The failure of the second law of addition is due (as we should say now that we have investigated the matter) to the fact that the bodies themselves have a finite heat capacity and do not give up all their heat to the water; the second law will not be true unless the sum of the heat capacities of A and B is the same as that of A' and B'. All this was discovered early in the history of calorimetry, and for a long time efforts were devoted to finding a method in which the second law was fulfilled. But I do not think it has ever been found; the difficulty experienced at the outset has proved insuperable. We are still not able to measure quantity of heat as a fundamental magnitude, although it is certainly and pre-eminently a quantity. We measure quantity of heat nowadays not as a fundamental magnitude but as a derived magnitude; we measure actually change of temperature or the product of current and potential difference or mechanical work, and we estimate quantity of heat from certain relations which we have discovered between these measurable magnitudes and certain assumptions concerning others. If the reader will ask himself if he can measure quantity of heat (in terms of any arbitrary unit) without measuring any of the three things just mentioned, I think he will have to confess that he cannot; and if he inquires why he cannot by any process which suggests itself, he will always find that it is because of a failure of the second law of addition which is due, according to modern methods of expression, to the fact that all bodies have finite heat

---

[1] Or, more accurately, the quantity of heat in excess of that contained in the body at the temperature of the water. It should be noted that "higher" and "lower" temperatures can be defined without any reference to measurement.

capacity. If we have not been able to find a satisfactory process of fundamental calorimetry up to the present time, it is extremely unlikely that we
shall find one in the future.

Addition and equality. The conclusion which I want to enforce is
that the second law of addition is quite as important in determining our
processes of measurement as either the first law or the form of the characţer-
istic relation, although it is not, like them, involved in the very meaning of
the quantity to be measured, but appears often only in the guise of experimental difficulties. For the fact, that while it might always be impossible
to fulfil the second law, even when the first law is fulfilled, actually it is in
the great majority of cases possible to fulfil it, is important and suggestive.
Our experience in this matter doubtless is the cause of our division of properties into quantities and qualities of substance; if we found many properties
which, while obeying the first law, would not obey the second we should
attribute much less importance to that distinction and to the conception of
substance. It is the almost invariable connection between the obeying of
the first and the second law which gives that conception such importance
in physics. To this matter we shall return later.

But one further question, suggested by the examples which have just
been given but unnoticed in order that the argument might not be interrupted,
requires brief notice. We have spoken throughout the last section of the
second law of addition being obeyed; but when difficulty was found in obeying
it, the alteration in the method of measurement which was made consisted
usually, not in an alteration in the definition of addition, but in an alteration
of the definition of "greater than" and "equal to". A consideration of the
attempts that have been made to measure the intensity of X-rays will show this,
but it is also shown in the case of weight. In order that the second law should
be true we must have a perfect balance satisfying certain conditions, but we
can reduce the number of conditions which are necessary by changing slightly
our method of weighing (i.e. judging equality) without altering our definition
of addition. It is well known that a balance which is imperfect if used in the
ordinary manner can be used with success if the "method of substitution"
is employed[1]. By this method difficulties arising from inequalities of the
arms are overcome; but these difficulties affect, as we saw, the nature of the
characteristic relation, as well as the second law of addition, and would
therefore have to be eliminated even if there were no question of addition.
However it also eliminates troubles which do not affect the nature of the
characteristic relation, but only the second law of addition, for instance
certain flexibilities of the arms. Now the employment of the method of
substitution rather than the ordinary method involves a change in the meaning
of "equal to" (and also of course of "greater than"); we now say that two
bodies are equal if, placed successively in the same pan, they balance the same

---

[1] The method of "double weighing" is also used to eliminate certain imperfections of
the balance. But that method assumes that the standard series of weights is already in
existençe; it cannot be used for making a standard series.

body in the other pan. On the other hand addition has precisely the same meaning as before. We have got over a failure[1] of the second law, not by changing the law of addition, but by changing the meaning of equality. It is to this that reference was made on p. 281, when it was pointed out that the relation of equality and the process of addition could not be separated.

It is interesting to observe that we do usually employ this method of overcoming difficulties arising in addition, for it shows that we regard the process of addition as even more intimately involved in the meaning of the process than the relation of equality. We do not feel that in changing the meaning of equality from that characteristic of the ordinary method of weighing to that of the method of substitution we have in any way changed the meaning of "weight"; but it is difficult to see how we could change the process of addition so as to be free from our difficulties without changing that meaning.

Is the Second Law necessary? After the long discussion which has been devoted to the second law of addition it may appear rather startling to inquire whether that law is really of any importance and whether measurement would not be quite as satisfactory if it were not true. Nevertheless I think it can be shown that the question is not wholly unreasonable.

Our discussion started from our desire to limit much further than is possible in the case of hardness the choice of numerals which can be used to represent a given property. By the method which has been described we have reduced ourselves from an infinite choice for every property to a single choice for one property, which then fixes all the other numerals. Can we reduce this choice further? No—the full reason will appear hereafter. Well, if we cannot reduce the arbitrary choice to nothing at all, would there be any very great harm in extending it slightly and allowing ourselves (say) two arbitrary choices; for if we allow ourselves this extra liberty a great many of the conditions which have been imposed on measurement could be removed? Let us consider this matter.

The removal of the infinite choice was effected by defining the process of addition. When we have defined addition and the body which has the weight 1, we have fixed, in virtue of the definition of 2 as $1 + 1$ and so on, which bodies are to have the weight 2, etc. It would seem then that so long as the process of addition was such that adding 1 produces a body with a weight different from 1, all that is required has been attained; for we shall then have a series of bodies all with different weights represented each by a definitely fixed numeral; the weights of all bodies which are equal in weight to any one of this series will be definitely fixed. Is not this all that we desire?[2]

---

[1] But not all failures. The imperfections arising from faulty hanging of the pans or of interaction between bodies placed in the same pan still remain.

[2] Of course there will be a large number of bodies the weights of which are not equal to those of any of the series, namely bodies which have weights which are not integral multiples of the unit. But the same is true, so far as we have gone at present, if the other laws about addition are insisted on. We shall deal with fractional weights later; for the present it may be observed that if we chose our unit weight small enough, then, whether the other laws of

Nothing has been assumed about addition, except the first law; why has the necessity for the second law been insisted on?

Suppose for example that, leaving our definitions otherwise unchanged, we allowed ourselves to use a balance with unequally flexible arms. Then the relation of equality would be transitive and symmetrical and the first law of addition would be true[1]; we could still calibrate weights and produce a series 1, 2, 3, 4, ... In what respects would this series differ from that produced by a perfect balance? There are two differences which it is important to note here. In the first place, unless all balances were exactly the same in the flexibility of their arms, weights calibrated on two different balances would not agree; "weight 2" made with one balance would not be equal in weight to "weight 2" made with another. But this is not a very serious matter. After all nobody ever calibrates weights for himself; he always refers them to somebody who makes a business of calibration; and as that person has to provide himself with a standard gramme, why should he not provide himself also with a standard balance? There is a standard current balance at the Board of Trade; why not a standard weight balance? We are forced to introduce one arbitrary element into our measurement in our selection of the unit; why not two arbitrary elements? That is the question which is asked, and I think that if this were the only matter in which the new series of weights differed from the old, it would be difficult to give any answer that would be felt to be really convincing. Arguments founded merely on experimental convenience should have very little importance unless there are none others forthcoming.

But there is a second difference. If the second law were not true, we should not find, when we had calibrated the weights 2 and 5 and the weights 4 and 3, that the first two added were equal to the second two added. (The proof that, if 2 + 5 is to be equal to 4 + 3, the second law must be true, need not be given in detail.) This appears more serious; but is it really so? Again it would be troublesome experimentally; we should not be able to weigh with the usual calibrated box containing 1, 2, 2, 5, ..., but should need a body to represent every weight, 1, 2, 3, 4, 5, ... Would there be any result which is anything worse than an experimental inconvenience? Having asked that question, we must leave its answer to a later stage.

Is the unit the only arbitrary element in measurement? One further question demands examination. In the system of measurement which has been described there is necessarily one arbitrary element, namely the choice of the unit[2]; that choice is not determined in any way by the laws

addition were observed or not, all other bodies would have weights which were sensibly integral multiples of the unit. This observation is made only to show that the problem of fractions has got nothing to do with the matter discussed here.

[1] I am not sure that this statement is quite accurate; but it is certain that some kind of balance could be devised which would be such that everything except the second law remained true It is such a balance that I am imagining.

[2] It should be observed that it has been assumed that the fulfilment of the laws of addition is independent of the choice of unit; and that, if they are fulfilled with one choice of unit, they will be fulfilled with any other. The assumption was necessarily true if a new unit is chosen

which underlie the process of measurement. Is this the only arbitrary element? It is not immediately obvious that the answer is affirmative, for the system of measurement involves the selection of one physical process rather than another for the combination of the bodies measured in the manner which is called addition. The choice of this process is not entirely arbitrary, because, as we have seen, the process must be such that the rules of numerical addition are obeyed; but is it possible that there should be two processes, both obeying these laws, and that our choice of one rather than the other is arbitrary?

The answer seems to be this. If there is only one process obeying the first law of addition, that is to say only one way of combining two systems so as to produce a third of which the magnitude is different from either, then there is nothing arbitrary in the system of measurement except the unit. But there may be as many independent processes of measurement as there are processes obeying the first law of addition.

The first part of the answer seems to follow by mere logical proof. For let us assume that there is only one way of combining two bodies so as to produce a third of different magnitude; and then, having established one satisfactory system of measurement, let us endeavour to establish another. The magnitude of a body measured according to the system already established will be represented by the numeral x; we shall call x the old magnitude of the body. If there is some other system of measurement, according to which the magnitude is represented by the numeral y, y will be termed the new magnitude of the body.

Now let us take two bodies of which the old and new magnitudes are respectively x_1, y_1 and x_2, y_2, and try to find a process of addition which shall be characteristic of the new system of measurement and shall produce the body which has the new magnitude $(y_1 + y_2)$. By our fundamental assumption this body must be produced by adding, in the manner characteristic of the old system of measurement, bodies having the old magnitudes x_1, x_2. However, we need not simply add the two original bodies in this manner. For since the definition of equality of magnitudes is prior to and independent of any system of measurement, in forming the body $(y_1 + y_2)$ I may make any number of bodies, each having the old magnitude x_1, and combine them with any number, each having the old magnitude x_2. If I combine together q bodies x_1 and r bodies x_2, then the old magnitude of the combination must be $(qx_1 + rx_2)$, for the only way in which I can combine them so as to produce a body different in magnitude is by the method which is addition on the old system of measurement. The only latitude which I have is in the choice of q and r. If q and r are not equal I must have some rule to determine of which body q specimens are to be taken and of which r. This rule can

from the members of the standard series established according to the method of this chapter; but, as we shall see in Chapter XII, that series does not include all bodies that form the field of the characteristic relation. Of course the assumption is universally true; but its truth appears to be an experimental fact, not a logical necessity.

be founded on the difference between $>$ and $<$, which again is prior to measurement. We may say for example that q of the greater and r of the lesser bodies are to be taken.

If this method is adopted, the body to which is assigned the new magnitude $(y_1 + y_2)$ must have the old magnitude $(qx_1 + rx_2)$, where q and r may have any integral values. But since to every x there must correspond a y and only one y, there must be between x and y an equation of the form $y = f(x)$, where f may have any form so long as it is single-valued. Accordingly

$$(y_1 + y_2) = f(qx_1 + rx_2)$$

or

$$f(x_1) + f(x_2) = f(qx_1 + rx_2).$$

If f is an analytic function, having everywhere a differential coefficient (and we shall see later reason to believe that such functions alone can be significant in physics), then this relation will be satisfied for all values of x_1 and x_2 only if $q = r = 1$, and if $f(x) \equiv Ax$. That is to say we must have $y = Ax$, where A may have any value; this relation clearly states that the new magnitude can differ from the old only in the choice of unit.

If however there is some other way of combining two bodies of old magnitudes x_1 and x_2 so as to produce a system of magnitude different from that of either of them, then it may be possible to find a new system of measurement differing from the old otherwise than in the unit. For if we can produce from the two bodies a system of magnitude $\phi(x_1, x_2)$, (where ϕ is not of the form $qx_1 + rx_2$), and if we can find a function f such that

$$f[\phi(x_1, x_2)] = f(x_1) + f(x_2),$$

then the new magnitude $y = f(x)$ will be satisfactory and will obey the second law of addition. Such related functions ϕ and f are possible; for instance, if $\phi = x_1 x_2$, f will be $\log x$, or if

$$\phi = \frac{x_1 x_2}{x_1 + x_2}, \quad f(x) = 1/x;$$

another example, which will be seen later to have some importance in connection with motion, occurs if

$$\phi = \frac{x_1 + x_2}{1 + \dfrac{x_1 x_2}{c^2}},$$

and

$$f(x) = \log \frac{1 + \dfrac{x}{c}}{1 - \dfrac{x}{c}}.$$

It is impossible to predict *a priori* whether or no such a function ϕ can be found; experiment and experiment only can decide the matter; and accordingly we must recognise the possibility that a system of measurement may be arbitrary otherwise than in the choice of unit; there may be arbitrariness in the choice of the process of addition.

On the other hand it must be noted that such alternative systems of measurement may not be regarded as measuring the same magnitude. Since it is fundamental to all measurement that the order of the numerals assigned as the result of measurement should agree with the order in which the bodies are placed by the characteristic relation defining the property which is the magnitude, two systems of measurement will not measure the same magnitude unless the order of the numerals assigned by both is the same. This condition places an additional limitation on the forms which can be permitted for the function f, if y is to measure the same magnitude as x; f must be such that df/dx is always positive. The condition is fulfilled if $f = \log x$, but not if $f = 1/x$; if a second method of combining the bodies were found such that

$$\phi(x_1, x_2) = \frac{x_1 x_2}{x_1 + x_2},$$

there would be a second system of measuring a magnitude of the bodies concerned, but the magnitude y could not be regarded as the same magnitude as x.

A simple example of this last possibility is actually provided in elementary physics.

Suppose we define the electrical resistance of a body as a property which is equal when, if one body is substituted for another in a circuit containing a source of potential, the current is unchanged by the substitution. If I have two coils, A and B, I can combine them to form a body of which the resistance is not equal to that of either of them in two ways; I can place them either in parallel or in series. Investigation would show (we shall consider the matter in a later volume) that both these processes of combination obey the law of addition. Whichever I adopt, the resistance of the combined bodies is independent of the order of combination, and the resistance of the body resulting from the combination of C with a body equal in resistance to the combination of A and B is equal to the resistance of the body resulting from the combination of B with a body equal in resistance to the combination of A and C. Accordingly our principle shows that there should be two distinct systems of measurement of resistance, and that the results of one should be related to the results of the other by an equation of the form $y = f(x)$. And there is such a relation; if both systems adopt the same unit, the relation is simply $y = 1/x$. But note that the order of the x's is not the order of the y's; it is the inverse order. Accordingly we say that the two systems of measurement are not measuring the same magnitude; we call one magnitude the resistance and the other the conductance.

There are not many cases, similar to that which has just been considered, in which two magnitudes, not exactly the same, but as closely connected as are resistance and conductance, can both be measured fundamentally; but all such cases as exist are naturally important. Of the other class of cases, which seem *a priori* possible, where the same magnitude can be measured in two different ways, I have not so far been able to think of a single example. The absence of examples is doubtless connected with the feeling, which will be mentioned presently, that all measurements are fundamentally measurements of numbers. Apparently measurement is actually unique except for the arbitrary choice of the unit, because there is only one way of combining two systems in respect of the property under consideration which obeys the first law of addition. However, a certain latitude must be allowed in interpreting the expression "one way"; several ways which differ in minor details are to be regarded as the same way, so long as they differ in no respect important for the process of addition. The criterion to be applied is this. If the two ways, A and B, of combining X_1 and X_2 to form a third system are such that, if X_1 and X_2 combined by A are equal to X_3 and X_4 combined by A, then X_1 and X_2 combined by B are equal to X_3 and X_4 combined by B, then A and B are to be regarded as the same way of combination, because any differences between them are immaterial for measurement.

Thus, for the property, weight, which has been used throughout as an example, there is only one way of combining two bodies so as to produce a third which differs in weight from either of them; this way is to establish a rigid connection between them so that they are not capable of relative motion or, more accurately, of relative motion in a vertical direction. But this way has really many forms; we regard as "placing in one pan with another" any method of preventing relative vertical motion of the two bodies; it does not really matter if the second body is placed actually in the pan; it will do if it is hung on a hook below. We so regard all these forms because they are equivalent for measurement, and if we analyse them, we shall find that they are distinguished from the methods that are not so regarded by the fact that they prevent relative vertical motion. All the ways that are equivalent for addition have a common property.

CHAPTER XI

PHYSICAL NUMBER

Summary. There is certainly a sense in which number is a property of a system and thus distinguished from both a Number and a numeral. "number", in this sense, or physical number, is a magnitude just as much as weight—though any statement beginning "number is" is really misleading.

The process which, in the determination of number, corresponds to weighing, in the determination of weight, is counting. The meaning of counting is explained; it involves no use of numerals (except possibly the numeral 1) and it is a purely experimental process. It is, however, difficult (indeed impossible) to express in words the laws on the truth of which the validity of counting depends, because they are assumed to be true by all language.

The only important difference, but it is a very important difference, between number and other magnitudes is connected with the choice of unit. Change of unit converts number into a different magnitude, while it leaves the nature of other magnitudes unchanged. This fact is expressed by the statement that a number must be a number *of* something.

The intimate connection between numerals and number arises from the fact that, by an extremely convenient and ingenious device, numerals are used to provide in a very compact form the standard series of number. The observation of this intimate connection enables us to dispense with the conception of Number in establishing a system of measurement; but it is not yet quite certain whether Numbers may not have to be re-introduced at a later stage.

Multiplication is comprehensible only if number is recognised as a physical magnitude. Two numerals multiplied together hardly ever, if ever, measure magnitudes of the same kind; one is almost always a number; the other may also be a number, but it must be a number of a different kind. Multiplication is most conveniently regarded as consisting in a change of unit.

Is number a magnitude? At the outset of our discussion measurement was defined provisionally as the process of assigning "numbers" to represent properties. We then proceeded to notice that "number" was often used indifferently for what we now call "numeral" and "Number". It has become clear that it is numerals which are assigned to represent properties in the course of measurement, though in the process of fundamental measurement their assignment is influenced by the properties of Numbers; when we call a body of weight 2, the 2 is a numeral, but the choice of the numeral 2 rather than 3 or 4 is dictated by something characteristic of the Number which is also conventionally represented by the numeral 2. But now we have to consider the last of the properties which are characteristic of the tray of crystals from which our inquiry started on p. 268, the property of "number". Is this "number" a numeral, or a Number, or something different from either?

It is certainly something different. "number" in this sense is a property of a system; that is, as we decided in Chapter II, when we say that the number of the crystals is 12 we are stating some uniform association in our external judgements. The number of the crystals is something to be ascertained by observation alone and fixed definitely by observation. It is not therefore a Number, which is something independent of observation, nor a numeral, which is a mere arbitrary symbol; in fact, number *is* nothing at all in the sense in which "is" is applicable to Number; it represents one of those cases, discussed before, in which the form of subject-predicate is misleading.

On the other hand number, the physical property, is represented by numerals in just the same definite way as weight is represented. The question therefore arises whether number is, like weight, a fundamental magnitude, and whether the process of enumeration is the same in principle as that of weighing and involves experimental laws to the same extent and in the same manner. The discussion is difficult because the conceptions connected with number are so familiar and so ingrained in all our thought that it is not easy to be sure whether propositions concerning them are or are not the result of experience; they may be necessary consequences of our manner of thinking now, but it is not certain that we have not come to think in that manner simply because we have been so accustomed to certain experimental or observational laws. But let us try how far we can trace step by step an analogy between the two processes.

Enumeration and counting. First, then, we must find a transitive asymmetrical relation which is characteristic of enumeration and generates the order of systems in respect of their numbers; this relation is "more numerous than". If this relation is analogous to "heavier than" we must be able to determine whether two systems are related by it, first without any reference to numerals and, second, in a manner imposed by experiment or observation. The first condition is certainly fulfilled; if a system is numerable at all I can tell whether a system A is more numerous than a system B without writing or speaking or (if I carefully refrain from doing so) thinking about numerals. In order to be numerable a system must consist of members each of which has some feature in common with each of the other members. If this condition is fulfilled, I take a member of system A and distinguish it in some manner from the other members, by putting a pencil mark on it or placing it in a box or by some method of that kind; I then take a member of B and distinguish it similarly (though not necessarily by the same method) from the other members of B; when I have so treated A and B I have performed a definite cycle of operations. I now repeat this operation, taking each time a previously undistinguished member from both A and B, until I have distinguished all the members of A or all the members of B. If I distinguish all the members of B before I have distinguished all the members of A, then I say that A is more numerous than B. I shall find that, according to this definition, "more numerous than" is a transitive and asymmetrical relation; and further that, if two systems have not to each other either this relation or its converse, but are such that in the same last cycle of operations I distinguish the last member of A as well as the last member of B, then they fulfil the remaining conditions for equality. The process will be called "counting A against B"; when the two systems are exhausted in the same cycle of operations they will be said to "fit".

It will be agreed, I hope, that this process needs no use of numerals whatever; in defining by it the characteristic relation I have not assumed that the property has already been measured and denoted by numerals. It will also be agreed that the use of the process to determine whether A or B is the more numerous depends wholly on experiment or observation; I could not possibly tell by it which was the more numerous unless I saw or handled the systems. But it is not so certain whether the proof that the characteristic relation is transitive and asymmetrical is as purely experimental as it was in the case of weight; it does not seem at first sight as if it required any experiment to prove that if A counted against B is more numerous than B, then B counted against A is less numerous than A, or that if A is more numerous than B and B than C, then A counted against C will be more numerous than C. But the appearance of inevitableness in these relations is due, I think, to assumptions which we made when we divided our systems into members, a very important part of the process to which we must return.

Is counting experimental? Two principles seem to be involved in the division into members of the system of crystals lying in the tray. In the first place all the members are judged to have some common quality and a quality which is important for the purposes to which the enumeration is directed. If they had not such common quality or, rather, if that common quality were not important for my purpose (for all objects have *some* common quality), I should not want to enumerate the system composed of them; in science we should never want to enumerate a system composed of a cow, my last birthday, and the House of Commons, for if the system were divided into members in that way, the members would have in common no quality important for science. In the second place the members must be permanent and retain their individuality. If the crystals were replaced by drops of water, I should not trouble to enumerate them unless I knew that the tray would remain undisturbed and would not be shaken, so as to cause the drops to coalesce or to split into new drops. It is difficult to state very precisely what is meant by "retain their individuality", but certainly one of the tests we should apply to ascertain whether the drops were permanent would be to count them and ascertain whether the number of the system composed of the drops was unchanged. Consistency in enumeration then is one of the criteria I shall apply when I am deciding how to divide the system into members. But, from the analogy with weight, we know that the enumeration will not be consistent unless the conditions are such that the relation generating order is transitive and asymmetrical; if it is not, then I shall arrive at different judgements concerning the relation between the number of the system and the number of any other system according to the exact method in which the counting process is conducted. Accordingly we may conclude that in dividing the system into members I have already assumed that the division is such that the counting process will fulfil the necessary conditions; if it turned out subsequently that it did not fulfil those conditions, I should say that the division of the system into members had been faulty. But whether the test is made in the course of the counting process or whether the result of it is known (from previous experience) before the division into members is made, the test remains experimental. For, in the example we have taken, nothing but experience could show that drops were likely to coalesce or to split and so lose their individuality, while crystals were not so liable. Indeed the position is much like that which we noticed on p. 285; if we stated in the definition that the process of weighing was to be carried out with a perfect balance, we found that the characteristic relation must necessarily have the requisite properties and the laws of addition be necessarily true. But when we inquired what we meant by a perfect balance, we found that we simply meant one which satisfied these conditions and that it was only by inquiring whether those conditions were satisfied that we could decide whether the balance was perfect.

Perhaps there will be an uneasy feeling that the analogy is not exact; and it is not quite exact. If the members of the system were drops of water and we subsequently shook the tray, the failure of the characteristic relation "more numerous than" to be transitive and asymmetrical would not be the only or the most prominent difference of the system from that of which the members were crystals. But it would be one difference; and I believe—though I cannot prove the statement by giving an example—that it would be possible to devise a system divided into members in such a way that this difference and this only existed. It would appear doubtless a fantastic system and a wholly unreasonable method of division into members, but that is precisely the point on which I want to insist. Our whole idea of what is an object and of what is a system made up of individual objects is intimately bound up with our experiences in enumeration; it is only those systems which can be enumerated that we can bring ourselves to regard, by any stretch of the imagination, as consisting of members which are individual objects. The division of our experience into individual objects is simply based on our experience of the conditions in which the conditions necessary for enumeration are found. What has been said about the division of a system into members, or individual objects, applies equally to the selection of the operation which is to be used to distinguish the objects in the process of counting. For the laws of measurement will not be fulfilled unless we choose rightly. Consider, for example, what would happen if we chose to distinguish an object by cutting it in two. But again our view of what is reasonable to select as a method of distinguishing is founded wholly on our experience of what selection actually makes enumeration possible and consistent.

It is probable, then, that the proof that the characteristic relation of enumeration, involved in the process of counting, is satisfactory depends on experiment or observation and on our judgements of the external world just as much as the corresponding proof for any other process of fundamental measurement. Exactly the same considerations present themselves when we consider the process of addition, the definition of which forms the second stage in the establishment of a process of fundamental measurement. Two systems are added in respect of number when their members are regarded as forming a single system for the purpose of counting. If we attempt to analyse the definition further or to prove that addition, so defined, obeys the necessary laws, we shall find as before that the assumption that these laws are fulfilled, or the decision in exactly what circumstances two systems are combined into one, is involved in the very core of our ideas of systems, their division into objects and their combination into other systems. No attempt will be made to elaborate the argument, for this is undoubtedly a matter in which words darken counsel. Our statements on the subject appear perfectly clear and significant until we try to analyse them; the confusion which results when analysis is attempted is not always due (as Socrates and others have fondly believed) to an indefiniteness of our ideas; it is quite as often due to the inadequacy of language. It is certainly due to that cause in this instance; for a moment's reflection will show that our language, even more than our ideas, is intimately bound up with the possibility of the division of the material world into enumerable systems composed of individual objects. Any assumption that conditions might occur in which a system is not enumerable immediately breaks all the associations between words and the ideas with which they are inseparably connected; if we talk of objects at all, we unavoidably think of them as permanent and individual. So long as it is recognised that the association is the result of experience, the purpose of the discussion is achieved.

Choice of unit. So far then we have no reason to believe that the process of enumeration is essentially different, either in its nature or in the extent to which it depends on experimental laws, from the process of weighing. We can define a transitive and asymmetrical relation which generates the order of "numerousness" and gives rise to a transitive symmetrical relation which is "equality in number"; we can define a process of addition which obeys the commutative and distributive laws; and there is every reason to think that the proof that the process obeys the laws and that the relation has the requisite property is purely experimental. But there is one matter in which the process of enumeration seems to differ materially from that of weighing, namely in the determination of the systems to which the unit property is to be assigned. In weighing we assign unit property arbitrarily to one system and then determine by means of the relation of equality arising from the characteristic relation to what other systems it is to be assigned. If we adopted this method in enumeration we should find that to all systems might be assigned the unit property, for any system or identifiable object whatever can be "counted against" any other. If we define a given member of the system of crystals as having the number 1, we can count against it the system consisting of the rest of the crystals, or any part of that system, we can count against it a house or a Prime Minister or a day of the week; these objects therefore also have the number 1, and any system composed of the crystal and any one of them has the number 2. As a matter of fact we limit our choice of other unit systems to other individual members of the system of crystals. But if we so limit it, we have no need of the relation of equality to decide to what else to attribute the unit property as we had in the case of weight; when we have decided into what members to divide the system to be enumerated, we have already decided on all our units.

Here apparently is a marked difference between enumeration and weighing, but once more the difference is really only an expression of the far-reaching effect of the decision which was made when we divided the system into members. When we made that decision we did in fact take care that the decision should be such that each individual member could be counted against any other individual member—that is indeed what we mean when we say that they are individual members. If that is so, we have already taken care that the transitive symmetrical relation characteristic of the measurement shall obtain among the individual members, and it follows at once that, when we choose one of the members as that possessing unit property, all the others have unit property also. All that we have done now, and did not apparently do before, is to *exclude* as units other things which, on the ground of the relation of equality alone, seem entitled to rank as units. This exclusion is very important; and if we express the matter in a rather different way we shall see what is the essential difference in this matter between enumeration and weighing.

The fact that we exclude as units things other than the members of the system to which the object arbitrarily selected as a unit belongs means that in physics what we are measuring is not simply "number", but "number of something". The only systems to which we are concerned to attribute number are those of which the members have some common characteristic; and the number we assign to the system is not simply its number but its number in respect of that characteristic. Thus we may have a system which has a "number of crystals" and another which has a "number of charwomen"; but we do not admit into physics the conception of a system which has a "number of crystals and charwomen"; we should only admit that a system composed partly of crystals and partly of charwomen was enumerable in so far as both kinds of members of the system had a common characteristic; we might, for example, admit an enumerable system which had a "number of things which begin with c"—though such systems would have little physical interest.

Accordingly in one respect two numbers, one of one thing and one of another, are distinct magnitudes, as distinct as weight and length; for just as a length and a weight cannot be added to make a measurable magnitude which is either a length or a weight, so also a number of crystals and a number of charwomen cannot be added to give a magnitude of the same nature as either; we cannot add numbers of different kinds any more than we can add other magnitudes of different kinds, or at least, the addition, if effected, is entirely different from that which consists in the adding of magnitudes of the same kind. On the other hand, it is possible to attribute a direct physical significance to the statement that numbers of different kinds are equal; such a statement gives the result of a direct physical experiment, namely that of counting the two systems against each other, for such counting can be carried out however different are the systems. It is not possible in the same way to attribute direct physical significance to the statement that a length is equal to a weight (see further, Chap. XIII). The importance of these considerations will appear when we inquire into "dimensions" and ask ourselves why "number", unlike all other fundamental magnitudes, is considered to have no dimensions.

Numerals and number. From the foregoing discussion care has been taken to omit all reference to numerals, in order to show that enumeration, like weighing, is not essentially dependent on the use of numerals, and that numerals are only introduced to express the result of experiments and other inquiry which can be carried on without their aid. But of course there is an especially intimate connection between numerals and numbers; into this connection we must now inquire.

When we have established a system of measurement, such as that of weighing, our next step is always to set up a series of material standards by means of which the magnitude of any system can be determined by a simple judgement of equality. And the same step is necessary in enumeration; we must have standard systems consisting of members and having the numbers represented by the numerals 1, 2, 3, ... against which other systems can be counted; the numeral 3 will be attached to the system with the number 3 just as it is stamped on the standard body which has the weight 3. And such a method in an elementary form was doubtless employed in the very early days of enumeration when men counted on their fingers and toes; it survived much later in the abacus. In this stage the systems of standard numbers were collections of material objects each of which could be readily identified and distinguished from the others[1]. But with the progress of civilisation a new method, much more flexible and convenient, was introduced. The standard systems were formed out of the numerals themselves. Numerals, which are material or quasi-material objects, are characterised by number; the collection 1, 2, 3, 4, 5 and the collection 18, 31, 24, 16, 2 have both the "number of

---

[1] These standards may seem rather different from those employed in the measurement of weight because the system characterised by the lower numeral was part of the system characterised by the higher. But the distinction is not significant; such systems, of which parts are used as standards, might be employed in measuring weight and are actually used in measuring length; we do not have a separate bar for 1 inch and 2 inches, but combine both in a single graduated scale. The use of such systems is doubtless connected with the employment of number (not numerals) in measurement as we shall note presently; but the distinction which I want to make here is between the material standard designated by numerals and the standard which consists of the numerals themselves.

numerals" 5; they can be counted against each other and against a member of any standard series which has been prepared according to the specification of Chapter X and to which, according to the principles of that specification, the number 5 is attributed. The adoption of numerals as the standard system has two advantages. In the first place numerals are much more portable than any other form of standard. If we employ them we do not have to carry about a material system whenever we want to count, as we should if we used an abacus[1]; for we can reproduce the system from ourselves whenever we want it; we have only to speak the numerals—and there is our standard system. In the second place a beautiful device enables us to remember without any effort what is the number of any given collection. The number of two collections of numerals may be the same though the members are different and is the same in whatever order the members, the same or different, are counted against another system. But the numerals have a conventional order, and at some time in the history of thought it occurred to an ingenious person that if they were always counted against any other system in this conventional order starting from 1, the numeral representing the number of the system would always be the numeral which was counted against a member of the enumerated system in the last cycle of operations, which exhausted that system; the number of 1, 2, 3, 4, 5 is 5 and that of 1, 2, 3, 4, 5, 6, 7 is 7. Accordingly we have not to retain in our minds the numbers of many different collections of numerals; we need not remember that it is the collection 52, 11, 28 which has the number 3 and 18, 31, 24, 16, 2 which has the number 5. We have only to begin counting any system to be enumerated against the numerals in order, and the numeral which is counted against the last member of the system will be the numeral which should represent its number. It is because numerals are used in this manner as the standard systems of number, while they cannot be used as the standard systems of any other magnitude, that the connection between numerals and number appears so much more intimate than that between numerals and any other kind of magnitude.

But one question is suggested by this explanation. I have spoken of numerals as material or quasi-material objects, and have suggested that when we use numerals for counting we speak them. But an educated person when he counts does not speak; he simply thinks of the numerals. If he spoke them he might be considered to be making judgements of the material world when he observed a relation between the object in the counted system which he "distinguished" and the sound which he heard himself make; but when he merely thinks of them, surely the judgement which he is making is not one of the external world. Counting is not, therefore, necessarily a process involving experiment or observation, and the conclusion that the number of a system, like its weight, is a "property of a system" implying a law of association between external judgements is false. This argument must be accepted. But it remains a fact that the counting of one material system against another

---

[1] Of course systems composed of the fingers and toes have the same advantage of portability, but then the range is so limited.

is a process consisting of judgements of the external world; and it would seem therefore that if we employ one process of counting number is a material property, if we employ another it is not. The difficulty will vanish if we remember why we call external judgements "judgements of the material world" and consider that they give us information about "material properties". It is because universal agreement concerning them can be obtained; experiment and observation inform us of material properties only because, or in so far as, universal agreement about them is possible. Now though the process of counting by numerals which are merely "thought" may involve internal judgements rather than external, the distinction is utterly unimportant for science, because in this instance internal judgements have the essential property which is normally characteristic of external judgements, namely that everyone agrees about them. Though the things against which I count systems are something personal and peculiar to me, something different from the things against which you count them, yet you and I, we and all other human beings and all animals (so far as we can ascertain), agree perfectly concerning the results of the process. The process has therefore exactly the same value for science as any other judgements about which we agree. This is one of several cases which will appear in our discussions where the criterion of universal agreement for the subject matter of science avoids difficulties which are insuperable if we adopt a criterion of "sensations" or "external judgements" or "matter".

Are Numbers required? But does not the admission of internal judgements as of equal value with external judgements in this matter abolish the distinction which has been maintained throughout between numerals, number, and Numbers? The question is not strictly relevant to our purpose; for so long as we are quite sure what is the meaning of and the foundation for our statements, we know all that concerns us; but a brief discussion of it may make some doubtful points clear. Of course all three conceptions have something in common, or they would not be so intimately associated; it is possible that the common feature is simply order and that from the possession of this feature all the other properties can be derived; the decision on that point must be left to logicians. What it is important for us to notice is that such a proposition as $4 + 3 = 7$, which may refer either to number, Numbers, or numerals, means different things and requires a different kind of proof in the three cases.

If the proposition refers to number it means the same kind of thing as if it refers to weight. In reference to weight it states a purely experimental proposition, namely that if I put on one side of a balance a body which balances the standard weight 7, and on the other bodies which balance respectively the standard weights marked 3 and 4, then the two sides will balance. If the proposition is to be true, the standard bodies 7, 4, and 3 must have been prepared by a certain process, but this process requires no reference to any numeral, Number, or number, except 1. The standard body 3 must be such that it will balance the body X and the standard 1 in the same pan, provided that body X balances (the standard 1 in the same pan with another body which balances the standard 1)—and so on for 4 and 7. Further it is to be understood that the balance used has the properties which characterise a "perfect" balance. In the same way, when the proposition refers to number it means that a system which "fits" the standard system 4 (a material system) and the system which fits the standard system 3 will, if counted as a single system against the standard system 7, fit that system. In order that the proposition shall be true the standards must have been prepared in a certain way (it is unnecessary to make all the long statements over again), and the members of the systems must be individual and permanent—this last proviso being analogous to that for a perfect balance.

If the proposition refers to Number it means something (we need not inquire exactly what) which has nothing to do with any experiment or observation at all; it is something which can be deduced by an immensely long, but entirely intellectual, process from certain axioms and certain definitions which do not apparently involve any conception resembling number or numerals; for instance, the axiom that, if A is A, then A is A, seems one of the most important. Moreover, the argument which leads to the conclusion is one concerning which people certainly do differ, though probably they "ought not to"; for in any exposition of it reference is sure to be found to the errors of those who have made previous attempts.

Lastly, if the proposition refers to numerals, it means that if I take the series of numerals in their standard order which ends in 4 (i.e. 1, 2, 3, 4) and the series which ends in 3 (i.e. 1, 2, 3) and count them as a single series against the whole series of numerals, then they will fit the series which ends in 7 and the numeral which is counted against the last of them will be 7. I may perform this counting by using material numerals thus:

$$1, 2, 3, 4, 1, 2, 3,$$
$$1, 2, 3, 4, 5, 6, 7, \mid 8, 9, \ldots$$

or I may perform it by a silent mental process. But in either case the judgement of the "fit", or the judgement of the numeral which is counted against the last member of the combined series, is a perfectly direct, simple and immediate judgement; it is one concerning which we cannot conceive any difference of opinion arising. The process therefore differs entirely from that employed with Numbers and resembles far more the process with number.

On the other hand, the use of the process of counting numerals against each other makes the introduction of Number into our systems of measurement superfluous. We have hitherto regarded physical addition as significant because it resembles in a certain manner the arithmetical addition of Numbers; we have chosen our process of measurement in such a way as to make the system produced by the physical addition of 3 and 4 equal to that produced by the physical addition of 2 and 5, because we know that there is a corresponding relation between the Numbers 3 and 4 and the Numbers 2 and 5. But now we see that the relation between 3 and 4 on the one hand and 2 and 5 on the other applies also to numerals, quite apart from any consideration of Number, and can be established by counting the numerals against each other; by the simple examination of numerals themselves we can find out all the relations which ought to exist between systems added physically and discover whether any proposed process of physical measurement has the properties which we desire. Moreover the proposition which the plain man means to assert when he says that 2 and 2 make 4 is probably one concerning numerals, and the implicit faith which he places in its truth is based on his examination of numerals and not on his examination of Numbers; for the plain man knows nothing about Numbers, nor indeed did the most skilled mathematician know anything about them until a period within living memory. The conception of Number is quite unnecessary for the purpose of establishing a process of physical measurement, but we cannot yet be sure that it is unnecessary for the use of such a process. For we are going to use measurement to discover numerical laws on which will be based mathematical calculation. That calculation seems certainly to involve the conceptions of pure mathematics, and the possibility must not be lost sight of that the use of these conceptions in physics depends on a relation between the results of measurement and pure mathematical conceptions, such as Number. Accordingly we shall not wholly reject Number as irrelevant to physics until we have had the opportunity of examining this possibility.

Multiplication. We have already noted that, though number resembles other fundamental magnitudes in most important characteristics, it differs from them in one matter, namely the choice of units. We have now to notice a second apparent difference which may be connected with the first. This difference is that multiplication appears to have a physical significance for number which it has not for other fundamental magnitudes.

We concluded that addition has a physical significance for weight but not for density, because in connection with the former but not with the latter, we could find a relation determined by experiment, which has some of the properties of arithmetical addition and, in particular, obeys the commutative and distributive laws. Now just as the meaning of addition is inseparable from these laws, so the meaning of multiplication is inseparable from other laws. Multiplication is an operation such that, if it is represented by the symbol $\times$, the following propositions are true:

$$a \times b = b \times a \qquad \qquad \text{......(1),}$$
$$a \times (b + c) = a \times b + a \times c \qquad \text{......(2),}$$
$$a \times (b \times c) = (a \times b) \times c \qquad \text{......(3).}$$

Here $(b \times c)$ means p, where $p = b \times c$. It may be noticed in passing that it is only the second proposition which distinguishes multiplication from addition; the others would be true if $+$ were substituted for $\times$.

If multiplication is to have physical significance for any magnitude, we must be able to find, corresponding to two systems A and B, a third P such that the relations between these three systems must be similar, in the sense of obeying similar laws, to those denoted by $\times$, $+$ and $=$. When we were considering addition we had to consider in detail whether any proposed relation obeyed the necessary laws, but now that we have measured the magnitude and expressed it by a numeral, we can abbreviate the inquiry greatly. For suppose the systems A, B and P have the magnitudes a, b, p; and that α, β, π are the Numbers represented by the numerals a, b, p. Suppose further that a physical relation can be found such that, whenever it holds between A, B, P, $\pi = \alpha \times \beta$; then after a very little consideration we shall see that this relation between the systems A, B, P must fulfil the required conditions. Accordingly the problem of finding a physical significance for the multiplication of weights is simply that of finding a rule whereby, corresponding to two bodies of weight a and b, a third can be found of weight p, such that $\pi = \alpha \times \beta$. In the case of weight this problem is insoluble or, at any rate, has not been solved; we know of no rule whereby, if we are given two bodies of weight 2 and 3, we can produce from them a body of weight 6. On the other hand we do attribute to addition a physical significance because we can produce from these two bodies a third having a weight which is the sum of their magnitudes, namely 5.

Now is there any difference in this matter between weight and number? No, if the problem is expressed accurately. If we are given two systems of which the numbers of members are 2 and 3 we know of no rule for producing from them a system with 6 members. But we do undoubtedly say, speaking of numbers, that $2 \times 3 = 6$. What then do we mean? We mean that, if we take a collection of systems of which the number is 2 and each of which consists of a collection of members, of which the number is 3; and if we combine these systems by addition into a single system, then the number of members of the combined system is 6. Now in this statement the 2 and the 3 are numbers of different things; the 3 is the number of members of each system and the 2 is the number of systems; they are therefore magnitudes of different kinds; we are multiplying together magnitudes which are as distinct as weights and lengths. numbers of the same kind can no more be multiplied together than weights; and multiplication appears to be applicable to numbers more than to other magnitudes only because there are many magnitudes, all of different kinds, which are all called "numbers".

Nevertheless there is an intimate connection between number and multiplication. $a \times b$ has generally no physical significance if a and b are magnitudes of the same kind, though it has in a few exceptional and very important cases, e.g. when a and b are lengths. And it has also generally no physical significance when a and b are magnitudes of different kinds, though here again there are exceptions. But it always has a significance if one of a and b is a number, whether or no the other is a number. The significance is this. If, in order to distinguish the magnitudes of different kinds, we write $A \times b$ in place of $a \times b$, A being the number and b a magnitude of another kind (whether a different kind of number or a totally different magnitude), then $A \times b$ is the magnitude, of the same kind as b, of the system which is obtained by adding together a collection of systems of which the number is A and each of which has the magnitude b. In other words, $A \times b$ is the magnitude of the system which may also be written $b + b + b + b \ldots$, where the number of the b's is A.

Accordingly when one of the magnitudes multiplied is a number, multiplication has a special significance which is nothing but repeated addition. From this definition of multiplication and the known properties of addition it follows that the multiplication sign obeys the commutative and distributive laws. In order to prove this we may consider first the case where b, as well as A, is a number. Then, since we are attributing no meaning to $A \times b$, except when A is a number of systems each of which has the magnitude b, the laws will have no meaning unless we write them in the form

$$A \times b = B \times a, \qquad A \times (b + c) = A \times b + A \times c,$$

where the capital letter always represents the number of systems which have the magnitude represented by the small letter and = means that the systems can be counted against each other. If this magnitude is also a number, the first of these equations means that the number of members in a system obtained by adding together A systems each of b members is the same as the number of members in a system obtained by adding together B systems of a members each. The second states that the number of members in a system obtained by adding together A systems, each of which is obtained by adding a system of b members to a system of c members, is the same as the number obtained by adding together A systems of b members, then adding together A systems of c members and lastly adding the two systems thus obtained. In fact it states generally that the number of members in a system obtained by adding together other systems depends only on the systems and their members and not on the order in which they are added together. The third law of multiplication is not, I believe, ever used in physics. It involves a third kind of magnitude, namely the number of "systems of systems". We should write it

$$\alpha \times B \times c = \beta \times A \times c = \beta \times C \times a = \gamma \times A \times b = \gamma \times B \times a = \alpha \times C \times b.$$

It is unnecessary to express it in a long string of words, but it will be seen that it is only a generalisation of the second law and states once more that the number of members in a system obtained by combining other systems depends only on those systems and not on the way in which the combination is effected.

The truth of these propositions follows from the very nature of the ideas involved in counting just as does the truth of the laws of addition; it is difficult to the same extent to say whether they are truly experimental. But at any rate they seem to follow directly from the laws of addition. Thus, if we have A systems each containing b members, we may take from each system one member and thus form a new system of a members, the unit of this number a being the same as the unit of the number b; further we can form B such systems, for the process of taking a member from one of the original systems can be regarded as the process of distinguishing that member. It follows that the system which has the magnitude $A \times b$ has, in terms of the same unit, the magnitude $B \times a$. Similar considerations prove that

$$A \times (b + c) = A \times b + A \times c.$$

It appears that the only proposition, other than those involved in addition, which is necessary to prove that the process of multiplication, defined as repeated addition and applied to magnitudes which are both numbers, obeys the commutative and distributive laws is that systems of enumerable objects are themselves enumerable.

The extension to instances when the magnitude, represented by the small letter, is not a number, but some other physical magnitude, is easy. Again, all that we have to assume, except the laws of addition for the magnitude, is the proposition that systems obtained by adding systems possessed of this magnitude are enumerable. This proposition is actually true for all magnitudes that are susceptible of addition. We may then argue thus: The system which has the magnitude $A \times b$ is, by definition, that obtained by adding together A systems each having the magnitude b. But a system having the magnitude b is equal (in the sense characteristic of this magnitude) to the system consisting of β units added together, where β is the number represented by the same numeral as b. Accordingly the system with the magnitude $A \times b$ will be equal (in the sense of the magnitude b) to the system which consists of $A \times \beta$ units added together, for the number of units in A collections each of β units is, by definition, $A \times \beta$. But the number of units $A \times \beta$ is equal (in the sense of number) to the number of units $B \times a$. This number of units is equal (in the sense of the magnitude b) to B systems each of which has the magnitude a; and this system, by definition, is to be represented by $B \times a$. Hence the system $A \times b$ is equal (in the sense of the magnitude b) to the system $B \times a$. It is unnecessary again to extend the proof to the distributive law. It may be noted that since $Ab = Ba$, we may write either ab, but it must not be forgotten that a and b are different magnitudes, and that ab means either Ab or Ba.

Multiplication as change of unit. There is another quite distinct significance that may be given to the symbol of multiplication. Suppose that we have measured the magnitude of a system B in terms of the unit A and found it to be b, and that we then change our unit and take in place of A a system X in terms of which A has the magnitude a. What will be the magnitude of B in terms of X? The answer is $a \times b$. It is unnecessary to go through the process of proving this proposition or of showing that if we adopt it as a definition of $a \times b$, then the symbol of multiplication obeys the commutative and distributive laws. If it obeys those laws it follows at once that the system of which the magnitude is $a \times b$ has also the magnitude p, where p is such that $\pi = \alpha \times \beta$, and π, α, β are the Numbers represented by the numerals p, a, b. The formal definition is: $a \times b$ is the magnitude of a system in terms of a unit X when it has the magnitude a in terms of the unit B and B has the magnitude b in terms of the unit X. Again a and b denote different kinds of things : b is a magnitude in terms of one unit, a a magnitude in terms of another. For complete clearness we should write in place of $a \times b$ either $A \times b$ or $B \times a$; but since the systems $A \times b$ and $B \times a$ are always equal, it is convenient as before to use the same symbol to denote both of them.

It should be noted that, whereas the first definition of multiplication was closely associated with number and was scarcely comprehensible without reference to that magnitude, the new definition is much less closely connected with number and appears at first hardly applicable to it. For while any other magnitude, such as a weight, is a weight in terms of whatever unit it is measured, a number changes its entire significance when the unit is changed. We may call "numbers" both the number of B in terms of A and the number of B in terms of X, but they are essentially magnitudes of different kinds. However we shall see that the definition of multiplication as a change of unit is very important for number.

Lastly we may ask, what is the importance of multiplication? Part of the importance arises directly from the meanings we have attached to statements in which it is involved. We often want to know what is the magnitude of some system which results from repeated addition. If we know our multiplication table we know at once the place in the order of magnitudes which will be occupied by any system composed by the repeated addition of other systems. We know that the system 3×4 will be greater than the system 2×5, less than the system 2×7 and equal to the system 2×6 or the system 12. Again, we do sometimes want to change our unit of measurement, and again a knowledge of the multiplication table enables us to tell at once how the numerals to be assigned to the magnitudes of various systems will alter in consequence of the change. These applications are obvious, but rather trivial. A somewhat more important application will concern us in the next chapter. It must be observed, in view of the discussions of that chapter, that every system represented by $A \times b$, where A and b are numerals included in the series which we established in Chapter X, will be equal to some system in that series; $A \times b$ may be regarded as a new numeral, but it will always occupy the same place in the order of numerals as one of the older numerals, and so may also be regarded as merely a new symbol equivalent to one of the older symbols. 3×4 is equivalent to 12 in just the same sense as "twelve" is equivalent to 12.

Lastly, any use of multiplication involves a knowledge of the multiplication table, just as any use of addition involves a knowledge of the "addition table". And since the multiplication which is defined here is always equivalent to repeated addition, we may obtain the multiplication table, just as we obtained the addition table, by the investigation of numerals without any consideration of Numbers. We draw up the multiplication table by counting numerals against each other. The statement that $3 \times 4 = 12 = 4 \times 3$ may mean, and to most people does mean, what is expressed in this table of counting:

$$1, 2, 3, 4, \mid 1, 2, 3, 4, \mid 1, \ 2, \ 3, \ 4, \mid$$
$$1, 2, 3, 4, \ 5, 6, 7, 8, \ 9, 10, 11, 12, \mid 13, 14, \ldots$$

or

$$1, 2, 3, \mid 1, 2, 3, \mid 1, 2, 3, \mid 1, \ 2, \ 3, \mid$$
$$1, 2, 3, \ 4, 5, 6, \ 7, 8, 9, 10, 11, 12, \mid 13, 14, \ldots$$

CHAPTER XII

FRACTIONAL AND NEGATIVE MAGNITUDES

Summary. If we left our system of fundamental measurement at the point reached in Chapter X we should be unable to assign numerals to many systems although they are included in the order of the magnitude. The standard series must be extended; its extension is possible only through the use of number.

Fractional magnitudes are defined; it is shown that the definition is satisfactory, if the proposition, not used hitherto, is added that if a pair of equal bodies added together is equal to another pair of equal bodies, then a body of one pair is equal to a body of the other.

There are no fractional numbers in the sense that there are fractional weights or lengths. A proposition involving a fractional numeral, if applied to number, can only be interpreted as stating something about change of units.

Negative magnitudes are also defined and shown to be satisfactory. There are no negative numbers: propositions applied to number which apparently contain negative numerals ought to be expressed so that it is clear that the − sign denotes an operation, not a numeral. But number is here not distinguished from other magnitudes. There are few negative magnitudes; weight and possibly resistance are exceptional.

Lastly, it is discussed in detail, in the light of the conclusions of this chapter, whether the method of fundamental measurement is unique. It is concluded that it is.

Fractional magnitudes. If we developed the process of measurement no further than the point at which we left it in Chapter X, we should find that, while the process was perfectly satisfactory as far as it went, it was impossible to measure the magnitudes of some systems at all although they were included in the order of that magnitude. The great majority of bodies would have magnitudes intermediate between those of two members of the standard series, greater than that of one and less than that of the next, but not equal to any. Further, the distinction between bodies of which the magnitude could be measured and those of which it could not would depend entirely on the choice of unit. In order to be able to measure the magnitude of all bodies we must increase the standard series and include in it many new members, which must be such that their magnitudes lie in between those of the existing members. Such increase is made possible only by the physical magnitude number.

The new members and the numerals to be assigned to them are defined as follows: Let A_1, A_2, ... be bodies all of which are equal in magnitude and such that a system of them, having the number P when the bodies are taken as unit members, and consisting of these bodies added together in accordance with the definition of addition, has the same magnitude as the body which is the unit. Then the bodies A_1, A_2, ... are members of the standard series and the numeral to be assigned to them is $1/p$. The definition may be expressed more briefly, by the help of the symbol of multiplication which has just been investigated, in the form that $1/p$ is the magnitude of a body such that $P \times 1/p = 1$. Other members of the series are those the magnitude of which is equal to that of the sum of any collection of such bodies; and if the collection has the number Q, the numeral to be assigned to the corresponding member is q/p; or, in symbols, $Q \times 1/p = q/p$. q/p might also be defined as the magnitude of a body such that p equal to it would balance the weight q; and we need only use the proposition that equals added to equals are equal to show that the two definitions are equivalent. For take q collections each of p bodies each of which has, according to the definition of $1/p$, the magnitude $1/p$. Then each collection is equal to the unit, and q of them balance the weight q. Now form p collections each of q bodies by taking one body from each of the first collections; this process is possible in virtue of the fact that the bodies possessing the magnitudes are enumerable. Then these still balance q; but each collection has, by the first definition, the weight q/p; therefore p bodies of weight q/p balance q.

All magnitudes are integral or fractional. $1/p$ and q/p, where p and q are numerals of the old (integral) series, are new numerals; that is to say—nothing more is meant—they are symbols which we have not used before. In Chapter XI when we introduced new numerals, ab or pq, to denote systems made, according to a defined specification, from those to which numerals had already been assigned, we found on inquiry that all the systems made according to that specification were already represented by numerals of the old integral series. But now, if we make bodies according to the specification involved in the definition of $1/p$ or q/p, we shall find that they are not generally represented by any of the old numerals and are not equal to any members of the old standard series. Indeed I think we can prove that generally they cannot be so represented, at least if we introduce one new and very obvious assumption. The second law of addition states that $a + b > = < a + c$, according as $b > = < c$. It follows that $a + a + a + ... > = < b + b + b + ...$ (the number of terms on each side being the same and equal to n), according as $a > = < b$. In virtue of the meaning of multiplication this is equivalent to saying that $na > = < nb$, according as $a > = < b$. The assumption that we must introduce is the converse of this proposition, namely that $a > = < b$, according as $na > = < nb$. This is a law to be proved by experiment; it is essential to all considerations of fractional magnitudes, and it is therefore desirable to introduce it at this early stage. It is clearly not a necessary consequence of the proposition of which it is the converse, but as a matter of fact it is always true so long as the converse is true; I have not been able even to invent with any plausibility a system and a magnitude for which it is not true.

Now consider the bodies represented by q/p and q'/p, where q' is an (integral) numeral greater than (i.e. occurring in the order after) q. Then p of these bodies added together are equal respectively to the bodies with magnitudes q and q'. On examination of the multiplication table we shall find that some of the integral numerals are equivalent to numerals of the form $s \times p$ and some are not; if q is a numeral to which a numeral of the form $s \times p$ is equivalent, then the next $p - 1$ numerals after q are not of that form; but the pth numeral is of that form and is equivalent to $s' \times p$, where s' is the numeral next after s. Suppose that q' is one of the $p - 1$ numerals between two numerals that are of the form $s \times p$ and $s' \times p$. Then p bodies q/p are equal to q: since q is equivalent to a numeral $s \times p$ or $p \times s$, q is also equal, in virtue of the meaning of multiplication, to p bodies s. Hence, according to our new assumption or experimental law, the body q/p has the same magnitude as s. q/p and s are, therefore, merely different symbols for the same numeral; or, more accurately, q/p and s occupy the same position in the order of numerals; for every purpose with which we are concerned one may be substituted for the other; q/p is not in our sense a new numeral. On the other hand, since p bodies q'/p are equal to q' which lies between $s \times p$ and $s' \times p$, the same law shows that q'/p must lie between s and s'. But there is no old numeral lying between s and s'. Consequently q'/p is a new numeral in our sense, occupying a new place in the order of numerals. The criterion that q'/p should be a new numeral is that q' should not be one of the old numerals to which is equivalent a numeral $s \times p$. Since all the old numerals are equivalent to a numeral $s \times 1$, none of the numerals $q'/1$ are new numerals; they are the same numerals as q'.

But not all the numerals q/p are separate new numerals, for it is easy to show by the same kind of argument that the numeral q'/p' occupies the same place as q/p if the numeral $q \times p'$ occupies the same place as the numeral $q' \times p$. We must take a number $p \times p'$ of each of the bodies having magnitudes represented by q/p and q'/p' and divide them respectively into p' collections each of p members and p collections each of q members. It then follows that the first set of $p \times p'$ bodies has the magnitude $q \times p'$, the second the magnitude $q' \times p$. These magnitudes are equal, and therefore again the magnitudes q/p and q'/p' are equal.

Again it can be shown—it is unnecessary to give the argument—that a numeral can be found for at least one body which has a magnitude between q/p and q'/p', whatever q, q', p, p' may be, so long as $q'/p' \neq q/p$. Such a numeral will be $(2qp' - 1)/2pp'$ or $(2q'p - 1)/2pp'$, according as qp' is greater or less than $q'p$. But of course it does not follow that a system having this magnitude can actually be found; nor does the fact that we can find a numeral which represents some one system having a magnitude between q/p and q'/p' prove that we can find a numeral to represent any actual system which occurs having such a magnitude. But as a matter of fact we can always find a system which has the magnitude $(2qp' - 1)/2pp'$ (taking qp' always greater than $q'p$), and by making in this way new systems intermediate between others, one of which is greater and the other less than some system to which a numeral is to be assigned, we can always find a numeral to represent the magnitude of any system to which a numeral has not been assigned previously. The introduction of the fractional magnitudes q/p does actually enable us to assign a numeral to represent any system whatever in the order of the magnitude and thus to fill completely all the gaps in the standard series which were left when we knew only integral numerals.

The truth of these statements will perhaps not be clear immediately to the reader who remembers that there are such things as "irrational Numbers", which, though intermediate between rational Numbers, are yet not equal to any of the rational Numbers which are so intermediate; the definition of fractional magnitudes which we have adopted permits only the addition to the standard series of magnitudes represented by rational numerals or fractions of which the numerator and denominator are commensurable. On the other hand it is often thought that various branches of science, and especially geometry, force us to recognise the existence of incommensurable magnitudes which ought to be represented by irrational numerals (i.e. the numerals which represent irrational Numbers). We shall inquire later into the truth of this view; but the statement which has been made will appear less objectionable if it is noticed, first, that we have so far omitted from consideration all questions of "experimental error"; second, that a rational numeral can always be found which differs by as little as we please from any irrational numeral. (By the difference of two numerals is, of course, meant the numeral which represents the Number which is the difference between the two corresponding Numbers. Though we have concluded that Number is irrelevant to the establishment of the integral standard series, it is convenient sometimes to use the conception to avoid circumlocutions necessary if everything is to be expressed in terms of numerals.)

The addition of fractional magnitudes. But we have still to inquire whether this extension of the process of measurement is satisfactory in the same sense as the previous process. The characteristic of the previous process, in virtue of which it was satisfactory, was that it was found that magnitudes obeyed the arithmetical laws of addition, so that two bodies of weight a and b would balance a third body c, if a, b and c were such that the Numbers A, B, C represented by these numerals obeyed the relation $A + B = C$. Since addition is the only process establishing a relation between magnitudes to which we propose to attribute physical significance (for multiplication is nothing but repeated addition or change of unit), if these laws of addition are obeyed, we shall have secured everything that is of experimental importance.

The satisfactoriness of the assignment of integral numerals was a consequence of the second law of addition (that equals added to equals are equal) and of the specification given for making the systems represented by the integral numerals. We may assume that the second law is obeyed by the system represented by the new numerals as well as by those represented by the old, for we imagined that we proved that law before we undertook the assignment of numerals at all and before we could make any distinction between the systems represented by the two classes of numerals. Further we may note that our supposed discovery that the success of our system of measurement did not depend on the choice of unit shows that the system must be to some extent satisfactory for the new numerals; for all the systems represented by q/p, q'/p, q''/p, etc. will be represented by integral numerals if we take as unit in place of our present unit the body which has the magnitude $1/p$ in terms of that unit. That conclusion follows at once from the first definition of q/p; and it implies in its turn that, if the system of measurement including the new numerals is to be satisfactory, the numeral which is to represent the sum of q/p and q'/p must be r/p, where r is the numeral equivalent to $q + q'$. A slight extension of the argument will show what numeral ought to represent the sum of q/p and q'/p', whatever q, q', p, p' may be. For if we take as our unit the body which, according to our previous unit, has the magnitude $1/u$, where u is equivalent to $p \times p'$, then in terms of this unit the two bodies have magnitudes s and s', where s and s' are the numerals equivalent to $q \times p'$ and $q' \times p$. Accordingly their sum must be represented by t, which is equivalent to $s + s'$ on the new system of units or by t/u on the old.

This method of arriving at what numeral should represent the system which is the sum of q/p and q'/p' is not very satisfactory, for it involves the idea of a change of unit every time we wish to add two fractional numerals, and changes of unit, being wholly artificial devices, are to be avoided as far as possible in establishing fundamental propositions. Moreover, when we have examined the questions to be raised in Chapter XVI we shall be less sure that our proposed system of measurement would be satisfactory if any unit, however small, is selected[1]; and the process we have considered compels us to take as unit the system $1/u$, however small this may be—and it may be very small. But a little inquiry will show that, though the consideration of the problem by means of the conception of change of unit is interesting and sometimes helpful, it is by no means essential. We should arrive at exactly the same conclusion if we considered the numeral which represented the sum of u groups, each group consisting of the system q/p added to the system q'/p', and made use of the proposition that, if collections equal in number of systems equal among themselves are equal, then any system in one collection is equal to any system in the other. Such an argument again would lead to the conclusion that the numeral which is to represent the sum of q/p and q'/p' must be t/u, if the measurement is to be satisfactory.

But *is* the sum of q/p and q'/p' equal to t/u or $(qp' + q'p)/pp'$? Let us consider what the question means. In considering the integral numerals and the magnitudes represented by them, we decided that the system of measurement would be satisfactory if the system 2 added to the system 3 was equal to the system 5, because the Number 5 is the arithmetic sum of the Number 2 and the Number 3; when we said that 5 is the sum of 2 and 3, and that measurement would not be satisfactory unless the same result was true of physical addition, we were at first thinking of Numbers and arithmetic sums. Now in this sense, of course, $(qp' + q'p)/pp'$ *is* the sum of

---

[1] Consider, for example, when that chapter has been read what would happen if the system with magnitude $1/pp'$ had a magnitude less than E, the maximum error and the step of the measuring instrument.

q/p and q'/p', for the Number represented by that numeral is the arithmetic sum of the Numbers represented by q/p and q'/p'. But later we found that we could exclude Number altogether from our consideration; we can obtain the result $2 + 3 = 5$, and all similar results, by simply counting numerals against one another. We now say that measurement will be satisfactory if the system 5 (and no other) is equal to the sum of the systems 2 and 3, because 5 is related in a certain manner to 2 and 3 in the counting of numerals. Can we similarly exclude Number from the process of finding what numeral should represent $q/p + q'/p'$, if the measurement is to be satisfactory? And if we do exclude it, what process can be substituted for it?

There is no method analogous to counting numerals against each other by which we can determine by pure experiment what that numeral should be. But just because there is no method of experimental test, it is permissible to define by pure convention that numeral as t/u, where t is the numeral equivalent to $(qp' + q'p)$ and u is the numeral equivalent to pp'. If we adopt such a definition we shall always be sure that the measurement is satisfactory, and at the same time we can determine in each particular case what the numeral should be; for by the process of counting numerals against each other we can determine t and u. For the integral numerals we could not in this manner define the numeral which was to be the sum of q and q' in such a way as to make the measurement satisfactory, because no mere definition would have been such that it could have been applied to give the result in any particular instance; nothing but the actual process of counting can give that result, and it has to be performed afresh for each sum which has to be determined—except in so far as the ingenious system of decimal notation makes the rule for numerals over 9 a simple modification of that for numerals up to 9. A definition is possible for fractions only because we know the multiplication table for integers and can thus find t and u when q, q', p, p' are given.

Our conclusion is then that, if the system of measurement is satisfactory for integral numerals, it will always be satisfactory for fractional numerals (if they exist), so long as we define the numeral that is to represent the sum of q/p and q'/p' as t/u, where t and u are the numerals equivalent to $(q \times p' + q' \times p)$ and to $p \times p'$ respectively. Satisfactoriness for fractional numerals, once satisfactoriness for integral numerals is established experimentally, is a question of definition. It so happens that the definition which is necessary accords with that suggested by the rules of arithmetic applied to Number—and it is possible that the accordance is not a mere coincidence. But it is not in the least degree essential to measurement; Number is as irrelevant to the measurement of fractional as to the measurement of integral numerals.

Decimal notation. The mention above of the decimal notation of numerals suggests that some slight attention should be paid to this matter. I do not feel that I have anything to say concerning decimal integrals that is not perfectly familiar, but a word should be said about the decimal notation of fractional numerals representing fractional magnitudes. The advantage of these numerals over the "vulgar" form are two; first they facilitate the addition, subtraction and multiplication of fractional numerals (we shall consider multiplication in a moment), second—and this is really much more important in measurement—they enable us to remember the order of the fractional numerals by a rule as easy as that which gives the order of the integral numerals. The principle of the decimal notation of fractions (or the part of it which concerns us) is the substitution for all numerals q/p of the numerals r/M, where M is the same for all the numerals, to which they are equivalent. If this principle is adopted the order of the fractional numerals will simply be the order of the r's, and that order is fixed by the rule which gives the order of the integral numerals; the introduction of fractional numerals does not require us to remember any new rules for determining order. Addition and multiplication of fractional numerals also becomes easy, because $r/M + r'/M = (r + r')/M$, and $p \times (r/M) = (p \times r)/M$.

But is the principle practicable? There will be a numeral r/M equivalent to q/p only if an integral numeral r can be found such that the numeral $r \times p$ is equivalent to the numeral $q \times M$. An examination of the multiplication table will show that such a numeral is not always discoverable; it will be discoverable only if either q or M is equivalent to a numeral of the form $s \times p$. We have seen that q for actually existing systems is not always of this form (if it were, there would be no need for the fractional numerals); M would be always of this form only if it were the numeral equivalent to Πp, the product of all actually occurring p's. It is unnecessary to inquire whether there is such a numeral, for actually the numeral M adopted is not of this form; M is always taken of the form 1000..., where the number of o's may vary according to the magnitude we are measuring and the method of measurement; and such numerals are not equivalent to a numeral of the form $s \times p$ unless p is either 2 or 5 or some numeral equivalent to a numeral of the form

$$2 \times 2 \times \ldots \times 5 \times 5 \times \ldots .$$

(By a numeral equivalent to $s \times p \times q$ is meant a numeral equivalent to $s \times u$, where u is equivalent to $p \times q$—and so on.) p is not always equivalent to a numeral of this form and therefore the principle is not strictly applicable.

On the other hand, if M, always of the given form, is chosen large enough, it is actually always possible to find a system represented, according to the definition of fractional numerals, by r/M which is equal to any other system in the order of the same magnitude, even though that system is represented by q/p where $q \times M$ is not equal to $r \times p$. The conclusion to be drawn from this fact—which will be the subject of much discussion later—is that one system may be equal to another although one is represented by a numeral which is not equivalent to that which represents the other. The explanation of the fact—which again will be discussed later—is based on the observation that, even when $r \times p$ is not equivalent to any numeral $q \times M$, a numeral r can be found such that the difference between q/p and r/M is as small as we please. If M' is the numeral nearest to M which is such that $q \times M'$ is equivalent to $r \times p$, then an examination of the multiplication table will show that $M - M'$ cannot be greater than $p - 1$. Accordingly the difference between q/p and r/M is never greater than that between r/M and $r/M + p - 1$, or $\dfrac{r \times (p - 1)}{M \times (M + p - 1)}$; and this difference may be made as small as we please by taking M great enough. Another way of expressing the fact that we can always find r/M as near as we please to q/p would be to say that we can always find a numeral of the form r/M intermediate between any q/p and q'/p'; and perhaps this is the more accurate mode of expression. But it is unnecessary to prove it or to work out its consequences in detail.

The final conclusion at which we arrive is that if we include in our standard series, not only members represented by the integral numerals, but also those represented by r/M, where M is some numeral of the form 1000..., then we shall be able to find a member of the standard series equal to any system included in the order of the magnitude and so be able to assign a numeral to represent that system. When such a standard series has been made, the problem of measuring the magnitude is completely solved. And it has been solved—this is the object of all the tedious periphrases that have been adopted—without any reference to Number. The only conception that we need is that of the ordered collection of numerals forming an enumerable system.

Fractional number. There is no fractional number; all the numbers of all enumerable systems are integral. The considerations just presented are applicable to every true magnitude except number. Of course we do speak of half an apple or a third of a company, but the systems to which reference is made by such expressions are not systems which have a number of apples or a number of companies. But, it will be said, we define $1/p$ when speaking of numbers in exactly the same way as we do when speaking of weight or any other magnitude; $1/p$ is the number of a system such that $P \times 1/p = 1$. True: but the symbol $=$ does not mean the same or the corresponding thing in the two definitions. When we define fractional weight, it means that the systems denoted by the two sides balance; the relation for number corresponding to balancing is "fitting" when one system is counted against the other. But the systems do not fit; three thirds-of-companies do not fit if counted against 1 company. If it is maintained, as seems to be necessary, that "counting against" is involved in the conception of physical number just as balancing is involved in the conception of weight, then the distinction in the meaning of the two definitions is essential. On the other hand $P \times 1/p = 1$ is true in some sense if applied to number. But it is true or even significant only if multiplication is regarded as involving a change of unit. The circumstances in which it is applicable are these. I have a collection of systems A, each of which for some process of counting I propose to take as a unit; from these systems A I form other systems B, each B consisting of p systems A; and for some other process of counting I propose to take each of the systems

B as unit. When such circumstances occur I define $1/p$ as the number of each system A in terms of the systems B. $P \times 1/p = 1$ then states the identical proposition that P of these systems make a system 1 in terms of the same unit. q/p is defined as the system which has the number q in terms of the unit which has the value $1/p$ in terms of the unit B, and it follows immediately that P of such systems have the number q in terms of that unit. It must be carefully observed that a fractional number has even this significance only if the systems B are actually divisible into systems A such that the number of B in terms of A is p. No fractional number has a significance applied to an indivisible system. Perhaps this limitation does not seem to amount to much because every system is conceivably divisible; but we only require to apply numbers to systems which have some importance, and there are systems of which the whole significance vanishes if they are conceived to be divided. Thus $\frac{1}{2}$ a sheep means nothing at all; for however we divide a sheep into two parts those parts must either be such that one of them is still a sheep—and $\frac{1}{2}$ a sheep cannot be a sheep—or a sheep ceases to be concerned in the matter at all because the sheep is mutton. It should be observed that when fractions are used in connection with number, it is always assumed that the systems have some very important characteristic; e.g. they are equal in magnitude. But the assumption is not essential to the significance of the conception.

We conclude then, that fractional numbers are only significant if the possibility of change of unit is borne in mind and every statement about fractional numbers is to be interpreted as a statement concerning the result of changing the unit. $1/p$ is a system such that, if I adopt it as a unit of counting, the system which, with some other unit, had the number 1 has the number P. The statement that $1/5$ of a company $+ 3/4$ of a company equals $19/20$ of a company means that if I take one of the system $1/5$ and three of the system $1/4$, combine them in a single system and count that system with the system $1/20$ as unit, then the number will be 19. Such statements are important because, as we have seen, change of unit in enumeration has a very important significance which it has not in connection with other magnitudes; herein lies the one fundamental difference between number and other magnitudes. But statements about fractional magnitudes other than number can also be interpreted as statements about change of unit in exactly the same way. We can, if we please, read the definition $P \times 1/p = 1$, applied to weight, as "$1/p$ is a body such that, if it is adopted as the unit of weight, the body which was previously adopted as the unit has the weight p." Such a statement has a meaning quite different from that which was given before, though it follows from the definition of the relation between the unit and any other weight that both statements are true or untrue at the same time. It is, moreover, a much less important statement, for we are concerned to find numerals to represent bodies which have weights not integral in terms of some unit, whereas we are very seldom concerned with changes of unit. But in the case of number owing to the difference in the method of choosing units and the change in the nature of the magnitude which accompanies a change of unit, the two statements are not equivalent; one of them is always false.

The absence of fractional number makes a slight alteration necessary in the statements of Chapter XI concerning multiplication, if they are to be applied to fractions. The significance of multiplication as a change of unit is, of course, unaltered. The assertion that a system has a magnitude ab may still mean, when a and b are fractional numerals, that it has the magnitude b according to some choice of unit, but that for the moment it is proposed to take as unit a system referred to which the first unit has the magnitude $1/a$. But it may also mean something involving the conception of number. ab cannot mean the collection of which the number is a, the magnitude of each number being b, for there is no such system; but, if $a = p/q$, it can, and does usually, mean the collection of p numbers, all equal in magnitude, such that a collection of q of them, regarded as a whole and as a unit for counting, has the magnitude b. It is unnecessary to state or prove all the propositions that are implied in the ordinary use of these conceptions of multiplied fractional magnitudes; for example that $\dfrac{q}{p} \times \dfrac{q'}{p'}$ represents the same system as $\dfrac{v}{w}$, where v is the same numeral as qq' and w the same as pp'. The establishment of such results does not introduce any new ideas.

These considerations may seem rather needlessly subtle, but they are important both in their origin and application. In their origin, because the absence of fractional numbers is a direct consequence of the basing of enumeration upon counting; enumeration is undoubtedly similar to weighing in that it consists of the assignment of numerals to represent the results of judgements of the external world; if these judgements are not those concerned in the process of counting, I cannot discover what they can be. Again the application of the considerations is important when we inquire into the conceptions of continuity and discontinuity; the difference between continuous and discontinuous magnitudes is not of much importance in the establishment of laws, for all magnitudes other than number are continuous; but it is of the very greatest importance in theories suggested by laws, for the substitution of discontinuous for continuous theories is the feature which distinguishes modern from ancient physics.

Negative magnitudes. The statement that, when we have established a standard series consisting of integral and fractional magnitudes, we can measure the magnitude of any other system is not quite accurate; it is not true for weight; we could not measure the weight of a balloon[1]. All the bodies

---

[1] Usually when we are speaking of weighing, and speaking accurately, we mean the weight *in vacuo*; but the weight of a body in air of given density is quite as definite a magnitude as its weight *in vacuo*. And of course what we measure is always the weight in air, so that when we are considering a process of measurement it is more satisfactory to take weight as meaning weight in air of some particular density.

In many chemical text-books and histories of chemistry, when the phlogiston theory of combustion is under discussion, the statement is made that "negative weight is inconceivable." I have not tried to trace the statement to its original source, but it must surely

we have considered so far have been such that, if the balance were balanced and we placed them in one of the pans, that pan would sink; that is to say, they were such that adding them to any other body produced a sum of greater weight. On the other hand the addition of a balloon makes the sum lighter; accordingly none of the standard series so far established are equal in weight to the balloon; new numerals are required to represent its weight, just as new numerals were required for the fractional weights.

Negative magnitudes are defined thus: If Q is a body such that, when added to a body the weight of which is $a + b$, the weight of the resulting sum is a, then Q has the weight $- b$; or, in symbols, $(- b)$ is such that

$$a + b + (- b) = a.$$

It is from this equation that the rules for the addition of negative numerals are derived just as the rules for the addition of fractional numerals are derived from the formal equations stating the laws of multiplication.

From the definition of negative magnitude and from the definition of subtraction as the operation which reverses addition, it follows that the effect of adding a body of magnitude $- b$ is the same as the effect of subtracting a body of magnitude b. Accordingly since processes involving subtraction are as satisfactory (in the sense of p. 281) as those which involve only addition, and since to every operation of the addition of negative magnitudes corresponds an operation of subtracting positive magnitudes, it follows that processes involving the addition of negative magnitudes will also be satisfactory. No new experimental laws are required. If, in any process of measurement which is satisfactory for the positive magnitudes first defined, we find systems having negative magnitudes, no further inquiry is necessary to establish that the process which includes the use of these negative magnitudes is still satisfactory. We may be sure that the laws of addition are obeyed and that the numeral which represents the magnitude of a system obtained by adding other systems will always be that which represents the Number resulting from the corresponding arithmetical operation.

In virtue of the fact that the addition of a negative magnitude is equivalent to the subtraction of a positive magnitude the proposition follows which is often expressed in the cryptic form $+ \times - = -$. For the purposes of physical measurement it would be more clearly expressed in the form $a + (- b) = a - (+ b)$; in which it must be remembered the $+$ and $-$ outside the brackets are symbols of operations, whereas those inside the brackets are inseparable parts of the numerals to which they are attached, and merely

---

have been copied blindly from one author by the next, for it is difficult to explain otherwise how a statement so utterly untrue and manifestly absurd could have become so widely current. Negative weight can hardly be inconceivable to anyone who has seen smoke come out of a chimney. Perhaps the original author meant that negative *mass* is inconceivable and there might be reason in his view if by mass he meant "quantity of matter." But if mass is defined dynamically, negative mass is not more inconceivable than negative weight; a body would have negative mass if another body striking it when at rest continued in motion in the same direction but with increased velocity. Such behaviour would be unusual and unfamiliar, but I find no difficulty in imagining that it might happen.

serve to distinguish two entirely different numerals which, if the sign were omitted, would be represented by the same symbol and liable to confusion. Similarly, the proposition $- \times - = +$ should be written $a - (- b) = a + (+ b)$, stating that the effect of subtracting a negative magnitude is the same as that of adding the corresponding positive magnitude; the truth of the statement may easily be seen to follow from the meaning of the terms. Of course all this is very elementary, but there is danger in forgetting exactly what is asserted by statements so familiar that their meaning is never questioned.

Just as there are no fractional numbers, so there are no negative numbers; there is no number q such that $a + b + q = a$. The symbol $-$ employed in connection with number always denoted an operation; it is not part of a symbol which is a numeral. $a - b$ always means $a - b$ and does not mean $a + (- b)$. In this respect number resembles most other magnitudes; it is weight that is exceptional. There are no negative lengths, areas, volumes, periods, electrical resistances (though perhaps some qualification is necessary in respect of this last); on the other hand there are negative distances and time-intervals, but it is not certain that these are fundamental magnitudes. These are matters which will concern us later.

These definitions enable us, in the case of weight, to establish a standard series containing a member corresponding to every numeral except one; this exception is o. The exception can be removed by the definition that a body has the weight o if it is such that its addition to (or subtraction from) any other body does not change the weight of the system. In symbols we express the definition that if $a + p = a - p = a$, then p is o; and this definition, regarded as a formal rule for handling symbols, enables us to find all the rules for the addition of numerals in which o is concerned. It is possible to find bodies of which the weight is o, namely such as have a density equal to that of the medium in which the weighing is performed. None of the other magnitudes mentioned in the last paragraph have a o, except possibly electrical resistance at sufficiently low temperatures and, possibly also, distances and time-intervals; there is no body which has a length or an area o.

Is fundamental measurement unique? We have now achieved the purpose for which we originally set out to discover a system of measurement. That purpose has become rather obscured in our discussions; it was to find some method of assigning numerals to represent all of those properties of systems which can be ordered by a single transitive asymmetrical relation. The method was to be such that it is perfectly definite, so that one and only one numeral can be assigned to each system possessing the property. The method that has been illustrated by the example of weight can be applied to any other magnitude capable of physical addition and it satisfies the specification. We have only to add to our knowledge of the generating relation a satisfactory definition of addition and a unit arbitrarily chosen, and we can then assign as the result of perfectly definite and indisputable experiments one and only one numeral to every property that is in the field of that generating relation; the order of these numerals will be the order of the properties.

But we have not really decided whether the solution of the problem that we have found is unique. In particular, on p. 289, we left it doubtful whether it was strictly necessary that the second law of addition should be true. The question could not be discussed there because, even if the second law were true, there were gaps in the standard series; we had established only the members of that series which are represented by integral numerals, and there were many properties in the field of the generating relation which would not be equal to any of those of the standard series. Now we have filled those gaps by fractional magnitudes and (where necessary) negative magnitudes; but we have done so on the assumption that the second law of addition was true. Could we have filled the gaps if that law had not been true? The question may seem quite unnecessary and the difficulties into which it will lead us quite artificial. Nobody, it will be said, wants to adopt a system in which the second law of addition is not fulfilled, so long as there is one available in which it is fulfilled; all the advantages are on the side of fulfilling the law. That is quite true; but it might be objected that some case may occur in the future, even if (as has been suggested) it has not occurred already, in which we could not fulfil the second law; it would be useful then to know whether we could still obtain a satisfactory system of measurement. But my true reason for discussing the matter is rather deeper and more important. The application of mathematical analysis to physical problems doubtless depends greatly on the introduction of measurement; but it raises some difficulties because mathematical ideas, being based upon "internal judgements", differ in their nature from physical ideas, based on "external judgements". Our view of the exact relationship of mathematics and physics is sure to be influenced by the view that we take of the exact nature of measurement; it will not do to show that we actually adopt certain processes; our conclusions will be uncertain unless we know that we could adopt no others.

In the discussion before us it will be well to be clear about the nature of the problem. Our object is to establish a standard series, such that the order of the numerals assigned to the members of it is the order of their properties, and such that any other system possessing the property in question will be equal to one of the members of the standard series. It will be convenient if the standard series is such that (e.g.) the members marked 2 and 5, added together, are equal to the members marked 3 and 4; for if they are, we shall be able to dispense with a large number of the members of the series which would otherwise be necessary, by building up those omitted from those that are included. And unless the second law of addition is true, such relations will not actually hold; we shall have to have the full standard series including (as we say now) members of every possible magnitude[1]. (We shall see in

---

[1] One possibility may be mentioned. If a standard series were made each member of which was equal to the unit multiplied by a power of 2, positive or negative, represented by a numeral, then there would be only one combination of these weights which, added together, would be represented by any numeral whatever. Accordingly even if the second law of addition was not obeyed, there could be no possibility of finding that two combinations of the members of the series were not equal though represented by the same numeral. On the

a later chapter that the number of such members is finite.) But this is a mere matter of convenience. We have not so far made any essential use of the relation between the 2 and 5 on the one hand and the 3 and 4 on the other; and when we have completed our discussion I believe that we shall still find that this relation is not in itself in any way essential to the process of measurement.

Let us first note, then, that it is possible for a standard series to exist which assigns uniquely a numeral to every magnitude, and yet is such that the second law of addition is not obeyed. For if we start with a complete standard series (i.e. a series in which every numeral is represented) prepared with a perfect instrument, we can alter the numerals marked on the members of the series, so that the desired condition is fulfilled. Draw axes of coordinates in the usual manner, and draw through the origin any curve whatever subject to the condition that dy/dx is always positive. Then if the abscissae represent in the usual manner the numerals marked on the members of the perfect standard series, the ordinates the numerals which are to be substituted for them, it is apparent that, since every magnitude can be represented by some numeral on the perfect series, it will also be represented by some numeral when the numerals on the perfect series have been changed; further, since dy/dx is always positive, the order of the changed numerals will again be the order of the magnitudes that they represent. The required conditions are therefore fulfilled. If the curve drawn is a straight line, the series will still obey the second law of addition after the numerals have been changed; it will be also a perfect series, differing from the first only in the unit. But if the curve is not straight, the second law of addition will not be fulfilled, if tested on a perfect instrument; it will not be true that the bodies 2 and 5 added together are equal to the bodies 3 and 4 added together. We shall call the series which does not obey the second law of addition, produced in this way, a "distorted" series, and the magnitudes assigned by it "apparent" weights; in contradistinction we shall speak of a perfect series which gives "true" magnitudes.

The question that we have to ask now is whether we could possibly produce such a distorted series by following out the specifications that have been given for the manufacture of the standard series, if our method of judging equality and our process of addition obeyed all the necessary laws except the second law of addition. I am inclined to think that we cannot, but it is impossible to prove that statement definitely; no amount of argument can prove what will happen if we make certain experiments[1]. The best plan

other hand if that law were not obeyed in the process of making the standard series and in combining them, there would be no certainty that the order of the numerals was the order of the magnitudes or that there were no gaps in the series and that to every magnitude could be assigned a numeral. This possibility must therefore be rejected. The standard series must include members represented by every numeral.

[1] This statement requires expansion. If we assume that certain laws are true, then of course we can prove, from the meaning of those laws, what will happen as the result of experiment. Such assumptions have been made throughout the preceding three chapters, where it has been shown that certain results follow from certain definitions.

But here, in order to obtain the required proof, we should have to assume that there are will be to imagine that we are trying to make such a series and to notice the difficulties that are encountered. We may take again the example of weight, and try to devise a balance which will give the desired result. It will, of course, be a ludicrously "artificial" and unnatural balance, the balance of a nightmare; but it is the bare possibility of achievement that concerns us here.

The arrangement we may try is suggested by noting (see p. 285) that a balance of the type we require might occur if the pan knife-edges were not parallel to the main knife-edge. We will suppose that we are going to weigh by the method of substitution, and that the right pan is an ordinary pan for the counterpoise. At the left end of the beam are a series of hooks, each of which will support one body only, hanging from knife-edges placed at different distances along the beam. The hooks are marked 1, 2, 3, ... and they are placed so that a body hanging on the hook n will balance a body of weight W in the counterpoise pan if its weight is $W/(1 - a_n)$. For simplicity we shall take $a_1 = 0$; every a_n is numerically less than 1 but may be positive or negative. We adopt a convention that if more than one body has to be hung on the hooks we fill up the hooks in the order of their numerals, and the heavier always goes on the hook with the larger value of n.

We now take the unit, place it in hook 1, counterpoise it, and make another weight so that it will still balance the counterpoise if hung on hook 1. Its true weight will be 1. We now leave this unit on hook 1, hang the original unit on hook 2, counterpoise and find a single body which, hung on hook 1, balances the counterpoise. The true weight of this body, the apparent "2", will be $1 + (1 - a_2)$. We now hang the unit once more on hook 1, the "2" on hook 2, and make a "3"; its weight will be $1 + (1 - a_2) + (1 - a_2)^2$, and so on. The apparent weight n, where n is integral, corresponds to the true weight $1 + \sum_1^{n-1} (1 - a_2)^s = \dfrac{1 - (1 - a_2)^n}{a_2}$; and it will not be true that the body with apparent weights x_1, x_2 balance those with apparent weights x_3, x_4, if $x_1 + x_2 = x_3 + x_4$. On the other hand the order of x_1, x_2, ... will always be the order of their true weights, the first law of addition will be obeyed, and there will be no inconsistent judgements of equality, if the conventional rules are followed strictly.

Now let us make the members of the standard series represented by $1/p$. It will be found by following out the specification that the true weight of the body that has the apparent weight $1/p$ is $1/(p - \sum_2^p a_s)$: again the order of the numerals $1/p$ is the order of their true weights, for p has only integral

---

no laws of a certain form. Such an assumption is wholly illegitimate; all that can be said is that no such laws are known.

It is always dangerous to try to prove that an experiment will turn out in a given way; the risk of unconsciously applying laws outside their proper range is great. It is especially great when "mental" experiments are involved—a phrase due to Mach—namely such as cannot possibly be tried. The fallacies of the ancients should be a sufficient warning against the pernicious practice (of which there has been a fresh epidemic recently in connection with relativity) of attempting to base proofs on such mental experiments.

values and, since $|a_n| < 1$, $p + 1 - a_{p+1}$ is $> p$. So far we have got on very well, but one feature must be noted. By suitable choice of the a_n's we can make the apparent weights less than 1 fit any curve determining the distortion of the standard series, but the form of the curve for weights greater than 1 is fixed wholly by the value of a_2. There is no doubt that, by a slight elaboration of the method, the weights greater than 1 could be made to depend on all the a_n's as do those less than 1 and not only on a_2; but all simple modifications of the procedure would have the common feature that the parts of the distortion curve above 1 are connected functionally with those below 1; they cannot be fixed quite independently.

But the series produced so far has gaps; in order to fill them we must produce the members represented by q/p. If the second law of addition is obeyed the two specifications given on p. 311 for making these members are equivalent; but now we must choose between the alternatives (1) making q/p equal to q weights $1/p$, or (2) making q/p such that p weights q/p equal q. If we adopt alternative (1) the weight produced will have the true weight

$$\frac{q - \sum\limits_1^q a_s}{p - \sum\limits_1^p a_s}.$$

If we adopt (2) it will have the true weight

$$\frac{1 - (1 - a_2)^q}{a_2 \left(p - \sum\limits_1^n a_s \right)}.$$

But, if either of these alternatives is adopted, will the order of the magnitudes of the members of the series be that of the numerals q/p by which they are denoted? In general they certainly will not. For it must be remembered that there are many numerals, $q_1/p_1, q_2/p_2, \ldots$, which are essentially the same numeral, although the q's and the p's are different: thus $25/50$ is the same numeral as $1/2$, and is placed in the same position in the conventional order. If the first alternative is adopted, the members of the series denoted by $q_1/p_1, q_2/p_2$ will be equal, when q_1/p_1 is the same numeral as q_2/p_2, only if all the a_n's (including a_1) are equal; for then the true weight of the apparent weight q/p is $\dfrac{q(1 - a)}{p(1 - a)}$ or p/q; the true weight is equal to the apparent weight But it must be remembered that q/p may be the same numeral as an integer greater than 1. The members of the series represented by integers greater than 1 have not true weights equal to their apparent weights unless $a_2 = 0$. Accordingly the possibility of two unequal members of the series being represented by the same numeral will not be avoided unless all the a_n's are 0 and the balance is perfect. If the second alternative is adopted, the same conclusion follows immediately from the formula given for the true value of the apparent weight q/p.

Thus the balance which we have imagined does not give the results that are sought; can we modify it so that it will give those results? I think not. The broad principle that was involved in our balance was that the deviation of an apparent weight from the true weight was determined by the number of bodies that had to be used in making that apparent weight. Many variants of that principle might be tried, but I think it will be found that they all break down in the same way. The only other broad principle that I can suggest might be tried consists in making the deviation depend on the magnitude of the weights weighed. Such a principle would be used if we made the arms of the balance flexible; but then the difficulty appears that, if weighing is by substitution, the balance is true; if it is not by substitution, judgements of equality are inconsistent—a different judgement is made if the objects are reversed in the pans. Another suggestion is that the two principles might be combined; the hooks of the previous balance might not only be suspended at different distances from the main knife-edge but they might be suspended by supports differently flexible. The relation between the true and apparent weight obtained with such a balance is extremely complicated and the formulae need not be given here; but the results show that the introduction of the previous principle, the apparent weight being determined by the number of bodies used, leads again to the same inconsistency when the members q/p are established.

Indeed I think that general considerations will suggest that the problem is insoluble. For let us return to the idea of a distorted series determined by a curve. Whatever form of balance we employ the general shape of the curve which represents the distorted series is fixed when we have made the members of the series represented by integral numbers. Now the members represented by q/p are those which would have been integral values if we had taken $1/p$ as the unit. It seems impossible to devise any balance which will not give the same general form of distortion curve whatever unit is adopted. Accordingly the distortion curve on which the members q/p lie will be of the same general form as that of the curve on which the integral members lie; it will be merely drawn on a smaller scale. But the condition that the q/p members must be consistent with the integral members is roughly equivalent to the condition that the q/p curve must fit the earlier part of the integral curve. But the only form of curve which is such that, if it is drawn on a reduced scale, it will fit the earlier part of the large-scale curve is the straight line. It is only if the distortion curve is a straight line (and therefore represents only a change of unit) that the q/p members will be consistent with the integral members.

Accordingly we shall conclude that if a satisfactory method of measurement is to be established on the general lines indicated in Chapter X all the conditions prescribed there must be fulfilled. And this conclusion indicates why it is important that they should be fulfilled; if they are not, we cannot measure at all. It may seem foolish to enter into all these intricacies in order to prove that it is necessary to define our magnitudes so that $2 + 2 = 4$, but

I cannot discover for myself any other connection than this in which that proposition is important. It seems to me that the proposition is important, not because it states some intensely important fact about magnitudes after they are measured, but simply because we cannot measure them at all unless it is true. Of course there may possibly be some other way of assigning numerals to represent properties differing in first principles from that described in Chapter X; but until somebody suggests such a way, it is hardly worth while to discuss the possibility; it is certainly not employed in the actual physics of to-day.

CHAPTER XIII

NUMERICAL LAWS AND DERIVED MAGNITUDES

Summary. A numerical law states relations of two kinds, physical and numerical. The physical relation need be nothing but uniform association; but in actual numerical laws other physical relations are often involved which have to be remembered when any application of the law is made. The uniform association asserted may be of any of the kinds considered in Chapter III.

The numerical relation is not a physical relation between the magnitudes that are measured. If it is a physical relation at all it must be a physical relation between numbers. But there are difficulties in accepting such a view and the alternative view that it is a mathematical relation between Numbers is considered. But this view is also open to an objection, namely that it would make the derived magnitudes, defined by numerical laws, hypothetical and therefore essentially different from fundamental magnitudes. In order to see whether such a distinction can be maintained a thorough discussion of derived magnitudes is undertaken.

It is concluded that derived and fundamental magnitudes are essentially similar; both contain an arbitrary element connected with the choice of unit, but both are definite properties of a system; indeed a derived magnitude may be exactly the same property as a fundamental magnitude. The only difference is that all fundamental magnitudes must be susceptible of addition, whereas derived magnitudes either may be or may not be so susceptible.

It is pointed out that all the "constants" of a numerical law may not be derived magnitudes. But if they are not, the law is an empirical law.

It appears impossible then to admit that derived and fundamental magnitudes differ as do hypothetical ideas and concepts. The impossibility is still further confirmed by observing that derived magnitudes can be measured by a purely experimental process by means of graphs. Some consideration is given to the process involved in the drawing of graphs, and the measurement of derived magnitudes by means of them.

The resolution of the apparent contradiction that one line of argument shows that derived magnitudes are hypothetical ideas and another that they are concepts is left to a later chapter (Mathematical Physics).

The process by which numerical laws are established is considered. It is concluded that, for the establishment of numerical laws as of other laws, there is no formal process of Induction, but that discovery proceeds by trial and error. However it may be possible to lay down a rule for the establishment of empirical laws.

Lastly a few remarks are made on the familiar problem of interpolation and extrapolation. It is insisted that there is here a great difference between empirical and true numerical laws.

Physical relations expressed by numerical laws. Measurement is only a means to an end; we want to express the properties of systems by numerals only because we are thereby enabled to state laws about them.

When we have measured two or more magnitudes characteristic of some system, we can usually find a general numerical relation between these magnitudes. The assertion of such a numerical relation is called a numerical law, and it is from laws of this kind that nearly all the advances made in the conscious history of physics have been made.

In Part I it was insisted often that a numerical law, Ohm's Law, for example, consists of two distinct parts. First there is a collection of statements that certain values of one magnitude (the current) are uniformly associated with certain values of another magnitude (the potential difference); second, there is the statement that a numerical relation, of the kind characteristic of mathematical variables, holds between the values which are so uniformly associated. Both these parts are usually expressed by a single statement of the form that $y = f(x)$; but it is important to realise that two entirely different kinds of relations are expressed by the sign $=$. That sign expresses, besides the numerical or mathematical relation between the numerals or Numbers which represent the magnitudes, a physical relation between the properties of the system which have those magnitudes. We will consider in greater detail each of the meanings expressed by $=$.

First it may be asked whether the physical relation is simply uniform association or whether it involves anything else which is worth considering.

In the process of establishing a numerical law we observe a large number of values of each of two magnitudes A and B, and we write these values down in our note book in two parallel columns; we then seek to find a numerical relation between the values in the two columns. In seeking this relation we compare one particular value of A from one column with one particular value of B from the other; the question may be asked on what grounds we select the particular value of B which is to be compared with any particular value of A. In any actual case the answer is so familiar that the possibility of any other may be overlooked. If the magnitudes which are being measured are (A) the distance that a body has fallen and (B) the time that has elapsed since the beginning of the fall, the values of A and B which will be compared are those that are simultaneous. If A is the electrical conductivity of an element and B its thermal conductivity, the values which will be compared are those that are characteristic of the same element. If A is the pressure of a gas and B its volume, the values to be compared are those of the gas in the same state, those namely which are measured without making any alteration to the apparatus; they need not necessarily be simultaneous. The feature common to all these relations between A and B, which leads us to select for comparison values between which they hold, is that all the relations are marks of uniform association; in each case the relation is such that, if the selected value of A can be observed, then the associated value of B can also be observed. But it should be observed that there is a difference between the first example and the two others. In these two the B which is selected to correspond to any A is the only B which is uniformly associated with that A; the only thermal conductivity which is uniformly associated with the electrical conductivity of any element is the thermal conductivity of that element, and the only volume which is uniformly associated with the pressure of a gas in a given state is the volume in that state. But in the first example (which is typical of many in which one of the magnitudes measured is the time) there is not this unique association of the corresponding magnitudes. All the values of the magnitudes, from the moment that the falling starts to the moment when it stops, form a connected series uniformly associated; and any distance is uniformly associated, not only with the time that is simultaneous with it, but also with any other time within this interval connected with it by any other fixed temporal relation. Thus, the distance the body has fallen is uniformly associated, not only with the time that is simultaneous with the moment at which it has fallen through that distance, but also with the time that is 2 seconds subsequent to that moment. If we chose as corresponding magnitudes the distance fallen and the time 2 seconds subsequently these magnitudes would still be uniformly associated. Is there any reason why such a correlation should not be adopted?

Of course if the values of the magnitudes which are made to correspond are changed, the form of the numerical relation will change; but is there anything important expressed by one relation that is not expressed by the other? A law may simply express the facts on which it is founded. If we are interested in the relation between the distance at one moment and the time at a moment two seconds subsequently, this relation would be expressed more conveniently by correlating in this manner the distance and the time than by correlating distances and times that are simultaneous. But laws are also sometimes used in combination for the deduction of other laws (see p. 117). For instance, the law relating the distance fallen by the body with the time may be combined with a law relating the distance travelled by the body in a horizontal direction with the time, in order to obtain a relation between the vertical and horizontal distances which represents the path of the body. If y is the vertical and x the horizontal distance, we may find $y = f_1(t)$ and $x = f_2(t)$ and thence deduce that $x = f_3(y)$. In order that such a deduction may be possible in the usual manner and may lead to the equation of the path of the body, it is necessary that the value of y which corresponds to any value of t is simultaneous with the value of x which corresponds to that value of t. This condition is fulfilled if simultaneous values are chosen as corresponding values for y and t and for x and t. But it will also be fulfilled if other relations define correspondence. Thus, if to any value of t corresponds the value of y 2 seconds previously and also the value of x 2 seconds previously, then again the values of y and x which correspond to the same value of t are simultaneous and the relation $x = f_3(y)$ deduced and interpreted in the ordinary way will give the path of the body.

These considerations may appear rather fantastic and unreal. Whenever one of the magnitudes measured is the time the values of other magnitudes correlated with the time are always in practice those that are simultaneous. But it may be worth while to notice that this choice of corresponding values, though the most convenient, is not absolutely necessary. It is always dangerous to overlook variations in our practice which are possible, though seldom convenient, for by so doing we may confuse arbitrary conventions with natural laws. And the danger of confusion is here increased by the occurrence of the symbol = in the numerical law. That symbol is often used to denote any relation that, like numerical equality, is symmetrical and transitive; and it might be thought that its occurrence indicated that the physical relation involved in the numerical law should also be symmetrical and transitive. Now simultaneity is such a relation, while "occurrence 2 seconds after" is not. But the suggestion is misleading. The symbol = is characteristic only of the numerical relation involved in the law; it gives no indication whatever of the physical relation. In any application of the law we have to consider what is the nature of the physical relation involved in that law, and it is not permissible to assume that applications possible for one law involving one kind of physical relation are necessarily possible for another law involving another physical relation. It may be added that no practised physicist and hardly any elementary student would be liable to error from the neglect of these considerations.

The remarks that have just been made suggest one further question concerning the physical relation involved in a numerical law. Must the uniform association between the corresponding magnitudes be of the symmetrical form, or are any of the varieties of it permissible? A very simple example will show that it need not be symmetrical; if we measure the deflection of a pendulum from the vertical and the time, we shall find that whereas any particular time is uniformly associated with a particular deflection, a particular deflection may be associated with many times. This feature of the physical relation will be reflected in the mathematical function, which will be "many-valued". But the fact that such many valued functions are permissible in numerical laws shows that the uniform association involved in them need not be of the symmetrical kind. Indeed, I think that there is no limitation on the physical relation between corresponding magnitudes in a numerical law other than that it must include uniform association of some kind.

Numerical relations of numerical laws. We must now turn from this discussion of the physical relations between magnitudes which are asserted by the law to more interesting and important questions concerning the mathematical relation which is the characteristic feature of numerical laws.

The first and most important question that arises is whether this mathematical relation is, after all, only a physical relation, expressible in terms of experiment and observation. The answer is very difficult and very important. Let us consider some possible numerical laws, and consider how far the "mathematical" relation can be expressed as one between physical magnitudes, or between any terms which can be clearly described in terms of observation and experiment alone. We may first take a numerical law between two physical magnitudes of the same kind, that is to say, between two lengths or two weights or two times. Suppose, for example, that we are measuring the lengths of the diagonals (L_1) and of the sides (L_2) of a series of squares. Then when we examine the results we shall find that there is a relation between L_1 and L_2 which we shall write $L_1 = a \cdot L_2$, where a is 1·414, so far as the accuracy of our experiments can determine it. What exactly do we mean by this assertion? First, we meant that the numeral representing the magnitude called L_1 is always the same numeral (in the sense of p. 311) as the numeral equivalent to 1·414 × x, where x is the numeral representing the magnitude called L_2. But it seems at first sight that we must mean something more. For we concluded that, in many cases, the fact that one numeral is the same as another is simply the consequence of a definition; and though that definition is suggested by physical facts, it remains actually purely arbitrary and formal. It seems impossible that the assertion of a relation so important as that we are considering should depend for its validity on an arbitrary definition. Can we not express it also as a physical relationship? Now in this special case it is perhaps possible to express it as a purely physical relationship between physical magnitudes. It is equivalent to the assertion that if we measure the diagonal of a square, using the side of that square as the unit of length, then the length of the diagonal always turns out to be 1·414. This, as we have seen, is a purely physical statement; we can describe exactly and completely in terms of observations what we mean by saying that a length is 1·414, if another length is taken as unit. In this case, then, it may appear that the relation expressed is purely physical. But, though the experimental evidence that has been obtained can be expressed in this form, it is very doubtful whether this form expresses what we really mean by the statement. For we have imagined that the unit of length is changed every time that we pass from one square to another; but that conception is not really in our minds when we make the statement and is wholly foreign to it. We are actually measuring all the lengths in terms of the same unit, and we should come to exactly the same conclusion even if we denied ourselves the right ever to change the unit of length. If we exclude the possibility of change of unit, I do not think we can express the assertion in terms of lengths at all. For there is nothing in the principles of Chapter X which allows us to give meaning to the conception of a length which is 1·414 times another, except on the assumption that we are using this second length as unit. I conclude therefore that even in this, the most favourable, case it is not legitimate to regard the relation which we are investigating as one between the physical magnitudes that are measured.

In all other cases, when we are measuring two magnitudes which are not of the same kind, this conclusion is perfectly obvious. If we are measuring the time and the distance a body has travelled with uniform velocity, we may find a relation $L = a \cdot T$, where a again is a definite numeral. It is again doubtful if we can regard $a \cdot T$ as a physical magnitude without introducing the conception, foreign to the experiment, of a unit of time which is different for every observation. But even if we could it would be clear that the symbol

= cannot express a physical relation between the distance and this physical magnitude, for our principles of measurement admit no relation between magnitudes of different kinds. If = here is to express a physical relation we must in some manner make the magnitudes which it relates of the same kind. There is a possibility of such a change if we introduce the magnitude number which, as we have seen, is involved in or applicable to the measurement of all kinds of physical magnitude. We might say that the collection of units of distance which, added together, are equal to the distance L is equal in number to (i.e. can be counted against) the collection which consists of a groups of unit times, each group being such that its members added together are equal to the time T. This statement is capable of a definite physical interpretation and asserts something that can be determined simply by experiment and observation, so long as there is no need to introduce fractional numbers, or only fractional numbers such that their denominators are sub-multiples of the number of the collection to which they are applied; for it is only then that fractional numbers have a meaning. This condition can be fulfilled if the units of distance and time are chosen small enough, so that the numbers of unit distances or unit times in L and T are very large. But here again we are binding ourselves to the use of certain units rather than others, and again we must note that we are introducing something foreign to the ideas which we really want to express.

Two further examples will enforce these difficulties and show that we cannot, even by the introduction of the conception of number and the ad-mission of units other than those actually employed, state a numerical law as a purely physical relationship. If the body of which we are measuring the motion is moving with uniform acceleration instead of uniform velocity, then we shall find a relation of the form $L = a \cdot T^2$. Now the symbol on the right of this equation does not represent a physical magnitude at all. By supposing that the unit of measurement changed at every observation we could represent $a \cdot L_2$ or $a \cdot T$ as physical magnitudes and the equation as stating some relation between physical magnitudes; but no admission of changing units will permit us to regard $a \cdot T^2$ as a physical magnitude or to regard the equation as stating a relation between such magnitudes. From a system characterised by a time-interval T, or from any collection of such systems, we cannot produce, according to any law, a system characterised by some magnitude which will be represented by the numeral which also represents the Number T^2. As this fact is important and is sometimes overlooked, it will be well to consider it rather more closely.

We may compare in this respect the magnitudes time[1] and length. If we are given a system characterised by a given length L, we can by a general law produce a system characterised by a magnitude represented by L^2; this

---

[1] In Part III we shall see that there are two magnitudes which are often confused under the single name "time", namely periods and time-intervals; we shall also have to distinguish between lengths and distances. But these distinctions are immaterial for the present dis-cussions, and a neglect of them will conduce to brevity.

system is the square of which the side is L, and the magnitude (which can be measured as a fundamental magnitude) is the area of the square. We can also produce by a general law[1] a system characterised by a magnitude represented by L^3, namely the cube with side L with the magnitude volume. But these possibilities are altogether exceptional and depend on our knowledge of certain laws which apply only to the magnitude length and to the powers 2 and 3. From a system characterised by a length L we cannot produce by a general law a system characterised by any magnitude represented by L^n, where n is any numeral, integral or fractional, rational or irrational, other than 2 and 3. Moreover, apart from length, area and volume, there is only one other magnitude which has a property of the same kind and is such that, from a system characterised by a value A of this magnitude, another system can be produced characterised by any other fundamental magnitude represented by A^n, for any value of n. This one other magnitude is electrical resistance; from a system characterised by a resistance R we can produce another characterised by a magnitude R^n, if and only if $n = -1$; this magnitude is electrical conductivity[2]. In general, if A is the magnitude characteristic of some system, there is not another system characterised by a magnitude represented by A^n or by any function of A other than $a \cdot A$.

It is to be concluded therefore that when we state that $L = a \cdot T^2$ we are not, as in the previous examples, stating a relation between physical magnitudes represented by the two sides of the equation. There still remains however the possibility (although we have already rejected it tentatively) that by the introduction of the physical magnitude number we can still make the numerical law represent a relation between physical magnitudes, but not between magnitudes of the kind that are directly measured in the experiment. Our last example excludes even this possibility. The motion which we are now supposed to be measuring is harmonic and the relation we find is $L = L_0 \cos aT$. Here again the right-hand side does not represent a physical magnitude derivable from the measured magnitudes, but it now cannot be made to represent even a number. Starting from a group of number T we can build up by physical operations according to the principles of fundamental measurement a system of which the number is aT or aT^2 or indeed aT^n, where n is any positive integer; but we cannot in general build up a system of which the number is $a \cdot f(T)$ where f is any mathematical function; and in particular we cannot build up a system of which the number is $\cos aT$. The relation

[1] It is unnecessary to stop here to inquire whether the general "law" is strictly an experimental law.

[2] It must be understood, of course, that at present magnitude always means fundamental magnitude, measurable according to the principles of Chapter X; at present we can know no other magnitudes, for what we are investigating is precisely the method by which magnitudes of other kinds are established. Among derived magnitudes, the reciprocal (and sometimes other functions) of one magnitude is always another derived magnitude. But among fundamental magnitudes, electrical resistance is the only one such that the reciprocal is also a fundamental magnitude—unless possibly we must make another exception in favour of electrical capacity. The mere fact that there is no generally accepted name for the inverse of a capacity indicates that the exception is doubtful.

between a number T and cos T is one which cannot be expressed in terms of the physical operations characteristic of measurement or, I think, of any physical operations at all. Accordingly we cannot represent both the terms related by the numerical law as numbers or both as physical magnitudes of the same kind, whatever that kind may be. The relation between the terms is not a relation between physical magnitudes and, since no other physical interpretation for it seems possible, it is not a physical relation at all.

Are numerical "laws" theories? What then is the relation? It may be one between the Numbers, mathematical conceptions, represented by the same numerals as the measurement magnitudes. L and T in the equation may be Numbers[1] of this kind, a another Number and the equation express between them the mathematical relations which are applicable to such Numbers. Indeed if this view is adopted, the numerical "law" appears to resemble in logical form what we have termed a theory rather than a law. For the relation "represented by the same numeral as" naturally suggests the dictionary of a theory. We may state the hypothesis that L and T are mathematical variables, a is a mathematical constant, and that $L = f(T.a)$. The dictionary then states that, in the special sense of p. 124, L *is* the distance travelled by the body, T the time, or, in other words, that the statement that L or T is the Number x implies that the distance or time has the magnitude x.

The conclusion that a numerical law states something about Numbers may seem so obvious that it was scarcely worth while to undertake this elaborate inquiry in order to reach it. But I do not think that it is quite so obvious as it appears. "numerical" might be the adjective either of number or of Number, two conceptions which are not always clearly distinguished. And in concluding that it is here the adjective of Number we have not entirely freed ourselves from difficulty. For it seems that this conclusion involves that numerical laws are not laws at all but, according to our definition, theories. This objection may be merely verbal; the fact that we have defined laws and theories so that propositions which are regarded as typical laws must be regarded as theories may only show that our definitions are bad and should be changed. Let us examine therefore in what degree numerical laws resemble what are regarded as typical theories.

In Chapter VI the definition of a theory was based on a certain logical form. That form was adapted to show how a theory might establish a connection between ideas of completely different nature, namely hypothetical ideas and concepts; and it was implied, but not stated, that a proposition (or set of propositions) was to be termed a theory only when by means of this logical form it established a connection between such different ideas. Now in this respect, if we admit that a numerical law states a relation between Numbers, it is undoubtedly a theory; for by its means a relation is established between Numbers, which are undoubtedly hypothetical ideas, and concepts,

---

[1] I am not sure whether a variable of which all the values are Numbers is properly to be termed a Number; but it is unimportant for our purpose to attain the full accuracy of statement which mathematical logicians would require.

namely physical magnitudes. But in the further discussion a condition was imposed that the hypothetical ideas must not only be different from the concepts but must also have some intrinsic value apart from the concepts; it is only in virtue of this intrinsic value that theories explain laws and, through additions to the hypothesis or dictionary, can predict new laws. The intrinsic value of the theories which we examined was always connected with an analogy between them and the concepts of some law. In this respect a numerical law is not a theory; the hypothetical ideas do not always, if ever, derive their value from any analogy with a law; for the only kind of law on which an analogy applicable to mathematical conceptions can be based is a numerical law. The hypothetical ideas of some numerical laws may possibly derive value from analogy with other numerical laws, but there must be some numerical laws which do not present analogy of this kind; these will be the most fundamental numerical laws and those, therefore, which most deserve our attention at present. If the hypothetical ideas of numerical laws have any intrinsic value—a value apart from that which they possess because they lead to the prediction of true experimental laws—that value is due to mathematical simplicity and not to any relation with physical concepts. It is because they lack the value derived from a connection with physical concepts that numerical laws have not two of the most important properties of true theories; they do not explain laws and they do not predict new laws. The laws deducible from the theory are those which form what has been called the first part of the numerical law, the assertions that certain magnitudes of one kind are uniformly associated with certain magnitudes of another kind. But the theory (if theory it be) involved in the numerical law does not explain these laws; nor are there suggested by the nature of the hypothetical ideas additions to hypothesis or dictionary which lead to the prediction of laws other than those of the first part of the numerical law[1].

On the other hand it must not be overlooked that in one respect a numerical law, expressed as a theory, appears to resemble true theories. We noted that it was one of the characteristics of such theories that they involved ideas, of great importance for science, which have no meaning apart from the theory of which they are hypothetical ideas; the velocity of a molecule is such an idea. Such ideas are involved in numerical laws; they are represented by the "mathematical constants" of the hypothesis. These constants, or some of them, are known as "derived magnitudes", and they are conceptions which play a part in science no less essential than fundamental magnitudes. A derived magnitude has no meaning whatever apart from the numerical law on which it is based. Thus, when the numerical law is of the form $L = a \cdot T^2$, the a is called a uniform acceleration and is an extremely important

---

[1] There may be exceptions to the last part of this statement which will have to be considered in a later volume. I cannot pretend to have arrived at a decision on the matter yet. One of these possible exceptions is the Fresnel law of reflection and refraction at the surface of a transparent body. Here the occurrence among the hypothetical ideas of an imaginary number suggested an addition to the dictionary which led to the prediction of a completely new law, namely that concerning the change of phase of the light at reflection.

derived magnitude; its importance and its meaning are based wholly on the fact that the numerical law in this case is of this form and of no other; to say that a body possesses a uniform acceleration and to deny that there is applicable to it a law of the form $L = a \cdot T^2$ would be self-contradictory and meaningless.

However, the importance of derived magnitudes could be explained just as well if the numerical "law" were really a law; they would then be concepts such as we discussed in Chapter II. If a numerical law is really a theory, derived magnitudes must all be theoretical or hypothetical ideas. A uniform acceleration, a density, a self-induction would be ideas as purely theoretical as the velocity of a molecule. The numerical value to be attributed to one of these magnitudes would be determined by experiment and experiment only, just as is the numerical value to be attributed to the velocity of a molecule, but the existence of such magnitudes and the possibility of their measurement would depend on the acceptance of ideas which are not completely definable in terms of experiment. From such a conclusion we shall all rebel. The test which distinguishes a theoretical idea from an experimental concept is the possibility of universal agreement concerning it. We shall recognise that other people may differ from us concerning the velocity of a molecule and that, if anyone denies the validity of that idea, we have no certain means of convincing him; but we shall not readily admit that a similar disagreement may occur concerning a uniform acceleration or a density. This is the difficulty to which we appear to be led by the admission that a numerical law states something concerning Numbers, ideas which are not definable in terms of experimental concepts, and that it is therefore a theory rather than a true law.

One way out of the difficulty is simply to include propositions about Numbers (or at any rate such propositions about them as are involved in numerical laws) with those that have so far been regarded as characteristically physical in the class of propositions concerning which universal agreement is possible. And there is something to be said for this view; for, after all, the statement "twice two is four" is often taken as typical of propositions concerning which there can be no dispute. But it is by no means certain that when this statement is said to be indisputable it is thought to concern Numbers rather than numbers; when it is asserted it may only mean that the number of a collection of men which consists of two groups each containing two men is four; this is a statement concerning physical magnitudes and does not concern Number. It is only recently that the distinction between number and Number and the true nature of Number have been recognised; and I do not think that those who have studied recent treatises concerning Number will always feel that there is attached to propositions concerning it the same indisputable certainty and impossibility of disagreement as is attached to statements concerning physical concepts. Personally I should never dream of venturing to suggest that there is error in the laborious process by which it is established in *Principia Mathematica* that $2 \times 2 = 4$; but at the same time I feel that I am powerless in the hands of its learned and ingenious authors, and that if they set out to prove that $2 \times 2 = 5$ they could produce in me an equal conviction; and I am by no means sure that in a second edition they may not undertake that very task. To me at least it seems intolerable to admit that conceptions so fundamental in physics as derived magnitudes depend for their significance on ideas and propositions which seem so extremely precarious. Mathematicians, of course, would not share that feeling; to them the ideas and propositions of mathematics are the most certain things in the whole realm of knowledge; mathematical knowledge is to them absolute knowledge; but—I am not a mathematician.

Now since the difficulties that we are discussing seem to depend ultimately on the nature of derived magnitudes, it is well to consider whether a meaning cannot be attributed to these extremely important conceptions by some different means which shall clearly involve nothing that is not purely experimental. For this purpose we must be quite clear what is the nature and significance of derived magnitudes; and since the matter is one of the most important parts of the present discussion, we must go back to fundamentals and consider it in detail.

The form of a numerical law. It has been stated already that a derived magnitude is a constant in a numerical law, and indeed that conclusion is so familiar as to need no formal statement. Nevertheless it will be well to inquire exactly what is meant by such a constant.

We are accustomed to speak of a numerical law between two magnitudes x and y[1]; but actually the relation found is scarcely ever simply between x and y; there are always involved in it other terms also represented by numerals. We do not find that $x = y$ or $x = y^2$ or $x = \cos y$, but we find that $x = 10y + 3$, or $x = 16y^2$ or $x = 24 \cos 17y$. There is an important difference between the numerals which are definitely stated and those which are implied by the use of the indeterminate x and y, namely that while the latter vary from experiment to experiment which proves the law, the former are characteristic only of the whole series of experiments and not of individual experiments. Nevertheless it is true that the relation which we find involves 10 and 3, or 16, or 24 and 17 as intimately as it involves x and y. Accordingly, if we express the relation between x and y by means of the generalised functional notation of mathematics, it might seem at first sight correct to say that we have found, not $x = f(y)$, but $x = f(y, 10, 3)$ or $x = f(y, 16)$ or $x = f(y, 24, 17)$.

The omission of the other terms represented by definite numerals might be due to their inclusion in the "f". The statement that $x = f(y)$ might only mean that to every numerical value of x corresponds one value (or a definite finite number of values) of y; that when the value of x is known the value

---

[1] Numerical laws are always actually discovered between *pairs* of magnitudes and not between three or more. Many numerical laws, e.g. the gas laws, express a relation between more than two magnitudes, but such more complex relations are always reached by deduction from simpler dual relations in the discovery of which one of the "variables" of the more complex relation is constant. I do not think there is anything important to be said about complex numerical laws which is not so familiar that there is no need to make reference to it here.

or values of y are known also; and that which values of x correspond to which values of y is determined by the form of the function f. If we give to f one form, one set of y's will correspond to a given value of x; if we give another form, another set will correspond to the same value. And if this were what is meant, the 10 and 3 in the first example would be an essential part of the function; the y which corresponds to any given x will change if we substitute 8 and 4 for 10 and 3 just as it will if we substitute cos y for y.

But as a matter of fact, when this notation is used, we do not regard f as determined by the value of the numerical terms, we regard f as the same, whatever the value of these terms, so long as the term involving y only is the same (i.e. y or y^2 or cos y). This point of view is often expressed by writing particular cases of the function with indeterminate symbols in place of the "constant" numerals, e.g. $x = ax + b$, $x = ay^2$, $x = a \cos by$. Each of these represents a different function f, but in each function, whatever numerals are substituted for a and b, the function remains the same. The basis of this practice is obvious; the notation is derived from mathematics. If the relation between x and y were one between pure mathematical ideas, there would be important propositions always true if the term involving y were always the same, even if the numerical terms changed. Thus, in the instance $x = 10y + 3$ it would be true, even if 8 and 4 were substituted for 10 and 3, that dy/dx is the same for all values of x. It is these propositions which are mathematically interesting, and for this reason we regard such propositions as fixing the form of the function f, so that all f's are the same for which the same set of propositions of this kind are true; we regard the particular values 10 and 3 as defining one particular function of this general form, and the particular values 8 and 4 as fixing another particular function of this form. But even if we adopt that practice, it may still be suggested that it would be better to write $x = f(y, a, b)$ and not merely $x = f(y)$. But the only additional information thereby conveyed is the number of terms such as a, b involved in the functions; and we shall see in the next chapter that this number can be determined immediately the form of the function f is specified. However, though the total omission of the a, b is formally justified on these grounds, it will be convenient for our immediate purpose to retain them.

If we write the relation $x = f(y, a, b)$ it must be remembered that there is an important distinction between the x and y on the one hand and the a, b on the other. This distinction is often expressed by calling x and y variables and a and b constants. But this must not be interpreted to mean that a and b can never vary without the proposition $x = f(y, a, b)$ becoming untrue; for if that were so there could be no possible reason for representing the terms by algebraical symbols rather than by numerals. If the proposition were only true when a was 10 and b 3, it would be foolish to insert in the relation anything but 10 and 3. Again the proposition does not mean that x would not change, y being constant, if a or b changed. The distinction between the variables and the constants is simply that the propositions, of which the truth defines the form of the function f, involve only x and y and not a and b.

Accordingly, if the possibility of a change in a and b is admitted by writing them as algebraical symbols and not as numerals, the terms variable and constant are slightly misleading. However since we want some name for the numerical terms which shall not prejudice our ultimate decision as to their physical significance we shall adopt the names, in place of inventing new ones, and shall call the numerical terms "constants".

Now it is clear that these considerations have a bearing on the problems of numerical laws only if relations similar to those which we have supposed to exist among the mathematical propositions are actually found among the numerical laws. If there were known only a law in which $x = 10y + 3$ and none in which $x = 8y + 4$, there would be no object in representing the numerical terms by algebraic symbols, and the conception of a constant which might change from one law to another, while the function in which it occurred retained its form, would be valueless. But actually it is a fact, and a fact of the very highest importance, that if we discover a law $x = f(y, a, b)$, where a and b have some assigned numerical values, we always expect, and almost always expect rightly, to find another law differing from this law only in the substitution for a and b of some other numerical values. And here it must be noted that "differing only" means rather more for a numerical law than for a mathematical equation. The law involves a physical relationship as well as a numerical; one law is not to be regarded as differing from another only in the numerical value of the constants, unless the physical relationship is the same as well as the form of the function. If in one law x and y are the distance travelled by a body and the time occupied in the travel, then x and y must have the same physical significance in any other law which is to be regarded as of the same form and differing only in the numerical value of the constants. We shall regard a term as a "constant" (in the present special sense) only if there are several laws, each expressing the same physical relationship and characterised by a function of the same mathematical form, differing from each other only in the numerical value of this constant. If such laws can be found we shall speak of the same constant having a series of different values. Of course the two constants occurring in the example we have taken are to be regarded as distinct; but in order to simplify the discussion we shall assume for the present that the law is characterised by only one constant; thus it may be of the form $x = a \cdot y$ or $x = a \cdot y^2$ or $x = a^y$ or so on.

And here, before we proceed, one question which might be raised may be answered. Among possible forms for $f(y)$ in numerical laws, there has been mentioned $a \cdot y^2$ or, in particular, $16y^2$. But the relation $x = 16y^2$ involves, besides the x, y, and 16, the numeral 2 which appears as an index of the y. Why is this numeral not included in the function; ought we not to say that the relation is $x = f(y, 16, 2)$? One reason why we do not include "2" in the function is that "y^2" may be regarded as a mere abbreviated symbol for $y \cdot y$, which does not explicitly involve a numeral at all. But a more important reason is this. We have concluded that it is not legitimate to regard the "2" as a "constant" in our special sense, unless we can discover a set of systems which are all characterised by laws which differ only in the substitution for "2" of other numerals. If we could find a set of systems for each of which a law was true, stating the same physical relation between magnitudes, x and y, of the same kind and expressible by the mathematical function $x = 16y^n$, the only difference between these systems being that the value of n for them was different; then and then only would n be a constant. I do not think that there are actually known any systems having a series of laws of this form; certainly there are no important ones. While therefore it cannot be said definitely that there is no case in which it would be right to regard such a law as a special form of $x = f(y, a, n)$, there are so many cases and such important cases in which it is not right, that it will be wise throughout our discussion, except when the contrary is stated explicitly, to suppose that we are dealing with such cases.

The variation of "constants". The important question which now faces us is this. In what kind of experiments do we find laws of the same form and differing only in the constants involved in them?

One kind of experiment in which the constant changes while the form of the relation is unaltered is that in which the system of measurement of the magnitudes or their correlation is changed. We have seen that the only way in which a system of fundamental measurement can be changed is by the alteration of the unit. As is obvious and well known, an alteration of either of the units in which the magnitudes are measured produces a change in the constant, if the properties of which the magnitudes are a measure are unchanged. In the next chapter we shall have to consider in much greater detail the relation between a change of unit and a change in the constant.

But there is also possible a change in the system of correlation. On p. 330 it was noted that in some cases more than one method of choosing corresponding values of the two magnitudes is possible. Let us take the example considered there. When we measure the distance fallen by a body starting from rest and the time occupied in the fall, then if we correlate distances and times that are simultaneous we arrive at a relation $L = a \cdot T^2$. Now we make a change and correlate the distance with the time b seconds subsequently; we shall now find a relation $L = aT^2 - 2abT + ab^2$. This relation is not of the same form as the original relation and changes of this nature do not therefore fulfil the necessary condition. It is doubtless for this reason largely that we do not adopt this form of correlation. If we once admit the possibility of correlating magnitudes that are not simultaneous, we are bound to introduce another constant b in some fashion in order to define which magnitudes we propose to correlate. But the presence of this additional constant changes the form of the relation, and since the choice of the constant is purely arbitrary there will be no reason why we should adopt one form rather than another. The fundamental condition upon which all considerations of constants rests, namely that the form of the relation by which they are defined should be unaltered, is not fulfilled and the conception loses its significance. These considerations are not of much importance, for nobody in such a case would propose to correlate magnitudes that were not simultaneous; but it is often worth while to discover why practices are so obvious.

The second class of experiments in which the constants of a numerical law change, while the form remains unaltered, is that in which the system on which the experiments are made changes. This conception needs a rather closer examination, since the experiment that originally led to the numerical law, and in which the constants were constant, is also one in which the system changes; for the changes in the magnitudes are changes in the system. But this difficulty is only apparent. According to our view, a system is a concept defined by the uniform association of certain properties; if there is another system in which some, but not all, of these properties are again uniformly associated, it is a mere matter of words whether or no we call this system the same as the first; it is in some respects similar, in others different. The statement that the constant may change when the system changes may be more accurately expressed thus. A set of systems can be found such that all of them are characterised by a law of a given form, that is to say by a uniform relation which consists of the same physical relation expressed by a mathematical function of the same form. Among these laws characterising the different systems of the set, some have one value for the constant some another, and those which have one value are to be regarded as different systems from those which have another. On the other hand, the fact that each of the systems is characterised by a law means that the variations of the magnitudes characteristic of it, which determine the law, are not to be regarded as constituting a change of system. The idea may be made clearer with the aid of an example. A certain uniform association of chemical properties will define a system which is called a substance; different systems in which the same chemical properties are uniformly associated are regarded as the same substance even though two magnitudes characteristic of them vary, namely the mass and the volume. For each substance we can thus determine a law between the mass and the volume; we find $m = a \cdot V$. If we take another substance, defined by the uniform association of other chemical properties, and perform the same experiments, we shall again find $m = a \cdot V$, but the value of a will be different. The class of substances thus form a set of systems all characterised by a law of the same form; but different substances in this class are characterised by different numerical values of the constant in the law of this form.

Constants and derived magnitudes. It is the fact that such sets of systems can be found which gives to the constants of numerical laws their great importance. If there were not classes of systems all characterised by laws of the same form, but with different numerical values of the constants, their importance would be very much less than it is. For it is this fact which gives to constants in numerical laws their character as magnitudes. A magnitude is a property of a system which can be fitly represented by a numeral because it is the field of a transitive asymmetrical relation that generates an order. But if things are to be ordered there must be several of them;

a magnitude, therefore, must be a property possessed by more than one system. Now in virtue of the fact that several systems can be found, all characterised by laws of the same form, but differing in the numerical value of the constant, the possession of some value of this constant is a property possessed by several systems. And this property, by means of the law, is represented by a numeral, namely the numerical value of the constant in the law of the given form applicable to it; and since the properties of different systems are represented by different numerals, they will (like magnitudes) have an order, namely that of the representing numerals.

But we cannot conclude immediately that the property of being characterised by a law of a given form and possessing a constant of a given kind is a magnitude; it will not be a magnitude unless it is the field of a physical relation that is transitive and asymmetrical. But as a matter of fact it will always be the field of such a relation simply because it is characterised by the law. The relation which leads to the association of a constant with these systems gives a method of ordering them in respect of the property associated with the constant. Thus in our example we might take the same mass of each of the systems, measure the corresponding volumes, associate each system with its volume and then order the systems in the order of the volumes (for volumes, being fundamental magnitudes, possess an order). The order of the systems reached in this manner would not always agree with the order of the associated constants; in this particular case one order would be the inverse of the other; in other cases the relation might be more complicated. But if we examine further we shall find that by altering the process slightly we can place the systems in an order that is the same as the order of the constants. We have only to measure the mass of the same volume of each, instead of measuring the volume of the same mass, and place the systems in the order of the resulting masses. Generally, if the numerical relation is $x = f(y, a)$, and f is such a function as occurs in any actual numerical law, we can deduce a relation $a = \phi(x, y)$, the function ϕ being such that either $\left(\dfrac{\partial \phi}{\partial x}\right)_y$ or $\left(\dfrac{\partial \phi}{\partial y}\right)_x$ is always positive; if we then compare systems characterised by the same value of y or x, and place the systems in the order of their x or y, this order will also be the order of the constant a characterising those systems.

This procedure appears, no doubt, artificial and yet we shall see that it is sometimes of great importance. We might not feel that the order in which the systems had been placed represented anything real or showed in any way that the property with which the constants were associated was properly to be regarded as a magnitude. When we had ordered the systems in the manner proposed by means of the volumes, we should not feel that we had shown chemical constitution to be a magnitude. (Actually it is not a magnitude, for substances cannot be placed in a single ordered series in respect of chemical constitution.) If the property is to be a magnitude the transitive symmetrical relation must be such that a variation in respect of it implies a variation of something that is in our minds when we speak of that property; in other words it must be something involved in the laws which give rise to the concept of that property. And this condition is not here fulfilled.

However, though the constants would not measure a magnitude which could be termed "chemical constitution", it might be possible to find some other magnitude, varying with chemical constitution, which the constants would measure. And in our example, such a magnitude could be found, namely density. In Chapter X we saw that density, a concept founded on flotation, could be regarded as a magnitude ordered by means of the transitive asymmetrical relation "floating in". We find, first, that all substances which are the field of this relation are also such that the relation between mass and volume is of the prescribed form $m = a \cdot V$, and, second, that the order in which substances are placed by the characteristic relation, generating the order of the magnitude density, is also the order of the constants, derived from the numerical law, associated with those substances; if the density of a substance A is greater than that of a substance B, the constant associated with A is also greater than the constant associated with B. When we have made this discovery, we can regard the constant as measuring the magnitude; we have found a way of assigning numerals to represent the property in a manner fulfilling the necessary conditions for a system of measurement. We assign to each substance the numeral representing the associated constant; the assignment of a numeral to each particular substance is thus fixed according to a definite rule and is free from all arbitrariness (except possibly that of the unit, a matter which we have yet to investigate); and the order of the numerals assigned is the order of the substances generated by the relation characteristic of the magnitude.

Accordingly the constant which occurs in the relation between the mass and the volume of a substance, in the form $m = a \cdot V$, certainly represents a property that is a magnitude, and the constant measures the magnitude. And of course there are many other numerical laws the constants of which are found similarly to represent magnitudes based on characteristic relations that are not apparently connected with the concepts involved in those laws. But historically the procedure has usually been rather different and indeed almost reversed. We have imagined that a numerical law is established and that it is found subsequently that the constant involved in it measures a previously known magnitude. It is generally difficult to be certain about the historical development of physical conceptions (there is a splendid scope for the historian who would attack the problems systematically), but I can only think of one instance in which it seems perfectly clear that the development that has been sketched was actually followed. This instance concerns temperature. The conception of temperature as a magnitude dates back to the pre-historic period, when the characteristic generating relation was based on direct sensation of warmth and cold; "feeling warmer to the hand than" is a transitive asymmetrical relation which can generate an order of temperature. At a much later stage in the history of physics it was found that this magnitude could be measured by the constant which occurs in a numerical law investigated quite independently; this was Boyle's Law, $p = a.v$, the experiments described by that law being all made on the same specimen of gas (i.e. a portion of gas of constant mass). In the example of density, it is probably not possible to ascertain whether the magnitude was first defined (roughly and vaguely, of course) by means of flotation and then measured by the constant derived from a numerical law between mass and volume, or whether the process was reversed. However what generally happens is that we form first a conception of a magnitude from purely qualitative observations; we then seek for a numerical law the constant derived from which shall measure this magnitude. This has been the procedure by which most qualities of substances have been defined as accurately measurable magnitudes. At the present time the process is being developed for the qualitatively defined magnitude hardness, and complete success does not yet seem to be obtained. The magnitude is defined either by scratching or by wear under some strictly prescribed friction; and attempts are made to measure this magnitude by means of a constant occurring in some numerical law between an impact and the dimensions of the resulting depression—magnitudes that are no more directly connected with hardness than are mass and volume with the basic idea of density regarded as defined by flotation.

For the purposes of clear exposition of the essential ideas involved, it was found convenient to take as an example of a magnitude measured by the constant of a numerical law one of which the basic meaning was not closely connected with the fundamental magnitudes concerned in the numerical law. But this example is not really typical. We saw that, even if we had not been able to discover any previously known magnitude measured by the constant of the numerical law, we could always invent a magnitude which would be so measured by means of the relations expressed by the law; we could always find a transitive asymmetrical relation which would place the systems in the order of the associated constants without the introduction of any system of measurement at all. This result is achieved by taking systems for all of which one of the fundamental magnitudes is the same, and arranging the systems in the order of the other fundamental magnitude; the determination of such order requires no measurement. Now the magnitude so defined may or may not have significance; in the example chosen, it was apparently not significant (until the connection with density was discovered), but in other cases it is certainly significant. Consider, for example, electrical resistance defined by Ohm's Law. From purely qualitative observations we arrive at a rough conception of a magnitude of this nature; we find that under a constant E.M.F. different bodies pass different currents, and that the same current is passed by different bodies under the influence of different E.M.F.'s. If we can order E.M.F.'s or currents we can define qualitatively a magnitude, resistance, and order systems in respect of it. When we discover that there is a numerical law relating current and E.M.F., it is at once apparent that the constant in this law is a measure of the magnitude and that the previous qualitative determination of the magnitude represents just the process that has been described. The magnitude determined by that process and measured by the constant immediately acquires significance. In this example, as in that of density, the magnitude derived from the numerical law is significant because its order agrees with that of a previously known magnitude; the difference is that in this example the magnitude derived from the law is of the same nature as that previously known. But it may also happen that the magnitude derived from the law does not agree in its order with any previously known, but acquires significance as soon as the law is known. Such a development probably occurred in connection with the derived magnitude, acceleration. Before Galileo showed that the relation between the distance fallen and the time occupied was $L = a.T^2$, no magnitude of the nature of uniform acceleration had probably been conceived. But as soon as the law was known, it became apparent that the constant involved in the law had a great physical significance; it measured a property, previously almost unsuspected, that was common to all bodies in the neighbourhood of the surface of the earth. A new magnitude, measured by the constant involved in Galileo's Law, was immediately defined[1].

Derived and fundamental magnitudes. The conclusion is then that the constant in a numerical law is always the measure of a magnitude. The magnitude which it measures may be important or it may not, but the property of being characterised by a law of a certain form is always a magnitude and is measured by the constant involved in that law. The importance of the magnitude will be determined by the importance of the law, which again is usually determined by the range of its applicability. Such magnitudes, measured by the constants of numerical laws, are termed Derived Magnitudes; for the process of their measurement, requiring the establishment of a numerical law which requires again the previous establishment of some fundamental process of measurement, depends entirely on the measurement of the fundamental magnitudes involved in the law; they are derived from these magnitudes. It is by the means that have just been considered at length that those magnitudes are measured which are not capable of fundamental measurement because they are not capable of addition.

But is there any other difference between fundamental and derived magnitudes other than susceptibility to addition, or rather does this difference indicate any other which is of importance? So far as I can make out it does

---

[1] This example suggests a consideration that deserves a moment's notice. On p. 342 it was said that experiments could always be found in which, by changing the system, the constant measuring the derived magnitude would change. But is this true of the derived magnitudes that are known as universal constants? As a matter of fact, all universal constants are purely theoretical conceptions, resembling the velocity of a molecule rather than a density; such theoretical constants will be treated later. But even if a universal constant occurred as the constant in a numerical law, I do not think the statements made would become untrue. What would happen would be that there would be a constant which did not change with change of system, although we expected it to change, because other constants, defining magnitudes which were somehow similar, changed with the system.

not; and perhaps the best proof that it does not is obtained from the fact that magnitudes derived from a numerical law are often fundamental magnitudes; they may be fundamental magnitudes well known before the law was discovered, or they may first have been found as derived magnitudes and subsequently discovered to be susceptible of fundamental measurement; the most striking examples of the last possibility is furnished by electrical resistance and capacity. The only limitation on the nature of the derived magnitude which may be found to be measured by the constant of a numerical law is that it cannot be of the same nature as one of the fundamental magnitudes on the measurement of which the law is based; the exact reason for this limitation will concern us in the next chapter.

Again though the measurement of some derived magnitudes necessarily involves the previous establishment of systems of fundamental measurement, there is no reason why, when derived magnitudes have been discovered and ways of measuring them found, these derived magnitudes should not take the place of fundamental magnitudes in the establishment of a numerical law. A numerical law may state an experimental relation between derived magnitudes as well as between fundamental magnitudes, and the constants determined by such laws may once again be found to measure other derived magnitudes. It is difficult to give a perfect example of this possibility of a law between magnitudes that are truly derived and could not by any possibility be measured as fundamental, and the discussion of the difficulties would lead us too far. But it may be suggested that the law relating the viscosity of a gas to the temperature is such a law, for viscosity and temperature are both obviously derived magnitudes; neither of them can be added.

On the other hand it must not be forgotten that, in some connections, the property of being capable of addition is very important. Thus much of the importance of mass and energy is derived from the fact that they can be added; much of the importance of the qualities of a substance (see p. 283), such as density or viscosity, from the fact that they cannot. Perhaps the best way to show to exactly what extent the property of addition, distinguishing fundamental from derived magnitudes, is important, without anticipating the results of the whole treatise, is to give a list of the magnitudes of the two kinds. It is impossible to give a complete list of derived magnitudes, for it would be equivalent to a list of all the known laws of physics, but it may be mentioned that probably the most important pure derived magnitudes, incapable of physical addition, other than qualities of substances, are uniform acceleration and temperature. A more complete list of fundamental magnitudes can be given; the following are believed to be all that are of any importance: Length, period of time, weight, electrical resistance; Angle, area, volume, energy, mass, moment of inertia, momentum, uniform velocity, quantity of heat, intensity of radiation, electrical capacity, self-induction, current, charge, conductance, potential difference, magnetic flux. It is to be understood that the inclusion of a magnitude in this list only means that it is capable of addition and might be measured by a fundamental process; it does not mean that in actual practice it is so measured; it is only the first four magnitudes that are actually so measured. Again it is well to note here that there are properties represented by numerals which are not magnitudes, either fundamental or derived; these are *defined* as certain functions of other magnitudes without the implication that the function is characteristic of a law. Velocity, other than uniform velocity, is such a property; it simply means ds/dt whatever the relation between s and t. In some connections it will be important to distinguish between such mere definitions and the physical laws that define true derived magnitudes such as uniform velocity or density.

An examination of the list will confirm the view that there is no general important difference between the two classes. Magnitudes so closely analogous as acceleration and velocity appear in different classes, while such typical derived magnitudes as resistance and uniform velocity, the very meaning of which is intimately associated with laws of a certain form, appear as fundamental. And this conclusion is important for the purpose which led to the discussion. There is no doubt that fundamental magnitudes are concepts, defined by laws which have as little theoretical about them as any laws. It seems intolerable that we should have to admit that derived magnitudes are hypothetical ideas. But as yet we have seen no way of escaping the admission.

True and empirical laws. But before we proceed to find grounds for asserting that derived magnitudes are also concepts, one matter must be noticed. It was said just now that all constants occurring in numerical laws must be magnitudes. The statement was true only because we had confined our attention to numerical laws involving only one constant. If there is only one constant it seems that it must measure a magnitude, though the magnitude measured may have little physical significance. But if there is more than one constant this conclusion does not follow. It often happens that two constants involved in the same law are both magnitudes and important magnitudes. Thus, in the law $I = I_0 . e^{-t/T}$, expressing the relation between the time and the activity of a pure radioactive substance, I_0 is the activity at the moment from which time is reckoned and T is the "life" of the substance; both of these are significant magnitudes. But in the law, $L = a + bt + ct^2$, expressing the relation between the length of a metal rod and its temperature, a, b, c are not all magnitudes. It will be recognised instinctively that this last statement is true, but perhaps it will not be clear so immediately why it is true. The reason is that when we vary these constants by varying the system on which the experiments are made (still keeping the form of the law unaltered), we cannot vary them separately; when one varies, so in general do the others. Accordingly so far as we can tell, all three constants are associated with the same property. Now a property which is a magnitude cannot be represented by more than one numeral, for the magnitude must have an order and this order cannot agree with that of more than one set of numerals—unless, of course, all the sets of numerals have the same order. In this case, the numerals representing the constants are not found to have the same order; for one rod b may be greater than c, while for another rod c may be greater than b; a, b, c cannot measure the same magnitude, and since there is at present no evidence that more than one property, and more than one magnitude, is concerned in the matter at all, they cannot all measure magnitudes of any kind.

However further inquiry may alter the situation somewhat. If we compare the constants for different rods, we shall find numerical laws between them; namely $b = b'. a$ and $c = c'. a$, where b' and c' are new constants characteristic of these new laws. We can now express the original law in a rather different but equivalent form, $L = L_0 (1 + b't + c't^2)$, and we shall find that some separate variation of the constants is possible. L_0 will vary and b', c' will not, if the length of the rod and not its material is changed; b', c' will vary and L_0 will not if the material of the rod and not its length is changed. L_0 varying alone with a single property is a magnitude; but the remaining constants, b', c', varying together and inseparably are not magnitudes[1]. More investigation might produce further simplification; we might find (though actually we should not) that the change of b' was associated with one set of the properties that determine the material and c' with another set. Again I might find a further numerical law between b' and c', e.g. $b' = 2.\sqrt{c'}$. If there is such a numerical law, the original law could be expressed in the form

$$L = L_0 (1 + \sqrt{c't})^2.$$

The constants are reduced to two; one varies only with the length, the other only with the material, and they may both be magnitudes.

Accordingly when there are two or more constants involved in a numerical law, they may or may not be magnitudes; if they can be varied separately they are magnitudes, otherwise not. The discovery of numerical laws between the constants in a numerical law may enable us to reduce the number of constants in that law and so convert constants that are not magnitudes into constants that are. The success that has attended our efforts on many occasions to convert into magnitudes constants that at first sight are not magnitudes leads us to believe that ultimately a similar success can always be attained. We do not regard as ultimate and perfectly satisfactory a numerical law in which there are constants that are not magnitudes; we term such a law (for instance that relating the length of a rod to its temperature) "empirical" and always entertain the hope that later we shall be able to express it in a form that is not empirical. On p. 153 we called laws empirical if they are not deducible from a theory; and the sense given to the term here is closely allied to that given before. For it is usually by the guidance afforded by a theory that we are able to discover the numerical law between the constants of an empirical

---

[1] An important question is raised here which will be discussed more fully in Chapter XIV. The use of symbols of b', c' has concealed the fact that they and the " 1 " are equally numerals. Why is the " 1 " omitted from the constants and the possibility of its being a derived magnitude not considered? The answer for the present is that the " 1 " cannot possibly change with anything; its presence is the result of a mere arbitrary definition or convention that I propose to write L_0 for a. It is not determined in any way by the physical properties of the system.

law which enables us to express it in a form that is not empirical; and it is only laws in which the constants are magnitudes that are ever explained by theories.

Graphs. We have now examined at length the nature of derived magnitudes and their relation to the constants of a numerical law. The question from which our discussion arose was whether it was necessary to regard these derived magnitudes as theoretical because they depended on the introduction of the hypothetical idea, Number. The question has not been answered, but we have obtained much evidence for answering it in the negative. For we have seen how closely derived magnitudes are allied to fundamental magnitudes, which are clearly concepts and not hypothetical ideas. We must now attempt to find evidence on which a definite negative answer may be based; it seems possible that we may be able to find such an answer through the use of the graphs that are so frequently employed in the expression of results which are expressed otherwise in numerical laws.

In forming a graph by the usual method of rectangular coordinates we take from our note book the numerals representing a pair of corresponding magnitudes and form two lengths which are represented by these numerals with some arbitrary choice of unit. We then find a point on a sheet of paper which is such that its distances from two perpendicular straight lines are equal to these lengths. This point represents the state of the system when it is characterised by these two magnitudes, and the collection of all similar points representing all possible uniformly associated pairs of magnitudes characterising the system within the limits of the experiment represents the whole system. In all cases where the relation between the two magnitudes can be expressed by a numerical law, it is found that the collection of points exhibits a certain regularity; they all lie on a smooth curve. The form of this curve is an expression of a general property of the system, just as in the form of the numerical law.

Such, of course, is the elementary principle involved in the use of graphs. It depends upon many geometrical propositions that will have to be considered in a later part of this work; all that concerns us now is that it is an experimental fact that by following this procedure we do arrive at a smooth curve. Further all the specifications for drawing the curve are purely experimental or else purely arbitrary; at each stage we are either making a purely arbitrary choice (as when we choose the unit for the scale of the curve or choose to place the symbols used as numerals in the order 1, 2, 3, 4, ... rather than in some other order), or we are doing something the correctness of which can be and must be tested by experiment or observation. We have not introduced anything which is asserted to be true and yet is not capable of being so tested.

It will sometimes happen that the smooth curve is of a form that can be described experimentally. Thus the "curve" may be such that it will fit a straight edge. This is an experimental statement; experiment decides whether any given edge is straight and experiment decides whether any edge which has been shown to be straight will fit the graph on the paper[1]. A graph which fits a straight edge is called a straight line, but it must be remembered that this definition is experimental and based on no geometrical considerations except such as are derived from experiment. Another form of graph that can be easily described experimentally is the parabola, which may be defined as the trace of a projectile on a vertical plane surface fixed relatively to the earth[2]. (Again it must be remembered that this is a mere definition; we merely propose to call any such trace a parabola.) Other graphs could be described in other ways by means of the physical properties of experimental systems, but in many cases the description would be very complicated and perhaps difficult to realise accurately in practice. Now if we move our straight edge about on the paper we shall find (again experimentally) that associated with every straight line there are two fundamental magnitudes, namely the length of the intercept on one of the axes and the angle which it makes with one of the axes; these two magnitudes fix the straight line, so that all straight lines for which they are both the same are coincident and are indeed the same graph. Accordingly if the graph which results from any experiment is a straight line, the properties of the system on which the experiments are made can be characterised by these two magnitudes. If further a whole class of systems on which experiments are made all have one of the magnitudes the same (if, for instance, the graphs all pass through the origin), then the other magnitude is a complete specification of that system sufficing to distinguish it from all others.

Similar experiments would show that a graph of any other form defined by experiment is characterised by a certain number of magnitudes which suffice to distinguish that graph from all others of the same class, that is, defined in the same way. Thus the members of the class of parabolas, defined as the traces of projectiles, would be characterised by the velocity of projection of the projectile (which determines the shape of the parabola) and a length and an angle (which determine its position on the paper relative to the axes). Every class of graphs (defined by some form of experiment) is thus distinguished from every other class by the association with it of a set of magnitudes, the nature of these magnitudes being different for every class; within the class members are distinguished from each other by different values of the same magnitudes. The graph which results from any given experiment is thus describable first by the nature of the set of magnitudes which is associated with it, and, second, by the value of these magnitudes.

These magnitudes, by means of which the graph which results from a given set of experiments can be described, are capable of replacing, for certain

---

[1] The conception of "fit" will be analysed further in Part III; but it will not be doubted that a judgement of fit is an experimental judgement of the kind concerning which universal agreement can be obtained.

[2] The best parabolas which I have seen realised in practice are the forms of water-jets flowing under a steady pressure from pipes approximately horizontal. Such jets must have been noticed by everyone who has travelled in the Alps. The shadows thrown by such jets on the white walls of the houses define beautiful smooth curves.

purposes at least, the derived magnitudes that are usually associated with numerical laws. For, substituting these magnitudes for the constants derived from a numerical law, we might repeat all the arguments of pp. 342-346, showing how and why they measure magnitudes characteristic of the system on which the experiments are made. Indeed, as is well known, we should find that to every constant involved in a numerical law corresponds a magnitude characteristic of a graph; and it is always possible to choose the magnitudes characteristic of the graph in such a way that the order of these magnitudes is the numerical order of the constants in the corresponding numerical law, though it is often, if not always, possible to choose the magnitudes so that the order is not that of the constants. Thus it turns out that if the system is such that the graph is a straight line, the corresponding numerical law is of the form $y = a.x + b$. The order of the angles between the graphs and the axis of x is the order of the a's, and the order of the intercepts on the axis of y is the order of the b's; on the other hand the order of the angles between the graph and the axis of y is not the order of the a's but the inverse order. And generally, whether or no the order of the magnitudes agrees with the order of the constants, numerical laws can always be found relating the magnitudes and the constants. If we can admit that the determination of the constants is experimental, then all these relations between the constants and the magnitudes are purely experimental.

It seems, therefore, that by the use of graphs we can measure derived magnitudes in just the same way as we can by the use of constants involved in numerical laws; the numerals representing the physical magnitudes characteristic of the graph may be used to measure those derived magnitudes. But the magnitudes are determined (in so far as they are not completely arbitrary) by experiment and experiment only. It would seem therefore that by the use of graphs we have overcome the difficulties which we encountered and have discovered a purely experimental way, involving no ideas that are not essential to physics, of defining and measuring derived magnitudes. Our previous conclusion that derived magnitudes must be theoretical because they involve the hypothetical ideas, Numbers, is clearly erroneous. We shall return to the subject later and try to discover why it is erroneous (the task is not difficult), but for the present the conclusion will suffice that derived magnitudes are experimental concepts and do not differ essentially in their nature from fundamental magnitudes; the only difference is that some, but not all, derived magnitudes are incapable of being added.

The establishment of numerical laws. We have now discussed fully the meaning of numerical laws; there remains the question how they are established. This matter cannot be discussed completely without paying attention to the existence of errors of measurement which will form the subject of Chapters XVI and XVII. But the question arises even when there is no such error; we may therefore discuss it on the assumption that the measurements are free from all error and inquire at a later stage to what extent it is necessary to revise our conclusions. If there were no error, would there be any rule or formal process by which we could proceed directly from the numerals entered in the note book to a numerical law which will represent them?

There is no need to describe the methods by which the form of a numerical law is determined in practice. The first stage in the process almost always involves the use of graphs. If the graph is a straight line (after the fit of the points has been examined in view of the experimental errors) then the problem is solved. If it is not, then we might seek for some other form of curve which would coincide with the graph. We do not actually do so, because the mechanical arrangements necessary for testing all the possible forms of any curve other than a straight line are so complicated as to involve prohibitive labour. With a single straight edge moved about on the surface of the paper, we can quickly produce all the members of the class of straight lines and examine whether any one of them coincides with the graph; but to produce all possible parabolas and to investigate their possible coincidence with the graph would be a task that is practically impossible. If we suspect that the graph is a parabola we proceed in a different manner. We know, for reasons into which it is unnecessary to inquire, that a parabola corresponds to a numerical law of the form $y = a.x^2$, and a straight line to a numerical law of the form $y = a.x$; accordingly if the experimental numbers give a parabola, we must be able to produce a straight line from numerals which represent the square of one column and the other column unaltered; and so we square one column or the other, plot the graph again and examine whether it is a straight line[1]. Now the only feature of this exceedingly familiar process to which attention is directed here is that it is essentially a process of trial and error all the way through and is conducted according to no rule or principle; it is by mere trial and error that we determine whether a given graph is a straight line and by trial and error which, if any, of the numberless functions of the measured values will give a graph that is a straight line.

Graphs, therefore, provide no rule for determining numerical laws; can we find a rule by making use of Numbers or other mathematical ideas? In a sense we can. Suppose that we have measured n corresponding pairs of the two magnitudes, and assume that the numerical relation is represented by some mathematical function involving n constants; for example let it be $y = \Sigma a_n x^n$, where n is a positive integer or zero. Then by substituting in this form the corresponding values of x and y, we get n equations to determine the n constants. This is a perfectly definite rule for representing the results of the measurements by a numerical law and a rule which will serve on all occasions.

But of course the rule is of no value. In the first place the numerical law so determined is empirical and the constants occurring in it will not generally measure magnitudes. It is possible that we might, as suggested on p. 349, find numerical laws between the constants by comparing the laws for many

---

[1] This process was not referred to on p. 351, because the plotting of a function of the measured values, rather than the measured values themselves, raises again the question whether the use of such functions does not necessarily involve the hypothetical idea Number.

different systems all of the same kind, and so reduce the number of constants until those that were left would all be magnitudes. But then how are we to determine these numerical laws? If we employ the same process again we are led to an interminable series of operations. As a matter of fact, when n is large, we should never need to take n terms of the proposed series and introduce n constants; for we have not got to find a formula which fits the observed magnitudes exactly, but only one which fits them within experimental error; in place of solving for the constants by the direct algebraical process, we could adjust them by the method of least squares and usually make three or four terms serve as well as 50. Nevertheless the number of terms and of associated constants will usually be greater than the number of magnitudes which can be discovered and separated. Such a method of establishing a numerical law is useful only when we are content for some reason or other to discover a numerical law that is merely empirical and do not expect to define derived magnitudes. It is of no service when we desire to establish a true law, characterised by the essential element of necessity. Such laws, whether they are numerical or not, cannot be discovered by any formal process; they can only be suggested by some considerations for which no formal rule can be laid down and then shown to be in accordance with experiment. There is no such thing as formal induction.

But it is well to notice that the proposed rule as it stands, even if it were not liable to this objection, would be liable to another. A law established by any such rule will not always have one of the most important properties of a law, the power of prediction. When we assert a numerical law as a result of certain observations, we mean not only that it represents the results of those observations but also the results of any others of the same kind that may be made. Now it is not always possible to find such a law at all. For instance, if we measured the mass and volume of a large number of bodies without selecting them in any special manner, then we should be unable to find any numerical law which would represent these measurements and also any others that might be made; a numerical law would only be found if we confined our observations to bodies made of the same material at the same temperature. But the mathematical rule that has been given would determine a numerical law in this case as well as in any other. It is interesting to inquire whether the rule can be amended so that it will give a numerical law only in those cases in which there is a true numerical law. The inquiry is not of any practical importance, for we have seen that laws derived from this rule are in any case merely empirical; still we do sometimes want to determine empirical laws. And again graphs provide a perfectly adequate means of determining whether there is a numerical law; there will be such a law only if the graph is "smooth". But "smooth" is not a term capable of accurate definition, and a brief discussion will bring out some points of interest.

The rule which may be suggested is this. If there are n observations, take some series $y = \Sigma f_n(x)$ having n terms and involving n constants, e.g. $y = \Sigma a_p x^p$

or $y = \Sigma a_p \sin \frac{2\pi x}{p}$. Out of the n observations select some smaller number m, and determine the first m constants of the series by substituting them in the equation $y = \Sigma f_n(x)$. Repeat the process selecting $m + 1, m + 2, m + 3, \ldots$ observations. Each operation will give different values for the first m constants; but if the values of these constants converge to definite values, as the number of observations is increased, then there is a numerical law relating x and y. The condition of convergence may be expressed more definitely thus: A constant converges to definite values if, after a certain number of values for it have been calculated, the variation of the values resulting from further calculations do not differ so much from those already calculated that the substitution of one for the other would produce a difference in the value of y for the corresponding value of x which could be detected by experiment. If however the constants do not converge in this sense to definite values, it is not proved at once that there is no numerical law. The process must be repeated with the substitution of some other function f_n. If, whatever f_n is selected (and in practice only a few need be examined), the constants still do not converge, there is no numerical law.

A little consideration will convince anyone used to physical investigation that the test is actually adequate; but I do not know that formal justification for it can be offered. The underlying idea is that, if the numerical law is really a law and predicts, the mathematical function representing it must be an "analytic function"[1]; for it is only in analytic functions that an examination of the values of the variables over part of the range of all possible values can lead to a prediction of the values over the remainder of that range. Now it appears that any analytic function, but only an analytic function, can be represented throughout any finite range with any degree of accuracy by such a series if n is finite.

The only importance of this rule lies in the possibility which it indicates of stating rather more precisely the condition for a numerical law which is usually expressed by saying that the corresponding graph must be "smooth". A smooth graph will correspond to a power series which gives constants that converge very rapidly after quite a few steps in the process; its form suggests therefore immediately that the numerical relation can be expressed by an analytic function, and thence that it is a true numerical law which will predict observations other than those on which it is founded. On the other hand many curves which appear to the eye by no means smooth can be represented by analytic functions and the corresponding laws could be deduced by means of the rule that has been given. Hence we are led to ask again a very familiar question, why we expect numerical laws to be represented by smooth curves and why, conversely, when a few observations seem to define a smooth curve we assume that this curve represents the numerical law and that the predictions made from it will be verified?

---

[1] An analytic function is one which has a differential coefficient at each point of the range, except possibly a finite number of separate points.

The usual answer is that smooth curves generally represent numerical laws simpler mathematically than those represented by curves that are not smooth, and that our expectation and belief is merely another instance of our general hope of simplicity and confidence in it. But perhaps in this instance it is possible to inquire rather further into the foundation of that hope and confidence. If the rule for expressing a numerical law as an analytic series is applied, it will certainly turn out generally that the less smooth the curve, the greater must be the number of terms taken in that series if it is to agree with the observed results within the limits of experimental error, and consequently the greater the number of constants involved in the law. It may turn out that there are numerical laws between these constants and that, by expressing the numerical relation in a rather different form, their number may be reduced, but in general, the less smooth the curve the more constants are required in any numerical law which represents it. But the more the constants, the less is the probability that all of them measure magnitudes; and it is only if the constants measure magnitudes that there is any likelihood that a continuation of the experiments will lead to results similar to those already obtained. For in making the experiments we mean to change two properties of the system and to leave the others unchanged; and we shall expect regularity in the results only if at each change we do in effect leave these others unchanged. If the constants measure magnitudes, these must be the properties of the system that are unchanged (or some of them); and we shall know that the conditions which it is intended to fulfil in making the experiments actually are fulfilled. But if the constants do not measure magnitudes, then our observations have given us no indication that those conditions are fulfilled, and we have therefore no reason to suppose that our future observations will resemble those already made.

Some such reason as this underlies, I think, our confidence in numerical laws corresponding to smooth curves. For such confidence is greatest when the curve is not only smooth but also straight. Then we know at once that there cannot be more than two constants involved in the numerical law and the probability that all the constants are magnitudes is a maximum. We should feel very nearly the same confidence if the curve turned out to be of some other easily describable form, such as a parabola; and indeed if by plotting a function of one of the magnitudes against another we can produce a straight line and so show that the original curve was of such a form, there is little loss of confidence. And if we can proceed so far as actually to show that the magnitudes characteristic of the curve are measures of some previously known magnitude, then all doubts vanish that we have really discovered a numerical law and that the graph will represent new observations as well as the old.

Interpolation and extrapolation. However in considering the likelihood that a graph or numerical law will represent observations other than those on which it is founded, a distinction is usually made between interpolation and extrapolation. Here again a very few remarks will suffice because the matter is so familiar and so adequately discussed elsewhere. If the experiments are such that we feel confident that there is a numerical law concerned at all (either because the graph defined is very smooth or because the test of p. 355 is satisfied), then we can always find a law such that we have no hesitation in placing complete trust in it, so far as interpolation is concerned; we are as sure that interpolation will lead to correct results as we are of anything connected with any kind of law. We attain to such confidence by making a sufficient number of observations evenly distributed over the range of interpolation. And the reason for the confidence is obvious; if a sufficient number of points are fixed it will be impossible to draw any graph through them which is at once smooth and so different from any other smooth graph through those points that the difference can be detected by experiment; smoothness here, as always, may be judged either by the eye or by the mathematical test of p. 355. Even if the numerical law we have stated is not the right one (i.e. that completely in accordance with all future observations), it must be so near the right one that no experiment can show the difference.

But in extrapolation the conditions are different. Through any number of points in a given range it is possible to draw many smooth curves which, though agreeing within experimental error inside that range, diverge widely outside that range. If the graph is empirical there is no reason whatever for preferring any one of these curves to any other, and there can be no certainty of prediction. Even when graphs are wholly empirical, they can be relied upon for interpolation if they are fixed by a sufficient number of observations, but they cannot be relied upon at all for extrapolation. However it might appear that if the graph is not empirical, there should be no difference between interpolation and extrapolation; for if the magnitudes defining the graph have been found to measure definite derived magnitudes, then the form of the graph is completely determined; the only matter requiring further determination is which of the graphs of this particular form represents best the observations. But the observations will always allow some slight latitude in the choice of the particular form; even if we know that the graph is to be a straight line and have made a great many observations to determine it within a certain range, the presence of experimental error will always leave some slight uncertainty as to which straight line fits the observations best. Straight lines, all of which fit the observations within the possible experimental error inside a given range, will diverge and differ by more than possible experimental error if they are continued far outside the range.

On this ground then extrapolation will always be less certain than interpolation, even if the numerical law is not empirical; but it is true and important that the uncertainty of extrapolation will be very much greater when the law is empirical than when it is not. There can be no certainty at all about the extrapolation of an empirical law; the extrapolation of a law that is not empirical involves only an uncertainty confined within definitely known limits. However there is an additional source of uncertainty in the extrapolation of laws that are not empirical; it is possible that there is involved in the law a derived magnitude of which the effect within the experimental range is so small that it has not been detected, while the effect outside that range is very appreciable. An obvious example occurs in the determination of the law of decay of a mixture of two radioactive substances with very different periods; observations made a long time after their separation from their parents would give a numerical law involving only one derived magnitude, namely the longer period; but the extrapolation of these observations to much earlier times would lead to error because terms involving another derived magnitude, the shorter period, which were inappreciable during the observations would become important.

Arbitrary and true measurement. One final question: Is measurement, as we have defined it, really necessary to numerical laws? It is possible, as we saw, to assign numerals to represent properties according to arbitrary scales which represent nothing but the mere order of the property. Could not such arbitrary measurement also give rise to numerical laws? It appears at first sight that the answer must be affirmative; if any two properties are both represented in any way by numerals, there must be some relation between these numerals. For instance, there must be a numerical relation between the numerals denoting the houses in a street and the numerals marked on the watches of the owners of them. An example nearer to the facts of physics may be based on the systems of arbitrary measurement that have served before for illustration. There must be some numerical relation between the hardness of a mineral on Mohs' scale and the numeral representing the crystallographic system to which it belongs. Is not such a numerical relation a numerical law?

It is not; and the discussion of p. 356 shows why it is not. The relation is not representable by an analytic function. If we attempted to carry out the process sketched there, we should find that the constants of the power series did not converge to definite values. Consequently any relation that might be found between the numerals, based on a consideration of some of the facts, would not lead to a knowledge of a relation which would fit the remaining facts. The relation would not predict; and therefore it is not a law. So much is obvious, but perhaps the answer to the main question is rather less obvious if another example is taken.

Before the establishment of the absolute scale of temperature, or at any rate before any method of measuring temperature other than that of the mercury-glass thermometer was adopted, measurements of temperature were all arbitrary; even if the fixed points were not arbitrary (a matter into which later inquiry will be made), the division of the stem between them into equal lengths is entirely arbitrary and unconnected with any laws of temperature. For our purpose we may suppose the measurements made still more arbitrary (as arbitrary as Mohs' scale) by simply making marks at random on the stem and numbering them in their order of remoteness from the bulb by the series of integers. Let us take two thermometers marked in this way, filled with different fluids, place them in the same bath, heat the bath and record the readings on the two stems at the same time. These readings may be plotted against each other in the same way as the distance through which a body has fallen and the time of fall; through the points may be drawn in a similar manner a smooth curve which can be represented by an analytic function. Does not this curve represent a numerical law, stating the relative expansions of the two fluids, in the same way as the curve between distance and time? And yet the numbers plotted are the results of entirely arbitrary measurements.

Let us note carefully the difference between the two curves. In the first place the curve based on arbitrary measurement is essentially discontinuous. For only a finite number of points on the arbitrary scale have been defined, so that there can only be a finite number of values of the abscissa or ordinate. But this feature does distinguish the curve from one based on true measurement, for we shall see later that, however perfect our system of measurement and however fine our instrument, there is always a limit to the number of readings possible. Again if the arbitrary scale were different from a true scale in this respect the difference could be removed by placing the marks on the scale, not at random, but according to some definite rule; the scale will be arbitrary in spite of the rule as long as the rule is not determined by anything characteristic of the property being measured[1]. Thus, the scale of temperature of the mercury in glass Centigrade thermometer is quite as arbitrary as that of the instrument with the random marks, in spite of the fact that the divisions are of equal length and the end points are not wholly arbitrary; for the selection of divisions of equal length is not determined by any of the laws on which thermometry is based. The adoption of such a rule would enable any number of points on the arbitrary scale to be fixed and assimilate it in this respect to a scale determined by true measurement. It would also remove another feature which may appear at first to distinguish the arbitrary and true scales, namely that extrapolation between the limits of the marks originally drawn is impossible. But even if this difference were not removed it would not make a vital distinction between true and arbitrary measurement; for if extrapolation beyond the limit of the experiments made is impossible with the arbitrary scale, it is highly dangerous with a true scale; it is only in very special conditions that we consider a numerical law determined by a true scale as likely to be valid outside the limits within which it was determined.

It must be admitted then that an arbitrary system of measurement may lead to a numerical law. And this law will involve constants. Are these constants derived magnitudes? Actually they are not; the law based on an arbitrary system of measurement is always empirical. Here is the great and fundamental difference between true and arbitrary systems of measurement:

---

[1] The possibility of thus producing a scale which, though arbitrary, is continuous, was not mentioned in Chapter X, because we were there discussing fundamental measurements. The rule which makes the arbitrary scale continuous is based on the measurement of another magnitude, namely length, and would not be possible unless at least one system of measurement had been established previously.

the former do and the latter do not define true derived magnitudes[1]. The recognition of derived magnitudes is one of the most fruitful sources of scientific progress and the search for them one of the most powerful instruments in the hands of an investigator. But that weapon cannot be used until true and not arbitrary systems of measurement are established. That is why the development of a science may be fitly estimated by the part that measurement plays in it, and why all other sciences rely ultimately on physics which provides them with their systems of measurement.

If it is asked why only true systems of measurement lead to the definition of true derived magnitudes, no answer can be given except that which has been so often given, that there would be no study of science unless, in this matter as in others, experimental facts were in harmony with our desires. It is the intimate connection with true derived magnitudes that makes us attach such importance to measurement and makes us feel that in making fundamental measurements we are discovering something real. But why there should be that connection—that question we must leave to those who expound to us, from their superior knowledge, the nature and functions of the human understanding.

---

[1] It may be observed that if the discussion at the end of Chapter XII had led to the opposite conclusion, and it had been decided that the system of fundamental measurement described in Chapter X was not unique, any other systems that might have been permissible would probably have been classed here with arbitrary systems. They would not actually have led to derived magnitudes.

CHAPTER XIV

UNITS AND DIMENSIONS

Summary. After a few trite remarks about fundamental units, we inquire into the changes introduced into numerical laws by change of units. It is observed that certain forms of law, but not other forms, are such that they are unchanged by change of unit; but any law which is changed can be altered into a form which is not changed by choosing a function of the constant which, in the first law, measures the derived magnitude to measure it in the second.

Consideration of this alteration draws attention to the very important terms which are called "formal constants" and are independent of units and of system so long as the form of the law is maintained. Every derived magnitude is associated with a formal constant.

Though the form of the law is unchanged, when the unit changes the numerical values of the derived magnitudes change. This observation leads to the conception of the dimensions of a derived magnitude; the difference between the unit of a derived magnitude and that of a fundamental is carefully noted.

The relation between the unit of a derived and the units of fundamental magnitudes is expressed by the conception of dimensions. The question why dimensions are always of a certain form is answered.

It is noticed that there are extremely important magnitudes which do not change with units and hence have zero dimensions. Some special properties of such no-dimensional magnitudes are considered and they are carefully distinguished from formal constants and other terms in numerical laws which resemble them in invariability with change of unit.

The question is raised whether, as is often stated, mass, length and time are in some way peculiarly basic magnitudes. Ultimately the conclusion is reached that they are not, and that such special features as they possess are derived partly from the importance of the dynamical equations in which they occur and partly to the especially high accuracy with which weights and lengths (but not times) can be compared.

In the course of this discussion certain problems raised by the magnitude, volume, and the electric units are discussed in detail. It is concluded that it is entirely misleading and incorrect to say that volume has the dimensions (length)^3, and that the K or μ should be omitted from the dimensions of electrical magnitudes. The important conception of a quasi-derived magnitude (e.g. volume measured by weight) is introduced.

A few final remarks are made on "practical" units and on the supposed "natural" units.

Units of fundamental magnitudes. In Chapter X we said that the choice of the unit of a fundamental magnitude was entirely arbitrary. By that statement was meant that it was not imposed on us by any physical law. But of course there is some reason, good or bad, for doing anything that we do, and there must be some considerations which determine that we select one system rather than another as a fundamental unit. The considerations that have finally determined the choice that has actually been made are either such as lie wholly outside the province of science—reasons of history and personal eminence and so on—or are connected with derived magnitudes in a way that we are not yet ready to consider. But some reasons which confine the choice within certain limits may be noted here—very briefly, for they are stated quite adequately in all text-books.

The first and much the most important reason is the necessity that the unit should be permanent and easily copied. Ease of copying needs no explanation; it only means that if we make two systems which are each intended to be equal to the unit we shall find on comparing them that the copies are equal. Permanence needs rather more explanation, for it might be asked what can be meant by a change in the fundamental unit; but the apparent paradox has been solved so often that the briefest account will suffice here. If we have made many copies of a unit and found, just after they were made, that they and the unit were all equal, and if we find later that the copies and the unit are not still equal, then we can say either that the copies have changed or that the unit has changed. If all the copies (or nearly all) are still equal to each other, though differing from the unit, then we shall say that the unit has changed; if the copies do not agree amongst themselves, then some at least of the copies must have changed, but we shall not know whether the unit has changed or not. When we say that we want the unit to be permanent we mean that we want to avoid such circumstances occurring at all; we want to be sure that if we make any number of copies with sufficient care then the copies and the unit will all be found to be always equal to each other.

Permanence and ease of copying are of great importance in deciding of what magnitudes we shall realise the units concretely; for we shall see that there is some choice in this matter. But they also determine to some extent what systems we shall choose as units. Thus for permanence it is well to choose a unit of mass as large as possible; for it will be less changed by accidental abrasion or corrosion. (The change must of course be measured in terms of the unit, for there is no other way possible.) But too large a unit would be difficult to copy; a compromise has to be made. The permanence of a unit of length is little affected, if at all, by the size; but there is a size which gives the greatest accuracy in copying. Special considerations, to which attention will be drawn in Part III, affect the choice of the unit of time; but the choice of the day is determined by ease of copying rather than by permanence.

A second consideration affecting choice of unit is based on the systems which it is desired to measure in terms of that unit; for the uncertainty of measurement will in general increase with the difference between the measured magnitude and the unit. Again the systems which will be measured depends to some extent on the instruments available for judging equality. Reasons of this kind generally reinforce reasons based on ease of copying;

but they are not of much importance in scientific work, because the magnitudes of the systems to be measured are so various and the instrumental facilities available for work of the highest accuracy so great.

Lastly there are reasons connected with derived magnitudes, to which we shall proceed immediately, which sometimes conflict with those already mentioned. It is sometimes possible to avoid the conflict by choosing in accordance with the first two reasons the body that is to be taken as the standard of the magnitude, but assigning to that standard body, not the value 1, but some other value. We have already seen that this procedure makes no difference to the possibility of a fundamental process of measurement. It is on such grounds that our practice with regard to the units of length, mass and time would be defended; our units are the centimetre, gramme and second, but the realised standard bodies are asserted to have in terms of these the values 100, 1000 and 86,400 respectively.

Numerical laws and changes of units. After these very brief remarks let us proceed to the real subject of this chapter and consider how a change of the units in which fundamental magnitudes are measured will affect numerical laws and the derived magnitudes that are determined by them.

Suppose that, with one set of fundamental units, there has been established a numerical law $f(x_1, y_1, z_1, ..., a_1, b_1, c_1, ...) = 0$, in which $x_1, y_1, z_1, ...$ are the fundamental magnitudes and $a_1, b_1, c_1, ...$ the constants which, if the law is not empirical, measure derived magnitudes. With a second set of fundamental units we measure uniformly associated values of the fundamental magnitudes $x_2, y_2, z_2, ...$ If the magnitudes of the second set of units measured in terms of the first are $\xi, \eta, \zeta, ...$, then, when the symbols refer to the same system in the same state, $(x_1, y_1, z_1, ...) = (\xi x_2, \eta y_2, \zeta z_2, ...)$. Consequently the numerical law expressed in measurements with the second set of units must be $f(\xi x_2, \eta y_2, \zeta z_2, ..., a_1, b_1, c_1, ...) = 0$. The important question arises now whether the numerical law expressed in terms of the second set of units is of the same form as that expressed in terms of the first; if it were not, the form of a numerical law would depend on a perfectly arbitrary selection of units and nothing of the smallest importance to science could be deduced from that form. Now we regard two numerical laws as of the same form if one can be derived from another by the substitution of one set of numerical values of the "constants" for another set; accordingly the second numerical law will be of the same form as the first if $f(\xi x_2, \eta y_2, \zeta z_2, ..., a_1, b_1, c_1, ...)$ can be expressed in the form $f(x_2, y_2, z_2, ..., a_2, b_2, c_2, ...)$, where $a_2, b_2, c_2, ...$ are constants with numerical values possibly different from those of $a_1, b_1, c_1, ...$, the nature of the fundamental magnitudes represented by the "variables" being unchanged. For this equation represents a relation between the same fundamental magnitudes, differing from the first only in the numerical value of the constants.

Before we consider whether the second numerical law can be expressed in this form, it will be well to notice one point which was unnoticed in Chapter XIII. When it is said that two numerical laws are of the same form if they differ only in the numerical values of the constants, one exception must be made; the possibility that the constants may have the numerical value o must be excluded. For if this value is not excluded it would follow that any numerical law may be of the same form as any other involving the same fundamental magnitudes. We can always write $f = 0$ in the form $1 . f + 0 . f_1 = 0$, and $f_1 = 0$ in the form $1 . f_1 + 0 . f = 0$. If o is permitted as a value for a constant, these two numerical laws are of the same form; the only difference between them is that the constant that has the value 1 in one law has the value o in the other; hence, whatever functions f and f_1 may be, the numerical laws defined by them are of the same form. But while in some cases the exclusion of o as a value for a constant seems obviously necessary, in others it may appear to raise difficulties. Everyone will agree that the numerical law $y = a . x$ should not be regarded as of the same form as the law $y = b . \sin cx$ or as the law $y = d$; but it is not so obvious that $y = a . x$ is not of the same form as $y = a . x + d$. This last example suggests perhaps that we ought to exclude from the value o only those constants that appear multiplied by any function of any of the fundamental magnitudes. However I do not think this amendment really meets the difficulty. The form of a numerical law is important only when the constants in it are derived magnitudes, and the statement that the constants, or any of them, cannot have the value o is equivalent to the statement that no system can have a zero derived magnitude. This proposition may appear difficult to accept.

However the difficulty is not really serious. When we speak of a system having zero derived magnitude, we are always comparing it with other bodies that have finite values of the same derived magnitude, and regarding it as a member of a series formed by such bodies. What we are saying is that the body differs from the other members of that series only in the fact that the numerical law characteristic of them all involves a constant of which the value is zero, and in the uniform association with this zero value of other properties that are also possessed in varying degree by the other members. This is a perfectly definite conception. It may be remarked in passing that the difficulty does not arise in connection with fundamental magnitudes capable of addition; for then zero magnitude can be defined as that of a system which, when added to some other system, produces a system equal in magnitude to this other system.

Let us now return to the main question.

If f is of one special type, the form of the numerical law will always be unchanged by a change of fundamental units; this type is $f = \Sigma a_{uvw...} . x^u y^v z^w ...$, where u, v, w may have any rational values, positive or negative, integral or fractional and $a_{uvw...}$ are the constants previously written a, b, c, ... For we may write

$$\Sigma a_{uvw...} . (\xi x)^u . (\eta y)^v . (\zeta z)^w ... = \Sigma a'_{uvw...} . x^u y^v z^w ...,$$

where
$$a'_{uvw...} = a_{uvw...} . \xi^u \eta^v \zeta^w ....$$

The form of the numerical law is precisely the same in terms of whichever set of fundamental units it is expressed.

But still a question remains. If $a_{uvw...}$ is a derived magnitude in the law with the first set of units, will $a'_{uvw...}$ be a derived magnitude with the second set? It must be observed at the outset that, if the law has this form, not every a can be a derived magnitude. For a derived magnitude is measured by a numeral that is definitely fixed by experiment, while in a law of this form only the ratios of the a's are so fixed; the law will still be true if we alter every a in the same ratio. When we express a numerical law of this form, we generally make one of the a's equal to 1; the remainder of them are then fixed by experiment and are true derived magnitudes. Thus we do not say that $ay - bx^2 = 0$, but that $y - ax^2 = 0$. This was the practice adopted in Chapter XIII. Some further remarks arising from this practice will be made later, but for the present it is sufficient to notice that all the a's may be a derived magnitude, if this practice is adopted, and all but one, if it is not. The question is then whether those constants that are derived magnitudes in the law based on the first set of units will also be derived magnitudes in the law based on the second part.

Of course the answer is yes. A constant is a derived magnitude if, by suitable change of the system on which the experiments are made, it can be varied while the other constants remain unchanged, and if the order of the numerical values of these constants is the order of the properties of the system which is so varied. The only effect of the change of units is to change in the same ratio all the derived magnitudes measured by one of the constants. The constant will therefore change with the same changes of the system and remain unchanged during the same changes; further the order of the numerical values of the constant measuring the same properties will be unchanged. Accordingly it may be concluded that, if the law has the form of a power series, its form will be unchanged by a change of unit; and that if the constants in the original form measure derived magnitudes, they will also measure derived magnitudes when the units are changed. But the numerical value assigned to any property measured as a derived magnitude will, in general, change with the change of unit.

Many functions which occur in numerical laws are not usually expressed by a power series such as we have been considering. It does not follow however that they could not be so expressed. It seems probable indeed that expression by means of a power series is always possible and therefore that it must always be possible to express a numerical law in such a form that this form is unchanged by a change of unit. However we are interested in the forms of numerical laws only when the laws are not empirical and when the constants involved in them are derived magnitudes. Even if all functions employed in numerical laws can be expressed as power series, it is not always immediately clear when they are expressed in this form whether the constants involved in them are derived magnitudes. The constants will be derived magnitudes usually only if, by the discovery of numerical laws between the constants, the many constants can be shown to reduce to a very much smaller number (p. 349). If there is a change of units, the new law will be, for our purposes, of the same form as the old only if the numerical law between the constants involved in it is the same as that involved in the old, so that the many constants reduce in the same manner to a smaller number, which are all derived magnitudes. It could be shown generally that this condition is (or can be) always fulfilled; but it will be more convenient to inquire directly whether the form of the function is preserved through a change of units, even when the law, though true and not empirical, is not expressible by a power series, the constants of which are independent derived magnitudes.

Consider, for example, the numerical law $y = b \cdot a^x$; numerical laws of this form can be found in which b and a are important derived magnitudes. If the unit of x is changed, the law becomes $y = b \cdot a^{\xi x}$, which is not of the same form, for it contains an additional constant ξ. ξ is not a derived magnitude, for it remains unaltered if the system on which the experiments are made is changed and changes only with a change of unit; accordingly the numerical law will have one form if the original unit is taken, but a different form if any other unit is taken. However by a simple device this highly objectionable feature of the law can be removed. In place of the constant a let us substitute a constant A^c, and let us assert as a simple convention that throughout all the experiments which we propose to consider A is to remain the same. With this convention we shall find, of course, that changes of system which previously led to changes of a now lead to changes of c, and, if A is greater than 1, the order of the systems in respect of the c characteristic of them is the same as the order in respect of the a characteristic of them. That is to say, c now takes the place of a as the derived magnitude characteristic of the systems; it has all the properties of a that make a an important derived magnitude; the derived magnitudes measured by c differ from those measured by a merely in the fact that the numerical value attached to any particular magnitude is different. But now the numerical law is of the form $y = b \cdot A^{cx}$; if the unit of x is changed, it becomes $y = b \cdot A^{c\xi x}$, or $y = b \cdot A^{c'x}$, where $c' = c\xi$. The law is now unaltered by a change of unit except for a substitution of one numerical value of a derived magnitude for another.

In other cases where it appears that a change of unit implies a change of form of the law a similar device will always remove the difficulty. I leave to competent mathematicians the proof that the device will always be successful; we all know that it actually is successful. It depends on the fact that if a is the measure of a derived magnitude, then any function of a, $F(a)$, is also a measure of the same derived magnitude, so long as $F(a)$ is single-valued and such that $F'(a)$ is always positive; for if this condition is fulfilled, the order of systems in respect of $F(a)$ is the same as their order in respect of a, and to every numerical value of a corresponds one and only one value of $F(a)$. All that we require in measuring a derived magnitude is some system of ascribing numerals which shall be definite and such that the order of the numerals is the same as the order of the properties which they represent. It may be noted in passing that it would make little difference if $F'(a)$ were always negative in place of positive; the order of $F(a)$ would then be the inverse of the order of a; but we regard two magnitudes as practically the same if the order of one is simply the inverse of the order of the other; such pairs of magnitudes are resistance and conductance, or density and specific volume. Moreover the reciprocal of $F(a)$ has an order that is the inverse of that of $F(a)$; accordingly in what follows no distinction will be made between a derived magnitude and its reciprocal; both will be called the same derived magnitude.

Formal constants. One consequence of the device should be noted, namely the introduction into the numerical law of "constants" that are not derived magnitudes; an example of such a constant is A. A differs from a derived magnitude and from the constants of an empirical law (which are also not derived magnitudes) in the fact that it does not change with the system on which the experiments are made. It also differs from most, but *not* all, derived magnitudes and constants in not changing with the fundamental units. It is defined to be unchangeable; and nothing can force us to change it. For a law $y = b \cdot B^{cx}$, where B is different from A, can always be expressed in the form $y = b \cdot A^{c'x}$, by a suitable choice of c'. On the other hand the choice of A is arbitrary; there is nothing in the form of the law to make us choose one value rather than another; the only effect of changing A will be to change all the numerical values of c in the same ratio. But if we are going to obtain comparable values of the derived magnitude c for all the systems characterised by the law $y = b \cdot A^{cx}$, that is values of c such that the order of the c's is the order of the magnitude measured by c, then in all experiments A must be given the same value; for if A were changed during the experiments then two different values of c might be found for the same system. The choice of A, therefore, determines the form of the law by which the derived magnitude is defined; it is only systems for which A remains the same that will be characterised by the derived magnitude. Accordingly we shall call A a "formal constant". The characteristics of a formal constant are (1) that it does not necessarily change either with change of unit or change of system, and (2) that, though it defines the form of the law and must be kept constant through any series of comparable measurements of the derived magnitude, the choice of the value to be attributed to it is entirely arbitrary. There is never any difficulty in an actual law in distinguishing formal constants from derived magnitudes, for the unchangeability of the former is always expressed by denoting it by a definite numeral[1] and not by an algebraical symbol. But we shall see immediately that not all terms denoted by definite numerals must be assumed to be formal constants in this sense.

But formal constants are not confined to laws such as we have just discussed in which a device, more or less artificial, is necessary in order to secure that the law shall remain of the same form when the fundamental units change. It is very important to observe that they occur in all numerical laws and that

---

[1] In this particular example A will probably be given the value e. But, for physical purposes, e is not an algebraical symbol but a numeral; it is a mere abbreviation for $2 \cdot 71828$, just as 3 is an abbreviation for three.

with every derived magnitude is associated a corresponding formal constant. Thus the simple law $y = a \cdot x^n$, which maintains its form through any changes of unit, might equally well be written $y = \frac{1}{2} a \cdot x^n$; and if it were agreed by convention that the $\frac{1}{2}$ should always remain unchanged whenever a law of this form was expressed, then a would be, as before, a derived magnitude which would change only with a change of the system or a change of the unit of y or x. The only difference would be that the numerical values of the derived magnitudes would be twice as great as they would be if 1 were put for $\frac{1}{2}$. Accordingly we must consider that before the a in the law stands a formal constant which, in the original form of the law, has been arbitrarily given the value 1; it might equally well have been given arbitrarily any other value. And what is true of the constant a in this law is equally true of any other constant measuring a derived magnitude; each such constant must be regarded as multiplied by a formal constant of which the value is usually fixed as 1. Moreover there are cases in which it is assigned a value other than 1. Thus the law of the falling body is usually written, not $y = gt^2$, but $y = \frac{1}{2}gt^2$; the $\frac{1}{2}$ is here a formal constant which has to be openly expressed because it is different from 1; but it would be there even if it were 1, and the choice of 1 would be quite as arbitrary as the choice of $\frac{1}{2}$. (The reason why we choose $\frac{1}{2}$ in this instance will appear later.)

But it should be noted that one of the statements made is not quite accurate; it is not really true that the law $y = a \cdot x^n$ is of the form that is independent of units; it is only of that form if it is written $b \cdot y = a \cdot x^n$. However that form suggests that there are two derived magnitudes, while really there is only one. Accordingly we may write it $a' \cdot x^n / y = 1$, where $a' = a/b$. In this form the formal constant 1 is openly expressed; it is a numeral which must be kept unchanged through any series of experiments which are to lead to consistent determinations of the derived magnitude a, and yet may be chosen arbitrarily with a consequent arbitrary choice of the scale of those derived magnitudes.

It is very important to distinguish carefully between these formal constants and the constants that represent derived magnitudes. A formal constant is something which determines the form of the numerical law and must remain constant so long as that form is to remain unchanged and the laws in which it is involved are to be comparable. On the other hand a constant measuring a derived magnitude changes either when the unit changes or when the experiments are made on a new system; as has been insisted before, it is not really a constant, but only a constant in respect of one particular kind of experimental variation, namely that in which the unit and the system remains unchanged, while change takes place in the properties of that system which are the fundamental magnitudes involved in the law.

And now there appears to be a possibility of finding a definite meaning for the index n which occurs in the law just quoted (cf. pp. 340, 341). Is this numeral a formal constant? It resembles a formal constant in so far that it does not change with the units and that it determines the form of the law.

On the other hand it has been noted that it might change with the system and measure a derived magnitude different in nature from that measured by the other constant in the law; and in this matter it differs from a true formal constant; for such a constant is intimately associated with the derived magnitudes, and variations in it can always and must always be represented as variations in the derived magnitude. It would make havoc of the theory of derived magnitudes if we admitted that in the law $y = \frac{1}{2}gt^2$ there were two derived magnitudes, one measured by the g and one by the $\frac{1}{2}$. However I do not think there are any laws in which an index such as n is a derived magnitude, and in practice n is scarcely distinguishable from a formal constant.

And another manner in which constants similar to this index occur should be mentioned. It has been said that many numerical laws can be expressed as a power series $y = b_0 + b_1 x + b_2 x^2 + b_3 x^3 + \ldots$, although they are usually expressed by functions of other forms. For instance, the law $y = b . A^{cx}$ could be expressed in this form. If it were expressed in this form, we should find in the manner mentioned on p. 349 that there were numerical laws between the constants; thus we should find $b_2 = b_1{}^2/2b$, and $b_3 = b_1{}^2/6b^2$. In virtue of these laws we can write the law $y = b (1 + ax + \frac{1}{2}a^2x^2 + \frac{1}{6}a^3x^3 + \ldots)$, which is now in the form independent of a change of unit. a might be taken as the derived magnitude in place of c; of course $a = c . \log_e A$, and the magnitudes measured by a will differ from those measured by c only by a constant ratio. This example shows how the results of expressing a law as a power series, independent of the change of unit, do not differ from those of expressing it by a function of some other form; but the immediate object of it is to draw attention to the numerals $1, \frac{1}{2}, \frac{1}{6}, \ldots$[1]. A little consideration will show that these are not true formal constants, for though they are independent of the change of unit and fix the form of the law, they might change with the change of system; there might be a series of systems characterised by some magnitudes, all characterised by a law of the same form but differing in these constants; and these differences would not be equivalent to differences in the derived magnitude a. Accordingly, as might be expected on mathematical grounds, these constants resemble the index n rather than the true formal constants; but once again, in actual practice they may be treated as formal constants, because the series of systems which would make them derived magnitudes do not actually exist.

Units of derived magnitudes. The main conclusion at which we have arrived may be put in rather a different way. Whatever the form of the numerical law, it is always possible to express it as a relation between terms of three kinds: (1) the "variables" measuring the fundamental magnitudes, (2) "constants" that vary both with change of unit and with change of system; if the law is a true law and not empirical, these "constants" measure derived magnitudes, (3) formal constants that change neither with the unit nor with the system, so long as the system remains one to which a

---

[1] It is clear that the omission of "1" before the term ax can be justified by nothing but convention.

numerical law of the form contemplated is applicable at all and therefore one possessing the derived magnitudes. It is, perhaps, interesting to observe that the three kinds of terms form a progression in respect of their variability with the properties of the system. The "variables" change with non-defining properties of the system; the "constants" do not change with these non-defining properties but only with those that distinguish one system of a given class from another; the formal constants do not change at all, so long as the class of the system is unaltered, but change if the class changes to one characterised by other derived magnitudes.

The fact that derived magnitudes vary with the units in which the fundamental magnitudes are measured leads to the conception of a unit of a derived magnitude, depending on the fundamental units, and to the conception of "dimensions" as expressing this dependence. If the form of the law remains unaltered, a change of fundamental units changes in the same ratio all the values of a single derived magnitude measured by the law. But in fundamental measurement a change in the same ratio of all the values of some magnitude is characteristic of a change of the unit of that magnitude. The change in a derived magnitude, consequent on a change in the units of the fundamental magnitudes involved in the numerical law by which it is defined, is thus very similar to the change in a fundamental magnitude consequent on a change in its unit; the resemblance between these changes is increased by the fact that some derived magnitudes are also fundamental magnitudes. It gives rise to the conception of a "unit" of a derived magnitude which changes with change in the units of the fundamental magnitudes by means of which it is measured.

On the other hand the difference between the "unit" of a derived magnitude and that of a fundamental magnitude must not be overlooked. A fundamental unit is the property of a system which is arbitrarily stated to have unit magnitude; and before any measurement of the fundamental magnitude can be made the system that has unit magnitude must be realised and made the subject of experiment. The statement that a body is 10 cm. long has no meaning whatever unless somewhere and at sometime there has existed a body 1 cm. long which has been compared, directly or indirectly, with the body of which the statement is made[1]. Now in order to measure derived magnitudes it is not in the least necessary that the system which has unit magnitude should be realised. We have never realised a rod which has unit Young's modulus on the c.g.s. system of units or unit electrical capacity on the electromagnetic c.g.s. system; and yet we have not the slightest difficulty in measuring Young's modulus or electrical capacity. The conception of a unit of a derived magnitude is not essential to its measurement at all; it is

---

[1] This statement is not inconsistent with the statement that the body which is realised concretely and preserved permanently need not be assigned unit magnitude, but may be assigned a magnitude 1000 or 86,400. Though it is unnecessary to preserve the unit permanently it must be made in establishing the standard series unless that series is to have gaps.

useful only when we are considering the change of derived magnitudes with the fundamental units or—in a manner we shall consider shortly—the change of fundamental units with a derived magnitude.

Again the unit of a derived magnitude is not arbitrarily chosen in quite the same way as a fundamental unit. Once the form of the law has been fixed and the unit of the fundamental magnitudes chosen, then experiment decides which system, if any, has the derived magnitude 1. However there is an arbitrary element in the selection of the unit of a derived magnitude (i.e. the system which shall have the derived magnitude 1); it is introduced by the formal constant which is inseparably associated with the derived magnitude. It has been noted that each constant measuring a derived magnitude must be regarded as multiplied by a formal constant of which the numerical value is selected arbitrarily; the selection of this constant will determine which system has unit derived magnitude. Thus we may write the law of motion of a uniformly accelerated body either $y = a.t^2$ or $y = \frac{1}{2}a.t^2$; as we choose one or other of these forms (and the choice is quite arbitrary), one or other of two systems will have unit acceleration; the body that has unit acceleration if the first form is chosen will have an acceleration 2 if the second is chosen. And here we must note a mis-statement that occurs in several well-known treatises. It is stated (I change the wording somewhat to accord with that used here) that the system which has unit derived magnitude *must* be that for which unit values of the fundamental magnitudes are uniformly associated; for instance, if we choose as fundamental units the cm. and the sec., then the body that has unit acceleration *must* be that in which the velocity increases at the rate of 1 cm. per sec. per sec. The use of "must" here is quite mistaken; it is not even true that the derived and fundamental units always *are* connected in this way. The relation stated holds only if the law defining the derived magnitude a is of the form $a.x^u y^v z^w \ldots = 1$. It does not hold if we substitute, as we may, for the 1 some other formal constant. And it does not hold if the defining numerical law involves more than one derived magnitude; for example if the law is $a.x^u y^v z^w + b.x^{u'} y^{v'} z^{w'} + \ldots = 1$ or if the law is $y = b.e^{ax}$; in these examples if we put both the derived magnitudes equal to 1, as well as the fundamental magnitudes, the equation is not fulfilled. Neither of these exceptions are practically important, for in a law defining a derived magnitude (and not merely using one already defined) we almost always do make the formal constant 1; and, so far as I can remember, there is no instance in which a derived magnitude is defined by a law which (in this sense) contains more than one derived magnitude. Nevertheless in order to keep our thoughts clear it is well not to neglect these possible exceptions.

Dimensions. The relation between the units of the derived and of the fundamental magnitudes is expressed by the conceptions of "dimensions"[1].

---

[1] The origin of the term "dimension" is based on geometrical relations. A plane surface has two dimensions where a line has one (the meaning of this statement will be considered in Part III). It is usually held that the magnitude especially connected with a plane surface, namely area, bears to the magnitude especially connected with a line, namely length, the relation which, if these magnitudes were derived, would be expressed by [area] = [length]².

We have seen that a derived magnitude can be always made to occur in a term of the form $a_{uvw} \cdot x^u y^v z^w$, and that when it so occurs the change in the derived magnitude consequent on a change of the fundamental units to those that, measured in the original units, have the magnitudes ξ, η, ζ is given by $a'_{uvw} = \xi^u \eta^v \zeta^w \cdot a_{uvw}$. This relation would also hold if the a's were fundamental magnitudes and the unit in which a'_{uvw} was measured had the value $\xi^u \eta^v \zeta^w$ in terms of the unit in which a_{uvw} was measured. Consequently a change in the fundamental units represented by ξ, η, ζ produces a change in the derived unit represented by $\xi^u \eta^v \zeta^w$. This relation is expressed by the statement that the dimensions of the derived magnitude a_{uvw} are u, v, w, or that $[a_{uvw}] = [x]^u [y]^v [z]^w$. It must be remembered that this statement is equivalent to the relation given between a'_{uvw} and a_{uvw}, and that it is true only if a_{uvw} occurs in the law in the form $a_{uvw} \cdot x^u y^v z^w$.

We can now answer one of the questions asked in the introduction (p. 4), namely why the dimensions of a derived quantity are always expressible as a product of powers of the fundamental magnitudes, and not by any other kind of function, such as $\log [x] \cdot \sin [y] \cdot e^{[z]}$. The conception of the unit, and so of the dimensions, of a derived magnitude is valid only if the numerical law is expressed in the form $f(a_1 \cdot x^{u_1} y^{v_1} z^{w_1}, \ a_2 \cdot x^{u_2} y^{v_2} z^{w_2}, \ldots) = 0$. For if it is not expressed in this form, then the change in the numerical values of the derived magnitudes consequent on a change of the fundamental units is not simply a change of all those numerical values in the same ratio; it will in general be a change in a ratio which is different for the different numerical values. If the law is of the form $y = b \cdot a^x$, then a change ξ in the unit x involves a change of the derived magnitude a from a to a^ξ; the ratio of the new to the old numerical value of the derived magnitude characteristic of any system will not be a function of ξ and of formal constants alone, but a function of ξ and of the old numerical value; it will be different for different systems. Such a change is not of the kind which takes place when we change the unit of a system. If the ratio of the new to the old value is a function of ξ and formal constants alone, and so is of the kind which takes place when a unit is changed, then that function must be of the form ξ^n, where n is a formal constant characteristic of the form of the law and determining that form; for it is only if $f(a, x)$ is of the form $a \cdot x^n$ that $f(\xi x)$ is equal to $f[a\phi(\xi), x]$ for all values of x.

These considerations explain why, if a derived magnitude has dimensions at all, those dimensions are of the prescribed form. It does not explain why all derived magnitudes have dimensions. This fact is explained, as has been stated already, by the latitude which is permissible in the choice of functions to measure a derived magnitude. If a is permissible as a measure of a derived magnitude, then $F(a)$ is also permissible, so long as F is single-valued and F' of the same sign throughout the relevant range. The latitude permissible in the choice of F is so great that we can always actually find an F such that $f(a, x)$ is identical with $f_1[F(a) \cdot x^n]$. If, having found such an F, we take $F(a)$, and not a, as the measure of the derived magnitude, the derived magnitude will change with change of the fundamental units in the manner characteristic of a change of unit of that magnitude.

And there is one other question. Not only are dimensions always expressible as a product of powers, but the indices of these powers are always small integers or simple fractions; we do not find derived magnitudes having dimensions − 0·038 in length, 56·42 in time and so on. Can any explanation of the fact be offered? It implies, of course, that we do not recognise as true (as distinct from empirical) laws any in which indices occur that are not small integers or simple fractions. The only reason that can be given is our constant association of mathematical simplicity with physical reality. If we obtain a numerical law with simple indices, such as $y = ax^2$, we are at once prepared to accept its mathematical simplicity as an indication of physical simplicity and ultimateness; it seems to us natural that the relation should represent some real physical fact and expect it to hold over a very wide range of experiments. Accordingly we attach importance to the derived magnitude defined by it, give it a special name and include it in our list of dimensions. But there are numerical laws in which indices that are not so simple occur, for instance Steinmetz' Law, $U = \eta B^{1·6}$, connecting hysteresis energy loss with the range of induction passed through in the cycle. η is here a derived magnitude, for it would measure the order in which specimens of iron would be placed according as they showed greater or less energy loss (a measurable magnitude) over the same range of induction; and yet η has dimensions which involve 1·6. But we find, as we should expect, that the numerical law is true only over a very limited range of specimens of iron; the derived magnitude, η or Steinmetz' constant, is not important and consequently it is never included in any list of dimensions. The simplicity of all dimensions in such lists is merely due to the omission of all of which the dimensions are not simple.

No-dimensional magnitudes. It appears then that dimensions are inseparable from derived magnitudes and that the statement of the dimensions of a derived magnitude indicates partially, though not completely, the form of the law in which it occurs and the relation between the fundamental magnitudes expressed by that law. But we have to notice that, though all derived magnitudes have dimensions, in the strict sense, in terms of the fundamental magnitudes by means of which they are defined and measured, not all of them change with a change in the fundamental units; in other words, though they have dimensions, these dimensions are zero. There are three classes of these derived magnitudes of zero dimension: The first class occurs when the law states a relation between two fundamental magnitudes of the same kind, measurable in terms of the same unit. They are of the greatest importance, chiefly in geometry, and it is the failure to recognise them as derived magnitudes that has made so much confusion in the theory of dimensions and when questions are raised how far geometry is experimental. Thus I may measure the length of the side and the length of the diagonal of a rectangle, or the arc and the radius of a segment of a circle. So long as all the rectangles are squares and all the segments of the same shape (i.e. their angles superposable) the two lengths will be proportional; the factor of proportionality is characteristic of the shapes on which the measurements are made and changes with those shapes; in the case of the segment of the circle, at least, it has the other property of a derived magnitude, namely that the order of the numerals representing it is the order of a known magnitude (angle). These factors of proportionality are simply and characteristically derived magnitudes, and yet the numerals representing them do not change with the unit of the fundamental magnitude by means of which they are measured. They have the dimensions $[x]/[x]$ or o.

The second class of derived magnitudes with zero dimensions are numbers. We have noticed that number differs from other magnitudes in the fact that the choice of unit is not arbitrary; a number is always a number of something, and this something defines the unit; to change the unit is to change the nature of the magnitude. Accordingly if a number occurs as a fundamental magnitude in a law, there is no need to consider the possibility of the unit of this fundamental magnitude changing, for it could not change without altering the whole meaning of the law; though formally a number ought to be included with other fundamental magnitudes in the dimensional equation, in practice it may be, and actually is, omitted without the possibility of error, so long as the dimensional equation is only regarded as a statement of the manner in which the numerical value of the derived magnitude varies with change in the fundamental units. In the same way, if a derived magnitude is a number it must be invariable in respect of any change of unit. It is not clear from what has been said already how we could be sure that any given derived magnitude was a number, and as a matter of fact, so long as we consider only laws and not theories, such a conclusion is impossible. The instances in which a derived magnitude is identified with a number had best be left until they are discussed in the normal development of the actual propositions of physics; for the present it is merely sufficient to note that there are such instances, and that this second class of derived magnitudes of zero dimensions does exist.

The third class of no-dimensional magnitudes (I do not think it actually has any members) is that of the constants, closely resembling formal constants, discussed on p. 369; e.g. the index n in the term x^n.

A no-dimensional magnitude, like any other, must have a unit; there must be conceivable some system for which the no-dimensional magnitude is 1, although this system may not actually exist; and this unit again will depend, like any other unit, on the formal constant associated with the magnitude. Thus if all of a set of systems are characterised by the law $L_1 = a . L_2$, between two lengths L_1 and L_2 characteristic of them, the unit system will be that for which these lengths are equal. But if we choose to change the formal constant and write $L_1 = \frac{1}{2}a . L_2$, then the unit system will be that for which L_2 is twice L_1. But there is one great difference between no-dimensional and other magnitudes. We have seen that, if the constant a occurring in a numerical law is the measure of some derived magnitude, then $F(a)$ is also such a measure, so long as $F'(a)$ has always the same sign; our choice of which of the number-less possible functions F, fulfilling this condition, shall be selected to measure the derived magnitude is determined by the necessity of expressing the numerical law in such a form that it is independent of a change of fundamental units. But if a is a no-dimensional magnitude, neither a nor $F(a)$, whatever F may be, will change with the unit; so long as F is single-valued and F' is always positive, it is perfectly immaterial which of the forms of F is selected; they will all equally measure the same no-dimensional magnitude. Thus if a is the ratio of the major and minor axes of an ellipse, a is a measure of a magnitude distinguishing different shapes of ellipses. And since a is no-dimensional, a^2 or $a^{\frac{1}{2}}$ or e^a or $\log a$ may be taken indifferently to measure the magnitude; for all the purposes with which we are concerned here they are the same magnitude. The conventional choice of the "eccentricity", which is $\left(1 - \dfrac{1}{a^2}\right)^{\frac{1}{2}}$, to measure the magnitude instead of any of the other functions has nothing to do with considerations of dimensions. Now this observation has an important consequence. Suppose that the same system is characterised by two or more no-dimensional magnitudes; such a case may arise if there is more than one pair of magnitudes of the same kind between which there is a law of proportionality; for instance if the system is characterised by two lengths such that $L_1 = a . L_2$ and two times such that $T_1 = b . T_2$. Then in virtue of the meaning of "characterised by", the two no-dimensional magnitudes must be uniformly associated and there must be some uniform numerical relation between them; some proposition of the form $a = F(b)$ must be true. Now we have seen that it is legitimate to regard $F(b)$ as the same magnitude as b; the two have precisely the same physical significance and differ only in the numerical values to which they lead. Accordingly it is always possible to choose the form of the no-dimensional magnitudes so that the numerical value of one is equal to the numerical value of the other, and so that all the no-dimensional magnitudes characteristic of a system are represented by the same numeral. This result may be expressed roughly by the statement that a system can only have one no-dimensional magnitude characteristic of it, and in some of our future considerations it will be useful to remember that statement. On the other hand it must be remembered that, even if all the no-dimensional magnitudes characteristic of the system are denoted by the same numeral, there is some physical distinction between them; for some will arise in a law between fundamental magnitudes of one kind and some in a law between fundamental magnitudes of another.

It is very important not to confuse these no-dimensional derived magnitudes with other terms occurring in a numerical law which resemble them in being invariable in respect of the fundamental units. One such kind of term has been mentioned already, namely, the formal constants that determine the form of the law. They differ from derived magnitudes of zero dimensions in the fact that they are invariable not only with respect to change of fundamental units, but also with respect to change of system, so long as all the systems are included in the class to which the law is applicable at all; on the other hand, derived magnitudes of zero dimensions change, like all other derived magnitudes, with change of system. And there is another kind of term involved in numerical laws which is invariable in respect of change of units, namely the "argument" of the function that expresses the law, consisting of the derived magnitude in conjunction with the corresponding fundamental magnitudes. Thus the law $y = y_0 \cdot e^{ax}$ may be regarded as a special case of the general function $f(y/y_0, ax) = 0$. It is expressed in this form rather than in the form $f(y, x, y_0, a) = 0$ because it is only if the "constants" are associated with the "variables" in the manner indicated by the first form that the form of the function will be unchanged by change of units. Now though the arguments y/y_0 and ax are independent of the units, they differ completely from the other terms, formal constants and no-dimensional derived magnitudes that are so independent, because they are not independent of anything but change of units; they vary both with change of the fundamental magnitudes, the system being the same, and with the system, one of the fundamental magnitudes being the same. There is only one special case in which these arguments are independent of the fundamental magnitudes and the system; that case occurs when there is only one argument, the remaining terms of the function being formal constants; for instance in the law $ax^2/y = 1$. Here the argument is invariable to the same extent as the formal constant 1, but it *is* not a formal constant, for the equations state something quite different from that which results from substituting a formal constant for the argument, that is from $1 - 1 = 0$.

There is a tendency to confuse these three classes of terms that are independent of change of unit—namely derived magnitudes of zero dimensions, formal constants, and arguments—under the general name "mere number". The name is objectionable in itself, for these terms are not distinguished from others in being either numbers or Numbers. Few of them are numbers; if any of them are Numbers (that is if the numerical law states a relation between Numbers) then all of them are Numbers, but so also are derived magnitudes of which the dimensions are not zero. The use of the word "number" to denote all terms that are independent of the fundamental units is the source of much of the confusion that attends the theory of dimensions.

Defined magnitudes. The statement, made at the beginning of the last section, that all derived magnitudes have dimensions suggests the question whether the converse statement is true and everything which has dimensions is a derived magnitude. If by "having dimensions" is meant "satisfying all the conditions that have just been discussed", the answer is obviously, yes; but if it merely means "changing its numerical value with a change of the units of fundamental magnitudes", the answer is, no. Derived magnitudes are connected with fundamental through definite numerical laws; there are other terms denoted by numerals that are not fundamental magnitudes, but connected with them by statements other than laws. For instance there are hypothetical ideas, such as the velocity of a molecule, which is connected with fundamental magnitudes by a theory; and again there are terms connected with fundamental magnitudes by a definition, such as the velocity of a body that is not uniform. Uniform velocity is a derived magnitude determined by the numerical law $x = at$, but velocity in general is a mere name arbitrarily given to ds/dt when there is a law of any form whatever connecting s and t. It is unnecessary to discuss in detail either of these classes of terms possessing dimensions, for the meaning and use of dimensions in connection with them will be obvious from what has been said already; indeed the difficulty is to distinguish them from true derived magnitudes rather than to trace the similarity to them. But the existence of magnitudes by definition or "defined magnitudes" must be borne in mind.

Again it must be remembered that fundamental magnitudes have no dimensions; there is nothing to force us to change the unit of one fundamental magnitude when we change the unit of another. On the other hand, it is useful for formal reasons to give to a fundamental magnitude the dimensions 1 in terms of itself, and to say that, while density has the dimensions [mass] × [volume]$^{-1}$, mass has the dimensions [mass]. But, it may be asked, what of fundamental magnitudes which are also derived magnitudes? Here again there is nothing to force us to give to such magnitudes one unit rather than another, so long as it is really practicable to measure them as fundamental magnitudes. If we insist on retaining full freedom of choice of the unit of such magnitudes, we simply create a new derived magnitude. Thus, in Ohm's Law all three magnitudes can be conceivably measured as fundamental and, if we intended so to measure them, we ought to write $I = a \cdot V/R$, where a is a new derived magnitude with the dimensions [current] × [resistance] × [potential difference]$^{-1}$. But when a magnitude can have either character we always do choose for its unit that which would be its unit if it were always to be measured as derived; we thus reduce the derived magnitude a to 1 and it disappears. Accordingly it is always permissible in dimensional arguments to treat a magnitude which can be either fundamental or derived as if it were a derived magnitude, and to omit totally from consideration the new derived magnitude that would appear if it were measured as fundamental.

Basic magnitudes. But the question, by the question at the beginning of the last section, that it is intended to raise is more important. In many discussions of the subject it is asserted that all magnitudes have dimensions in terms of certain "fundamental magnitudes". In the older treatises these "fundamental" magnitudes are usually asserted to be mass, length and time; in more recent work it is realised that others must be added to the list, and for this purpose, temperature and one of the electrical magnitudes (usually dielectric constant or permeability) are chosen It will appear in our discussion that the conclusions which it is desired to draw are unaltered whether or no these two additional magnitudes are included. And since by omitting them we avoid certain special difficulties connected with temperature[1], the proposition that will be discussed is that there are only these

---

[1] See note at end of chapter.

"fundamental" magnitudes, in terms of which all others have dimensions, namely mass, length and time. Further an alteration in nomenclature will be necessary, since we have appropriated "fundamental" to another use; I shall therefore substitute in this connection the term "basic".

According to our discussion the proposition must mean that all magnitudes are either

(1) masses, lengths, or times,

(2) derived magnitudes defined by numerical laws[1] in which the fundamental magnitudes are either masses, lengths, or times or are derived magnitudes defined by other and more ultimate laws in which the fundamental magnitudes are masses, lengths, or times, or

(3) mere names for some functions of masses, lengths, and times or of some derived magnitudes satisfying (2).

Is this statement true? If it is, would it still be true if any other magnitudes were selected as basic in place of mass, length, and time? If so, why are mass, length, and time selected? And so on—an endless series of interesting questions is indicated.

At the outset three considerations will be suggested, chiefly in order to show that the statement is not so obviously true as it is often thought to be. First mass, length, and time are not the magnitudes that we habitually measure as fundamental magnitudes[2]; the practical fundamental magnitudes are weight, length, time and electrical resistance. And here it may be well to offer an explanation on a very elementary point which might, if it was left unnoticed, raise unnecessary doubts. I have substituted weight for mass as a practical fundamental magnitude; nevertheless the magnitude which is determined by the process of weighing is often called the mass. What is actually measured in the fundamental process of weighing is the weight of a body in air at a given region of the earth's surface relative to the weight in the same air at the same place of the standard unit body. If all the bodies are of equal density, we believe that their weights measured in this way are proportional to their masses; if they are not, a "correction", involving the densities of the bodies and of the air, is introduced, and it is believed that the values so corrected are proportional to the mass. But this belief depends upon the truth of some proposition which is not involved in weighing at all; what is its nature, whether it is a numerical law, a definition or a theory, is a question of some difficulty. But it is obvious that the fundamental process of weighing itself does not involve dynamical mass in any way whatever; it is a measurement of weight and not of mass. In that process mass may be

---

[1] For the purpose of this discussion I propose to make no distinction between laws and theories or between concepts and hypothetical ideas. It is impossible to avoid this step— which does not affect the main discussion—until the exact nature of all the propositions that will be mentioned has been determined in the course of a systematic investigation of the part of physics to which it belongs.

[2] In ordinary laboratory experience we do not ever undertake a fundamental measurement; we use calibrated instruments and rely on the maker to calibrate them. But the statement is true if by "we" is here meant our instrument makers.

regarded as a mere name for that function of the weight, of the density of air and of the body weighed, which is independent of these densities, and also of the position on the earth's surface. Mass, thus defined, would have a definite meaning if Newton had never lived and if there were no science of dynamics.

However, owing to the necessity for the correction, mass, so defined, is measured by a process which is not truly fundamental. But for our present purpose it will be convenient and permissible to overlook this fact; and in what follows mass will be regarded as a fundamental magnitude determined by weighing. The inaccuracy would raise difficulties only if we inquired into the reason why force and energy are given dimensions in terms of mass, length and time; for dynamical mass, the magnitude that is not simply a name for a certain function of weights, enters into numerical laws only through these two magnitudes and through those which are, in their turn, derived from these magnitudes. Accordingly in order not to raise these difficulties, which belong properly to a much later stage of our inquiry, we shall simply assume, without giving or asking for any reason, first, that dynamical mass can be determined as a fundamental magnitude and, second, that force and energy have the dimensions in terms of mass, length and time that are usually assigned to them. It will be seen that none of the conclusions that are about to be advanced are affected materially by this assumption.

To resume after this digression—the second consideration, suggesting that the statement under discussion is not indubitable, is that there are important magnitudes which are not usually given dimensions in terms of mass, length and time. One of these is temperature; but since it is now generally admitted that temperature must be included among the basic magnitudes, no importance can be attached to this example. Others are the photometric magnitudes based on the standard candle and not on energy. What is there distinguishing such magnitudes from those of which the dimensions are always given in terms of these three fundamental magnitudes?

The third consideration is suggested by the magnitude volume, which is always given the dimensions [length]^3. Does the attribution of these dimensions imply that the volume of a rectangular block means nothing but the product of the lengths of its edges? or does it imply that the volume is a magnitude derived from some numerical law known to exist between these lengths and (possibly) the mass of the block and the time of it—whatever that may mean? The second alternative will scarcely be accepted by anyone. The first may be accepted for a moment, but will scarcely survive the suggestion that what volume means is something to do with the quantity of liquid the block will displace, and that the product of the lengths of the edges is merely an indication of this quantity. But if the attribution of the dimensions implies neither of these things, what does it mean?

Quasi-derived magnitudes. Having shown that there is need for inquiry, we will proceed to the inquiry itself. The problems that we have to consider are best solved by indirect attack; let us start with some very simple and obvious facts concerning a law which has been used as an example before, namely that defining the derived magnitude density. This law states a relation between the mass and the volume of any substance. In order to establish it, it is necessary that there should be some way of measuring both mass and volume which is independent of the truth of the law. Now mass (according to the assumption we are making) can be measured by a fundamental process, and volume can also be measured by a fundamental process, a fact which is sufficiently proved by the undoubted applicability to volume of the conception of addition. The exact process of measuring volume as a fundamental magnitude will be discussed in detail in Part III, but it may be suggested briefly that the volume of a vessel is the number of times the liquid contents of a vessel of unit volume can be emptied into it in order to fill it. Since both mass and volume can be measured fundamentally, it is possible to establish the law without making any previous assumptions about its truth and so to define the derived magnitude density.

Now once the law has been generally established, a single measurement of volume and mass, instead of a whole series, will suffice to determine the density of any particular substance; and indeed we can dispense altogether with any measurements of one of the two fundamental magnitudes. If we always employ as our volume the arbitrary unit of that magnitude, then the density of any substance will be simply the mass of this volume. Further we can reverse the rôles of fundamental and derived magnitudes and, in place of using measurements of volume and mass to determine density, use measurements of density and mass (or volume) to determine volume (or mass). If we use for the experiment the substance of unit density a single measurement of mass will determine the volume, for the volume will be simply equal to the mass. In place of the substance of unit density we might use any other of which the density has been determined, but this possibility is of no importance for the moment.

This reversal is quite general. Whenever we have established a numerical law between fundamental magnitudes, x and y, defining thereby a derived magnitude a, and determined what system has unit value of a (or indeed determined the numerical value of a for any system), we can measure one of the fundamental magnitudes in a manner characteristic of a derived rather than of a fundamental magnitude; that is to say, we can measure it by measuring a magnitude of some other kind. And this possibility may be of great practical importance, for it may well happen that the measurement as a derived magnitude is experimentally more accurate and convenient than the measurement by the fundamental process. By "more accurate" is meant that successive determinations of the magnitude for the same system agree better, and by "more convenient" either that the process is easier to handle or that it is readily applicable over a wider range. Thus the process is certainly more accurate in the case of volume, and all accurate measurements of volume are actually made by weighing portions of a substance of known density.

Now if such a derived process of measurement proves thus more satisfactory than the fundamental process, all necessity vanishes for realising and preserving a concrete unit of one of the fundamental magnitudes x. We take the system for which the derived magnitude a has been determined to be 1 (or other definite value) and assign that value of the derived magnitude to it by definition. The unit of x may then be defined simply as the system characterised by unit a and y (or by any other assigned values of a and y). If this procedure is adopted, it becomes not only unnecessary but actually undesirable to realise the concrete unit; for if it were realised, we might find with the progress of the experimental art that the realised unit was not characterised with perfect accuracy by unit a and unit y as defined. We should then be faced with the choice of abandoning the realised unit and making a new one or denying that the derived magnitude for the standard system was really 1. Formal considerations would probably lead us to prefer the latter alternative, but practical convenience would probably point in the other direction; a situation would arise which would please nobody but those who enjoy international congresses. But any difficulty of this kind is avoided quite simply by refusing to realise a concrete standard at all; nobody can then possibly maintain that it is wrong. And this, again, is the course actually adopted with volume; the litre is not now defined as the volume of a certain vessel (or even of a vessel that might be constructed according to certain specifications); it is defined as the volume of 1 kilogramme of pure air-free water at the maximum density and a pressure of 760 mm. of mercury.

When the unit of volume has been defined in this manner and not by the property of some realised system, the resemblance between it and a derived magnitude is greatly increased; for derived magnitudes are distinguished from fundamental by the fact that their measurement does not require the realisation of a concrete unit. Accordingly it is suggested that volume ought to have dimensions, like a derived magnitude, and further that these dimensions are [mass]/[density]. For if the form of the definition of unit volume is maintained, while there are substituted for the original systems of unit mass and unit density those which have the magnitudes μ and δ in terms of those units, then the new unit of volume will be μ/δ times the old. The relation between the units is therefore exactly the same as that given by the dimensional equation of a true derived magnitude; and it only holds if the law $m = aV$ is true. Nevertheless there is an important difference. If that law were not true, it would still be possible to measure volume, and unit volume might still be defined as that of a portion of some definite substance which possesses a definite mass. On the other hand, if the law were not true, it would not be possible to measure density, for there would be no concept density to measure. We might still, if we pleased, give a name to the mass of unit volume of the substance, but the numeral denoted by this name would have very little significance; if the unit of mass or volume were changed the "densities" of different substances would not, in general, change in the same ratio.

And just as the fundamental magnitude volume has been changed into something very like a derived magnitude, so the derived magnitude density has been changed into something very like a fundamental magnitude. For by refusing to realise a unit of volume, we have converted the statement that the standard substance has unit density from a result of experimental measurement into a definition which cannot be proved or disproved. The selection of a certain substance as possessing unit density is precisely analogous to the selection of a certain body as possessing unit mass. But again it must be remembered that the resemblance is not complete. The important fact always remains that volume can and density cannot be measured in terms of the unit by a fundamental process; unless volume could be measured as volume, the law defining density could never be established; while density can never be measured as density, but only by measuring something that is not density.

It will be seen that measurement of a fundamental magnitude in this manner involves the substitution of a unit realised in a substance for a unit realised in a body. (The distinction between a substance and a body is explained in Chapter III.) For a derived magnitude, being defined by a law which is applicable to each of several systems, can only be the characteristic of a substance; the measurement of the derived magnitude, requiring the investigation of a law, involves the alteration of properties which distinguish different bodies but characterise the same substance. Herein lies one of the great advantages of quasi-derived measurement, for since the transition from a body to a substance involves the removal of restrictions, the specifications necessary for the realisation of the unit substance will always be less severe than those for the realisation of the unit body.

Derived units. The dimensional equation [volume]=[mass]×[density]$^{-1}$ is seldom if ever included in a list of such equations, but the considerations that have been advanced suggest that it might be with some show of reason. If it were, it would express a determination to measure volume in the way that has just been described or, as will be said in future, to measure it as a "quasi-derived" magnitude. Now there are other instances in which a unit of a magnitude is defined in a manner very similar, and yet are such that it would certainly not be proper to treat the magnitude as quasi-derived and to write a dimensional equation for it. Such instances are electric current and electric resistance. The international ampere and the international ohm are defined respectively by the quantity of silver deposited by a current and by the resistance of a column of mercury of constant cross section and stated mass and length. Analogy with density might possibly suggest that current ought to be given the dimensions [mass] × [time]$^{-1}$ × [Faraday's constant]$^{-1}$, and resistance the dimensions [mass]$^{-1}$ × [length]^2 × [density] × [specific resistance]. But there is an important difference which makes the analogy false. The laws on which the attribution of these dimensions is based are not used actually in the measurement of current and resistance by the most accurate and convenient methods. The definitions of the ampere and the ohm are definitions of mere units and not of processes of measurement; they might remain unchanged even if the laws by which they are suggested were found to be untrue; and the units might not be changed with changes in the units of mass, length and time as is suggested by those definitions. Accordingly current and resistance are not, in the sense defined, quasi-derived magnitudes, or at least they are not quasi-derived magnitudes defined by the laws which suggest the units adopted.

Units which are not realised and are defined in terms of magnitudes other than those of which they are the units and other than the fundamental magnitudes in terms of which the magnitudes of which they are units are measured—such units, of which we have just considered examples, may be termed "derived units". It must be remembered that a derived unit may not be the unit of a derived magnitude or a derived magnitude have a derived unit; but in spite of this fact the use of the term derived in both cases is probably justified; indeed it is justified because it compels attention where it is needed. Some further consideration concerning derived units will be offered later in this chapter.

Example of electric charge. From these very trite and familiar remarks, let us proceed to another example of the same type and scarcely less familiar, which is provided by the magnitude "electric charge". Here we have the numerical law $Fr^2 = K.e^2$, where F is the force between two small bodies with the charge e separated by a distance r *. The law defines the derived magnitude K, the dielectric constant, which is, of course, found to measure a definite property of a system, namely the medium in which the charges are immersed. Accordingly the dimensional equation

$$[\text{charge}] = [\text{force}]^{\frac{1}{2}} \times [\text{length}] \times [\text{dielectric constant}]^{-\frac{1}{2}}$$

is exactly analogous to the equation $[\text{volume}] = [\text{mass}] \times [\text{density}]^{-1}$. By asserting arbitrarily that some particular medium has some definite numerical value for the dielectric constant, a unit of charge can be defined which depends upon the units of force and length. By making all measurements on a single medium electric charges can be measured as derived magnitudes, using length and force as fundamental magnitudes; there is no need to realise a concrete unit of electric charge.

In fact the example is so precisely similar to the last that it has been cited only to raise the question why it is treated differently in ordinary text-books. It is not usual, even since the definition of the litre as the volume of a

* The question may be raised here whether force and electric charge are really fundamental magnitudes and so analogous to the magnitudes involved in the laws previously considered. Whether force is a derived or a fundamental magnitude is a matter on which much will have to be said in a subsequent volume; I believe that it is, but even if it were not there is no doubt that here it acts as a fundamental magnitude; for, even if it is derived, it is derived from some law quite other than that under discussion. With electric charge the matter is rather different; for if it is a derived magnitude, it is derived from this very law (or from some other closely connected with it). This question again must be postponed, but it will probably be realised that, if the magnitude is derived, it is not, like K, derived solely from this law; other laws are involved in the derivation. But the reader will probably accept the statement that electric charge may be measured as a fundamental magnitude, and may be regarded as such for the purpose of the present discussion, when he remembers that charges are undoubtedly capable of addition.

decimetre cube has been abandoned, to give volume the dimensions [mass] × [density]$^{-1}$; but it is usual to give electric charge the dimensions

$$[\text{force}]^{\frac{1}{2}} \times [\text{length}] \times [\text{dielectric constant}]^{-\frac{1}{2}}.$$

In so far as there is any difference, it would seem to be in favour of a reversal of this practice. For while volume is always measured in all accurate work as a quasi-derived magnitude by means of the law of density, charge is not always, or usually, measured as a quasi-derived magnitude by Coulomb's Law. It might be argued that according to modern practice the definition of unit charge resembles the definition of the international ohm rather than that of the litre and therefore, since nobody would give to the ohm the dimensions suggested in the last section, it ought not to give rise to a dimensional equation.

One actual reason why the dimensional equations based on Coulomb's Law is always stated is probably that electric charge is thought of as a pure derived magnitude defined by this law; it is not always realised that electric charge might be measured as a fundamental magnitude or that it must be so measured (or at least measured in some way which does not depend simply on the truth of the law $Fr^2 = K.e^2$) if that law is to be the expression of experimental facts. But another reason is suggested by the observation that in some text-books the dielectric constant is wholly omitted and the dimensions of electric charge simply stated as [force]$^{\frac{1}{2}}$ × [length]. This omission would probably be justified on the ground on which the omission of number from dimensional equations is justified, namely because it is inconceivable that the unit of dielectric constant should ever be changed or that any other medium other than that selected at present should be selected as the standard. If there is such a ground, it must imply that there is some essential difference which distinguishes this medium from all others, for otherwise there could be no reason to force us to select it rather than any other. We realise that our choice of water rather than mercury as the substance of standard density is arbitrary and dictated by nothing but practical convenience (if indeed it is dictated by that); on the other hand, there is a very essential difference, indicated by the electronic theory, between a vacuum and any other medium in respect of dielectric constant. We can therefore assign a good and definite reason for our refusal to contemplate ever taking any medium other than a vacuum as the standard of dielectric constant. If we make that selection, the equations of the electric field for a vacuum will always be free from any symbol representing the dielectric constant and yet will be invariable in respect of changes of the other fundamental units in terms of which the unit of electric charge is fixed. The symbol will only occur when media other than a vacuum are considered, and since, according to theory, the equations for such media have a significance rather different from that for a vacuum, there is no disadvantage, but rather advantage, in the appearance of the symbol in one and not in the other. If this view is accepted the deliberate omission of the K from the dimensional equation is completely justified.

But it still remains to justify the use of a dimensional equation at all.

It is doubtless justified because it does express the manner in which we should actually change the unit of electric charge if we were to change the units of mass, length and time. But why are we so certain that we should change the unit of charge in this manner, when we are by no means certain that we should change in the corresponding manner the international ohm? The answer is given by the considerations which have just been mentioned. The equation stating Coulomb's Law in a vacuum is a very important equation, much more important than the equation connecting the resistance of a body with its mass, length, specific resistance and density; it is more important that the form of this equation and any constants involved in it should be unchanged by a change in units. We do not mind the occurrence in the equation of resistance of a constant the numerical value of which may have to be changed, but we do mind the occurrence of such a constant in Coulomb's Law. But if this is so, we must clearly determine always to give K for a vacuum the numerical value 1; and it would seem therefore that if the dimensional equation is to be stated at all, it should always be stated with the omission of the K and the possibility of choosing as the standard medium any but a vacuum should be rigidly excluded.

The same considerations apply to the electromagnetic units of electric and magnetic magnitudes. Here again the attribution of dimensions to the magnitudes can be justified only on the ground that we are determined to keep the equations expressing other laws (e.g. Ampère's Law) clear of "constants" which change with the units of the fundamental magnitude involved in those laws. And since in respect of these laws a vacuum is again distinguished from all other media, there is good reason for choosing the units so that μ, being 1, disappears from those laws applied to a vacuum and appears only when the media are magnetic. But it follows that electrical units cannot have dimensions both on the electrostatic and the electromagnetic systems. If we assume $K = 1$, then experiment tells us that μ is not 1, and vice versa. We cannot keep both sets of equations clear of the variable constants. I do not mean that the occasional use of both systems is not justified; we may first use one and then use the other, just as we may sometimes measure lengths in feet and sometimes in metres. But the two uses involve contradictory assumptions and cannot be used at the same time. However, all this is quite clearly recognised by all competent physicists.

The example of volume. And now let us revert to the magnitude volume and consider some relations that are equally familiar but not usually clearly stated.

We have noticed that volume is measurable, not only as a fundamental magnitude, but also by means of measurements of length. The possibility of measuring it in this manner again depends on experimental laws. If I take a series of hollow parallelopipeds of the same shape, each having all its edges equal, and measure for each the length of these edges and the volume, measured as a fundamental magnitude, then I shall find a law $V = a \cdot L^3$. a is a derived magnitude characteristic of the series of parallelopipeds. If a series of different shape is taken, again it will be found that $V = a'.L^3$, but the derived magnitude a' will be different from a. There is a complete analogy with the density law $m = \rho V$. To m corresponds L^3, also determined by fundamental measurement, to V corresponds V, to ρ corresponds $1/a$, also a derived magnitude; just as ρ is constant while the system remains constant in one respect (being the same substance), although the fundamental magnitudes characteristic of it vary, and changes if the system changes in that respect, so a remains constant if the shape of the parallelopiped remains constant, although the fundamental magnitudes characteristic of it vary, and changes when that shape changes. And as we could obtain a unit of V without realising it in a definite vessel by defining arbitrarily the density of some substance to be unity, so we can obtain a unit of V by defining arbitrarily the shape, a, of some particular set of parallelopipeds to be unity; and as we actually do so define a unit by means of a particular substance, so in the past we have actually defined it by means of a particular parallelopiped, assigning the value $a = 1$ arbitrarily to the cube.

Accordingly, the position is very similar to that we have just discussed in connection with electrical magnitudes. We have the choice of defining our unit of volume as a quasi-derived magnitude in two ways, indicated by the two dimensional equations [volume] = [mass] × [density]$^{-1}$ or [volume] = [length]^3 × [shape]; and it is just possible that we might define it in both ways. Having selected our substance of unit density and our parallelopiped of unit shape, it would be possible so to choose the units of mass and length that the unit defined by one equation was equal to the unit defined by the other. But such a method would be open to the objection mentioned before that increasing experimental accuracy might show that the two units were not exactly equal, and that, if this happened, we should be faced with the necessity of abandoning one of the two definitions or of altering the unit either of density or of shape or of mass or of length; it would be difficult to obtain agreement which of the alternatives was to be adopted. As a matter of fact we do not adopt this method; unit volume is defined by mass and a substance of standard density and it is actually known that the unit so defined is not the volume of a cube with edges of unit length; it is the volume of a cube of which the edges (according to the latest measurements) have a length 10·00009. What then does the statement of the dimensions of a volume in terms of length mean? It might still mean that we were fully determined, if the unit of length were changed, to adopt as a new unit of volume a cube of which the edges had the length 10·00009 in terms of the new unit; it might also mean that to the shape of the cube we propose, once and for all, to attribute the value 10·00027. But as a matter of fact there is not the slightest foundation for either of those statements. Once more then what does the attribution of such dimensions to volume mean?

In attempting to answer that question our attention is, of course, at once drawn to the universal omission from the dimensional equation of the derived magnitude that is here called shape. If it is asked why it is always omitted, I think the only possible answer (which will have to be justified in subsequent discussion) is that the actual reason is to be found in a confusion of thought. We realise that we might change the substance of which the density is arbitrarily asserted to be 1, although it is extremely improbable that we shall ever do so; but we do not realise that we might change the parallelopiped to which the shape 1 is arbitrarily assigned. And the failure to realise the possibility of such change is merely due to the knowledge that geometers have used a conception, which they also term "volume", which is *defined* to be L^3 for the cube. This definition conveys the true meaning of the conception, and it would be as foolish to deny that this "volume" is equal to L^3 as it would be to deny that a cube is a parallelopiped with its edges at right angles to each other; to dispute the proposition would be to enter on squabbles about words. But to deny that this volume is the same as the physical volume measured by a fundamental process—that is not to squabble about words, but to state something that is as obvious as that a house is not the same as the legal right to occupy it.

Nevertheless it may be asked whether the omission of shape can be justified on any more adequate grounds, such as those given for the omission of the dielectric constant. Let us try to justify it, assuming for the moment that we are going to define the unit of volume, regarded as a quasi-derived magnitude, by the shape of a cube and not by the density of water. Numerical laws can be found relating the a for any particular shape to angles and other no-dimensional geometrical magnitudes of the kind mentioned above. Any a can be expressed in the form $a'.f(x, y, z)$, where x, y, z are these magnitudes and the function f contains nothing but these magnitudes and formal constants. a' is a constant for all possible shapes, which differ only in the values of x, y, z or in the form of the function f; it is a true universal constant[1] depending only on the choice of the units of volume and length; it differs from a (and from ρ) in being the same for all the systems to which it is applicable at all. Accordingly if we fix its value arbitrarily there can be nothing ever to make us change that value except mere caprice; there can be no reason similar to that which might make us think one substance better than another as that of standard density. It may be argued, therefore, that, since there is no prospect of it ever being changed, it may be safely left out of the dimensional equation which is significant only if the terms involved in it are capable of change. And then it may be argued that, since $f(x, y, z)$ is also of no dimensions it also may be safely left out, and the dimensional equation simply reduced to [volume] = [length]^3. But the last step in the argument is inadmissible; for though $f(x, y, z)$ has no dimensions it is a derived magnitude,

---

[1] This highly important universal constant, probably the most important of all universal constants, is dismissed without the smallest reference, so far as I can discover, in all text-books. It is, of course, implied in the statement that eight pint pots will fill a gallon jar whether water or mercury or beer or any other incompressible liquid is used for the measurement. This is clearly an experimental assertion and one which could not possibly have been predicted. The only objection to this view that can possibly be raised is that it is merely a definition of what is meant by incompressible. I do not think the objection can be sustained, but the full discussion must be left until we consider "space".

depending on and changing with the system on which the measurements are made, and unless it is inconceivable that we should choose for defining the unit any but one of all the systems which have this derived magnitude, the possibility of a change of choice and a consequent change of unit of volume must be considered. The omission of shape will, therefore, be justified only if a cube differs from all other solid bodies in the same ultimate way that a vacuum differs from a material medium; personally I cannot see any reason for asserting that it does so differ. A cube is a very important solid body, but so is a sphere. Why should we not adopt as the unit shape that of the sphere rather than that of the cube?

Another defence might be offered. In stating any relation between volumes and lengths, we always do insert the function $f(x, y, z)$ and do write $a' . f(x, y, z)$ in place of a; consequently the only effect of changing our choice of the standard shape of solid body, the unit of length and a' being unchanged, would be to change the form of f characteristic of each shape. There is therefore no need to mention shape in considering how the unit of volume would change. On the other hand, if we changed the unit of length (having agreed to keep a' the same), then we should have to change the unit of volume in the manner indicated by the dimensional equation [volume] = [length]³. But the statement made in opening the defence is untrue. We shall see in the next chapter that the $f(x, y, z)$ is habitually omitted in exactly those cases in which, for any use that can be made of dimensions, it is essential that it should be inserted. Moreover it is by no means certain that we have agreed always to keep a' the same. The argument just given was based on the assumption that volume was to be measured as a quasi-derived magnitude in terms of length. But it is not actually so measured. If we discovered that our experimental determination of the relation between the litre and the volume of a cubic decimetre was slightly in error, we should probably wish to alter the value of a'. We have seen from the example of electric charge that our choice of a particular way of defining a unit is determined largely by the desire to keep constant the form of some specially important equation, and that when it is so determined it is usual and useful to state a dimensional equation based on that equation. Now in the matter of volume there are two equations of great importance in which the magnitude is involved; one is that defining the density of substances, the other that stating a relation between volumes and lengths. We cannot be sure of keeping the forms of both equations always unchanged. In the earlier days of physics, the second was regarded as the more important; but the re-definition of the litre seems to indicate that the first is now the more important. Even in the earlier stage of opinion, the dimensional equation [volume] = [length]³ was a very inadequate way of expressing the relation which it was desired to maintain between the units of volume and length; it now expresses nothing whatever that is true about the relations of units and should be wholly abandoned.

Basic magnitudes resumed. The foregoing discussion doubtless appears inconclusive and confused; but that, I maintain, is because an attempt, which is bound to fail, has been made to exhibit a consistency in current practice that is essentially inconsistent. The conclusion which I would draw is this. There are three things which may be usefully and clearly expressed by a dimensional equation of the form $[p] = [x]^u \times [y]^v \times [z]^w \times [a]^r$: (1) If p is a true derived magnitude or a mere name for the function $x^u y^v z^w a^r$, the equation expresses the only manner in which p can be measured and in which its (fictitious) unit can be defined. (2) If p is a fundamental magnitude which it is convenient to measure as a quasi-derived magnitude by means of the law $p = x^u y^v z^w a^r$, then the dimensional equation expresses the nature of this process of measurement. Of x, y, z, a, one (a) must be a pure derived magnitude; the unit of p will vary in the manner shown by the equation with the arbitrary choice of the system which has unit of this derived magnitude and with the arbitrary choice of the units of the fundamental magnitudes x, y, z; and in order to express this fact a must be kept in the dimensional equation. (3) If p is a fundamental magnitude of which it is convenient to choose the unit in a certain manner in order that an important law may always retain its form, however the units of the fundamental magnitudes x, y, z are changed, then the equation expresses how the unit of p must be chosen to attain this object. In this case it is impossible that a should change if the object of the definition of the unit of p is to be attained, and therefore a should be omitted from the dimensional equation; a will always be given the value 1.

But these three uses of the dimensional equation do not coincide with current practice. (1) is often employed, e.g. in the statement

$$[\text{velocity}] = [\text{length}] \times [\text{time}]^{-1}$$

or $$[\text{acceleration}] = [\text{length}] \times [\text{time}]^{-2}.$$

(2) is not employed, but would be if we said that

$$[\text{volume}] = [\text{mass}] \times [\text{density}]^{-1}.$$

(3) is employed in connection with electric charge, but the K is not, as I hold it should be, always omitted; in fact some writers pride themselves on their correctness in including K on every possible occasion[1]. And in addition to these uses there is one for which I can find no justification, e.g. when it is stated that $[\text{volume}] = [\text{length}]^3$, or even $[\text{volume}] = [\text{shape}] \times [\text{length}]^3$. The first means nothing that is true, the second means only that there is a relation between volume and lengths of the form $V = a'.b.L_1.L_2.L_3$, where a' is a universal constant and b is no-dimensional. It does not state anything true about methods of measuring V or about the definition of its unit; and since elsewhere dimensional equations always express something about methods of measurement or about units, this use should be abandoned. If it is not

---

[1] They usually fail to notice their inconsistency in omitting another constant which should occur in passing from electrical to magnetic units. Experiment does not prove that the μ in $F = \mu \dfrac{ii'\,ds\,ds'}{r^2}$ is the same as the μ in $F = \mu \dfrac{mm'}{r^2}$, but only that the two are proportional. A universal constant expressing the factor of proportionality is wanted—but all this must wait till we treat electricity and magnetism systematically.

abandoned, a magnitude might have any number of different dimensions[1], one for each of the laws in which it is involved with any other magnitude, and these dimensions would not be inconsistent.

There are only two reasonable methods of treating the magnitude volume (and area of plane surfaces) in the matter of dimensions. One method, and this is certainly the best, is to treat it throughout as a fundamental magnitude; in that case it has no dimensions in terms of either mass, length or time. The other is to treat it as a quasi-derived magnitude, according to the law by which it is actually measured; in that case it has the dimensions [mass] × [density]$^{-1}$. In neither case are its dimensions expressible solely in terms of mass, length and time.

We may now return to our original question and ask whether it is true that mass, length, and time are basic magnitudes, such that all other magnitudes have dimensions in terms of them. It is obviously not true; for volume and area are instances to the contrary. Mass, length, and time are not the only fundamental magnitudes; and a fundamental magnitude will have dimensions in terms of other fundamental magnitudes only if the use (3) happens to be applicable to it. It is not even true that all pure derived magnitudes have dimensions in terms of mass, length, and time; the magnitude density is an instance to the contrary, for density has the dimensions [mass] × [volume]$^{-1}$ and we have decided that volume has not dimensions in terms of these three. The only question that now seems reasonable to ask, and to which an affirmative answer would still enable us to regard mass, length, and time as basic, is whether all magnitudes that have dimensions by use (3) have dimensions in terms of the three "basic" magnitudes.

And the answer here is in the affirmative, for the only magnitudes given dimensions by use (3) are the electrical and magnetic magnitudes. (It would take us too far to discuss whether this limitation is justifiable.) And the three magnitudes are basic here because, in the equations which are so important that it is desired that they should retain their form, the only fundamental magnitudes involved, other than the electric or magnetic magnitudes, are forces, lengths and times. But the association here is not a mere coincidence. The equations are important because they involve these fundamental magnitudes, because they are dynamical equations and because they are connected with the supremely important dynamical laws. Here then is one reason why dimensional equations involve these three fundamental magnitudes, namely that numerical laws in which they are involved are of peculiar importance.

---

[1] There is already the possibility that a magnitude might consistently have more than one dimension. Thus a derived magnitude might have one dimension derived from the use (1) and one from the use (3); a fundamental magnitude might have one from the use (2) and one from the use (3). Such alternatives do not occur in practice, for (2) is not used, and the only magnitudes for which (3) is used are not pure derived magnitudes in terms of the fundamental units used in (3). But a magnitude may have magnitudes derived from (1) and (3) in terms of different fundamental units. This electrical resistance has the dimensions [potential difference] × [current]$^{-1}$ from use (1) and the dimensions [length]$^{-1}$ × [time] or [length] × [time]$^{-1}$ from use (3)—these last two being inconsistent.

However it is seldom permissible to dismiss as simply erroneous a proposition accepted by the vast majority of men of science; the certainty which admits such presumption can only be obtained by those whose ignorance is positively philosophic. There must be some basis for the general impression that mass, length, and time are in some way peculiarly basic. I believe it is derived from the process of quasi-derived measurement, which might, though according to current practice it does not, give rise to a significant dimensional equation. For there is an important distinction (rather neglected hitherto) between the derived and the fundamental magnitudes in the dimensional equation of a quasi-derived magnitude. The derived magnitude is usually kept constant, while the fundamental magnitudes are varied; it is by their variation that the quasi-derived magnitude is measured. And this observation, of course, gives the clue to the specially important part played by mass, length and time in this connection. We have seen that the object of measuring a magnitude as quasi-derived is the attainment of greater experimental accuracy; but this object will not be attained unless the fundamental magnitude employed in that process can be measured with greater accuracy than the fundamental magnitude which it is used to replace. The fact that we tend to replace the measurement of other magnitudes by measurements of mass, length and time suggests that these last can be measured more accurately than any other fundamental magnitudes[1]. Is this suggestion true? A hundred years ago it was true, and the predominance of mass, length and time as the fundamental magnitudes *par excellence* is, I believe, largely an historical survival. It is probably still true of mass (measured on a balance) and length, but such values of time as occur in laboratory practice are probably less accurately measurable than electrical resistances; in fact it is definitely stated in the latest determination of the absolute value of the ohm that the limit of accuracy is set by the measurement of time. It is only when very long times are concerned that measurements are very accurate, for time differs from most other magnitudes in the fact that the error in its measurement is absolute and not relative; it is often as easy to determine to ·0001 sec. a time interval of several days or even years as a time interval of a single second. But it does not follow at once that we should attempt to measure time always as a quasi-derived magnitude, replacing it by resistance; for it would probably be difficult to define with sufficient definiteness the system of which the derived magnitude, involved in the process, is unity (or some other fixed numerical value). In most experiments, but not in all, we do attain greater accuracy by using time as a fundamental magnitude than we should be replacing it by some other. However it must be insisted once more that there is not always a gain in accuracy by replacing other magnitudes by these three; in electrical and thermal measurements there is a decided loss of accuracy.

But one possibility should be considered. Would there be any advantage

---

[1] This is a reason often given for the predominant position of these magnitudes. But it is to be noted that it justifies their predominance only in connection with that kind of dimensional equation which is seldom, if ever, stated in ordinary text-books.

in measuring one of the three fundamental magnitudes as quasi-derived in terms of the other two. It has been proposed to define the unit of mass in terms of the centimetre and the density of water, and the centimetre (by means of the pendulum) in terms of the second and the acceleration due to gravity. But these proposals have concerned only the units of these magnitudes, and if they had been accepted the definitions would only have resembled that of the ampere in terms of mass and time and the Faraday's constant for silver. It was never proposed to measure mass throughout as a quasi-derived magnitude in terms of length, and therefore, even if the proposal had been accepted, there would have been no grounds for giving one of the magnitudes dimensions in terms of another; and as a matter of fact the proposal has been rejected, and none of the units of the basic magnitudes are derived units.

This is the best case I can make out for regarding mass, length, and time as basic magnitudes. The attempt to amend the proposition we have discussed by adding temperature and permeability to the list seems to me to destroy even those doubtful arguments. The idea which seems to underlie it appears to be this. If we confine our attention to the more important laws of physics (and still more if we confine our attention to its theory) we shall find that all these laws are expressed in terms of (1) the 5 basic magnitudes, (2) derived magnitudes which have hitherto always been accepted as having dimensions in terms of (1) and (3) not more than one other magnitude. Accordingly, if the group (2) is rightly classified, group (3) can be given dimensions in terms of groups (2) and (1), and thence in terms of group (1) above. But I protest, first, that this statement is not true if *all* the laws of physics are included, as they should be; it is not true, for example, if the law that illumination from a point source varies as the square of the distance from the source is included. This objection may not be serious, for it is doubtful whether these laws are truly physical according to the criterion of Chapter I; illumination, defined by candle power, would have no meaning for the blind. Second, that though all laws may be expressed so that group (3) in each law has only one member, they should not always be so expressed; this group appears singular only because of the unfortunate habit of neglecting many no-dimensional magnitudes and associated universal constants. The factor of proportionality mentioned in the footnote of p. 389 is an instance of such neglect. Third, and most important, that group (2) is classified by methods that are quite indefensible. I have urged that volume, always included in group (2), is not properly regarded as having dimensions in length only; shape must also be included. And later I shall urge the same conclusion in connection with many dynamical magnitudes, in particular force. In order to avoid trespassing on the matter of Part IV, it was agreed to accept, for the sake of argument, the conventional dimensions of force; but as a matter of fact, I deny totally that force is properly regarded as a derived magnitude at all; it is fundamental, just as volume is fundamental.

If this last protest is accepted, the whole case for 5 basic magnitudes falls to the ground. It appears plausible just because dynamical magnitudes are so important in our laws and theories and because group (2) is so large. If nearly all that group has to be transferred to group (3), the group becomes the largest of all; most numerical laws will contain at least 2 magnitudes which have not dimensions in terms of the 5 basic magnitudes and the assignment to them of such dimensions becomes indeterminate.

Accordingly I find it impossible to avoid the conclusion that in this matter the consensus of physical opinion has been wrong; but the error has been shown to be plausible and, I hope, the charge of presumption rebutted. Our main discussion is at an end and we may proceed to our next inquiry, what is the use of dimensions? But first a few miscellaneous questions may be asked.

First, if there are not three or five basic magnitudes, are there basic magnitudes at all? If this means, Are there any magnitudes which must always be regarded as basic, the answer is no, whether we are thinking of the necessity of choosing units for systems of measurement or of the applications of the theory of dimensions. But if it means, Must we regard some magnitudes as basic, then the answer is yes, whichever process is in our thoughts. There must be as many basic magnitudes as there are magnitudes which, for the purpose of establishing laws experimentally, must be taken as fundamental and not as derived. But there is considerable latitude of choice which magnitudes we shall take as basic. Thus of the three electrical magnitudes, current, potential difference, and resistance, two must be taken as basic in order that Ohm's Law may be established; but any of the three possible pairs may be taken, and any of the three magnitudes may be regarded as derived.

And the further question may be asked, Must we realise concretely a number of units equal to the necessary number of basic magnitudes? Yes; but we need not realise them in concrete bodies; some of them may be realised in concrete substances (or geometrical systems). And by this process the number, though theoretically equal to the number of basic magnitudes, may be actually less. Thus we might use mercury as the standard substance not only for fixing the unit of resistance but also for fixing the unit of density.

Lastly, what are the standard bodies and systems actually used in fixing basic units? The following list is taken from Kaye and Laby's Tables; it is probably not complete, but a discussion of its deficiencies would lead us much too far: The mean solar day; the international prototype meter and kilogramme; water (for volume, quantity of heat, and temperature); the square (for area); hydrogen (for temperature); silver (for current); mercury (for resistance); vacuum (for dielectric constant and permeability); the standard of candle-power.

Practical units. Very few words are necessary here on this familiar topic. We have seen that there are two reasons, one given in the first section of this chapter and one in discussing electric charge, which may make us wish to fix as a unit of a fundamental magnitude one system rather than another. Occasionally the choice determined in this manner causes all the numerical values of magnitudes which occur in our work to be inconveniently large or small. When the reason which has fixed the unit is the first of these two, and the unit has been realised in a concrete system, the objection can be overcome by attributing to the realised standard some other numerical value than 1; for we have seen that so long as some numerical value is attached to some realised system a process of fundamental measurement can proceed. On such grounds might be defended the practice of attributing to the realised standards of mass, length and time, the values 1000, 100, and 86,400 respectively. But an examination of any tables of physical constants, and the observation how often large positive and negative powers of ten occur, will hardly convince us of the strength of the defence, for the ostensible object is very imperfectly attained. It is probable that our preference for the c.g.s. to the metre-kilogramme-day system is really based on mere historical accidents.

When the second reason has led to the choice of unit, the unit is not realised, and the attribution to it of any value but unity would immediately defeat the object for which the unit was chosen. When we are considering the numerical law the importance of which determines the choice of unit, we must use the unit so determined. But when we are not considering it, there is no reason why we should adhere to this unit, and we are at liberty again to attribute any value that we please. Since the importance of the determining law is usually theoretical rather than practical, we thus adopt a convention that in dealing with practical matters we attribute to the standard one set of values, when we are dealing with theoretical another set. A rather curious position has been created by the International Electrical Congress of 1908 which realised concretely the chief electrical units, or rather gave specifications for their realisation, which do not depend on laws and, in particular, do not depend on the laws which make it desirable to choose the electrical units in one manner rather than another. The practical units are defined by giving certain numerical values, prescribed once and for all by the Convention, to the realised standards; but the absolute units are defined by reference to the fundamental laws. The determination of the ratio between the two is a matter to be determined only by experiment and therefore can never be known with absolute precision. If physicists continue to use the absolute units, as they seem still inclined to do even since the Congress, they are in the position of being liable to alter all their numerical values with every fresh determination of the relation between the realised and absolute units. The alternatives would be (1) the introduction into the fundamental equations of constants which would need explicit expression because they are rather different from 1; but they would need to be noticed only when we were comparing with experiment a numerical law predicted by theory or (2) the definition of the absolute unit in terms of the practical, e.g. the definition of the electromagnetic unit absolute of resistance as 10^{-9} of the International Ohm, with the consequence that the fundamental equations would not be quite accurately true, so long as the convention that K (or μ) is 1 is maintained. It is not my business, since opinions differ, to express any preference between the alternatives.

Natural units. Concerning this last matter we may be almost equally brief. Attempts have been made from time to time to rid the choice of fundamental units of its arbitrariness, and to choose some set which has a wider and deeper significance than that which can be obtained from the voluntary choice of any collection of men. The philosophers of the French Revolution sought such a set by choosing as their units magnitudes characteristic of the earth and of water, systems which must always have a peculiar significance for the human race. But of late an even more ambitious scheme has been proposed, nothing less than to choose units "which shall necessarily retain their significance for all times and for all intelligences, even if they be non-human or non-terrestrial" (Planck). The scheme depends on the discovery of various "universal constants" which have the same value for all portions of matter and might, ideally at least, be determined from any portion of it whatever; it is thought that the object would be attained if the units of the "basic magnitudes" were so chosen that the numerical value of all these universal constants was unity. Such a choice seems possible, for the units of mass, length, and time can be fixed by making equal to unity the velocity of light, Planck's constant, and the constant of gravitation; if, as Planck recognises, temperature is also a basic magnitude, the unit can be fixed by making the gas constant unity. It has been urged that the list of basic magnitudes must be extended, but since we have also recognised universal constants that are generally overlooked it is possible that the system of natural units might be extended to these also. However I do not propose to inquire whether all the units which it is necessary to fix in order to have a complete system of measurement could be defined as natural units; I only want to consider whether there is any reason for adopting the scheme at all.

So far as I can see, there is no reason whatever for adopting it, if the object to be attained is that quoted above; for there is not the slightest ground for believing that it can be attained. Even if we propose to fix basic units by means of universal constants, there is more than one way of doing so, and there is no reason to think that other intelligent beings, even though they did not differ very greatly from ourselves, must necessarily select the same alternative out of the many possible, if they started afresh without knowing what we had done before. For (1) there are two distinct ways in which the unit of mass might be fixed in terms of universal constants; one way by making c, h, γ all unity; the other by making the mass of the electron unity. A more complete inquiry would show alternative methods of fixing other basic magnitudes. (2) All the universal constants, if they were concepts, would be derived magnitudes, with the possible exception of the mass of an electron. A derived magnitude is always associated with a formal constant, to which any value we please may be arbitrarily assigned. We are in the habit of assigning to most, but not all, formal constants the value unity; but that is only because most of us find little pleasure in numerical computation. A race of "calculating wonders", who revelled in the intricacies of long division, might very likely choose quite different values for the formal constants. Even without differing from us greatly in this matter, there are (as will appear from later discussions) reasons which might easily have led us to choose 2 or *e* or *π* for some of the formal constants instead of 1. (3) As a matter of fact, all the universal constants ordinarily recognised are hypothetical ideas and not concepts; the only universal constants that are concepts are never recognised. Accordingly another race of thinkers would only arrive at the same universal constants as ourselves if they accepted the same theories; it would not be sufficient for them to accept the same laws.

On such grounds I can find no word milder than ridiculous to characterise Planck's suggestion. If it were true (I do not think it is true) that by fixing arbitrarily the values of universal constants we could fix uniquely the units of all basic magnitudes, that discovery might have a considerable theoretical importance. But it would provide no ground whatever for actually fixing the units in that manner. The choice would be as arbitrary as any other—not to mention the practical disadvantages: the only advantage gained would be that the arbitrariness would be concealed from those who did not think carefully. And that is a very doubtful advantage. It is surely better to distinguish as clearly as possible between what is arbitrary in science and what is imposed by the material world; and, in the matter of units, the distinction cannot be made better than by referring all our measurements to casual lumps of matter preserved at the Bureau at Sèvres.

Note on the Dimensions of Temperature.

Temperature is the magnitude with which all those who have discussed dimensions find it most difficult to deal. A total neglect of these difficulties might suggest doubts of the complete adequacy of the exposition of dimensions offered here; accordingly, since at least one other volume of this treatise will have to be written before we are in a position to deal in detail with thermal conceptions (which present some of the most interesting problems in the principles of science), it may be well to offer a few remarks on the matter.

The choice of the numerals which are to represent temperatures is certainly independent of the choice of the system of measurement of any other magnitude; we can employ any of the scales of temperature in conjunction with any system of units for other magnitudes. It would appear to follow from our discussion that this freedom of choice must mean that temperature is either a fundamental magnitude or is a derived or defined no-dimensional magnitude; for it is only magnitudes which fall into one of these two classes that do not necessarily change their numerical values when the units of other magnitudes are changed.

The first alternative is obviously not correct. There is no physical process of addition for temperatures. Whatever scale of temperature is adopted, there is no rule whereby from two systems at temperature 1 we can produce a system at temperature 2. The second alternative must therefore be accepted, if temperature is a magnitude at all. Nevertheless measurement of temperature presents differences from measurement of most, or all, other no-dimensional magnitudes, such as the eccentricity (of ellipses) or the sine of an angle. (An angle is a no-dimensional magnitude, but since it is also a fundamental magnitude, it does not provide a good illustration.) The most obvious difference is that, whereas in these other no-dimensional magnitudes it is not necessary to assign arbitrarily a value to any specified systems, in measuring temperature, it is necessary to assign arbitrarily values, not only to one, but to two specified systems, namely melting ice and boiling water. It is true that in measuring sines we have to specify one particular class of systems (right-angled triangles) on the examination of which the measurement shall be based, but even such specification is not necessary for eccentricity; measurements of eccentricity can be made on all systems that have the property at all; and in both cases, as soon as the nature of the magnitude is stated, and the class of systems in which it is to be measured defined, the numerical values to be attributed to the magnitudes follow without any further arbitrary specification. There is no need, as there is for temperature, to assign arbitrarily numerical values to the magnitude for any definite members of the class possessing the magnitude.

This difference arises from the fact that it is only by an extremely arbitrary and artificial device that temperature can be made a no-dimensional magnitude. If we could free ourselves from the relics of the arbitrary system of measuring temperature (a system as arbitrary as Mohs' scale of hardness) which prevailed before modern conceptions of temperature were developed, then we should be forced to conclude either that temperature is a derived magnitude with perfectly definite and finite dimensions or that it is not a magnitude at all. It is our desire to escape from these conclusions and at the same time retain as far as possible some features of the old arbitrary scale that leads to all the difficulties. If a similar desire existed in respect of other magnitudes, e.g. density, precisely the same peculiar features would recur.

Suppose that, before we had discovered that density (a magnitude defined by flotation) could be measured as a derived magnitude by means of the ratio of mass to volume, we had been in the habit of using an arbitrary scale of density, according to which water was represented by 0 and mercury by 100. We now find that $m = \rho V$, and that ρ measures density. We may throw over entirely our arbitrary scale and in future measure density as an ordinary derived magnitude of which the unit will depend on the units of mass and volume. On the other hand, we may find that our arbitrary scale was very nearly "right", and that if, by some device, we can make the densities of water and mercury, measured as derived magnitudes, again 0 and 100, the densities of other substances will also come very near to those previously assigned to them. If matters turn out in that way, there will be some advantage in retaining the densities assigned to these two substances as far as possible, for we shall be saved a good deal of trouble in re-calculating all our old results when only approximate accuracy is required.

It is not possible to retain the old value 0 for water without altering the form of the law we have discovered; for by that law the body which has density o must be that of which a finite volume has no mass. On the other hand it is easy to retain 100 for mercury; we have only to fix the volume of which the mass is to represent the density so that the mercury which fills this volume is 100 grams; this volume would be between 7 and 8 c.c. But there is another alternative which may be adopted; we can abandon the precise values o and 100 for water and mercury but retain a difference of 100 between their densities. For this purpose we have to agree that density shall be represented by the mass of a definite volume of the substance, and that this volume shall be such that the difference of the masses of water and mercury which fill it is 100 grams; the volume is about 8 c.c. The density of water will then turn out to be about 8. Having gone so far, we might go further and make the densities of mercury and water agree exactly with those on the arbitrary scale by defining density, not as the mass of this chosen volume, but as this mass less 8; but this procedure is so obviously forced and artificial, and the practical advantages gained by it so small (for it is easy to add 8 to all the arbitrary densities), that we shall probably not adopt it.

Now what effect has this procedure had on the dimensions of density? An assertion of dimensions may state one of two things; it may state what is the form of the law which defines the derived magnitude, or it may state how the unit (and so the numerical values) of the derived magnitude will change with change of the units of the fundamental magnitudes involved in that law. If we adopt the natural course which was considered in the body of this chapter, the same assertion states both things; but by our artificial procedure we have divorced the two meanings. We have not, of course, changed the form of the law defining density as a derived magnitude, and we have not therefore altered any statement about it which has physical, as distinct from arbitrary, significance; but it is no longer certain that we shall change the numerical values of density, if we change the units of mass and volume, in the way suggested by that law. The new definition of density rather suggests that density now will vary with the unit of mass as if it had the dimensions of mass; for it would so vary if we always kept the same the concrete realised vessel, the mass of the contents of which is to measure density. However as our whole procedure is arbitrary and artificial there is no guarantee that we shall so keep it. If we changed our unit of mass or of volume we might change that vessel. Strictly, density now has no dimensions at all, the conception of dimensions is not applicable to it; for there is no physical rule by which we can determine whether or how the numerical values of density will change with change of unit; the change, if any, is a matter of mere caprice.

As a matter of fact, it is probable that, if we do change our units of mass and volume, we shall not change the numerical value of density, but shall change the standard vessel by means of which it is measured; for the reasons which led us to desire that the densities of water and mercury shall be represented by certain numerals will be unchanged by change of those units. And a further change in our method of measuring density will make our intention clear; we can change the definition so that density appears formally as a no-dimensional magnitude the numerical values of which are independent of all changes of unit; for this purpose we must define density as the ratio of two magnitudes of the same kind, so that the difference of the densities of water and mercury shall be 100 whatever the unit of those magnitudes. This object is attained by defining the density of a substance as $\rho = \dfrac{100\,m}{m_2 - m_1}$, where m is the mass of the substance, m_1 the mass of water, and m_2 the mass of mercury which will fill any vessel of constant volume. In virtue of the truth of the law $m = \rho V$ for all liquids, it appears that the numerical values of density obtained by this definition will be the same whatever vessel is selected, and accordingly we may omit from our definition any mention of the actual vessel by which measurements of density are to be made.

By this definition, as has been said, density is made to appear a no-dimensional magnitude, because it is the ratio of two masses. But it must be remembered that the statement that it is a no-dimensional magnitude means something very different from the assertion that eccentricity is a no-dimensional magnitude. The latter statement is intimately connected with the law that there is a class of bodies having many important properties in common and differing only in the ratio of the major and minor axes; it is because there is such a law that eccentricity is an important conception and that it is measured as a no-dimensional magnitude. The former statement is not based on a law at all; the law which gives to density its importance is the law $m = \rho V$, and according to that law density has finite dimensions in mass and volume. The propositions by which it is made to appear as a no-dimensional magnitude have nothing to do with that law (except in so far as the specification of the actual vessel to the used can be omitted); they could be asserted equally well if the law were not true and mass was not proportional to volume. The assertion that any substance has an assigned numerical value according to the definition that has been adopted does not imply the assertion of any law at all; measurement of density according to the new scale is really as arbitrary as measurement according to the old; the new system of measurement is only suggested by a law of a certain form; it does not depend necessarily on that law. And as the only physical significance of dimensions is to state physical laws, it is hardly correct to say that density, defined as $\dfrac{100\,m}{m_2 - m_1}$, has any dimensions at all; the conception of dimensions is applicable to it no more than to hardness on Mohs' scale. However there is one difference between density so defined and hardness, namely that the numerical value of density will agree throughout with those obtained from determination of density as a true derived magnitude by means of the law $m = \rho V$, so long as one particular choice is made of the units of mass and volume. If we happened to choose these units then the proposed system of measurement would cease to be arbitrary, and density would become once more a true derived magnitude with a unit suggested by the dimensions indicated by that law.

The analogy with temperature is obvious. Temperature on the international scale defined by the constant volume hydrogen thermometer is measured by a method suggested by the law $p = a . \rho$, where p and ρ play the part of fundamental magnitudes (for, though derived, they are derived from laws other than this), and a is a constant, maintaining its values so long as the chemical nature of the gas and its thermal relations are unchanged. If we had known nothing about temperature before the discovery of Boyle's Law, we should probably have measured it simply by the constant a, which would have been a true derived magnitude with the dimensions (subject to considerations which will be noticed presently) [pressure] × [density]$^{-1}$. But as there was already in existence an arbitrary scale of temperature measured by the mercury in glass thermometer (and as the discovery that a is a constant was actually made by means of its identification with t, the temperature on this scale), it was desired to make the new measurements of temperature agree as far as possible with the old; the desire was the more reasonable because the arbitrary scale proved to be very nearly "right". The manner in which the two were forced into agreement and the consequences of the process have been sufficiently discussed in connection with density.

However there are certain differences in this matter between temperature and density arising from (1) the discovery that gas law is not strictly true, (2) in so far as it is true, a connection of a with certain other constants, (3) the existence of the thermodynamic scale of temperature.

(1) makes it necessary, in order to obtain a definite scale, to specify p at one of the standard temperatures, just as, if the law $m = \rho . V$ had not been true, it would have been necessary to specify the volume to be used. And since the law suggesting the new scale of temperature is not strictly true, the scale becomes more clearly arbitrary than ever; not only is it not defined by a true law, it is not even suggested by a true law. The failure of the law leaves us without any true experimental magnitude, temperature, at all. t is not a constant in a law $p = t . \rho$; it is at most one of the constants in a law $p = f(\rho, t, a, b, ...)$. And all the forms of f which represent the facts quite correctly are empirical; the constants involved in them are empirical constants and none of them are magnitudes. It is only if we succeeded in establishing a function f which was not empirical, and all the constants in which could be identified by a magnitude measuring some property of the gas, that t would become a true derived magnitude. The international scale of temperature is as arbitrary as Mohs' scale of hardness; the only difference is that we have certain reasons for believing that it may be possible to establish a scale which is not arbitrary and which will agree very nearly with this arbitrary scale.

(2) introduces new considerations. It is found that the law $p = a . \rho$ is accurately true within certain limits for many gases and not only for hydrogen. If we use different gases at the same temperature (and the same temperature can be defined independently of measurement), we find that a is not the same for all of them. But the ratio of a for hydrogen to the a for oxygen turns out to be the same as the ratio of certain constants (they are really hypothetical

ideas) characteristic of the gases. These constants have the dimensions [mass]$^{-1}$; if we represent them by $1/M$, we may write the law $p = a' \cdot 1/M \cdot \rho$, where a' is now a constant the same for all gases which obey the law at all. We may now take a' to be a measure of temperature, as we formerly took a; it is a true derived magnitude with the dimensions of energy. Accordingly, since it is obviously better to measure temperature by the universal constant a' rather than the particular constant a, if there had not been in existence the arbitrary scale, we should have measured temperature as a derived magnitude with the dimensions of energy. And if we want to convey by a statement about the dimensions of temperature the most significant physical assertion, and not one merely about an arbitrary and artificial method of measuring it, then the only choice is to say that temperature has the dimensions of energy.

However, since we are determined to force temperature to appear formally as a no-dimensional magnitude—although thereby we rid a statement of its dimensions of all physical significance—we split up once more the constant a' into a product of two factors. We write $a' = Rt$, where R is a universal constant, independent not only of chemical constitution but also of thermal condition, and t is the constant which we propose to use, according to our artificial scale, for the measurement of temperature. Since the whole object of the artificial scale is to represent t as a no-dimensional magnitude, we must give to R the dimensions of energy formerly attributed to t. I maintain that to attribute to R any dimensions but those of energy is definitely wrong and inconsistent—except in so far as we shall have to revise the conventional conclusion concerning the dimensions of energy, and their relation to the dimensions of force. It is foolish, for example, to say that it has the dimensions of a specific heat.

(3) The relation between the gas scale and the thermodynamic scale is a very difficult matter which cannot possibly be considered at this stage. But it will probably not be disputed that, according to our definition, all thermodynamics is essentially theoretical, and that consequently thermodynamic temperature is a hypothetical idea, not a concept. This conclusion does not necessarily prevent statements about the dimensions of thermodynamical temperature from being significant; for if that magnitude is included in one of the propositions of the hypothesis together with others, all of which are analogous to concepts and true magnitudes, then it may reasonably be given the same dimensions as it would have if the proposition concerned were a law and the concepts were substituted for the hypothetical ideas that are analogous to them. However it appears that this possibility does not actually help us to attribute dimensions to temperature, for in all fundamental propositions of the hypothesis the thermodynamic temperature T occurs in the form of a ratio T_1/T_2. This ratio will always be no-dimensional, whatever dimensions are attributed to temperature. Accordingly the dimensions of the thermodynamic temperature are completely indeterminate, and there is no reason for attributing to the magnitude one dimension rather than another.

Our conclusions are then that, if we had not been hampered by a pre-existing arbitrary scale of temperature, we should have attributed to temperature the dimensions of energy and varied it with change of other units in the same way as, at present, the gas-constant varies. But owing to the pre-existing arbitrary scale we have defined temperature in such a way that it resembles a no-dimensional rather than any other; variations of temperature scale (e.g. from Centigrade to Fahrenheit) are to be regarded as representing changes in a formal constant—for no-dimensional, like all other derived magnitudes, are associated with formal constants, and change their numerical values if those formal constants change. However, from the strictest point of view temperature is not a magnitude at all, because the perfect-gas law does not hold within experimental accuracy for hydrogen of the density which is employed in the international temperature scale, even within the limited range of temperature to which the hydrogen thermometer is actually applied. The scale is as arbitrary as that of the mercury-in-glass thermometer. Thermodynamic temperature has dimensions which are completely indeterminate; there is no reason for assigning one dimension rather than another; accordingly, since experimental temperature approaches more nearly to no dimensions than to any other, it is probably best to regard it also as of no dimensions.

CHAPTER XV

THE USES OF DIMENSIONS

Summary. The use of the theory of dimensions expounded in the preceding chapter is based on the fundamental fact that the dimensions of a derived magnitude indicate, though imperfectly, the form and physical significance of the law by which it is defined.

The chief use of the theory is in connection with the "argument from dimensions". The argument is stated formally and criticised in connection with a simple example, that of the pendulum. It is concluded that the argument, as usually stated, must be fundamentally unsound, because its conclusions are inconsistent with the premisses.

This inconsistency arises from a neglect of no-dimensional magnitudes. The argument is applicable only to such systems as have the same value for the no-dimensional magnitude characteristic of them. The recognition of the part played by this no-dimensional magnitude removes some of the difficulties which attend the argument.

The conception of physical similarity is then introduced and examined carefully. The doctrines called by such names as the Principle of Physical Similarity are examined at some length. It appears that the only formally satisfactory statement of them is conveyed by the assertion that there are physically similar systems. The discussion leads to the examination of some prevalent errors, based chiefly on the neglect to realise that dimensions have no physical meaning or importance, except as the expression of laws established experimentally.

The formal exposition of dimensional arguments is now complete. It remains only to decide why it gives any information in cases where complete dynamical reasoning is not available. The question is investigated in détail in connection with the pendulum; it is concluded that for the application of the argument from dimensions everything involved in the dynamical reasoning is required except the numerical values of no-dimensional magnitudes. The argument merely permits us to dispense with certain mathematical operations when we are content to remain ignorant of these numerical values.

It is inquired whether our conclusion that mass, length, and time are not peculiarly basic magnitudes affects in any way the application of the argument. It does not; the right conclusions will be attained so long as all magnitudes that are fundamental are regarded as fundamental. The conventional treatment of volume (e.g.) as a derived magnitude arrives at the right result only by the cancelling of errors or, if they are not actual errors, propositions which are gravely misleading.

An answer is attempted—not very successfully—to the question why the "undetermined constant" is always near unity.

The application of the argument from dimensions is extended to cases where the dimensional equation is indeterminate. If the meaning of physical similarity is clearly understood these cases present no difficulty whatever.

Two other minor uses of dimensions are noticed, namely those which depend on numerical coincidence and on the similarity in dimensions of magnitude of different physical significance.

The use of dimensions. But what is the use of all this complicated and difficult theory of dimensions? It might be urged plausibly that if dimensions are a conception only necessary in view of the possibility of a change of units, the best and simplest plan would be to agree once and for all on the units that we are going to use, and so to render the conception unnecessary. And except for certain ambiguities in connection with electrical units that agreement has been obtained; we all agree to use the c.g.s. units and the Centigrade scale of temperature. Even where there is ambiguity, dimensional considerations are not actually much help. For every person who could say off-hand what are the dimensions of electric current or potential or what are the units of length, mass, and time on which the "practical" electric units are founded, there are twenty who know that an ampere is a tenth of the c.g.s. electromagnetic unit of current and that an electrostatic c.g.s. unit of potential is 300 volts.

In fact the only use made of dimensions, which is founded on their original and fundamental meaning, is very trivial. It is sometimes useful to check the accuracy of a calculation by seeing that the two sides of an equation always remain of the same dimensions. That use would certainly not justify the long consideration that has been given to the matter. But there are more important uses; and they are founded on a very important fact, on which it is impossible to insist too strongly or too often, that magnitudes, derived as well as fundamental, are concepts. Any statement concerning a derived magnitude, if it is to have any experimental basis, must imply the truth of a law; there would be no sense in talking about density if mass were not proportional to volume in certain circumstances, or about uniform acceleration unless the distance travelled varied as the square of the time. Now the dimensions of a derived magnitude are determined by the form of the law in which it occurs, and, conversely, the statement that a magnitude has certain dimensions is equivalent to saying that a law of a certain form is applicable to the system of which that magnitude is characteristic. It must never be forgotten that it is this fact, and this alone, which gives to dimensions their great physical significance. If we defined density as the ratio of a mass to a volume, without introducing the provision that this ratio must be constant over some important range of conditions, the dimensions of density would not have the slightest physical importance.

The "argument from dimensions". The most interesting and valuable application of this principle is undoubtedly that known as the argument from dimensions. The rule to which the argument leads is perfectly familiar, but it may be well to state it formally in order to fix our notation. Suppose that it is known that the behaviour of each of a set of systems is determined wholly by the magnitudes $p, q, r, s, \ldots$, these magnitudes being different for the different systems; and that these magnitudes have in terms of the fundamental magnitudes $x, y, z, \ldots$ the dimensions $P_x, P_y, P_z, \ldots, Q_x, Q_y, Q_z, \ldots$, the dimensions of the different magnitudes being all different. (Actually three fundamental magnitudes, x, y, z, are taken, namely mass, length, and time; but it is well to express the matter so that formal relations would not be altered if this condition were removed.) Suppose further that a set of constants $\lambda, \mu, \nu, \rho, \ldots$, can be found which are determined uniquely by the simultaneous equations:

$$\lambda P_x + \mu Q_x + \nu R_x + \rho S_x + \ldots = 0,$$
$$\lambda P_y + \mu Q_y + \nu R_y + \rho S_y + \ldots = 0,$$
$$\lambda P_z + \mu Q_z + \nu R_z + \rho S_z + \ldots = 0,$$
$$\vdots \qquad \vdots \qquad \vdots \qquad \vdots \qquad \vdots$$

Then the conclusion is to be drawn that, in each of the systems, the determining magnitudes are related by the numerical law,

$$p^\lambda q^\mu r^\nu s^\rho \ldots = a,$$

where a is a constant, the same for all the systems.

It should be noted if there are n fundamental magnitudes $x, y, z, \ldots$ and n' magnitudes $p, q, r, s, \ldots$[1], the simultaneous equations will be n in number and will involve n' variables of which $n' - 1$ are independent. Accordingly $\lambda, \mu, \nu, \ldots$ will be determined uniquely only if $n' - 1 = n$. If n' is less than $n + 1$, there will not necessarily be any set of values $\lambda, \mu, \nu, \ldots$ satisfying the equations. If n' is greater than $n + 1$, the equations will be indeterminate and there will be more than one set. In the first case, the conclusion to be drawn is that the assumption that $p, q, r, s, \ldots$ are the only determining magnitudes is false; in the second case the procedure to be adopted will be discussed later. For the present we shall assume that $n' = n + 1$. Further it must be noted that this assumption involves that there is among $p, q, r, s, \ldots$ at least one which is not of the same kind as $x, y, z, \ldots$, but is a derived magnitude defined in terms of them. We shall further simplify the conditions for the present by assuming that there is only one such derived magnitude p. Then $q, r, s, \ldots$ are of the same nature as $x, y, z, \ldots$, and the list of determining magnitudes may be written $p, x, y, z, \ldots$ of which p is true derived and $x, y, z, \ldots$ fundamental. The relation stated by the argument is then $p^\lambda x^\mu y^\nu z^\rho \ldots = a$; of course one or more of $\mu, \nu, \rho \ldots$ may be zero, but λ cannot be zero.

Criticism of the argument. The question that we have to ask is what is the foundation for this conclusion? Let us take for discussion a very simple case provided by the pendulum. The argument here states that T, the period of the pendulum ($P_x = 0$, $P_y = 0$, $P_z = 1$), depends only on L, its length ($Q_x = 0$, $Q_y = 1$, $Q_z = 0$) and g, the acceleration due to gravity ($R_x = 0$, $R_y = 1$, $R_z = -2$). The only values of λ, μ, ν satisfying

$$\lambda.0 + \mu.0 + \nu.0 = 0, \qquad \lambda.0 + \mu.1 + \nu.1 = 0,$$
$$\lambda.1 + \mu.0 + \nu. - 2 = 0,$$

---

[1] The magnitudes p, q, r, s need not be derived in our special sense of the word; all that is necessary is that they have some dimensions in terms of x, y, z. Thus some of the $p, q, r, s, \ldots$ may be of the same kind as the $x, y, z, \ldots$; that is to say, (according to the usual convention as to the nature of x, y, z) p, q, r, s may include masses, lengths, and times as well as true derived magnitudes based on these.

are given by $v/\lambda = \frac{1}{2}$, $\mu/\lambda = -\frac{1}{2}$; consequently we must have

$$T = a\sqrt{\frac{L}{g}} \quad \text{or} \quad L = \frac{1}{a^2}gT^2.$$

Here it may seem that the nature of the argument is perfectly clear and its cogency is indubitable. When we say that b is a uniform acceleration, which is a pure derived magnitude, all that we mean is that it is a constant in a numerical law of the form $s = \frac{1}{2}bt^2$, where s is a length and t a time; it is only if b occurs in a law of this form that it is called a uniform acceleration and it is only because it so occurs that it is given the dimensions assigned to it. Accordingly, it may be argued, if we have to make a numerical law out of a time, a length, and an acceleration (and this is what is asserted by saying that the period depends only on the length and the acceleration), then it must, from the very meaning of the words, have the form assigned to it by the argument from dimensions.

This is, I think, the reasoning by which the argument would often be supported, though it is seldom expressed. But by forcing ourselves to express it in words we have shown its falsity. For the law derived from the argument from dimensions is not that which is inseparably connected with the meaning of acceleration; the argument does not assert that $L = \frac{1}{2}gT^2$, and, if it did, the assertion would be false. But if we can change the "formal constant" $\frac{1}{2}$ without altering the form of the law $s = \frac{1}{2}bt^2$ and depriving b of its meaning as an acceleration, why should we not, without altering that form, also change the exponent 2 in the term t^2? But if we allow that b is an acceleration when it occurs in a law of the form $s = \frac{1}{2}bt^n$, when n is other than 2, the argument fails. Again an acceleration does not mean a constant b occurring in any numerical relation of the form $s = \frac{1}{2}bt^2$, but only one occurring in a numerical law stating, besides a numerical relation, a physical relation. If b is to be an acceleration, s and t must be, not any magnitudes or even any length and any time, but the distance from a starting point and the time-interval from the starting moment which are simultaneous. But L, the length of the pendulum, is not the distance through which some body falls in the time T, the period of the pendulum. However similar the numerical relations may be, the physical relations stated by the laws $L = \dfrac{g}{a^2}T^2$ and $s = \frac{1}{2}bt^2$ are utterly different. Even if we write $L = \frac{1}{2}(2g/a^2)t^2$, $2g/a^2$ in the former does not, like b in the latter, mean an acceleration; the whole argument breaks down.

In fact the argument must be unsound because its conclusion contradicts its premisses. We start by assuming that there is nothing which determines the period of the pendulum except its length and the gravitational acceleration. We end by finding a relation between these magnitudes and a "constant" a. What is the nature of this constant? The considerations that have been advanced show that it is not a "formal constant", one arbitrarily assigned to designate a particular form of law. It is a magnitude in the sense that its numerical value is assigned to represent the property of a system which is determined by experiment[1]. For a is not the same for all pendulums for which the relation $L = gT^2/a^2$ is true. a is the same for all pendulums consisting of a spherical bob at the end of a weightless string; it is also the same for all pendulums consisting of a straight rod of constant cross section; but it is not the same for the first set of pendulums as for the second. Its different numerical values measure different properties of these systems. a is a magnitude, and the assumptions from which the argument starts are true only if it is included in the list of determining magnitudes.

Why then is a omitted? How does it differ from the magnitudes that are included? There are two important differences. First, a is a no-dimensional magnitude. It has been insisted that $A = 2g/a^2$ is not an acceleration; that is to say, the statement that A has some assigned numerical value does not mean that we know of some system moving so that the distance travelled and the time occupied is always represented by the numerical law $s = \frac{1}{2}At^2$. On the other hand, A may have the same numerical value as an acceleration. But this admission, standing alone, is trivial; for it may have the same numerical value as a magnitude of any other kind. The special connection between A and an acceleration, which would not hold if for an acceleration were substituted any other kind of magnitude, is that if they have the same numerical value when one set of units is taken, they will also have the same numerical value if any other set is taken. This relation is precisely what is expressed by saying that they have the same dimensions. But it does not imply that they have the same physical significance; for, even if the mathematical form of the laws in which they occur is the same, the physical relation expressed by the laws may be quite different. Second, whereas the other magnitudes determining the period differ from system to system among those that are considered, a is the same for all of them. Though a might vary from system to system, all systems except those for which it is the same are deliberately excluded from consideration, and the relation which it is sought to obtain by means of the argument is one valid only so long as this magnitude is unaltered.

The conclusions at which we have arrived are essential to any clear understanding of the argument from dimensions. The proposition on which the argument from dimensions is usually founded, namely that T is determined wholly by L and g, is simply inconsistent. For it leads to the result that T is related to L and g by a numerical law which involves, besides L and g, another magnitude a. This magnitude differs from the remainder by being no-dimensional and the same for all the systems to which the argument is to be applied. If that magnitude is omitted from the list of the inter-dependent magnitudes the statements on which the argument rests are untrue. Even if they were true, it is difficult to see how anything could be deduced from them by an argument depending on dimensions, for there is nothing in the assumptions that

---

[1] It is also a magnitude in the sense of something of which the numerical order is identical with the order characteristic of the property: for it is determined by the ratio of the radius of gyration to the distance of the c.g. from the point of suspension. This ratio can be ordered.

refers in the remotest manner to that conception. But if the assumption is added that one of the magnitudes is no-dimensional and constant, then not only do the assumptions become true, but it also becomes obvious why the conception of dimensions can be used in making deductions from them. For we may now argue thus. If p is the derived magnitude characteristic of the system, the fact that there is only one set of constants $\lambda, \mu, \nu, \rho, \ldots$ means that the derived magnitude $(x^\mu y^\nu z^\rho)^{1/\lambda}$ is the only one characteristic of the system that has the same dimensions as p. Accordingly $a = p/(x^\mu y^\nu z^\rho)^{1/\lambda}$ is a no-dimensional magnitude characteristic of the system. But our assumptions assert that the no-dimensional magnitude characteristic of the systems has the same value for all of them. Consequently a must be constant for all systems. On the other hand our assumptions do not tell us what the numerical value of the no-dimensional magnitude is, so that while we know that $p = a \cdot x^\mu y^\nu z^\rho$, where a is the same for all systems, we do not know what is the numerical value of a. This argument is perfectly rigid and depends for its truth on nothing but the meaning of the terms involved in the assumptions on which it is based—at any rate subject to an interpretation of part of it which will be discussed presently.

The feature that has been noted in the example that has been taken is common to all in which the argument from dimensions is applied. The argument might be applied when there is no constant no-dimensional magnitude involved, but then it is valueless. Thus we might use the argument to prove that if T, the time occupied in the fall of a body, is determined by its constant acceleration, b, and by L, the distance through which it falls, then the relation is $L = \frac{1}{2}bT^2$; but now it has not even the appearance of adding anything to our knowledge; the conclusion is not only a consequence of the premises, but means precisely the same thing as the premises. When the argument is actually applied, the fundamental magnitudes involved are such that, though they can be used to define a derived magnitude of the same dimensions as the derived magnitude involved in the assumptions, their physical nature and relations are not such that the derived magnitude so defined *is* the derived magnitude involved in the assumptions. If the two derived magnitudes are not the same, their ratio defines a no-dimensional magnitude; the assumption that this no-dimensional magnitude is characteristic of, and has the same numerical value for, all the systems concerned is as necessary as any of the other assumptions.

It is the partial ignorance about this no-dimensional magnitude that gives rise to the partial indeterminateness in the results obtained from the argument. Most intelligent students, when they first encounter the argument from dimensions, experience difficulties which might be expressed by some such questions as these. If it is true that the period of the pendulum is determined wholly by its length and by gravitational acceleration, and if the numerical values of both of these last are known, how comes it that a process of deduction which leads to some relation between these magnitudes does not lead to a complete determination of the numerical value of the period?

Why is the constant indeterminate? It is not really indeterminate, as the complete dynamical reasoning shows; it has a definite numerical value. If this value is not determined by the magnitudes that are said to be alone concerned in the determination of the period, by what is it determined? The answer is obvious. The period is determined not only by the magnitudes usually mentioned, but also by a certain no-dimensional magnitude. We know that there is such a magnitude and that it has the same value for all systems, but we do not know what that value is. The "constant" depends on this value and it is indeterminate because the value is unknown.

Another difficulty is also felt by many students. Just as the argument from dimensions appears in one direction to prove too little, so, in another, it seems to prove too much; from extremely simple premisses, so obvious that they can hardly be doubted, the argument deduces nearly as much as may be proved by the use of the whole armoury of abstract theoretical physics. The formal answer to objections of this nature is that they merely show that in making the assumptions on which the argument rests we are assuming much more than appears at first sight; and we have already noticed that, in the usual method of statement, very important assumptions are concealed. However such difficulty as is felt can only be removed wholly by examining carefully the deduction of the same law, first by dimensions and then by strict dynamical reasoning, and deciding exactly in what measure the assumptions introduced into the two methods of deduction differ. But before we make such an examination it will be well to regard the whole matter from another point of view and to notice a form of the argument which, though logically equivalent to that given already, has a rather different significance.

Physical Similarity. This form is based on the conception of physical[1] similarity, which is a development of the conception of geometrical similarity. Systems are said to be geometrically similar when, if one of the systems is characterised by a set of lengths $L_1, L_2, L_3, \ldots$, the other is characterised by a corresponding set of lengths $L_1', L_2', L_3', \ldots$, such that

$$(L_1', L_2', L_3', \ldots) = k.(L_1, L_2, L_3, \ldots),$$

where k is some constant; in other words systems are geometrically similar if corresponding lengths are in a constant ratio. Physically similar systems are those in which similar propositions are true, not only for lengths characteristic of the systems, but for magnitudes of all kinds characteristic of them (or at least of all kinds that influence the dynamical behaviour). If $x_1, x_2, x_3, \ldots$ are magnitudes all of one kind characteristic of one system, then any physically similar system must be characterised by a corresponding set of magnitudes $x_1', x_2', x_3', \ldots$, of the same kind as $x_1, \ldots$, and such that

$$(x_1', x_2', x_3', \ldots) = k_x.(x_1, x_2, x_3, \ldots).$$

The proposition must be true for all kinds of magnitudes characteristic of the system, i.e. for forces and masses and times as well as for lengths; but

---

[1] More often called "dynamical" similarity, but the more general term is preferable because the application of the conception need not be confined to dynamical magnitudes.

k_x need not be, and in general will not be, the same for magnitudes of different kinds; it will have one value when the x's are masses, and a different value when the x's are times and so on.

This definition of physically similar systems may be expressed more easily and, for our purpose, more conveniently by the aid of the conception of no-dimensional magnitudes. If the conception of geometrical similarity is to apply, there must be at least two lengths L_1 and L_2 characteristic of the system; we should not call systems geometrically similar if they were characterised each by one length only (but actually such systems are not possible). Any other geometrically similar system will be characterised by L_1' and L_2', where $(L_1', L_2') = k.(L_1, L_2)$. Consequently $L_1'/L_2' = L_1/L_2$. This relation is true for all the systems. Accordingly they all are subject to a law $L_1 = a_{12}.L_2$, where a_{12} is a no-dimensional magnitude characteristic of all the geometrically similar systems. If there are more than two characteristic lengths, there will be other no-dimensional magnitudes of the same kind characteristic of all the systems, and the assertion of geometrical similarity is equivalent to saying that they are all constant for all the similar systems. We may therefore define geometrically similar systems as those which are characterised by the same no-dimensional geometrical magnitudes, where by "the same" we mean the same in number and in physical meaning, as well as the same in numerical value. The definition is obviously easily extended to physically similar systems. They are such as are characterised by the same no-dimensional magnitudes of all kinds and not only by the same geometrical no-dimensional magnitudes.

Such then is the meaning of physical similarity. Its connection with the argument from dimensions is obvious. For we have seen that that argument assumes that all the systems to which it is applied are characterised by the same numerical value of a no-dimensional magnitude; if this is the only no-dimensional magnitude characteristic of the system, then the assumption is simply equivalent to saying that all the systems considered are physically similar. But is it the only characteristic no-dimensional magnitude? In our example we took for this magnitude the ratio of the acceleration g to the derived magnitude L/T^2; we might also have taken that defined by the ratio of the period to the derived magnitude $\sqrt{L/g}$; is not this another no-dimensional magnitude? This question has been discussed already (p. 375) We have seen reasons for regarding as the same magnitude any two magnitudes of which one is a single-valued function of another, the function F being such that F' has always the same sign; the reasons for doing so are especially cogent when the magnitudes are no-dimensional. Accordingly it would seem that the two no-dimensional magnitudes should be regarded as the same; and, if this were all, it would be true that the pendulum was characterised by a single no-dimensional magnitude. But there is a more important consideration raised by the question. It has been assumed that a single time, the period, is determined by a single length and a single acceleration; and this assumption is actually true. But the further assumption, sometimes made implicitly, that the pendulum system is characterised by only a single time, a single length, and a single acceleration is untrue; when we come to examine the basis of the first assumption we shall find that it is necessary to deny this further assumption. The pendulum is characterised by many lengths, times, and accelerations and, consequently, by many no-dimensional magnitudes determined by the ratios of magnitudes of the same kind. In a single system it may be convenient to regard all the no-dimensional magnitudes as mere variants of a single magnitude; but here we are considering, not a single system, but many systems. If that practice is adopted, the relation between the corresponding magnitudes in the several systems must be expressed in some other way. The fact has somehow to be expressed that in any system there are many no-dimensional magnitudes, defined by the ratios of different magnitudes of the same kind, and that to every such no-dimensional magnitude in one system corresponds an equal no-dimensional magnitude in any other. If we regard each system as characterised by only a single no-dimensional magnitude (as is sometimes convenient) we must say that to every function of this magnitude in one system which has a definite physical significance must correspond the same function in another system with the same physical significance. The argument from dimensions will really apply only to systems which are physically similar in all their parts, and in which all no-dimensional magnitudes or all forms of the same no-dimensional magnitude have the same numerical value.

On the other hand, if the systems considered are known to be physically similar, and if the nature of the magnitudes characteristic of them are known, then the result of the argument from dimensions follows directly. For if one of the characteristic magnitudes p is derived and has in terms of the characteristic fundamental magnitudes x, y, z the dimensions u, v, w, then if p, x, y, z represent some uniformly associated magnitudes of these kinds characteristic of any one of the systems, $p/x^u y^v z^w$ is a no-dimensional magnitude characteristic of this system; and if no other magnitudes are involved, all no-dimensional magnitudes must be of this form. Since other systems are physically similar they have the same value for this no-dimensional magnitude; in other words, if p, x, y, z always represent physically corresponding magnitudes in the different systems, $p = a x^u y^v z^w$, where a is the same for all.

The same argument may be expressed in a form that is sometimes convenient by means of the constant k, which represents the ratio of a magnitude in one system to the corresponding magnitude in another. Let k_p, k_x, k_y, k_z represent the ratios of the p's, x's, y's, z's in the two systems. Then, corresponding to any p in one system we have $k_p . p$ in the second. But we have also derived from any x, any y, any z in one system the magnitude $x^u y^v z^w$, and to this magnitude must correspond $(k_x^u k_y^v k_z^w) x^u y^v z^w$ in the second. But this magnitude has the same dimensions as p, so that

$$p/x^u y^v z^w \text{ and } k_p/k_x^u k_y^v k_z^w . p/x^u y^v z^w$$

are similar no-dimensional magnitudes. Since, by assumption, the two systems are physically similar the values of these no-dimensional magnitudes must be the same, and $k_p = k_x^u k_y^v k_z^w$.

This result leads to a very simple expression of the argument from dimensions in some important cases. It often happens that we are only concerned to deduce the relation between the fundamental magnitudes for physically similar systems which are all characterised by the same value of the derived magnitude. Thus, in the pendulum, we may desire to know the relation between L and T, g being always the same. Accordingly k_p must always be 1, so that $k_x{}^u k_y{}^v k_z{}^w = 1$. It follows immediately that $x^u y^v z^w$ must be the same for all systems; consequently the relation which is sought between x, y, z is $x^u y^v z^w =$ constant.

The "Principle" of Physical Similarity. It will be observed that in making these deductions from the conception of physical similarity no use has been made of any general proposition about physically similar systems. We have only assumed that the systems to be compared are physically similar and have not asserted anything that could be called a Principle of Physical Similarity. Yet in many discussions of the subject it is implied, or definitely stated, that there is some such Principle, although it may not be precisely formulated, and that the principle is essential to the deduction of the results. I believe that this implication is erroneous, and that the results of the argument from dimensions follow simply from the statement that the systems are physically similar (together with a statement of the magnitudes in respect of which they are similar), and that the deduction requires nothing which is not involved in that statement, interpreted according to the definition of similarity which has been given. On the other hand, the results do not follow unless they are physically similar.

The proposition which is often introduced under the name of the Principle of Physical Similarity may be stated in some such words as these: Systems which differ in nothing but scale will behave in similar fashion. Though this is the form in which the proposition is expressed by able writers, a very little examination will show that it requires amendment or elucidation. For what can be meant by differing *only* in scale and by behaving in similar fashion? If the statement is not to be self-contradictory, the second expression must be defined so that systems may behave in similar fashion although they differ in scale; but if it is so defined, then, whatever other meaning is attached to it, the similarity of systems which differ *only* in scale must be so great as to include their behaviour in similar fashion. The proposition is either self-contradictory or tautologous; in its present form it is not significant.

However we have admitted that it is not a serious objection to a scientific proposition that it is open to such formally logical objections, so long as it is an adequate means of calling to mind important ideas. If we examine how the proposition is used we shall find that "behaving in similar fashion" means almost exactly the same thing as "physically similar". Two systems behave in similar fashion if to every magnitude in one system corresponds a magnitude of the same kind in the other, while the physical relations (or the forms of uniform association) between two magnitudes in one system are the same as those between the two corresponding magnitudes in the other. This definition differs from that of physical similarity only because the latter includes the further condition that the ratio between the numerical values of two magnitudes in one system, and not only the physical relation between them, shall be the same as that between those of the corresponding magnitudes in the other system. Thus a pendulum with a small bob at the end of a thick rod would be held to behave similarly to one with a large bob at the end of a thin rod; but it is not physically similar to it. But in the application of the proposition we are considering this greater latitude allowed by "similar behaviour" is of no consequence, for it is always actually used in the narrower sense of physical similarity.

With this interpretation the proposition states that systems which differ in nothing but scale are physically similar. But again in this form it is tautologous. For if "scale" has its original sense of geometrical scale, differing in geometrical scale means nothing but geometrically similar; and of course systems which are geometrically similar and otherwise identical would be physically similar, if they existed—but actually they do not. And if "scale" is generalised to apply to magnitudes other than lengths, areas, and volumes, differing in scale can still be only used reasonably to mean similar in respect of such other magnitudes; and it is still a mere truism, a consequence of the meaning of words, to say that systems which are similar in respect of some magnitudes and otherwise identical are physically similar.

Nevertheless the proposition does state an important truth, though it is one which is difficult to formulate briefly in words. What it states is that there are such things as physically similar systems and that they are easy to produce and of constant occurrence. It states, in the case of the pendulum for example, that it is possible to find a pendulum B which differs from A in geometrical scale or in its scale of mass, and yet is physically similar to A. The geometrically similar pendulums will be physically similar, so long as both are of homogeneous density, even if the densities are different or if the densities, though not homogeneous, are similarly distributed. The pendulums which differ in scale of mass will be physically similar if they are geometrically similar. But it must be noted that the geometrically similar systems, which are physically similar, do not differ in nothing but geometrical scale, even if both are made of homogeneous material of the same density; they will differ in their periods, unless they differ in a certain definite manner in the gravitational fields in which they are placed.

It is this fact that it is impossible to make two systems which differ in nothing but the scale of a single magnitude, geometrical or other, which makes it difficult to formulate the proposition very precisely. For we must admit that, when we change the system in respect of such a single scale, we must change it in respect of other things as well; while, if we remove all limitations on the changes which are to be admitted concurrently with the change in the single scale, the proposition obviously becomes untrue; there are obviously changes (e.g. in the distribution of density in the pendulum) which, if they accompany change of geometrical scale, will lead to systems which do not behave similarly to the original system. On the other hand, if by differing in scale we mean differing in the scale of several magnitudes and not merely of one, then the proposition once more is tautologous, for systems which behave similarly are simply those which differ in the scale of several magnitudes. It seems necessary to assert the proposition formally by simply stating that physically similar systems, behaving similarly, are possible, and not to attempt to define precisely the means by which they may be produced. But while so confining our formal statement we must bear in mind that physically similar systems are produced by changes which, psychologically, are changes in nothing but scale (cf. p. 63). If we set out with the deliberate intention of changing the scale of a single magnitude or of a limited selection of magnitudes, then, although we shall not actually achieve our aim, but shall change the scale of other magnitudes as well, we shall produce a system which is physically similar and behaves similarly. Thus, to revert once more to the pendulum, if we mean to change nothing but the linear scale, we shall take care not to change the density, either in scale or in distribution, and not to change the gravitational field; and if we take such care we shall actually produce a physically similar system. Nevertheless we shall have changed more than the linear scale to which our attention was directed; we shall have changed the scale of area, of volume, and of period. As a practical direction of the steps we must take to obtain physically similar systems, the proposition is adequate and useful; but as a formal statement of the result of those steps it is either tautologous or untrue.

The explanation of the proposition which has just been given probably conveys its true meaning and importance; the expression, though formally objectionable, indicates properly the ideas that are in our minds when we make use of the proposition. The question now arises why is the proposition true? Is it simply a consequence of things which are implied in the use of the conceptions involved in it, or does it represent some new and important physical principle, which must be accepted as ultimate and beyond analysis? In many discussions of the matter there seems to me a tendency to answer the question in accordance with the second suggestion and to regard the proposition as a definite Principle of Physical Similarity which is something external and added to the remaining assumptions of the argument from dimensions. Definite statements to that effect can certainly be quoted from widely-used text-books and original memoirs; but that is no proof that they are worthy of serious consideration. As I have indicated already, I believe that the first suggestion is correct. But since there are passages in the writings of Rayleigh, who is not often in error and is responsible for much of the attention that has been given to the subject, which might be interpreted in support of the second suggestion, it is worth while to give the matter careful attention.

Let us once more use our example. The proposition states that two pendulums can differ in geometrical scale and yet be physically similar, behaving in similar fashion and both executing harmonic vibrations characterised by definite periods. We shall see presently that this proposition follows from two vital assumptions that underlie the application of the argument from dimensions to this example, namely, (1) that the motion of the pendulum over any very small range of position is uniformly accelerated or, in other words, that the distance travelled is proportional to the square of the time occupied, and (2) that the uniform acceleration in any position is determined by the product of a magnitude depending on the gravitational field by a geometrical no-dimensional magnitude defining the position of the pendulum. So long as these assumptions are true the pendulums will be physically similar; the proposition we are discussing asserts that they are true; under what conditions could we imagine them being false? They would be false, if either the form of the law of motion, or the numerical value of the gravitational acceleration, or the numerical value of the no-dimensional magnitude changed with the size of the system. The point which I want to make is that we have already denied that such changes occur in stating the magnitudes on which the period depends and in attributing to them certain dimensions.

For our assumptions may be expressed by the statement that the motion of the pendulum is represented by a numerical law $s = \frac{1}{2} (g\theta) t^2$, where g is the gravitational constant and θ a no-dimensional geometrical magnitude, and where the factor $\frac{1}{2}$ and the index 2 are formal constants. If it were true that the change from a larger to a smaller system changed the motion in a given position of the pendulum, defined by a given θ, from uniformly accelerated to some other form of motion, then the index 2 would not be a formal constant. It would depend on the size of the system; it would be a magnitude and it would have dimensions in terms of the geometrical magnitude, length, which fixes the size of the system[1]. Similarly, if, although the motion remained uniformly accelerated, the acceleration changed with the scale, then we should have to conclude either that the $\frac{1}{2}$ was not a formal constant, but had dimensions in terms of length or that θ was not no-dimensional, but had such dimensions. But we have expressly denied these conclusions; we have stated that the geometrical magnitude is no-dimensional, and (in denying that there are no magnitudes involved other than length and acceleration which are not no-dimensional) we have asserted that the $\frac{1}{2}$ and the 2 are formal constants. The feeling that any special proposition has to be introduced to state that the form of the motion does not depend on the geometrical scale is due merely to overlooking what very important and far-reaching assertions were made when we made out our list of determining magnitudes, assigned to them dimensions, and asserted that any other relevant numerical values were formal constants.

[1] This statement is only strictly true if the index turned out to be of the form aL^n, where L is the size of the system. But if, while depending on L, the functional relation were of some other form, we should have to regard some function of the index as having dimensions in terms of length, or, perhaps, regard the index as a function of several magnitudes of which at least one has dimensions in terms of length. But the essential conclusion is unchanged.

This conclusion cannot be emphasised too often or too strongly. It seems to us nowadays a very simple thing to assign dimensions to magnitudes, so simple that we are apt to forget the extremely important implication of the assertions. When we assert that a certain derived magnitude always has certain dimensions, we are in fact asserting the complete accuracy of the law which determines that derived magnitude under all possible conditions. If there is any doubt whatever about the universality of the law, then there is a corresponding doubt about the dimensions of the derived magnitude or even about its existence. When we say that acceleration has the dimensions [length] × [time]$^{-2}$, and proceed to assert that all systems of a certain class are characterised by uniform accelerations, we are simply asserting the validity of the law of uniformly accelerated motion for all those systems; we are asserting that in a certain respect they behave similarly. If it appears that from that assertion we can deduce consequences far beyond the possibility of experimental confirmation, then we must conclude that we are asserting the validity of that law far beyond the possibility of experimental confirmation, and we must be correspondingly cautious in accepting the result of the argument. If the argument from dimensions is a magical process which results in the production of experimental knowledge from anything but experiment, then we must conclude, not that it is valuable, but that it is absolutely fallacious.

I fear, however, that some people may not be wholly convinced by the explanation that has been given of the supposed Principle of Physical Similarity. Accordingly it may be well to attack directly some views which have been expressed in recent years which, though they are so fallacious as to deserve no serious consideration, unfortunately seem to have produced much confusion of thought.

An attempt is sometimes made to base the argument from dimensions or arguments similar to it upon a doctrine which may be epigrammatically expressed in the words, Absolute magnitude has no physical significance, or, If the whole universe were reconstructed on a different scale, no experiments could detect the change. I do not propose to interrupt the argument to urge objections against the form of these expressions, involving the highly dangerous words "absolute" and "universe". For it will probably not be disputed that the proposition stated in the following form is a consequence of the doctrine, even if it is a single case of a more general assertion:—Suppose that we examine the behaviour of some system (e.g. a pendulum), and, in place of measuring the magnitudes characteristic of it in terms of the conventional and fixed units, measure them in terms of selected magnitudes of the same kind characteristic of the system (e.g. measure all lengths and periods in terms of the length and period of the pendulum), then any proposition which is true of that system is also true of any physically similar system, differing in geometrical scale.

In the example we have taken this proposition is true. If we measure all lengths in terms of the length of the pendulum and all periods in terms of its period, then, so long as the pendulums are geometrically similar, of similarly distributed densities, and in similarly distributed gravitational fields, all propositions true of one pendulum will be true of the other, including propositions asserting the numerical values of any magnitudes, lengths, times, or accelerations characteristic of it. The truth of it depends on nothing but our definition of fundamental measurement (implying the statement that the measurement is satisfactory), and on our knowledge that the law of gravitational acceleration is true and complete in the sense that we have discussed lately.

But the proposition is apt to be used in a way which, though it does not lead to an actually false conclusion, is dangerous because it displays confusion of thought. It is argued that if the geometrical scale of the pendulum is changed, while it remains in the same gravitational field, the doctrine asserted shows that the change will not be detected, if all measurements are made in terms of units characteristic of the system; consequently, by an easy train of reasoning, all periods must have changed in the ratio of the inverse square of the lengths. But the proviso about the gravitational field remaining unchanged is misleading. If all measurements are made in terms of units characteristic of the system, then no measurement will detect the change in geometrical scale, even if at the same time the pendulum is moved to another homogeneous gravitational field. Consequently, from the two facts (1) that the geometrical scale has been changed, (2) that measurements made in terms of units characteristic of the system discover no change, it is not permissible to conclude that the periods must change as the inverse squares of the lengths. That conclusion follows only if the gravitational field, measured in fixed units, is unchanged during the change in geometrical scale; if it does change, the change cannot be detected by measurements in terms of units characteristic of the system; and the fact that the change cannot be detected thus is no evidence that it has not occurred, or of any conclusions concerning the change of the periods, measured in fixed units, which are based on the assumption that it has not occurred.

However, as has been said, error does not seem to have arisen from the confusion of thought displayed here. It arises only when an attempt is made to develop the doctrine further. Suppose now that our "system" consists not only of a pendulum, but of a pendulum and a resonator, consisting of a box tuned to some pitch. We now increase the geometrical scale of both pendulum and resonator. We have noted that we cannot increase only the geometrical scale, and the question arises at once what else we are going to change and what we are going to leave unaltered. The other magnitudes characteristic of the system are the periods, the gravitational acceleration and the velocity of sound. The "natural" course is to leave the last two unchanged and let the periods alter. If that course is adopted, the two periods (referred to the conventional and fixed units) will change in different ratios; if lengths are changed in the ratio p, the period of the pendulum will change in the ratio p^{-2}, the period of the resonator in the ratio p^{-1}. Accordingly, although the whole system after the change is dynamically similar to that before the change, the numerical value of the period of the resonator measured in terms of the period of the pendulum will have altered. If that value was T before the change, it will be T/p after the change. Qualitative propositions about the system will be unaltered by the change; but certain statements of numerical values will be altered. And exactly the same feature will be found, if we adopt some other course; we might make the numerical value of the periods, measured in terms of one another, the same before and after the change by changing at the same time the gravitational acceleration or the velocity of sound; but then we should find that numerical values of accelerations or velocities had altered during the change. It is quite impossible in this case to keep all propositions concerning the system unaltered during a change of geometrical scale, even if all magnitudes are measured in terms of units characteristic of the system.

Accordingly if a "system", in the statement of the doctrine, is to include such a combination of a pendulum and a resonator, the doctrine is untrue. And it is quite clear why it is untrue of the combination although it would be true of either component, regarded as a system. The reason is that the combined "system" is characterised by two periods, and not only one, and that these two periods are not related by any law. A pendulum or a resonator, considered alone, is also characterised by two or more periods, but the periods of the pendulum are connected by a law, and so are the periods of the resonator; on the other hand there is no law relating the periods of the pendulum to the periods of the resonator. If the word is used in the sense described in Chap. II, the combination of the pendulum and resonator is not a "system" at all; an assertion about it is not an assertion about the uniform association of properties; it is not a law. And since, once more, the whole argument from dimensions or from similarity depends entirely on the assumption that certain laws are strictly and completely true, any attempt to apply it when no laws are known is certain to lead to error.

Now the erroneous applications of the doctrine which is under discussion are due to the false assumption that the "universe" is a system in our sense, and that statements about it are all statements of laws and of uniform association. But if the "universe" is given any reasonable meaning, even if it includes combinations so limited as a pendulum and a resonator, that assumption is utterly untrue. We have not reduced the entire universe to order and stated all its properties in terms of laws; until that feat is achieved, an attempt to apply any arguments based on dimensions, and, because they are based on dimensions, implying the complete and accurate knowledge of laws, is bound to land us in the most extravagant absurdity.

The particular form of absurdity to which we may be led in this instance is illustrated by this argument:—If the scale of the universe is changed, the doctrine asserts that it will be impossible to detect the change; therefore the velocity of light must be the same in both universes; consequently, if the scale of length has been increased p times. the scale of time must also have been increased p times. From this conclusion and others obtained by similar applications of the doctrine, the form of most of the important laws of physics can be deduced. But the conclusion does not follow unless it is known that an increase in the scale of the universe would be accompanied by no change in the velocity of light, measured by an observer who maintained his units unchanged during this change of the universe; and since not only the velocity of light, but any velocity, might be used to measure time in conjunction with a standard of length, all velocities must similarly be unchanged during the change of the scale of the universe. Further constant accelerations might be used to measure times; if accelerations were unchanged during the change of scale, it would not be true that the change could not be detected, for times measured by velocities would not have their original numerical values in terms of times measured by accelerations; in order that the change should be incapable of being detected by measurements of times, if the velocities are unchanged, the accelerations, measured by an observer with fixed units, must change inversely as the lengths.

Accordingly the doctrine on which these conclusions are based is not true, and the conclusions which it is desired to draw do not follow, unless it is known that a change in the scale of the universe is accompanied by certain definite changes in the derived magnitudes associated with it, as measured by an observer whose units remain fixed during the change. If velocities remain unchanged, accelerations must change; if accelerations remain unchanged, velocities must change. The conclusions which will be reached by the application of the doctrine will differ entirely according to which of these alternatives is adopted. Is there the slightest reason for adopting either of them or adopting one rather than the other; is there indeed any meaning in assertions concerning what would happen during a change of scale of the universe? It is unnecessary to criticise further such fantastic notions.

Yet the space occupied in their discussion has not been entirely wasted. If such arguments can be published in a serious scientific journal and gravely discussed by professors of physics, it is surely proof that the nature of the argument from dimensions or physical similarity is not properly understood. Moreover they draw attention to a most dangerous tendency of recent years, against which the strongest protest should be entered, the tendency to revert to the scholastic practice of attempting to deduce experimental conclusions from doctrines that have no experimental foundation. It is as absurd to pretend to prove that the laws of physics must have a certain form from an assumption about what would happen if the scale of the universe were changed, as it is to attempt to deduce the law of falling bodies from the doctrine that bodies tend to move to their "proper place". The reappearance of errors which were thought to have been permanently buried 300 years ago is largely due to the misunderstanding of one of the most remarkable and successful theories of modern physics. Until men of science are prepared to give much more attention than they have been doing in the past to the real meaning and foundation of the propositions which they assert, they would do well to abandon entirely any use of the theory of dimensions.

The use of dimensional argument. So far we have been concerned mainly to state formally the argument from dimensions and to expose certain fallacies which may easily arise in its application. It has been insisted that, if the argument is to prove anything valuable, it can only be because very intricate and complex assumptions are implied in the apparent simplicity of its premisses. Nevertheless there is no doubt that the argument is useful, and it remains to consider why it is useful and how it can lead to any true conclusions which cannot otherwise be attained except by far more elaborate and difficult arguments.

For this purpose let us revert once more to our simple example of the pendulum, and inquire exactly how the argument from dimensions differs from full dynamical reasoning, first, in the assumptions made, second in the conclusions reached.

To simplify matters further the pendulum will be supposed to consist of a point mass at the end of a weightless string or rod, and the arcs of vibration to be so small that they can be considered straight. We will first consider on what physical propositions the assumptions of the principle of dynamical similarity are based and next those on which the full dynamical reasoning is based; a comparison of the two will answer our question.

The full dynamical reasoning starts from the equation $\ddot{x} + g \cdot \dfrac{x}{L} = 0$. By purely mathematical reasoning we integrate the equation and find that it is logically equivalent to the equation $x = A \cos\left(\dfrac{2\pi t}{T} + \alpha\right)$, where $T = 2\pi \sqrt{\dfrac{L}{g}}$. This equation implies that x will return to the same value after a lapse of time T, which is therefore the period of the pendulum. But though the passage from the first equation to the second is effected by purely mathematical argument, the result would not be physically significant unless it corresponded to the tracing out of some physical process. The process involved here is the addition (the physical operation) of the periods occupied by the pendulum in moving over parts of its path so short that, in each part, the motion can be regarded as uniformly accelerated; the physical assumption underlying the mathematical argument is that the whole period occupied by the pendulum in its return to a position previously occupied is the physical sum of periods during each of which it moves with uniform acceleration. The exact significance of this assumption will concern us in Part III, but it is clear that, if the assumption were not true, the mathematical operation of integration would not lead to any results of physical significance.

Now turn to the dimensional argument. What is our reason for asserting so confidently that the period is determined by the length and the gravitational acceleration? First, we know that the period occupied in the passage between any two positions of the pendulum must be the physical sum of periods during each of which the pendulum moves with uniform acceleration; for that is simply the assumption on which all theoretical dynamics rests. This assumption then is common to both forms of reasoning. Second, we know from our study of gravitation that the uniform acceleration of any body in a gravitational field is the product of a constant, determining the field, by a geometrical no-dimensional magnitude; we know that a geometrical no-dimensional magnitude characteristic of any system must be a function of the ratio of any two lengths characteristic of that system, in particular it must be a function of x/L. Consequently we know that the uniform acceleration corresponding to any value of x must be $g\theta$, where θ is $f(x/L)$.

Having reached this conclusion we argue thus, introducing the assertion that acceleration has the dimensions $[\text{length}]/[\text{time}]^{-2}$. Consider two pendulums starting from rest and from positions which are geometrically similar. Then their accelerations are equal and represented by $g\theta$, where θ is a no-dimensional magnitude characteristic of the position. They move to some other positions which are again geometrically similar and so close to the original positions that the accelerations along the paths may be considered constant; the lengths which they traverse in so doing are proportional and in the ratio of the lengths of the pendulums; let them be $\lambda L_1, \lambda L_2$. Since, by the meaning of constant acceleration, the length travelled must be related to the time occupied by the equation $s = \frac{1}{2}(g\theta).t^2$, the times occupied must be

$$T_1 = \sqrt{\frac{2\lambda L_1}{g\theta}} \quad \text{and} \quad T_2 = \sqrt{\frac{2\lambda L_2}{g\theta}} \quad \text{or} \quad T_1 = \phi\sqrt{L_1/g} \quad \text{and} \quad T_2 = \phi\sqrt{L_2/g},$$

where λ and ϕ are some no-dimensional geometrical magnitudes; further, by the meaning of velocity, their velocities must be $g\theta T_1$ and $g\theta T_2$. In the position which they now occupy the accelerations are $g\theta'$; from these positions the pendulums pass to yet other positions which are still geometrically similar and so close that the acceleration may again be considered equal over the whole passage; the same argument, taking into account the fact that the pendulums now start with finite velocity, will again prove that the times occupied in the second passage must be $T_1 = \phi'\sqrt{L_1/g}$ and $T_2 = \phi'\sqrt{L_2/g}$, where ϕ' is some no-dimensional magnitude which is a function of θ, θ', λ, λ'. And this relation will hold good for any subsequent passages from one geometrically similar position to another. Now the period of the pendulum is the time of passage from a given position to the same position again. The argument can not show that the pendulum will ever return to the same position, but it shows that, if it returns, then the periods must be $T_1 = \Phi\sqrt{\dfrac{L_1}{g}}$

and $T_2 = \Phi\sqrt{\dfrac{L_2}{g}}$ where $\Phi = \Sigma\phi$, the sum of the ϕ's for all the passages

between the occupation of one position and the return to it.

Accordingly we conclude that the only physical assumption in which the argument from dimensions differs from the full dynamical reasoning is that concerning the nature of the function $f(x/L)$. The argument from dimensions merely asserts that the function is single-valued; the dynamical argument asserts that it is x/L; the latter, but not the former, gives to the function at each position of the pendulum a definite numerical value. And as the premisses differ, so also do the conclusions; one argument, but not the other, gives a numerical value to a no-dimensional magnitude which is a function of that introduced originally. The undetermined constant is simply a function of the originally undetermined no-dimensional magnitude.

The connection between the two forms of argument is exceptionally clear in this very simple example. To trace out the relation between them in more complex cases is a very interesting problem, but it is always soluble. It will always be found that the mathematical process of integration leads to physically significant results only because it corresponds step by step to some physical process; and that, if it is assumed that the laws of this physical process are known, the argument from dimensions will lead to exactly the same results as the dynamical reasoning, except in the matter of the numerical value of some no-dimensional magnitude. The assumptions concerning the magnitudes on which the behaviour of the system depends are always simply based on the form of the differential equation from which the full dynamical reasoning proceeds; if we did not know the form of that differential equation we could not proceed with the dimensional argument any more than with the dynamical argument. The only difference between the two is in the attribution of a numerical value to some no-dimensional magnitude—usually a geometrical no-dimensional magnitude; the lesser intellectual effort required by the argument from dimensions arises solely from the neglect of these numerical values. If it should appear in any case that these statements are not true, and that there is some other assumption made by the full dynamical reasoning which is omitted by the argument from dimensions, then the conclusion to be drawn is that the results of the latter are precarious, and that they have not the certainty which would attach to results obtained by complete dynamical reasoning.

If these very obvious considerations are borne in mind, the argument from dimensions will prove valuable and reliable. If they are neglected it will be a fruitful source of error. And now let us leave the main problem and turn to a few considerations which have been neglected.

Does the argument apply only to "basic" magnitudes? So far consideration has been limited to cases in which there is only one set of constants $\lambda, \mu, \nu, \rho, \ldots$ and only one derived magnitude. The second part of the limitation has been inserted only for convenience in exposition; so long as the first part is maintained no difference would be made to anything that has been said if there were two derived magnitudes in place of one. In fact when there is only one set $\lambda, \mu, \nu, \rho, \ldots$, two derived magnitudes, p and q, reduce to one, r, for they must always occur in the form $p^u q^v$, and it is easy to see that, if we call this r, r has all the properties of a derived magnitude. In fact this practice is often adopted. In hydro-dynamical problems the viscosity η always occurs in conjunction with the density in the form ρ; η/ρ is accordingly called the kinematic viscosity. It may be noted that it is not a true derived magnitude, for there is no law $\eta \propto \rho$.

But these remarks are true only so long as the magnitudes are truly derived. We have seen that there are magnitudes, notably area and volume, which are always treated conventionally as derived, but are really fundamental magnitudes, although they may be, and actually are, measured as quasi-derived. How does the denial that volume is a derived magnitude, to which the dimensions [length]^3 can be properly assigned, affect arguments based on dimensions?

Let us take an example. A familiar acoustical argument states that T, the fundamental period of a resonator, depends only on its volume V and on the velocity of sound U. If we attribute to V, in the conventional manner, the dimensions [length]^3, it is known that the argument from dimensions proves that $T \propto V^{\frac{1}{3}}/U$. If on the other hand we call V a fundamental magnitude and attempt to find a set λ, μ, ν, which will lead to a law of the form $T^\lambda V^\mu U^\nu = $ constant, we fail; there is no such set. But our failure is due to inconsistency; if we are going to take V as a fundamental magnitude in one connection, we must take it as fundamental in all. If we inquire into the dynamical propositions on which the assumptions made in applying the argument are founded, we shall find that they involve the proposition that, in a medium consisting of a given substance (of which only the quantity is varied), the elasticity q is proportional to the density ρ. We have in fact $q = \alpha\rho$ where α is a magnitude characteristic of the medium. This magnitude, as can be proved by dynamical reasoning, is proportional to the square of the velocity of sound in the medium; we have therefore $\alpha = \beta . U^2$ where β is another magnitude characteristic of the system; it so happens that the same value of β is characteristic of all systems; β is a "universal constant", but this special feature of it is irrelevant to the argument. Now (assuming as always that force has the dimensions [mass] $\times$ [length] $\times$ [time]$^{-2}$), the dimensions of β are [volume] $\times$ [length]$^{-3}$. If we assign to volume the dimensions [length]^3, β has zero dimensions, and in that case there is no need to include it in the dimensional argument; for though it is essential to that argument that there should be some no-dimensional magnitudes characteristic of the system, any assumptions concerning them can only affect the undetermined constant; unless therefore we can assign values to them all there is no purpose in noticing them formally at all. But if we do not assign to volume those dimensions, then we must not omit β from the dimensional equation; it is a derived magnitude characteristic of the system as much as η or ρ. Accordingly we must write $T^\lambda V^\mu U^\nu \beta^\rho = $ constant; we shall now find a set λ, μ, ν, ρ and the relation $T \propto V^{\frac{1}{3}}/U\beta^{\frac{1}{3}}$. Since β is a universal constant, this result differs in no manner appreciable by experiment from $T \propto V^{\frac{1}{3}}/U$.

One more example may be taken to show that the explanation of the matter offered here is quite general. In aerodynamics it is assumed (subject to a condition to be discussed presently) that the air forces F acting on a body as a resistance are determined by v, its velocity, ρ the density of the air, and A the area of cross-section of the body, all systems being assumed geometrically similar as usual. Consequently, if to A is given the dimensions [length]^2, we should have $F \propto A\rho v^2$. Again if we regard A as a separate fundamental magnitude, no set λ, μ, ν, ρ can be found. It is much less obvious here than in the previous example where else an area enters into the characteristic magnitudes. But the only basis for the assumption that F, A, ρ, v are the only relevant magnitudes is to be found (as was suggested before) in the differential equations of aerodynamics; and if we turn to them[1], we shall find that in establishing them the proposition is involved that (the length dx) $\times$ (the area of the rectangle with sides dy, dz) = (the volume of the parallelepiped with sides dx, dy, dz). Now if area (as well as length and volume) is a fundamental magnitude, we must write, not $LA = V$, but $LA = \gamma . V$, where γ is a derived magnitude characteristic of the system (and again of all systems). We must introduce γ into the list of magnitudes and write $F^\lambda A^\mu \rho^\nu v^\rho \gamma^\sigma$ = constant. We can now find a set λ, μ, ν, ρ, σ and reach the conclusion[2] $F \propto A\rho v^2 \gamma^{-1}$. Since γ is universally constant, this again is equivalent to $F \propto A\rho v^2$.

In these examples—and the examination of others would show that the conclusion is quite general—we arrive at exactly the same conclusions whether we treat volume and area as fundamental or as derived from length. And the reason is that they are always connected with some other magnitude mentioned in the assumptions by means of a law. This connection is necessary. The only reason for including a magnitude in the list of those characteristic of the system is that it is connected with some other magnitude in the list by a law; so much was indicated by our analysis of the reasons for selecting the list characteristic of the pendulum. But if two fundamental magnitudes are connected by a law, they must define a derived magnitude; this derived magnitude is characteristic of the system and must be included in the list of those on which its behaviour depends. It is only if it is so included that the argument from physical similarity can lead to right results.

But this only proves that area and volume, being essentially fundamental magnitudes and not derived, should always be treated as fundamental. It does not justify the practice of assigning to them dimensions in terms of length, and yet that practice does always lead to correct results. Why does it not lead to error? The reason is this. In dynamical systems in which volume and area are concerned at all, there always is a law connecting the

---

[1] See e.g. Rayleigh, *Theory of Sound*, § 237.

[2] It may be noted that not only are the equations sufficient to determine the set, but are redundant. That is because, as an examination of the fundamental equations will show, we have omitted two of the magnitudes necessarily involved in the fundamental assumptions, namely length, which occurs in such terms are dp/dx, and volume. The equations show that in this particular application the index of length is o. By giving to area dimensions in terms of length, we obscure, what might be important in other applications, that length, area and volume are all determining magnitudes.

areas and volumes that are concerned with some lengths. There may also be laws connecting them with other magnitudes (e.g. volume with mass, giving rise to the derived magnitude density), but whether there are or are not such laws, there are always the laws connecting them with length. Accordingly the derived magnitudes defined by these laws should always be introduced. But these derived magnitudes are of a special kind; as we have seen they may be regarded as the product of a true derived magnitude a', with dimensions in terms of area (or volume) and length, with a no-dimensional magnitude, shape. No error is committed by omitting either of these factors. The last may be omitted because it is no-dimensional; the first because it is a universal constant; both are absorbed in the "undetermined constant". Such is the reason why the omission of the derived magnitude introduces no error and why it is permissible to omit it. But I must protest that the omission is formally unjustifiable and actually unfortunate. Even though "shape" is a no-dimensional magnitude, I believe the significance of the results of the argument would be clearer if it were mentioned explicitly and if we wrote (in the case of the resonator) $T \propto V^{\frac{1}{3}}/U \, (\text{shape})^{\frac{1}{3}}.(a')^{\frac{1}{3}}$; that mode of expression would show clearly that the period was partly determined by the shape. The presence of it would also show—it is actually a fact—that, since the unit of volume is not now defined as that of unit cube, in the most accurate work the factor $1 \cdot 00009$, representing the ratio of unit volume to that of the unit cube, must be taken into account.

In defence of the usual omission of "shape" it might be urged that it is always really present, even when the magnitudes area and volume are not concerned, and yet is always omitted. The statement is not true. The systems considered are always geometrically similar and characterised by the constant no-dimensional magnitude, shape; and, since the geometrical similarity usually determines the complete physical similarity (owing to the uniform distribution of density, the parallelism of the forces and so on), it is practically the only no-dimensional magnitude involved; the undetermined constant is usually simply the shape, if area and volume are not mentioned, and though shape is not mentioned explicitly, it is mentioned if the undetermined constant is introduced and the relation stated as equality and not as proportionality. But even if the statement were true, it might be replied that two wrongs do not make a right; it would be a very good thing if, in place of the undetermined constant, "shape" were actually written, until everyone realises that " a " is simply an abbreviation for "shape", just as ρ is for density. And further, even if the argument were admitted as justifying the omission of shape, it would not in the least justify the omission of the very important universal constant a', which is present whenever area and volume are among the determining magnitudes and are treated as having dimensions L^2 and L^3. It is very important to realise that, if the usual practice is adopted, the undetermined constant, when these magnitudes are involved, is not no-dimensional and includes, besides the no-dimensional magnitude shape, this universal constant. Nobody would propose to omit " c " from numerical laws because it is universally constant; at the present time it is even more unfortunate to omit a' simply because, while everyone knows that there is a universal constant c, it does not seem to be at all widely known that there is a universal constant characteristic of "space".

It appears therefore that, if due care is taken to include all the relevant derived magnitudes, a fundamental magnitude may be either treated as such or given the dimensions it would have if it were measured as quasi-derived. And if the numerical law by which it is measured as quasi-derived is one that is involved in the process under investigation, the procedure has sometimes some advantages. It is always followed conventionally in the case of area and volume, but it might be followed in other cases. Thus, we might give volume the dimensions [mass]/[density]; in that case we should arrive at the relation for the resonator $T \propto m^{\frac{1}{3}}/U\rho^{\frac{1}{3}}$; that relation is quite true, and in some circumstances would be more important than that stated in terms of volume direct. The basis of such procedure is that we might if we pleased measure volume as a quasi-derived magnitude, using as system of density 1 the medium filling the resonator. It is also formally possible to give to any fundamental magnitude the dimensions which it would have if it were measured as quasi-derived by some law not involved in the process under investigation. Thus we might measure volume by means of the electrical resistance (R) of a rod of known length L and shape filled with a substance of which the specific resistance r is asserted to be unity. The relation for the resonator would then become

$$TU \propto \{RL^2/r \, (\text{shape})\}^{\frac{1}{3}}.$$

But this mode of expression has no advantages whatever; for the specific resistance occurring in it is not that of the medium under discussion (which, for all we know in following the argument, has no specific resistance) but that of some entirely different system which has been arbitrarily chosen to represent the standard. The representation of a fundamental magnitude as quasi-derived is justifiable only when the numerical law by means of which it is measured as quasi-derived is one that is characteristic of the system considered. It is the fact that, if area and volume are measured as quasi-derived in terms of length and shape, the laws always are involved in any system we consider—it is this fact that distinguishes the measurement of area and volume as quasi-derived from all other quasi-derived measurements and justifies, formally but not physically, the universal practice.

These considerations show that the practice of basing the argument from dynamical similarity on dimensions expressed only in terms of mass, length and time is a mere convention and has no experimental justification whatever; indeed it is liable to lead to misunderstandings. The best and most consistent plan would be to introduce into the dimensional equations all the fundamental magnitudes that are characteristic of the system. If we do not adopt this practice there is no logical reason why we should not go to the other extreme and measure all the fundamental magnitudes except one (including mass, length, and time) as quasi-derived. The only argument that can be advanced for the present practice is that mass, length, and time are the most important magnitudes in all dynamical systems. But I maintain that such a statement is simply untrue. The most important dynamical magnitude is acceleration; the whole theory of dynamics is intimately bound up with the recognition of the supreme importance of acceleration. And I think in many cases it would actually make the significance of the propositions clearer, if we gave to one of the three "fundamental" magnitudes (usually mass, but sometimes time) dimensions in time of the others and of acceleration.

The "undetermined constant". There remains one question raised in the introduction to which no answer has been attempted. Why is the undetermined constant a, in a relation of the form $p^\lambda x^\mu y^\nu z^\rho = a$, deduced from the argument from dimensions, never very different from unity?

The formal answer is that it is sometimes very different. It is true that if we express the relation for the pendulum in the form $T^2 = a.L/g$, a is not very different from unity; but if we expressed it (as we might with equal justification) in the form $T^{200} = a.L^{100}/g^{100}$, it would be very different indeed. Again a is only nearly 1 if L is the length of the pendulum. Suppose that the pendulum consisted of a thin rod with a sphere at the end; then the relation would only be true for pendulums, geometrically similar, in which the length and diameter of the rod and the radius of the sphere were all in the same ratio. The relation would be equally true if L were the diameter of the rod, but this diameter might be very small compared with the length and a correspondingly great. It is clear that the question which we want to ask is this, Why is it always possible, by suitable choosing of magnitudes of the same kind, to make a nearly unity, and why does this choice seem "natural" and any which make a very different from unity foolish and artificial? It is clear that no logical considerations can give the answer; it must be somehow based on ideas much more vague.

I think the assumption that a is always nearly unity would be defended in some quarters by such an argument as this. If I watch an occulting light and notice that it appears for 15 seconds once every minute, then I shall be justified in concluding that, involved in the mechanism of the lighthouse, is some process which takes for its complete happening a time not very different from a minute. For suppose that there were involved only processes requiring a small fraction of a second; then the light would appear or disappear only after some very large number of these processes had been completed, and there must be involved some complicated mechanism which enables a distinction to be made between (say) 300 happenings and 301. If I have any reason to believe that the mechanism is essentially simple, I must reject this hypothesis and suppose that the time of the process is a small multiple of the times of occultation or vice versa. Similarly in the pendulum, if the period is one second, there must be something happening in the pendulum about once a second; this something, I am imagining, is determined by a length and an acceleration. I can make a the ratio of the period of this something to the period of the pendulum; and then a cannot be very different from unity.

Considerations of this kind have been put forward; and, though I have done my best to be fair to them, any attempt at expressing them openly shows, as so often happens, that they are entirely false. The argument about the lighthouse is valid only if a very narrow interpretation is given to the idea of simplicity. The period of the light probably depends on the number of teeth on a wheel or the number of holes in a shutter; and a wheel or shutter with a large number of holes is not much more complicated in any reasonable sense than one with a small number. As a matter of fact in actual lighthouse mechanism, the period of the light is often a very considerable multiple of the fundamental mechanism determining it. The application to the pendulum is no less objectionable. It is not true that $(L/g)^{\frac{1}{2}}$ is the period of any fundamental mechanism determining the period; it is not the time in which anything at all important happens in the pendulum. It is the time in which something simple might happen; e.g. the fall and rebound of a small elastic particle sliding down the whole length of the vertical rod. But as a matter of fact, there is no such particle; and if there were, it would have no effect on the period. It is quite untrue that the period is determined by anything happening in the time $(L/g)^{\frac{1}{2}}$; and with the recognition that it is untrue vanishes, I believe, any chance of supporting the assumption by some loose application of a vague "Principle of Sufficient Reason".

Such basis as there is for the assumption is to be found in another direction. The undetermined constant is always a function of magnitudes of two kinds, universal derived constants and no-dimensional constants; of these the geometrical magnitudes determining shape, which are called a' and $f(x, y, z)$ on p. 387, are the most important, for these are the only magnitudes that there is a constant tendency to omit from explicit expression. Now a' is always nearly unity, because we choose our units of volume and area so as to make it unity; that a' is unity is the consequence of a purely arbitrary definition. $f(x, y, z)$ on the other hand depends on the no-dimensional magnitudes characteristic of certain simple geometrical forms; e.g. π (the circle), $\sqrt{2}$ (the square), $\sqrt{3}$ (the equilateral triangle); none of these are very different from unity. The reason why they are not very different from unity is that we choose, as standard shapes, figures of which the most important dimensions are equal; all the radii equal in the circle, the sides equal in the square and triangle; it is because these dimensions are equal that we regard the figures as simple. But it would be perfectly possible to take as standards of shape an extremely elongated ellipse, a parallelogram with very unequal sides, and a scalene triangle. And if we made that choice the magnitudes that would replace π, $\sqrt{2}$, $\sqrt{3}$ would be very different from unity.

The fact that all the magnitudes of which a is a function are near unity is then the result of deliberate choice, all formally arbitrary, but all dictated by reasonable considerations of some kind. But a, though a function of these, will be near unity itself only if the function is comparatively simple; if it involves terms like $e^{\pi^{\pi}}$ it might be very different from unity. Now a simple function, according to a principle of which several applications have been noted already, corresponds to a simple system. So long therefore as we know that the system to which the argument is to be applied is simple, there are some grounds for assuming that a will be near unity. And it may be urged that, if it were not simple, we should not be able to find out about it the kind of information that is required for the application of the argument, unless we solved the whole problem completely by rigid analysis and already knew what a was.

Such seems the explanation of the undoubted fact that in all the usual applications of the principle the undetermined constant is not very far from unity. It is doubtful how far it provides a basis for belief that in all other cases it will be so. The assumption has usually been made in the application of the principle to fundamental atomic and molecular structures, and accordingly the necessary condition that the systems are simple may be plausibly held to be fulfilled. But the greatest caution in basing conclusions on the assumption is clearly necessary.

Indeterminate dimensional equations. We must now remove the last of the restrictions made on p. 405, and consider what happens when there is more than one set of constants $\lambda, \mu, \nu, \rho, \ldots$ satisfying the equations. The application of the argument to dimensions to such cases is apt to prove confusing to students; but if we introduce the conception of physical similarity there are no difficulties whatever.

The procedure adopted depends on a simple algebraical proposition. If we have a set of simultaneous equations

$$\lambda P_x + \mu Q_x + \nu R_x + \rho S_x + \ldots = 0; \qquad \lambda P_y + \mu Q_y + \nu R_y + \rho S_y + \ldots = 0, \text{ etc.}$$

satisfied by more than one set of values of $\lambda, \mu, \nu, \rho, \ldots$; and if, by omitting certain of the P's, Q's, R's, etc. (e.g. the P's and Q's), we can find another set of equations

$$\nu R_x + \rho S_x + \ldots = 0, \text{ etc.}; \qquad \nu R_y + \rho S_y + \ldots = 0, \text{ etc.}$$

which are solved *uniquely* by the values $\nu_1, \rho_1, \ldots$; and if, further, by other omissions of the P's, Q's, and R's, etc., we can find so many other sets of such equations, giving sets of uniquely determined $\lambda, \mu, \nu, \rho, \ldots$, that we have determined at least one λ, one μ, and so on. Then all the values of $\lambda, \mu, \nu, \rho, \ldots$ satisfying the original indeterminate equations will be of the form

$$\lambda = a.\lambda_1 + b.\lambda_2 + c.\lambda_3 + \ldots,$$
$$\mu = a.\mu_1 + b.\mu_2 + c.\mu_3 + \ldots,$$
$$\nu = a.\nu_1 + b.\nu_2 + c.\nu_3 + \ldots,$$
$$\vdots \qquad \vdots \qquad \vdots \qquad \vdots$$

where a, b, c are any constants.

To apply this proposition we note that all the expressions $r^{\nu_1} s^{\rho_1} \ldots,$ $p^{\lambda_2} q^{\mu_2} \ldots, \ldots$ denote no-dimensional magnitudes. Consequently any function $\phi\,(r^{\nu_1} s^{\rho_1} \ldots,\ p^{\lambda_2} q^{\mu_2} \ldots, \ldots)$ with these expressions as arguments will be a no-dimensional magnitude. Therefore if the systems considered are physically similar, this function must be the same for all of them, and the magnitudes must be related by the equation ϕ = constant. Now the dimensional argument asserts that the relation between the magnitudes must be

$$p^\lambda q^\mu r^\nu s^\rho \ldots = \text{constant},$$

where $\lambda, \mu, \nu, \rho, \ldots$ are sets satisfying the original indeterminate simultaneous equations. In virtue of the proposition just quoted any $p^\lambda q^\mu r^\nu s^\rho$ will be no-dimensional only if it is of the form $(r^{\nu_1} s^{\rho_1} \ldots)^a \cdot (p^{\lambda_2} q^{\mu_2} \ldots)^b \ldots$. Such an expression is included among the possible forms of the function ϕ. Accordingly that function represents the most general relation between the magnitudes.

This may sound rather confused, but its meaning is quite clear if an example is taken. Let us revert to the aerodynamical example. The list of characteristic magnitudes F, L, A, ρ, v is complete only if the viscosity of the medium is zero and the velocity very small compared with that of sound; if the conditions are not fulfilled, the viscosity (or preferably the kinematic viscosity ν) and U the velocity of sound must be included in the list. There are now 3 fundamental magnitudes (L, A, V) and 5 derived (F, ρ, v, ν, U); the equations for determining the indices are indeterminate. But examination shows that $FA^{-1}\rho^{-1}v^{-2}$, vU^{-1}, $\dot{\nu}v^{-1}L^{-1}$ are all no-dimensional magnitudes. Therefore, in accordance with what has just been said, the most general relation between the magnitudes compatible with the physical similarity of the systems is $\phi\,(FA^{-1}\rho^{-1}v^{-2},\ vU^{-1},\ \nu v^{-1}L^{-1})$ = shape = constant. So much follows from the principle, but it cannot decide at all what is the form of the function ϕ.

In most treatises this result is stated in the form

$$F = A\rho v^2 \cdot f\left(\frac{v}{U}, \frac{\nu}{vL}\right).$$

This form is perfectly equivalent mathematically to that which has just been stated, so long as it is understood (as it must be understood) that the unknown function f involves a "constant". This constant is the no-dimensional magnitude characteristic of the geometrical properties of the systems. The form obscures the important fact that logically the expression $F/A\rho v^2$ is precisely similar to v/U or vL/ν; the physical significance of all three is that they measure no-dimensional magnitudes. The first is distinguished from the others only in the applications of the result. We know experimentally that, in certain conditions, the relation $F \propto A\rho v^2$ is an adequate expression of the observed facts. As we depart from these conditions, it ceases to be adequate, and we want to know what terms must be added to the relation to make it adequate generally. The answer is that we must introduce some functions of v/U and vL/ν; in other words if we make all our experiments on bodies for which $v/U, vL/\nu$ and the geometrical no-dimensional magnitudes are the same, then the relation will always be $F \propto A\rho v^2$. This statement is of great practical importance and it is conveyed suitably by the form. It is also sometimes conveyed by saying that the systems will not be physically similar unless, in addition to being geometrically similar, they are such that v/U and vL/ν

are the same for all of them. This is quite true, but for completeness it should be added that they are not physically similar unless $F/A\rho v^2$ is the same for all of them. The whole argument is based on the assumption that the systems are familiar in respect of *all* the magnitudes characteristic of them.

For completeness it may just be noted that it is considerations of experimental importance that decide that the relation is to be expressed in the form given and not in one of many equivalent forms such as

$$F = A\rho \frac{v^2}{l^2} \cdot f\left(\frac{v}{U}, \frac{v}{Ul}\right).$$

Other uses of dimensions. In conclusion we must notice two other applications of the theory of dimensions which, though not identical with that which we have been considering, are closely connected with it. The first arises in connection with numerical coincidences. Suppose that we have measured one or more derived magnitudes for some system and we find that there is some very simple relation between the values of these magnitudes (and possibly of those of the fundamental magnitudes), then, it is said, the importance of the discovery depends entirely upon dimensions. If the relation is such that it would vanish if other units were employed in the measurement, then it is of no importance at all; but if it is independent of units then it doubtless has some physical significance, though what significance will depend on circumstances. The classical instance of such an application is connected, of course, with the electromagnetic theory of light. It is said (I do not know on what evidence) that his theory of light was suggested to Maxwell by observing that the numerical value of $\sqrt{K\mu}$ for many transparent media was the same as the numerical value of v, the velocity of light in those media. Investigation shows that the dimensions of $K\mu$ are the same as those of (velocity)^2; consequently the numerical equality will remain unaltered if the units are changed, and the conclusion is therefore drawn that it represents no mere coincidence, but a fact of great physical significance[1].

But what physical significance? It is sometimes said that the numerical coincidence and the agreement in dimensions prove that $\sqrt{K\mu}$ *is* the velocity of light. This statement is untrue in the same way and for the same reason as the statement that L/T^2 for the pendulum *is* an acceleration. If we recognise that it is untrue we are naturally led to ask whether the physical significance would have been altered if it had been found that $K\mu$ was numerically equal, not to v^2 but to $2v^2$ or $1\cdot5v^2$ or $1\cdot5839v^2$. If with the last alternative the significance is unchanged, numerical coincidence can have nothing to do with it, for the numerical value of every magnitude must bear some relation to the

---

[1] It should be mentioned that if μ is defined, as it usually is, by reference to magnets, $\sqrt{K\mu}$ is *not* of the same dimensions as velocity; it involves another universal constant with definite dimensions. This constant is involved in the statement that, if a certain current distribution is equivalent to a certain magnet in one medium, it will be equivalent in any other. It is very surprising how, in modern physical discussions, immense importance is attributed to some universal constants, e.g. c and h, while others are entirely ignored.

numerical value of any other, and the number 1·5839 has been selected entirely at random.

I think it must be concluded that the numerical coincidence is not the sole source of the physical significance and that the significance would have remained if the ratio had been other than 1. For after our previous discussions it need only be pointed out that the similarity of dimensions means that the constant ratio $K\mu/v^2$ defines a no-dimensional magnitude. The importance of no-dimensional magnitudes is that they usually represent the properties of "space", which are concepts that are involved in almost all other concepts; the introduction of a no-dimensional magnitude does not usually involve the introduction of any entirely new physical ideas. The similarity of the dimensions of $K\mu$ and v^2 shows that there may be a numerical law between the two involving, besides these magnitudes, nothing but the properties of space, and this observation suggests further that this law may be explained by a theory which introduces no hypothetical ideas other than those analogous to these concepts. If the dimensions had not been similar, the constancy of the ratio would still have been significant; it would still have shown that the electrical properties of a medium must have something to do with the optical properties. But any theory which was invented to explain the constancy of the ratio might have had to introduce ideas which were not already implicit in all electrical and optical theories. The conclusion suggested by the similarity of dimensions is that any theory that is competent to explain electrical properties ought at the same time to explain optical properties. The numerical coincidence seems to me relatively unimportant, except as a mere coincidence which drew attention to the dimensional coincidence. Whatever the ratio of $K\mu$ to the v^2 of light had turned out to be, so long as it was constant and defined a no-dimensional magnitude, the same conclusions would have been justified. If the ratio had proved very different from unity, the arguments of the last paragraph might have been adduced to prove that any theory connecting electrical and optical properties must be very complex; but we have concluded that no great reliance can be placed on those arguments.

However there are other instances in which the mere numerical coincidence appears to be much more important.

It was pointed out a few years ago that the numerical values of $\dfrac{(4\pi\epsilon)^2}{c}$ and $\dfrac{h}{2\pi}$ are nearly the same[1] and that, if ϵ is measured in electrostatic units, their dimensions are the same. From what has been said already it is clear that the dimensions are not really the same, for K, the dielectric constant, must be introduced if any valid argument from dimensions is to be made. That K has the value 1 for a vacuum is either the result of purely arbitrary definition (if ϵ is measured as quasi-derived), or is a consequence of an

---

[1] It is quite clear now that they are not the same, for with the latest values of ϵ and h, c would have to be $3\cdot45 \times 10^{10}$ if they were to be the same. The difference from the known value is far greater than can be attributed to experimental error.

arbitrary choice of the unit of charge (if ϵ is measured as fundamental); in either case the numerical coincidence would be changed by change in a purely arbitrary assumption. However the necessity for the introduction of K does not alter greatly the position; it only indicates that any theory which is to explain the numerical relation must introduce, besides no-dimensional magnitudes, the magnitude K, or rather ideas analogous to these magnitudes. But in introducing K we are not really adding to the physical ideas involved, for K is so intimately associated with ϵ that if we introduce one we expect to have to introduce the other[1]. There does not seem then to be any important difference between this numerical coincidence and that between $K\mu$ and v^2. Yet there doubtless is a difference, for while the physical significance of the dimensional relation between $K\mu$ and v^2 would not have vanished if their ratio had been found not to be exactly 1, nobody would attach any physical significance to that between $\dfrac{(4\pi\epsilon)^2}{c}$ and $\dfrac{h}{2\pi}$ now that it is known that the ratio is not exactly 1. This difference arises from the fact that there is a law $K\mu \propto v^2$, and that there is not and cannot be a law $\dfrac{\epsilon^2}{c} \propto h$. For a law implies that something remains the same while something else changes. K, μ, v can change while the ratio $K\mu/v^2$ remains constant, for there are different systems[2] characterised by different values of K, μ, v. On the other hand ϵ, c, h cannot change; it is part of their essential meaning that they are universal constants. There is a reason, namely the existence of the law, quite apart from all numerical coincidences, for believing that a theory may be evolved concerning K, μ, v; there is no reason whatever apart from the numerical coincidence for believing that any theory can be evolved connecting ϵ, c, h. The introduction of 4 and π into the relation in order to secure numerical coincidence is justified on the ground that, if there is any theory, it is highly likely that these constants will be brought in with the spatial conceptions; but if any constants have to be brought in which are not closely connected with spatial conceptions, then all reasons vanish for believing that any theory at all cannot be produced which will explain the relation.

There is one other use of dimensions, yet vaguer and more inconclusive, but nevertheless of some importance. It is best illustrated by an example that might have occurred, but actually did not. Boyle's Law defines a constant $= pV$ which, for a given quantity of gas, is a function of the temperature only; pV changes when the temperature changes and is constant when it is constant.

[1] So long as we are thinking of that property of electric charges in virtue of which they attract each other. If we were thinking of the properties of electric charges in motion, then we should expect to introduce μ and not K. The conclusion to be drawn from the fact that the numerical relation remains only so long as electrostatic units are used is that the theory which explains it must be based on analogy with the properties of charges at rest, not on those which are characteristic of charges in motion.

[2] Or there were according to electrical theory in Maxwell's time. According to modern theory K for material media has such an entirely different meaning from K for a vacuum that it is hardly correct to regard all the K's as the same magnitude.

The constant has the same dimensions as energy. The observation of this fact might have suggested to somebody that a theory might be conceived in which changes of temperature were represented in the dictionary by the changes of the energy of some system. It is not in the least necessary that the theory should be of this form; the dictionary might relate temperature to some function such as [mass] × [velocity] × [time]$^{-1}$ and the dictionary might state that changes of temperature were represented by changes of mass. The representation of temperature by energy is only one of an infinite number of possibilities which the dimensional relation will admit.

But in one instance considerations of this kind did undoubtedly suggest a theory. Bohr has confessed that he was led to the fundamental ideas of his theory of atomic structure by noticing that the constant h, in the numerical law[1] $E = h\nu$, has the dimensions of a moment of momentum. Up to that time it had always been called an "element of action" and such theories as had been put forward to "explain" it had attempted to represent it as an "action". These theories are not disproved by the new view of the matter; but there is no doubt that the newer view that h "is" a moment of momentum has led to theories and hypothetical ideas of very great fruitfulness. It may be noted that the main assumptions of Bohr's theory might also have been suggested by the observation of a numerical coincidence, namely the coincidence of Rydberg's constant with a function of other universal constants. This coincidence, being a relation between numerical constants, would have been similar to that between $\dfrac{(4\pi\epsilon)^2}{c}$ and $\dfrac{h}{2\pi}$; but even if it had been noticed it would only have suggested that some theory could be found relating N with ϵ, c, h, m_0; it would not have directly suggested the theory which was based on regarding h as a moment of momentum.

Dynamical similarity and graphs. In Chapter XIII we concluded that a numerical law could be adequately expressed by a graph and that no representation involving numerals or Number was really necessary to convey the full meaning of the law. The question ought to be asked whether this conclusion extends to the application of reasoning based on the principle of dynamical reasoning. If the numerical laws on which that reasoning is founded were expressed by graphs instead of by numerals, could we still deduce our conclusions? We could. I shall not attempt to give a complete demonstration but merely such indication as will probably satisfy the reader.

Let us take once more the example of the pendulum, and consider first what form the argument sketched on p. 421, on which the reasoning is based, would take if we had our laws expressed by graphs. Starting with the pendulum at rest in a given position, we want one graph expressing the relation between the distance it travels and the time, and another expressing the relation between the velocity acquired and the time. Our fundamental assumption is that they are of the form characteristic of the corresponding

---

[1] Of course it is not really a law, but a theory. We have agreed for the present to neglect this distinction.

curves for a body falling freely; that is to say, if we plot them with suitable scales of abscissae and ordinates they can be made to coincide (at any rate in the initial part) with those corresponding curves. From these curves we determine the time required for the pendulum to reach a new position, for which we have other similar curves, and the velocity it acquires in reaching that position. From the time so determined we plot the first point on a curve giving the relation between the position of pendulum and the time. We then proceed to examine the curves for the new position and obtain a second point for our curve, and so on. We get finally the time-interval after which the first position is regained, and this time interval is the period.

When we say that any other pendulum is dynamically similar to that for which we have carried out this process, what we mean is this. The pendulums are both characterised by certain fundamental magnitudes of different kinds. To each magnitude in one pendulum corresponds another of the same kind in the other. If we plot magnitudes for one pendulum against corresponding magnitudes of the same kind for the other pendulum, the points will lie on a straight line. Let us choose the scales of plotting for the magnitudes of the same kind in the two pendulums so that this straight line is equally inclined to both axes. Thus if for pendulum 1 we choose, in plotting lengths, to represent 1 metre by 1 centimetre, we may, in order to make the straight line equally inclined to both axes, have to represent 1 metre by 4 cm. for pendulum 2; if we choose, in plotting time-intervals for pendulum 1 to represent 1 second by 1 cm., we may have to represent 1 sec. by 2 cm. for pendulum 2. Now all the laws which are true of a pendulum are expressible by graphs the axes of which represent these fundamental magnitudes. The Principle of Dynamical Similarity asserts that if in plotting these graphs, expressing the laws characteristic of the pendulum, we use the same scales as we did when we made the straight line of corresponding magnitudes equally inclined to the axis, then the graphs will be identical for all the pendulums. If for pendulum 1 we plot the graph for the motion of the pendulum from its first position with 1 cm. to the metre for length and 1 cm. to the second for time; and if for pendulum 2 we plot the graph with 4 cm. for length and 2 cm. for time, then the graph for pendulum 2 will be exactly the same as the graph for pendulum 1.

The assertion of the Principle of Dynamical Similarity in this form is again obviously based on the conception of similarity as a change of scale. The no-dimensional magnitudes which characterise all the similar systems are represented by the angles which the straight lines of corresponding magnitudes make with the axes. By making these lines equally inclined to both axes, we have in fact chosen our scales of plotting so that all the no-dimensional magnitudes are equal. Since, then, the no-dimensional magnitudes determine the motion, the motions must, on the scale adopted, be precisely the same in all the similar systems. It is for this reason that the graphs representing any law must be identical.

It is now not difficult to see that if we plot the length of the pendulum against the period using the appropriate scale for each pendulum, all pendulums will be represented by the same point; for the period is determined throughout by the same graphs whatever the pendulum. If we now plot the lengths against the period, using the same scale for all pendulums, we shall obtain the information which the Principle of Dynamical Similarity is designed to give. Of course the form of this curve will be determined by the form of the graphs representing the laws of the pendulum; for corresponding to each form of law there is only one (if any) possible relation between the scales of the fundamental magnitudes which is such that the graph will remain unchanged when we pass from one pendulum to another.

CHAPTER XVI

ERRORS OF MEASUREMENT

I. METHODICAL ERRORS

Summary. Our discussion of fundamental measurement in Chapter X was based on the assumption that the laws of equality and addition are strictly true. But they are not generally true. It is generally possible to find three systems A, B, C, such that $A = B$ and $B = C$, but $A \neq C$.

The failure of these laws is reconciled with the fundamental idea that a magnitude can be represented by a single definite numeral by the introduction of the conception of "errors of measurement". It is pointed out that these errors are of two kinds, errors of method and errors of consistency: if it is only the laws of equality and addition that fail, we are concerned with errors of method alone.

The results of the failure of these laws is examined carefully. The failure does not prevent us establishing a self-consistent standard series, though it cannot be made by the specification given in Chapter X.

The problem of establishing a system of fundamental measurement which shall be free from errors of method is then attacked. We must alter either our definition of equality or of addition. Reasons are given why it seems more plausible to alter the former.

The new definition of equality proposed depends on the conception of a "real magnitude". The direct observation of equality involved in our previous definition is considered to show, not that the real magnitudes are equal, but only that they differ by less than some amount, which is the error of measurement. In order to apply this new definition to the determination of real magnitudes some further proposition about the errors must be introduced.

It is insisted that the new definition and all the propositions connected with it are theoretical. The theory of measurement is stated in the standard form of Chapter VI.

It is examined how far the theory is in accordance with experiment and how far the hypothetical ideas involved in it (real magnitudes and errors) can be determined by experiment. It is concluded that no facts are known contrary to the theory, but on the other hand it is impossible, without introducing further propositions, to determine any of the hypothetical ideas and so produce direct confirmation of the theory. These additional propositions must include a "law of errors"; discussions of possible laws are reserved for the next chapter.

Though it has been found so far impossible to determine real magnitudes uniquely and so avoid all the consequences of the failures of the laws of equality and addition, some progress has been made. Our measurements, though still "inaccurate", are not so inaccurate as they would have been if the theory had not been introduced. The very important conception of a "stepped" measuring instrument is introduced; it will concern us greatly in future discussions.

Lastly it is asked whether all fundamental magnitudes are affected by errors of method. All are, except one; the one exception is number. Number is, however, affected by errors of consistency, an observation which enforces the essential distinction between the two kinds of error.

Failure of the laws of addition and equality. In considering the process of fundamental measurement we concluded that such a process could be established only if the laws of equality and addition were true. But they are seldom strictly true. We must now turn our attention to the modifications in the process which are rendered necessary by their failure. Of the two "laws of equality", namely that the relation of equality must be transitive and that it must be symmetrical, the second is always true, for its truth is necessarily implied by the definition of equality. If A is neither greater nor less than B, then, in virtue of the meanings of greater and less, B is neither less nor greater than A. But the truth of the first law is not implied in the definition, and, as a matter of fact, the law is not generally true. In most systems of fundamental measurement it is possible to find three systems A, B, C, such that A is neither greater nor less than B, B neither greater nor less than C, and yet A is either greater or less than C; sometimes A will be found greater than C, sometimes less, and sometimes the law will be true and A will be equal to C.

The laws of addition are also not generally true. The first law, that $a + p$ is greater than a will occasionally fail. Thus, if we take again weighing as an example of fundamental measuring, it is possible to find a body such that, if it is placed in the same pan as one of two bodies which balance each other, the balance will not be disturbed. If we were to choose such a body as our unit—and we have so far imposed no limitation whatever on the choice of units—the first law would be untrue in the more specialised and more important form, $a + 1$ is greater than a. At first sight it might seem that such observations only prove that the body which can be added without disturbing the balance has the weight o; but this method of avoiding the difficulty is impossible for two reasons. First, though the body P may not disturb the balance of the bodies A_1 and A_2, when placed in the pan with either of them, it may disturb the balance of two bodies B_1 and B_2, when placed in the pan with one of them. (If such conditions are found, it will usually be found also that, though P placed in the same pan with B_1 disturbs the balance, it will not disturb the balance if placed in the pan with B_2.) Second, if we find a number of bodies P, such that when placed in the same pan with one of two balancing bodies, they do not disturb the balance, and add all these bodies P together by placing them on the same pan, they depress the pan and can be balanced against some other body which has not the weight o, because, whenever it is placed in a pan with either of two balancing bodies, it depresses that pan. But if all the bodies P had the weight o, their sum would have the weight o, if the process of measurement were satisfactory.

The second law of addition is equally untrue. It is possible to find four bodies A, B, C, D, such that A balances B and C balances D, and yet, if A and C are placed together in one pan, while B and D are placed together in the other, the sums will not balance. It is not generally true that equals added to equals are equal.

These facts when they are pointed out are obvious and familiar; and yet it is probable that they did not occur to many readers during their reading of Chapter X; unless they had thought a good deal about the matter before, they probably accepted without hesitation the statements that the laws of equality and addition were true in the process of weighing with the balance. And when their attention is drawn to the discrepancies which have just been described, they may be inclined to say that the laws on which weighing depends are, at any rate, "very nearly true". This conception of "very nearly true" demands a moment's consideration. We have seen in our consideration of probability that scientific truth, or at least scientific belief in truth, is a matter of degree and that it cannot be maintained that every proposition is either definitely true or definitely untrue. But it is not degree of truth in this sense which is in question here; there is no doubt whatever that the laws of equality stated in the form of Chapter X are quite definitely untrue; indeed at a later stage of our inquiry important considerations will be founded on the fact that they are not true. What is meant here when it is said that the laws are very nearly true is, first, that a very large number of cases can be found in which they are true, and that there are definitely true propositions which differ very little from the laws in question. But here again "differ very little" is a phrase which demands examination, for there are other cases in which laws which, apparently, "differ very little" are held to be supremely important just because of that very little difference—the laws, for example, of the properties of thorium and ionium.

The feeling that the laws of equality and addition are very nearly true, and that they differ very little from the strictly true laws by which they are to be replaced, is due, I believe, to the way in which the new laws have developed out of the old. In some cases when we find that a law which we have believed to be true is not strictly a law, we have to abandon it altogether and start entirely afresh; such, for instance, has been the case in the development of thermometry. But in other cases, of which that which we are considering is typical, the new development does not wholly abandon the old path. Our ideas of the measurement of weight and of most other fundamental magnitudes were founded by those who believed (unconsciously, of course) that the laws of equality and addition were true; when it was discovered that they were not strictly true, the old ideas were still retained and the new ideas developed without wholly abandoning the laws on which the old ideas were based. The conception of "errors of measurement" was introduced. The very phrase "errors of measurement" seems to imply that there is some method of measurement free from error; and that the existence of errors does not force us to abandon measurement, but only to "correct" the errors to which it may be liable. The retention of words and ideas based on laws which are known not to be true is doubtless dangerous; indeed it has actually caused error and confusion. It is therefore necessary to consider very carefully the process of correction, and to discover how far it can be stated in a manner wholly free from fallacy and ambiguity. The process is of particular importance in connection with fundamental measurement, but similar processes occur in many later developments of physics. We must be careful in the discussion not to use prematurely ideas that can properly result only from the completed discussion. On the other hand, since those ideas are extremely familiar, it would be pedantic to refuse to use terms based on them, for the ideas themselves are sure to be present in the reader's mind.

Errors of consistency and errors of method. We have then to consider what we mean by "errors of measurement", how we determine what the errors are and how we arrive at measurements which are free from error. At the outset it will be convenient to distinguish clearly two kinds of error of measurement which, though closely connected and often confused, are not inseparable and have to be considered apart. Often, perhaps usually, when we speak of errors of measurement, we are thinking of cases in which successive measurements on the same system are not consistent with each other; if we repeat a measurement, we arrive at a result which is clearly not the same as that which we had obtained before. Such "errors of consistency" are not those which have been described in the opening paragraph. Perhaps it is doubtful—for a reason which we shall consider in a moment—if it is possible to find any system of measurement which is wholly free from errors of consistency, but it seems that the most accurate fundamental measurements, those of length, time, weight, and electrical resistance, are very definitely free from them (in the most suitable conditions); if we are using a very good balance in the best circumstances, then whether we judge that the weight A is greater or less than B, or judge that it is neither greater nor less, we can repeat that judgement if we repeat the observation under those conditions which are known to be most free from errors of consistency. However if even the most careful measurements are not perfectly free from these errors, the errors are entirely different from the "errors of method" or "methodical errors" which we are considering [1]. For these methodical errors only appear in the comparison of measurements on at least three systems, and they appear if we only make a single measurement on each of those systems, so that no question of consistency can arise. It is conceivable (even if it is not practically possible) that conditions should exist in which methodical errors should be found in the total absence of errors of consistency; and in what follows we shall suppose that such conditions obtain, and inquire later into the questions which arise when errors of consistency and errors of method are both present.

Consequences of error. First let us examine rather more closely exactly what happens when the laws of equality and addition are not fulfilled. We shall suppose as usual that all the measurements that are to be used directly in our experiments are made by use of a calibrated instrument, and that all magnitudes are determined by judging them to be equal to one of the members of the standard series included in that instrument. The fundamental process of measurement enters only in the making of the standard series. This series must include a member equal to every system which it is desired to measure,

---

[1] Systematic errors would perhaps be a better phrase, but it is already appropriated to a rather different sense.

but all these members are not always realised separately; some of the members are made by combination of other members. Thus we do not usually have a standard set of weights or resistances one of which is equal to any weight or resistance that we may possibly want to measure; we have such a series as ·01, ·02, ·02, ·05, ·1, ·2, ·2, ·5, 1, 2, 2, 5, ..., and make up a member equal to any system which is not equal to one of these by adding two or more of these together. For members less than ·01 we again have members of the standard series, but they are usually realised in a rather different way; thus the weight ·001 may consist of a rider in a certain position on the beam, and the resistance ·001 of a certain deflection on a galvanometer scale; but in principle these members are precisely the same as the members realised in the normal way, and they require no separate consideration. The same principle is employed again in a slightly different way in setting up the standard series of length; we do not usually carry the finer graduations all along the scale; and it is employed in yet another manner in the standard series of time, though the detailed consideration of this series must be left for the present.

Other magnitudes than these are usually measured as quasi-derived magnitudes by means of scales calibrated in terms of these basic magnitudes. Accordingly we have only to consider for our present purpose what will be the effect on measurement, by means of such a standard series as that of weight, if the laws of equality and addition are not obeyed.

The main difference will be this; the standard series will either not be self-consistent, or it will have gaps, so that there are some systems which are not equal to any members of the standard series. By self-inconsistency is meant that members which, when added together, should be equal to each other (because the numerals assigned to them are such that the corresponding Numbers added together are equal) will not actually be found to be equal. Such inconsistency can always be avoided (and is avoided in some objectionable instruments) by choosing the members of the series so that one and only one collection of members, added together, is to be represented by any given numeral; the easiest way to prepare such a series is to make every member represented by a power of 2, positive or negative. But if inconsistency is thus avoided, then, if the series is prepared by a method which does not obey the laws of equality and addition, we fall on the other horn of the dilemma, and there are gaps in the series (as we saw in one particular case of failure at the end of Chapter XII). Accordingly, if we measure by means of such a series, either there will be ambiguity and it may be possible to assign two different numerals to represent the same system, or there will be gaps and it will be impossible to assign a numeral to some systems at all. In either case the fundamental purpose of measurement is unfulfilled.

However, it should be noted that, if the failures of the laws of equality and addition are such as are considered here, the difficulties that have been mentioned will not always arise. If we went on long enough preparing standard series, one after the other, according to the prescription, after a sufficient number of trials we should always obtain a standard series, both unambiguous and without gaps. Or we might attain the result by departing from the prescription and, after we had made a standard series which was not satisfactory, tinker at it by mere trial and error, till we had found one which was satisfactory. By either means trial and error would ultimately lead to the result that we want. That it would so lead is a mere experimental fact; no ideas that have been introduced so far could possibly prove that the result must ultimately be obtained.

A minor effect of the failure of the laws of equality and addition will appear if systems measured by comparison with the standard series are compared among themselves. Two systems equal to the same member of the standard series will not always be equal to each other; and systems equal to 2 and 5 of the standard series will not, if added together, always equal those equal to 3 and 4. But this effect is not, I believe, as serious as appears at first sight; for it is very seldom that we have any occasion to compare among themselves systems which we have once measured. It may be replied that we have no occasion to do so, only because we know what the result of the comparison would be; that may be part of the truth, but it is not the whole truth. In Chapters XIII to XV we have discussed with some thoroughness all the most important applications of measurement to physics; but in discussing them I do not think we have made any use whatever of the laws of equality and addition applied to systems when once they are measured; those laws are important only as an indication that the system of measurement is satisfactory. If it could happen (it is not easy to devise an instance of its happening) that the standard series and the method of judging equality with the standard series were satisfactory, and yet the bodies measured did not obey the laws of addition and equality, it is by no means certain that their failure to do so would have any scientific importance whatever. It certainly cannot be proved from any of our previous discussions that it would be important.

The judgement of equality. Such are the symptoms of the disease we have to cure; now let us examine the necessary features of the remedy.

In order to find a new system of measurement which shall be free from the discrepancies which have been noted and yet shall fulfil the essential purposes of measurement we must in some manner make the laws of equality and addition true. This end cannot be achieved without altering our definition of equality, for the discrepancies affect relations in which only equality, and not addition, is involved; but it may be necessary to alter the definition of addition as well. But reasons are immediately apparent why the definition of addition need not be altered. For we have seen that there are certain laws which must be true, if the process of measurement is to be satisfactory, which do not involve equality at all, but only greater and less.

In the first place the relations of greater and less have to be transitive and asymmetrical. This proposition is strictly and accurately true if a suitable balance and suitable conditions of weighing are adopted. The characteristic relation generating the order of weight is perfectly satisfactory and is not, as in the case of hardness, liable to exceptions and irregularity. Further there are the laws of addition involving only greater and less which were mentioned on p. 284. Among these laws involving only greater and less is the first law of addition. Now this law in the form essential to measurement, namely that $a + 1$ is greater than a, is not true if we impose no conditions whatever on the choice of unit; it would not be true if the unit were very small, but on the other hand it is always possible to choose the unit so that the law is true. Accordingly to make this law true all that is necessary is to impose some slight limitation on the choice of unit; this limitation does not make any other alteration necessary and it is of no practical importance, for it would be imposed also by other considerations which will be noted later. Accordingly the first step in establishing a new system of measurement is to limit the unit chosen so that the first law is always true.

The other laws of addition which do not involve equality correspond to the second law of addition. They state that, if A is greater (or less) than C, and B than D, then the sum of A and C will be greater (or less) than the sum of B and D; also that it is only the nature of the bodies placed in one pan, and not the order or position in which they are placed in the pan, which determines whether one collection will be heavier or lighter than another. Now there are conditions in which these laws are strictly and accurately true, the conditions, namely, which define an accurate balance and bodies suitable for accurate weighing. If weighing is by substitution, it seems impossible to devise a balance which will weigh at all (i.e. for which the first law of addition is true) and does not obey the second law, so far as it applies to relations of greater and less. Accordingly if we consider only the relations of greater and less, all the laws involved in measurement are accurately true. Discrepancies arise only when we introduce the relation of equality; and it is strongly suggested that, if we change suitably the definition of equality, the discrepancies will vanish.

This suggestion is enforced when we consider in what a judgement of equality consists. The judgement which we make is not really a judgement that A is definitely not greater and not less than B, but only a judgement that we cannot decide that A is greater or less than B. We can sometimes judge perfectly definitely that A is greater than B and sometimes that it is less; and, as we have seen, when we can definitely make those judgements then no discrepancy in measurement arises. Our judgement of equality is merely a refraining from making one of two definite judgements, and we are aware in our own minds of a lack of certainty in the matter. We feel there is no perfectly sharp distinction between the cases in which we are prepared to make a definite judgement and those in which we refrain; the truth of judgements of equality, unlike the truth of judgements of greater or less, is felt to be a matter of degree. It is for this reason, of course, that we consider that errors of consistency are likely to be associated always with errors of method. As we are conscious that our judgements are not perfectly definite, we can readily understand that we may not always make exactly the same judgement if we repeat the observation.

Real magnitudes. These observations would be expressed in uncritical discourse by the statement that the discrepancies which are under discussion arise from the fact that our judgements of equality may be erroneous and that we sometimes judge weights to be equal when they are not really equal. Now this is obviously one of these cases when the word "really" may cover a multitude of confusions; and if we are to make any progress its use must be avoided. There is no harm in using the word so long as we are sure that the ideas expressed by it can also be expressed in language which is not open to the same charge of ambiguity; but we must be sure that the ideas can be so expressed. It is merely meaningless to say that our judgement of equality is wrong, unless we can set up some standard according to which it could be right. So far the only meaning which has been attached to the term "equal" is that of balancing (or analogous operations for other magnitudes), and there is no sense whatever in saying that bodies which do balance are not equal. Such a statement will have sense only if we lay down some new definition of equality.

The definition which is implied by the loose expression from which we started may be expressed more strictly thus: Bodies which are equal in weight balance, but the converse proposition is not always true. Bodies may balance although their weights are not equal, but differ by some "small" amount. The fact that a and b balance does not show that the "real weights" A and B are equal, but only that A and B do not differ by more than a certain amount; in other words a and b will balance if their real weights are such that $|A - B| = \epsilon$, where ϵ, "the error", is not greater than some assigned amount E. Such is undoubtedly the idea to which we are led by observing the peculiarities of our judgements of equality as compared with those of greater and less. Let us examine it.

It is clear at once that the definition will not define anything useful, unless we can fix E independently of it; for if E is a perfectly unknown amount, A and B can have any values. But a simple development of the idea immediately fixes E. Though we are going to change our definition of equality, we propose to leave our definition of greater and less unchanged; we cannot change that definition without changing the meaning of weight, for weight simply is the property of all bodies which form the field of the relation of greater and less as we have defined it. The real magnitude of a will be greater than that of b, if a weighs down b. Accordingly if a weighs down b, we must have $A > B$, or $|A - B| = Q$, where Q is different from o. But this relation is of exactly the same form as that defining equality, namely $|A - B| = \epsilon$; the distinction between equality and inequality must lie in a difference between ϵ and Q. In order to carry out our general idea the difference must be that ϵ is less than Q. Accordingly the following definition for E is suggested; E is equal to the least difference between the magnitudes of any two bodies which are such that one weighs down the other.

It follows then that the difference of the weights of any bodies which balance can never be greater than the difference of the weights of bodies which do not balance, and that consequence of our definitions is once more in accordance with our general idea. The reader will probably notice that a difficulty has been introduced, but we will leave it on one side for the moment and proceed.

The new definition of equality will be no better than the old unless it permits us to assign a numeral to every system in the order generated by the characteristic relation, and to assign only one numeral to each system. It is apparent that whether this condition is fulfilled depends entirely upon what is known about the errors. We can apply our definition to experiment only by observing what sets of bodies balance; each time we find a balance we get an equation between two real magnitudes and an error. If the error of each such observation is independent of that of any other, then every time we add an equation to our list we add also an independent variable; since there must be at least two independent variables other than the errors (namely, two real magnitudes), the number of variables will always be greater than the number of equations, the solution will be indeterminate and there will be an infinite number of possible real weights for each body. On the other hand, our definition sets some limit on the errors; it states that they must all be less than E. If E is assigned, it might turn out that no set of ϵ, all less than E, would satisfy the equation, or that only one such set would; these are mathematical possibilities which cannot be disproved *a priori*; but as a matter of fact it is always found that, even when an upper limit E is set to the values of the ϵ's in the manner we have discussed, the number of possible solutions of the equations given by the observations, and the number of possible real magnitudes for each body, is still infinite.

There is only one way, consistent with the ideas underlying the new definition, by which this number can be reduced and the determination of the real magnitudes made definite. That way is to introduce further propositions about the errors ϵ, so that some of them are made dependent on the others and the number of independent variables is reduced. This course is actually adopted; but before we examine the matter further it will be well to stop for a moment and consider carefully the position at which we have arrived.

The theory of measurement. We started to escape from the discrepancies arising from the failure of the laws of addition and equality by taking a new definition of equality. Now no mere definition—the mere giving of a name to a thing or the invention of a new symbolism—can extricate us from any difficulties which arise because the laws of nature are not what we should like them to be; to imagine the contrary is to admit the fallacy against which men of science had to fight so long for victory. Accordingly we should have anticipated from the first that we should have to add propositions to our definition. We have already added two; we have added a proposition about E and one about the relations of the errors ϵ. There is no doubt that the second is an assertion and not a mere definition, and if at first sight the proposition about E appears a mere amplification of the original definition, a very short inquiry will convince us that it is not. For we have assumed implicitly that Q is (within certain limits at least) independent of A and B; if it varied with every A and B, the definition of E would not convey our ideas unless E were equal to the least Q for the same A and B. E would also vary with A and B; and before we could determine E we should have to determine A and B—which, of course, is absurd[1]. Now the proposition that Q is independent of A and B is of supreme importance. For if Q is not determined by the magnitudes of the bodies on the balance, by what is it determined? By the balance, of course; that is the natural answer, but it represents none the less a very important step forward in the argument. We have now introduced a wholly novel idea that the real magnitudes are determined by the bodies weighed and the errors by the process of weighing them. This idea is involved intimately in the method of fixing E, and without it we should have never got past the original formal definition.

And not only have we introduced new ideas and new propositions, but we have also explained why the old definition was unsatisfactory. The idea of an error, depending on the instrument of measurement, explains why it is satisfactory up to a certain point and no further. Now this is the important matter. For the fact that "explanation" is involved indicates here, as elsewhere, that we have passed from the realm of laws into that of theories; a little consideration will show that the new conceptions of "real magnitude" and "error" which have been introduced are distinctively theoretical. It is characteristic of theories that the conceptions of the propositions stated cannot be adequately described in terms of experiment alone; they can only be given a meaning if the truth of some proposition which is not purely experimental is assumed. In the original system of measurement, based on the assumption that the laws of equality and addition were true, we could describe adequately and exactly what we mean by saying that a body has the weight 3 in terms of experiment alone; we mean that it will balance the unit weight in the same pan with another body which in turn will balance a unit weight and another weight balanced by the unit weight. But when we say, according to our new definition, that the real weight of a body is 3, we cannot say exactly what we mean in terms of experiment alone. Any experiment only gives information about a relation between real magnitudes and errors; but real magnitudes and errors can only be distinguished and evaluated separately in virtue of the propositions about the nature of errors, namely that they

---

[1] It may be said that, according to our definition, we should in any case have to know some A and B in order to determine Q. This is perfectly true as the definitions are expressed, but the objection might be avoided by expressing it differently. It is possible to put the definitions in a form which leads to equations, based on observations of balancing, involving the real magnitudes and the errors, and connecting the criterion of equality to that of greater and less without assuming that, in the application of the criterion, any magnitude has been previously assigned a numeral. But the form is very complex, and the considerations to which we are proceeding show that any attempt of the kind does not really avoid the ultimate conclusion.

depend on the instrument and are related in a certain way. And the meaning of this proposition is not clearly conveyed by any statement about the observational equations resulting from balancing. It is possible that it may be proved by them—we have yet to inquire into that—but the proof does not convey the meaning.

If it is recognised that the definition of equality which introduces error is theoretical, it can be described quite simply and clearly in the standard form of propositions and dictionary. The propositions are: (1) Every system which has a place in the order of the magnitude concerned is characterised by a numeral called its real magnitude A or B; (2) The magnitude of a combination of bodies in a manner called addition (differing according to the kind of magnitude) is the sum of the real magnitudes of the bodies in the combination; (3) The instrument of measurement is characterised by a numeral E, called the maximum error; (4) Some proposition about the relation between the individual errors ϵ or their distribution; this matter will be considered presently. The dictionary then states that the propositions $|A - B| >$ or $< E$ mean that the body A is greater than or equal to the body B, according to the definition of these terms by means of the characteristic relation which generated the order of the bodies.

Not only can the proposed criterion of equality and greater or less be stated in this form, but this form conveys accurately the true meaning of the criterion and the ideas that underlie it. It will hardly be doubted that the "definition" of equality is really part of the hypothesis of a theory, and that "real magnitudes" and "experimental error" are theoretical conceptions or hypothetical ideas. We shall now accept this view and discuss the matter further on the assumption that we are dealing with a theory and that the examination that must be conducted is that appropriate to a theory. But before we proceed one point should be noted. In the first three chapters of this Part great care was taken to show that the process of measurement did not necessarily involve the introduction of mathematical conceptions; our reason for taking that care was that, if measurement involved necessarily mathematical conceptions, all the results of it must be theoretical and state propositions concerning hypothetical ideas and not concerning concepts. But now we are forced to the conclusion that if by measurement we mean the process of determining real magnitudes, theory must necessarily enter; there is no object in endeavouring to exclude mathematical conceptions, even if it were possible. We may therefore suppose that to every observational equation between real magnitudes and errors, arising from the results of balancing, corresponds a similar equation between Numbers; and that any conclusion drawn from the equations (other than that concerning the physical relation between the magnitudes) will be determined by the validity of a similar equation about the Numbers. I do not know whether this is equivalent to saying that a real magnitude "is" a Number, but I am inclined to think that it is not. For Number, according to those who expound its character, "is" undoubtedly something; on the other hand it seems that a statement that '*a* real magnitude is" anything is one of those misleading abbreviations which must be rejected if perfect clearness is to be attained. All that the theory states is the meaning of the proposition that "*the* real magnitude of so-and-so is such-and-such".

Examination of the theory. Assuming then that our "definition" of equality is really part of the hypothesis of a theory, which is more completely stated at the end of the last paragraph, we have next to inquire whether the theory is true. It will be true if it leads to an unique determination of the real magnitude of every body and to the error of every instrument. On the other hand, if it does not lead to this result, it is not a necessary conclusion that the theory is untrue; it will only be proved untrue if it is shown to be impossible to assign to every body a real magnitude, and to every instrument an error, so as to satisfy the propositions of the hypothesis. Between these extremes lies the alternative that we shall be able to find several values of the real magnitudes of each body, and several errors for each instrument, all of which are such that they fulfil the conditions of the hypothesis. If that alternative results, the theory will be shown to be true, but it will not perform perfectly the purpose for which it was designed, namely the assigning of one and only one numeral to represent the magnitude of every body.

We must note first that the theory provides a way of determining E, the maximum error, by experiment. E can be estimated as follows. Place in the two pans two bodies, a and b, which balance; and search for bodies, p, which have the following two properties: (1) they can be placed in either one pan or the other without disturbing the balance, (2) if placed in either one pan or the other they will disturb the balance—this pan being, of course, that opposite to the first pan. Such bodies can be found. Now[1] place the unit weight on one pan and determine the number of bodies p which must be placed on the other so that the addition of the nth turns the balance over on the side of the p's. Then we may argue thus. The real magnitudes of a and b are such that $|A - B| < E$. If any p fulfils condition (1) its real magnitude P cannot be greater than $2E$, because, if P is greater than $2E$, $|A - B + P|$ is always greater than E. If any p fulfils condition (2) its real magnitude cannot be less than E, for if P is less than E, both $|A - B + P|$ and $|A - B - P|$ may be less than E. Accordingly the real magnitude of the n bodies lies between nE and $2nE$; but the real magnitude of the n is greater than $1 + E$, while the real magnitude of $n - 1$ of them is less than $1 + E$. The limits of E are fixed by $2nE > 1 + E$, $(n - 1) E < 1 + E$, or E lies between $1/(2n - 1)$ and $1/n$.

Having thus found the limits between which E must lie, we can inquire whether these limits are independent of the weights which are already in the balanced pans when the experiment is made; we shall find that they are independent over a considerable range, and shall thus confirm the truth of

---

[1] If the bodies p are the same rider in various positions, the second part of the experiment may be unnecessary. But since the use of the rider involves the previous establishment of a system of measurement, in order to prove the laws of the rider, it is well to consider the fundamental case.

the theory, if it is only used for weights all of which lie within the range. It may be noted in passing that we have already assumed such independence in taking E to be the same when the unit is in one pan as when the original bodies were in the pan. This assumption could have been avoided, but as we have now proved it is true, the additional complication is unnecessary. On the other hand we can inquire whether the limits of E vary with the balance; we shall find that they do so vary.

So far the theory is satisfactory. We can determine E, at any rate within certain limits, and those limits turn out to be independent of the bodies weighed and dependent on the instrument. In what follows we must take the larger limit of E.

We must now investigate whether we can actually assign the real magnitudes and the errors of the individual observations so that these errors are all less than the E which has been determined. The following is the procedure that we must adopt for the purpose. We take any number of bodies of any kind whatsoever, such that the collection includes the body selected as unit weight, and such that the number of pairs of combinations of the bodies which will balance each other is greater than the total number of bodies. If the real magnitudes of these bodies are denoted by capital letters, the observations of the combinations which balance against each other give a series of equations of the form

$$(A + B + C + \dots) - (F + G + H + \dots) = \epsilon_1;$$

$$(1 + M + N + O + \dots) - (P + Q + R + \dots) = \epsilon_2; \text{etc.}$$

the number of these equations being greater than the number of bodies $A, B, C, \dots R, \dots$ If the ϵ's were known, there would be thus more equations than are needed to determine the unknowns $A, B, C, \dots R$, so that a direct test of the theory would be possible; for we could inquire whether any single set of values $A, B, C, \dots R$ would satisfy all the equations; actually the ϵ's are not known, but the superfluity of equations limits the possible sets of values to be assigned to them and to the $A, B, C, \dots R$. In order to choose one definite set out of these sets of possible values and so to choose a definite set of values for the real magnitudes, it must either turn out that there is one and only one set of ϵ's which fulfil the condition that they are all numerically less than E, or, if there is more than one set fulfilling that condition, some additional proposition of the nature of (4) on p. 447, must be added, which will reduce the number of possible sets to one. Such a proposition might assert, for example, that out of the total number of ϵ's, so many must have the value ϵ_1, so many ϵ_2, and so on.

Of course it is usual to add such a proposition, as a result of which an unique set of values for the real magnitudes may be obtained; as it is usually employed, it does not lead to the result that all the ϵ's are less than E. However I propose to postpone entirely to the next chapter any consideration of this or any other "law of errors", and to suppose merely that some "law" can be found which will satisfy the observational equations and give unique values to the real magnitude, together with errors all less than E. If it can be found in every case, then the theory will be true. It only remains to ask whether these unique values of the real magnitudes will be satisfactory and whether the problem of measurement will be solved.

But before we consider that question it may be noted for interest that, in the carrying out of the process just described, any collection of bodies might be used which fulfils the conditions that the unit is included[1] and that the number of pairs of combinations which balance is greater than the number of bodies. But in practice we select the bodies in a definite fashion. The bodies which are selected are a standard series made according to the prescription founded on the original definition of equality and therefore not entirely self-consistent. But this is merely a matter of convenience and the old definition is not used at all in the final result. The choice is convenient because it enables us to be sure that we shall find a sufficient number of pairs of combinations which balance; for the standard series can be so arranged that some combination of its members (including different positions of the rider or other "fine adjustment" as equivalent to different members) will balance any other body within a certain range. Moreover we shall find that the resulting real magnitudes of the series differ from the magnitudes originally assigned by amounts small compared with the differences between successive members of the series; this feature again is of great convenience when the series has to be used to determine the weights of other bodies. But it must again be insisted that the real magnitudes finally assigned are quite independent of judgements made in establishing the original standard series.

The system of measurement will be satisfactory if (1) a group of bodies a is greater than, or equal to, a group of bodies b (in the sense determined by the relation generating order) according as the real magnitudes A and B are such that $|A - B| > E$ or such that $|A - B| < E$; and (2) any body outside the original collection which is greater than, equal to, or less than some group of bodies in that collection is greater than, equal to, or less than any other group of bodies in the collection which has the same real magnitude.

If the observational equations by means of which the real magnitudes were determined included the examination of every possible combination of the bodies which balanced some other combination, then (1) must be true so far as the relation of equality is concerned. Actually it is also always true of the relation greater or less; but it is not necessarily true. It would probably be possible to devise an assumption of the distribution of errors which, in some special case, would fulfil the condition that the observational equations were satisfied, and yet would lead to discrepancies when relations of greater and less were examined. But in that case we should simply seek a new assumption concerning errors, and, so far as our experience can indicate, should always find one to avoid the discrepancy.

[1] Of course the actual unit need not be included so long as some body the weight of which is supposed to be known in terms of the unit is included; for many purposes it is sufficient to select arbitrarily one of the bodies to be determined as unit, most conveniently the largest.

But (2) is not necessarily true, and cases could actually be found in which it is untrue; we shall not be able to assign a magnitude uniquely to any body outside the series by simply weighing it against the series, and this failure is fundamental; it shows that our definition of equality is not satisfactory. Like the old definition, and in just the same way, it leads to inconsistent values being attributed to the magnitude of the same body. "Real magnitudes" are not consistent any more than the magnitudes attributed by the original process. Of course it must be inquired whether any further alteration of the definition will remove the discrepancy. Two ways of avoiding the difficulty might be tried. One is to make, as before, a standard series by comparison with which the magnitudes of all other bodies are to be measured, and to make it so that each possible value of a real magnitude is represented by one combination only; no disagreement between two combinations having the same real magnitude could ever occur. It would be rather a cowardly way, but we need not stop to discuss ethics, for fortunately it is practically impossible. By our old method of making a standard series, assuming that the law of equality was true, we could make a member of the system having any magnitude we pleased. But now we can only select a large collection of bodies and find out what their magnitudes are; if some member of the series which we should like to have does not occur, the only way to get it is to take a new collection (which may or may not include some of the old) and start the process all over again. Doubtless the result of the first trial would give us a broad hint how to proceed in the next, but the task of making successive trials and forming a really complete standard series with no over-lapping would be almost endless. It has certainly never been achieved. On the other hand, it seems probable that if we did ever find such a series, we should not be faced with the same difficulty as before, namely, that in avoiding over-lapping we had produced gaps. However there is no experimental proof of that assertion; it is a mere deduction from the general ideas of the theory.

Another method would be this. If we want to determine the magnitude of the body X we may include it in a collection of other bodies and proceed to perform on this collection the experiments of p. 449. If there were a sufficient number of combinations, each including X, which would balance, we should obtain, by solving the observational equations, a value for the real magnitude of X which we could be sure would never be discordant with any of the other real values in the collection. This plan is also cowardly, but, if we are sufficiently cowardly, it will work. We must take at the outset a collection which will give sufficient balancing combinations with all the bodies we may ever want to measure, and we must make all our measurements with this one collection and with no other; it would be no good making copies of the collection and giving them to other people to use, for we could not be sure that X determined by a copy of the original collection would agree with that determined by that collection. Accordingly though this method seems just possible, it is not one which we should ever think of adopting; it is full of that arbitrariness which it is our special object to remove from science.

We may say, therefore, that actually it turns out that we cannot assign numerals uniquely to represent real magnitudes, any more than we can to represent magnitudes, as we originally conceived them. Our theory as a method of measurement has failed.

But it is important to note that the failure does not prove that all the theory is false. The fundamental proposition of the theory is that, though a and b balance, A and B may differ by any amount not greater than E. Accordingly if the real weights A and A' may differ by αE, while X, not lying between them, differs from the nearest by βE, X will differ from the other by $(\alpha + \beta)E$, which may be greater than E although $\alpha + \beta$ are both proper fractions. All that is proved by the failure of X to balance both A and A' is that we have been wrong in assigning the value o to the error $A - A'$. The assignment of this value depends on the proposition about the "law of error"; we may retain the essentials of the theory if we admit that the "law of error" is wrong. Now since the discrepancies which have been described undoubtedly do or may occur, our conclusion is that the law of error which is actually adopted is false; and the more we inquire into that law the more reason we shall have for believing it false. The only question that remains is whether we can find a law which is true; in the next chapter reasons will be given for believing that it is impossible to discover such a law. We may be able to discover a distribution of errors which, if it is assumed in any particular instance, will lead to a confirmation of the theory; but we cannot discover by any possibility a law which will enable us to predict what the distribution of errors will be in any future instance. It may be well to indicate briefly here the grounds for this conclusion; it is that the "law of error" is based on considerations of probability, and that any law which leads to a confirmation of the theory must be such that any error within some finite range is equally probable with any other in that range; such errors cannot be distinguished by a law based on probability.

The practice of measurement. But though we cannot assign real magnitudes uniquely and therefore cannot attain the ideal of measurement, yet some progress has been made by the introduction of the theory of error. In the system based on the definition of equality as meaning simply balancing there was no limit to the inconsistency which might occur. The greater the number of steps in the process of establishing the standard series which separated a given member from the unit, the greater in general would be found to be the difference between its magnitude defined by that process and its real magnitude determined by the process which takes account of error, and the more likely it would be that this member would not balance the corresponding member of another series prepared in exactly the same way; there is no reason to suppose that, if we made a sufficient number of standard series, and examined corresponding members sufficiently removed from the original unit, the difference between the real magnitudes of these members might not exceed any defined limit. But in the process which takes account of error, so long as an assumption concerning distribution can be found which always leads to definite values for real magnitudes and always makes the errors less than E, there is a limit to the inconsistency which can occur. If X balances A but not A', though A and A' have been given the same real magnitude, then, if the real magnitude of X were determined by including it in a collection with A and A', it will not differ from that of A' by as much as $2E$, where E is the limit set to errors by observations of inequality. Again if A and A' are redetermined by using a different set of standard bodies, their new real magnitudes will not differ from their old by more than E. In all such cases, it can be shown that, if a suitable assumption for the distribution of errors can be found, the maximum difference between two determinations of the real magnitude of the same system cannot exceed some quantity which depends on E. As we usually express it, the consideration of errors increases greatly the accuracy of our measurements.

The process is actually adopted when accuracy is desired. In making a standard series of weights or electrical resistances[1], a maker takes a collection of bodies which he believes will be near the series he requires and sends them to a standardising laboratory to be calibrated. The calibration undertaken, there follows very closely the process already described (but see p. 519) and leads to the assignment to the bodies of real magnitudes which are consistent; two combinations having the same real magnitude will always balance, if tested on an instrument of the same kind as that with which the calibration was made, though, of course, bodies of which the real magnitudes are not exactly equal may also balance. We determine the magnitude of any other body by comparing it with the members of such a calibrated standard series.

It is important to inquire what conditions the real magnitudes of the standard series must fulfil in order that it may serve our purpose. One of the conditions that we exacted previously must be abandoned, because it is impossible to fulfil, namely that a body which balances one combination of the series must balance any other of equal real magnitude; but the second condition remains, namely that any body must balance some combination of the standard series. In order that this condition should be fulfilled, it is sufficient that the real magnitudes of the standard series should be arranged in steps, differing by less than $2E$; for then it is impossible that any body, the magnitude of which lies between those of two members of the series, should differ from both by as much as E. But it must be remembered that the real magnitudes which are assigned are not strictly the real magnitudes of the theory or the "true" real magnitudes; even after the process of calibration has been performed, the assigned real magnitude may differ from the true real magnitude by as much as E, so far as the theory can predict. Now if the assigned real magnitudes could actually differ from the true by as much as E, if these differences were in opposite directions in two consecutive members of the series and both tended to increase the nominal difference, then, however small was the nominal difference, a gap might be left between them, and a

---

[1] The procedure is slightly different with standards of length and time, but we can leave it until we consider these magnitudes in detail.

body might be found which, lying between them, would balance neither. Fortunately such cases do not occur, and their absence shows that the law of error which we use is not so bad as it might be; on the other hand these considerations show that, on the basis of theory, no definite limit can be assigned to the permissible step between consecutive members of the standard series. Still the fact remains that steps are permissible; for all our standard series in use are characterised by steps. There is always a finite number of combinations of the members of the system which have real magnitudes all different and all lying within a given range; and yet we can always measure any body which lies in that range. There is, therefore, a permissible step, although we cannot estimate its magnitude except by trial. But it seems that the permissible step is roughly equal to E, and that assumption will be adopted in future discussions; the argument based on it would not be changed if we supposed that the step was αE, where α is any proper fraction.

The conception of a "stepped" standard series is so important that it requires further emphasis. It is not always recognised, as it should be, that, whatever measuring instrument we adopt, we can only attribute to any body, as a consequence of its use, a finite number of different magnitudes. This statement is true, however many "fine adjustments", riders or microscope scales or so on, we employ. In weighing, we have first the realised weights in a box; to subdivide the intervals between these we have the rider moving over a scale with a finite number of graduations; we may perhaps subdivide the graduations either by eye or by a microscope with a divided scale; and if we use the latter we may divide once more the scale of the microscope by eye. But we never divide by eye into more than a finite number of divisions (usually ten), and however far we carry this process of subdivision, the number of values which we can assign to any magnitude always remains finite. The point to which attention is directed here—it is sufficiently obvious, though its consequences are not always recognised—is that this finitude of the number of possible values represents an important experimental fact, namely that there is no use in carrying the process of subdivision beyond a certain limit; when the steps are so small and the number of members of the standard series so great that any other body will be equal to one of them, then there is no meaning or sense in making further subdivisions. In a well-designed instrument the limit will be represented in the construction; in a good balance the step produced by moving the rider half a division is usually a fair measure of E, and there is accordingly no need to carry further the subdivision of steps. Of course it must be noticed that the permissible step, being determined by E, varies with the instrument used in comparing bodies with the standard series, and that it is useless to employ in comparing bodies with the standard series an instrument more accurate than that with which the series was calibrated. However, standard series are always calibrated with the most accurate instrument available at the time; and at any given time there is a definite smallest E which is experimentally attainable; it may change with the development of experimental methods.

Have all magnitudes errors? In this chapter, as in Chapter X, the magnitude weight has been consistently used as an example. We must guard against the danger of drawing general conclusions from facts which are really only applicable to the example. Doubtless many of the statements that have been made in the preceding paragraphs will appear rather sweeping, especially those which involve the idea that E is a definite thing to which a definite numerical value can be assigned as the result of experiment. And perhaps some of the statements are rather too positive, but the considerations to which we shall proceed in the next chapter will show that even if they are, no important false conclusions are involved. However we must inquire very briefly whether they are any less applicable to other magnitudes. Of the other "basic" magnitudes (p. 391), electrical resistance, length and time, the first seems to me precisely similar in all respects to weight; the only difference, and it is quite unessential, is that the "fine adjustment" for subdividing the steps of the realised standard series is not usually embodied in a definite instrument, but is set up whenever measurements are to be made. Length and time, on the other hand, do present some new features, but since we shall devote great attention to these two magnitudes in the next Part, the matter had better be left till then. All other magnitudes in accurate work— and it is only with accurate work that we are concerned here, for otherwise the original crude process of measurement would suffice—are measured as quasi-derived in terms of these basic magnitudes. We have yet to consider how the existence of errors of method affect the establishment of the numerical laws on which such measurement depends, but once those laws are established, the measurement is reduced simply to that of one of the basic magnitudes.

However there remains another basic magnitude which, though not included in our previous list, must never be forgotten; I mean the magnitude number. Here we do meet with a very great difference. The laws of equality and addition are strictly and absolutely true for number; there are no methodical errors. I cannot find, however much I search, three collections such that B can be counted against both A and C, while A cannot be counted against C. Herein number is distinguished from all other magnitudes.

This absence of error in the determination of number is, of course, intimately connected with the absence of fractional numbers and the fact that it is not always possible to find a system which has a number intermediate between those of any two other systems. This consideration leads to important conclusions which will concern us later; but it may be noted here that if it could be shown that all other magnitudes are numbers of some systems, then there might be a hope that perfectly consistent systems might be found for the measurement of such magnitudes. It is on this idea that the importance and attractiveness of "atomic" theories of all kinds are based; for in so far as a theory is atomic it indicates that all the magnitudes concerned in it are numbers of some system. On such grounds we may perhaps think it not wholly impossible that perfect systems of measuring weights and lengths might be devised, while we shall feel very doubtful whether such systems could ever be found for measuring periods of time or electrical resistances, although at present the inconsistencies which affect the former are no less than those which affect the latter.

Again, the absence of methodical errors in the determination of number makes very clear the great and essential distinction between errors of method and errors of consistency. For number, like any other magnitude, may be subject to errors of consistency. If I am determining the number of alpha particles emitted by a radioactive substance in a given time, by counting scintillations, I shall not usually find the same number on repeating what is, to all appearance, exactly the same observation. But as the result of any observation I shall be able to state a number perfectly definitely and without any uncertainty of any kind. There are errors of consistency but no errors of method.

It is because the distinction between these two kinds of error is so often overlooked that it has been necessary to consider at such length the questions raised in this chapter. The application of our conclusions (and even to some extent the conclusions themselves) will be affected by the discussion of errors of consistency to which we must now proceed. But any discussion of these errors which overlooks the existence of errors of method can only lead to confusion.

CHAPTER XVII

ERRORS OF MEASUREMENT

II. ERRORS OF CONSISTENCY AND THE ADJUSTMENT OF OBSERVATIONS

Summary. The considerations of the preceding chapter were directed towards establishing a satisfactory standard series of fundamental magnitudes by means of which these magnitudes and others could be measured. We now make measurements and find that we have not rid ourselves of all errors; our measurements are not always consistent with each other.

On the other hand the measurements, even if inconsistent, show some kind of order; if they did not, no further progress could be made, for mere ignorance and disorder is not a basis for any argument. During the first part of this chapter it will be assumed that the measurements show the order characteristic of what is termed a "complete collection". Briefly it is a collection which permits the determination of the probabilities of the various inconsistent values.

We must now find, as in Chapter XVI, a theory which will explain errors of inconsistency and enable us to determine from inconsistent measurements "true values". The question arises immediately, What are true values? The failure to answer clearly this question is responsible for many ambiguities and confusion in the theory of errors.

By a "true value" is always and without exception meant a value connected with some other true value by a law. This law is often recognised in the conventional theory under the name "equation of condition". But all true values are inseparably connected with an equation of condition, even though it may be concealed by an habitual terminology. If there is no equation of condition there is no true value. Errors of consistency are not errors of measurement, but errors in the systems measured.

Since this conclusion may appear startling at first sight it is supported by a brief inquiry why we desire accurate measurement.

The problem to be solved is then re-stated. It is to find a way of combining inconsistent observations in such a manner as to produce true values which satisfy some law which may or may not be known accurately.

The rule always adopted for solving the problem is to take the arithmetic mean of the inconsistent observations. It is inquired how far direct experimental proof can be obtained for the rule; it is concluded that if there are complete collections known the rule can be established as a definite experimental fact with all the certainty that can be attached to any law.

An exception is usually recognised to the rule when there is "systematic error". It is maintained that the presence of such error only means that the assumed equation of condition is not accurately true; it may be convenient to use the term, but for our purpose the problems of systematic error are merely those of determining whether the equation of condition is accurately true.

The problem is now formally solved for complete collections. But it is desirable to explain the solution, and for this purpose a theory of errors of consistency is required. The theory offered (it is involved implicitly in all physical thought) states briefly that errors of consistency are magnified errors of method. The theory leads directly to a law of errors of consistency which is not, except in special circumstances, identical with the usually accepted law. Evidence is probably not available (but it might be obtained) for establishing the law, but it is urged that such evidence as there is tends in favour of the proposed law rather than Gauss'. Much of the evidence often adduced for the latter is irrelevant.

The remaining problem of the study of errors of inconsistency is to find true values when the collections of observations are not, as we have supposed so far, complete. If the collections are really incomplete the true values cannot be determined and there is no more to be said; but our theory suggests a method by which several incomplete collections may be combined in some cases to form a complete collection; that method is to distribute the errors of the incomplete collections in the manner in which they would be distributed if they were the errors of a complete collection.

But the rule thus obtained is not definite; a further criterion is required. That usually adopted is that the true values are to be chosen so that they are the most probable causes of the actual distribution of errors, assuming that the errors are distributed according to the law of a complete collection. The general formula to which this rule leads is deduced, assuming (as is always done if this rule is adopted) that Gauss' law is true.

The application of the rule is made by the Method of Least Squares. The problems solved by this Method are two: (1) the determination of the true values of magnitudes when they are related by an equation of condition of which the form and coefficients are known, (2) the determination of the coefficients of the equation of condition when the form is known. It is inquired how far the Method accords with the theory in solving these two problems. It appears that it is in accord with the theory in solving the first (though some applications of the Method are illegitimate); but it is not at all in accordance with the theory in solving the second. Moreover the fact, often quoted, that the residuals are distributed according to Gauss' law does not seem to justify the foundation of the Method on that law.

The difficulties of the Method, as of any other method which is based on considerations of probability, are even more apparent when the "probable error" is considered. It seems that a definite meaning can be attributed to the "probable error of a single observation", but we fail to find any definite meaning which can be attributed to "the probable error of the general mean". The discussion of the questions raised leads to a complete distrust of all methods of determining true values (except possibly from complete collections) by considerations of probability. If the collections are really incomplete and cannot be made complete by the device proposed, then it is useless to try to determine true values.

But can any less objectionable method be proposed? Certainly not for determining true values from collections essentially incomplete. If, however, the collection can be made complete by combining incomplete collections, a better method can be suggested. It is to make the arithmetic sum of the errors zero. It is urged that this method is preferable (1) because it is much simpler to apply in all cases, (2) because it is always an adequate expression of the theory on which it professes to be based, (3) because it does not require the same detailed knowledge of the law of errors, (4) because it is suggested directly by the most fundamental fact in the whole study of errors, (5) because it tells us plainly when we can and when we cannot determine true values and does not pretend to achieve more than any method can achieve.

The bearing of all the foregoing discussion upon the problem of establishing numerical laws is considered. Numerical laws state relationships between real magnitudes. This conclusion requires some unessential alterations in the statements of Chapter XIII. Rules are given based on the Method of Least Squares and the alternative method for deciding, as far as it is possible, whether a proposed numerical law is in accordance with the facts. But complete decision is not possible unless the collection of observations is complete.

Lastly we return once more to the problem from which we started, that of establishing and calibrating a standard series for fundamental measurement. It is finally concluded that by no process whatever is it possible to get entirely free from errors of method and that some uncertainty in assigning real magnitudes is perfectly unavoidable.

Inconsistent measurements. Complete collections.

We have now established the standard series of our basic magnitudes and may proceed to make measurements by comparing systems with these standard series. We may measure, for example, the distance through which a body falls in a given time-interval. We shall probably find that successive measurements of this distance, made under conditions which are to all appearance the same, are not identical. The measurements are inconsistent. On the other hand, we shall not find that the measurements are entirely random and that at any trial any distance may be found. We shall find rather that all the measurements lie within certain limits, and that, though we cannot predict which of the possible measurements within these limits will result at any trial, there is a certain similarity between any two collections of a large number of trials. The arithmetic mean of the magnitudes measured in two such collections will be "nearly" the same.

This statement will not tell us much unless we can give a definite meaning to the word "nearly". As a result of the discussion of the previous chapter we seem able to give such a meaning. Owing to the unavoidable presence of methodical errors, there can be no meaning in the statement that a magnitude has a value lying between those of two steps of the standard series. Generally a magnitude will be equal to one and only one member of the series. In a few exceptional cases it may happen that it is equal to both of two consecutive members, and in such cases we shall probably attribute to it a value intermediate between those of these members; but such attribution is merely a short way of saying that the magnitude is equal to both, and there is no reason, apart from mere convention, why we should attribute to it one of such intermediate values rather than many others. If the two steps are marked 2 and 3, we shall probably call the magnitude that is equal to both 2·5, but that statement does not differ, except conventionally, from the assertion that it is equal to 2·4 or 2·6 or 2·5001. Accordingly when the means of two collections of measurements both lie between the values of the same two consecutive steps of the series, they differ in a way that no experiment could detect, if they were values of individual magnitudes. In such circumstances it is reasonable to say that they are nearly equal. Such is the meaning that will be attached to the phrase in what follows.

If the two collections of measurements are sufficiently numerous, and if we can take as many measurements as we please in the same conditions, further inquiry will probably bring to light other regularities of the two collections. Not only will the arithmetic means be nearly the same, but they will be means of the same values, occurring in nearly equal proportions. Or, to state the facts more definitely, if p_s is the number of times a value a_s is observed in N trials, the difference between the ratios p_s/N for the two collections can be made to remain less than any assigned Number during any assigned number of consecutive trials by increasing sufficiently the number of trials. That is to say, according to the discussions of Chapter VII, the conditions necessary for the application of the conception of probability are fulfilled, and the occurrence of the value a_s will have a definite probability p_s which will be the same in any two collections of trials.

If an indefinite number of measurements can be made, and if they turn out in this way, we shall say that we have a "complete collection" of measurements. Whether such complete collections can be obtained is perhaps doubtful, but I propose to base the treatment of errors of consistency on the examination of complete collections. Such a procedure seems necessary, for mere failure to repeat an observation does not afford any basis for the application of an ordered argument, any more than mere ignorance affords a basis for the application of the theory of probability. There must be both knowledge and ignorance of a definite kind; the knowledge and ignorance which give rise to the theory of errors of consistency is that characteristic of a complete collection of inconsistent measurements. It may not always be possible to realise the conditions supposed, but, if we knew that investigation would not sometimes disclose those conditions, we should not believe in the theory.

Errors of consistency are not errors of measurement. And now what is the theory? Unlike many of the matters which have been considered in this volume, it has been the subject of so many discussions by so many distinguished writers that it may seem presumptuous to attempt to say anything new. But though, as usual, the conclusions at which we shall arrive are, in the main, entirely familiar, those which we have reached earlier may make somewhat clearer their basis and significance. Let us therefore begin once more at the beginning. It is recognised that the theory of errors of consistency is a theory; can it be stated in the form which we regard as characteristic of theories?

At first sight perhaps we shall be inclined to state it in a form almost exactly the same as that used for errors of method. We shall say that the system we are measuring has a true real magnitude which is always the same; that our methods of observation are affected by error; that the measurements which we make are the sum of the real magnitude and the error; and that the inconsistency is due to variation of the error and not to variations of the true real magnitude. These statements can be put, as before, in the form of hypotheses and dictionary. But do they really represent our view of the matter?

They seem certainly to represent the view which is usually expressed in the conventional treatment of errors of measurement, but many instances can be brought to show that we are in the habit of accepting tacitly and without consideration propositions which have only to be stated clearly to be rejected. Our answer to the question will, I think, depend on what exactly we mean by the "methods of observation" that are affected by error; if we mean by these the methods of observing the magnitude of which the errors are being considered, then the statements do not represent our views and are simply untrue. We do not believe, in this example, that by adopting more accurate methods of measuring distance we could reduce considerably the limits of inconsistency in the measurement of the distance fallen in a given time; by changing those methods we shall change only the methodical errors. If we start measuring the distance with a foot-rule on which the inches are not sub-divided, the range of inconsistency may well be a tenth of an inch, tenths being estimated by eye. If we now substitute a millimetre scale the range may possibly be reduced to a tenth of a millimetre; but if we now have recourse to a reading microscope, it is unlikely that the range will be further reduced. A stage will be reached at which the range of inconsistency is greater than the step of the measuring instrument, and once that stage is reached a further reduction of the step will not reduce the range of inconsistency. The obvious explanation of the fact is that the greater range of inconsistency when the step is very large simply represents the methodical errors which we have discussed already, errors which would be present even if there were no errors of consistency.

An even better example—and since the matter is important it is well to multiply examples at the risk of prolixity—is provided by the measurement of the weight of a given volume of liquid; the volume being fixed by filling a vessel to an assigned mark on the neck. It is well known that in such experiments it is of no use to use a balance of the very highest accuracy and all the finest precautions in weighing. As the accuracy is increased and the precautions multiplied, a stage is soon reached at which the range of inconsistency far exceeds the errors of weighing, that is the methodical errors. If we fill our vessel once and for all, and use it as one of the collection for determining the standard series, we shall find that series characterised by a certain maximum error E which will depend on the balance and the precautions. If we empty the vessel and refill it, we may very well find a difference from the first weight very much greater than E; and this difference will not in general increase with E, until E becomes greater than any of the differences found with smaller E's.

Of course these facts are perfectly familiar. We should express them by saying, in the first case, that the error arose from the difficulty of determining the time or, perhaps, from the difficulty of releasing the falling body without velocity; in the second case, that the error arose in filling the vessel to the mark (that is, in judging the volume) or in always filling at the same temperature. But the implications of these statements are not always realised.

We are referring errors in the measurement of distance to errors in the measurement of time or velocity, and errors in the measurement of weight to errors in the measurement of volume or temperature. The errors arise, not in measuring the distance or the weight, but in realising the systems of which the distance or the weight are to be measured. They arise because we are measuring, not the distance between *these* lines on a carefully prepared rod or the weight of *this* carefully prepared lump of material, but a distance defined by means of time and velocity or a weight determined by volume and temperature; the error is in realising the system so defined and determined.

To adopt any other view would be to abandon the entire theory of measurement. The basis of that theory is that it is possible to assign definitely a numeral to represent the property of a system; if the system remains the same the numeral must remain the same. If the numeral apparently does not remain the same, then the only conclusion consistent with measurement, or even with the very meaning of the property of a system, is that the system has changed. Errors of inconsistency are not errors of measurement, but errors arising from unintentional changes of the systems measured. This may seem a very trivial conclusion, but nevertheless in it lies, I believe, the clue to most of the difficulties and disputes that attend the theory of errors.

True magnitudes. For let us turn to a question which has been asked since the days of Gauss. What is the justification, when the measurements turn out in the manner described in the first paragraph, for choosing one of the observed values for the magnitude rather than another, or for choosing one function of the observed values rather than another function? Why should we choose the arithmetic mean rather than any other mean? Ought we to choose a mean at all? Would it not be better to choose the most probable value or, possibly, the probable value[1]; if the most probable and the probable values are not the same, which is it correct to choose? The answer to these questions is that they are unanswerable. The problem is not stated fully. If the questions are asked about the inconsistent measurements of a single magnitude, and nothing is stated about its relations to other magnitudes, then there is not the smallest justification for taking any one of its values to represent "the true magnitude". The mere fact that there is inconsistency shows that there is no "true magnitude"; there are many magnitudes, at least as many as there are inconsistent values (probably more, for we must remember that the number of possible values is limited by the step of the measuring instrument). Before we choose "the true magnitude" we must decide on what grounds we are going to choose it; such grounds can be provided either by some relation of "the true magnitude" to some other magnitude or magnitudes; these other magnitudes might simply be the inconsistent values themselves. Thus we may define "the true magnitude" to be the most probable value or the value nearest to the arithmetic mean; but then any question how to select the true magnitude becomes trivial; for it is not experiment, but a mere definition which decides what is the true value.

---

[1] The probable value is $\Sigma p_s a_s$, where p_s is the probability of the value a_s.

On the other hand we might say that the true value is that which is related in some way to a magnitude of a different kind measured in some other experiments; then the question is not trivial; it is supremely important, but the answer to it cannot be based only on the consideration of the "inconsistent values"; it must be based on the experimental investigation of the relation to this magnitude of a different kind.

The examples which have been quoted show that the second alternative is adopted and show further what this relation must be. "The true magnitude", to be determined from the various "inconsistent" measurements, is a value the relation of which to some other magnitude is a particular case of a numerical law. If this law defines a derived magnitude the value required must be such that, together with this derived magnitude and the value of the magnitude to which it is related, it satisfies the numerical equation stated by that law. The "true" distance which we require in our first example is that related to the time and the gravitational acceleration by the equation $y = \frac{1}{2}gt^2$; the "true" weight which we require in the second example is that related to the volume and the density of the liquid by the equation $W = \rho V$. If there is such a distance and such a weight, there is good reason for distinguishing it from all other values of the measured magnitude and for calling it the "true" value. If the arithmetic mean turns out to be the value which is required in each case, then adequate grounds will have been found for choosing that mean rather than any other function. But it must be insisted that our reason for choosing it will be based on considerations quite other than those of the "inconsistent" values of which it is the mean. No examination of these values alone could ever give us a reason to select one of them rather than another; it is only when we examine their relations to measurements which have no necessary connection with these "inconsistent" values that such a reason can be found.

The problem of finding some means of combining observed values so as to obtain "true" values which obey a numerical law is quite familiar. It is discussed in all treatises on the theory of errors and is termed the adjustment of observations subject to equations of condition. What is not always realised is that all problems of errors of consistency are of this kind, and that there is no other problem; that fact is concealed by the suggestion, contained in the phrase, that observations could be adjusted if they were not subject to equations of condition, a suggestion which is absolutely false. If there were no equations of condition there could be no question of adjusting observations; there would be nothing to adjust them to and nothing to suggest that one method of adjustment was better than another. The reason why this conclusion is not always accepted or openly expressed (for there are indications that it is accepted implicitly) is that some equations of condition are so simple and familiar that their existence is not realised. Treatises on error usually begin by considering the process of determining the "true" value from a number of independent observations on a single quantity. One of the examples which is almost sure to be used is that of the observations made in a levelling survey.

There are observed directly the heights of several points one above the other, and it is required to find the true heights of these points above each other. It will be found, and must always be found, that in the process of adjustment the proposition is used that, if x is the height of A above B, y the height of B above C, then the height of A above C is $x + y$. Now of course this is a law; it is an experimental fact which depends on the geometrical properties of rigid bodies and the facts of gravitational acceleration (in so far as height means distance perpendicular to a level surface). It is only because this law is believed to be true that there can be any adjustment of the observations, and the only adjustment there can be is that which makes the observations obey this law. The law is an "equation of condition", just as much as the proposition that the three angles of a plane triangle must add up to two right angles. That proposition is usually stated as an equation of condition and adjustments which depend on its use included under "conditioned observations". So also should be those which depend on the use of the "law of levels".[1] The observations doubtless are "direct", that is to say, the measurements are made to determine the magnitude of some system concretely realised. But that is true also of the weighing of the flask filled with liquid; we weigh an actual concrete flask. But in one case as in the other, the conception of a "true" magnitude is introduced because it is believed that this concrete system is made according to a specification involving a relation to other magnitudes. We speak of a true height only because we believe that the point the height of which above A is measured is the same point as that the height of which above B is measured. If these points were not the same, and if there were not a law relating heights of a series of points, we should not speak of true heights.

The object of measurement. The same remarks apply to all the other examples which are quoted of direct and independent observations; in all cases they will be found to be merely examples in which the equations of condition are concealed, often by a conventional notation. For in truth it is only when there are equations of condition that we are interested to assign numerical values to properties; the sole object of measurement in science is to state numerical laws.

Perhaps this last statement requires a little more examination before it can be accepted without reserve. It may be thought that we do often go to considerable trouble to ascertain the exact numerical value of a magnitude, even when there is apparently no numerical law connected with it. Thus a great deal of valuable research has been directed to the exact measurement of the wave-length of the red cadmium line, of the velocity of light, of the charge on an electron, and of other physical constants; and in such research attention has to be paid to the errors of inconsistency such as we are considering. It is not at all obvious that it is directed to the discovery of magni-

---

[1] It is interesting to notice that in two well-known treatises, problems in levelling, practically identical, are treated both under "unconditioned" and under "conditioned" observations.

tudes that are related to some other magnitudes by equations of condition, or that systems of which the "true" values which are sought are defined by the numerical laws between them and other systems. But it is to be noted that none of these magnitudes are fundamental (in our special sense); as a matter of fact they are all theoretical magnitudes (and that fact is significant), but the position would not be altered if they were true derived magnitudes. The characteristic feature of them, which they share with derived magnitudes, is that the magnitudes would have no meaning unless certain propositions were true. If we denied the undulatory theory of light the wave-length of a given line would have no meaning and the velocity of light (as the term is used at present) would have none; if we denied the electronic theory there would be no meaning in the charge on an electron. In just the same way, density would have no meaning if mass and volume were not proportional. Any very accurate determination of density would necessarily assume the truth of the law which defines density; in fact the most certain way of proving that law might well be to undertake a very accurate determination of the density of some substance. Similarly the most certain way of proving the undulatory theory of light might be to measure a wave-length with great accuracy, and the most certain way of proving the electronic theory to measure with great care the charge on an electron; in fact the recent determination by Millikan of the electronic charge is regarded by himself and by most other people as the best proof of the theory. Accordingly, in spite of first appearances, these magnitudes of which an accurate knowledge seems intrinsically valuable are really connected with laws just as intimately as those which we took as examples before.

Moreover—and this is the important point—the errors of inconsistency which occur in their determination are connected with equations of condition in the same way. It is true that there is no equation of condition involving the charge on an electron, but then there is also no error of consistency, in our sense, connected with it. We do not measure the charge directly at all; we measure some other magnitudes and from them, by the use of the laws (including those which give the charge on an electron its significance), calculate the charge. Inconsistency in the values obtained for the charge is merely the consequence of the inconsistency of the magnitudes measured directly. This inconsistency may be immediately apparent; we may obtain different results when we measure the same magnitude in apparently the same conditions; or it may be concealed, and due to the fact that, though the measurement of each magnitude separately is affected by no error of consistency, the pairs of associated magnitudes which should satisfy a numerical law do not actually satisfy it. In any case the inconsistency of the calculated charge is due to the failure of the fundamental measurements to give results in accordance with a certain law; this is precisely what we regard as the typical form of errors of inconsistency. The fact that we attach importance to the accurate determination of such physical constants is only one more proof that errors of consistency are only worthy of attention, and are only "errors", when they represent a failure to satisfy a law.

There is another type of magnitude which might be suggested as an instance of errors of consistency being significant and important, even when there is no equation of condition; it should be noted because it is always discussed in treatises on error. It may be urged that it is all-important for a surveyor to know which to select out of several inconsistent values of a length or an angle; the recognition that one of these values (or some function of them) is the "true" value seems here independent of any numerical law which that value has to satisfy. Of course the value has to satisfy a law, namely the law which makes this value fit with others on a map; and it is by the equation of condition represented by this law that the value is actually selected. But it seems that the conception of a "true" value has a meaning independent of this necessity and, in a sense, more important, because on it depends the value of the map when constructed; quite apart from maps it is important for us to know whether the next village is one mile or two distant. If our measurements were so inconsistent that we sometimes found the distance to be one mile and sometimes two, would there be any criterion other than that of fitting on the map by which one rather than the other might be judged to be the "true" value? I believe that our feeling in this example that there would be a criterion is due simply to the belief that there is some other system of measurement that will fix the distance within narrower limits; thus we might be sure that the distance was nearer one mile than two, because we could walk it easily in a quarter of an hour. When there is such a more accurate system, and we use a less accurate, we are simply increasing the error of consistency by increasing the methodical error; and we can reduce the error of consistency by employing the more accurate. If we can reduce it to nothing, then of course there are no alternative values from which to select and the whole problem falls to the ground; but if, as is more often the case, a limit is reached when a further reduction of methodical error does not reduce the error of inconsistency, then of course an attempt to select the "true" value by using a more accurate method fails entirely. I believe the feeling that there is some criterion for determining the "true" value, apart from any equation of condition, is always based on a false analogy of this kind. We know that we can often decide between some, at least, of a set of inconsistent measurements by employing better methods; and unconsciously we imagine that we can always decide between all of such a set by the same process. If the belief is stated clearly it is at once seen to be false. Anyone who thinks that a "true" value could be determined from inconsistent measurements when there is no equation of condition will alter his opinion if he will force himself to realise that circumstances may occur in which the range of inconsistency cannot be reduced by the employment of any other method of measurement whatever.

Re-statement of the problem. We conclude then that the "true" value to be derived by any adequate theory of errors from the inconsistent collection which is the result of measurement is always the value which satisfies some law that plays the part of an equation of condition. We must now examine the problem rather more closely. If we knew that law and also the value of the magnitude with which the required true value was to be associated by the law, then we should know the true value and there would be no problem to solve. There is a problem only if we do not know the value of that other magnitude or do not know the law or do not know either. The first alternative is simple and is represented by a very large number of important cases; it arises when measurements on this other magnitude are also inconsistent. The problem then is to find some way of treating in the same manner both sets of inconsistent measurements, so as to find from them a single pair of values which satisfy the law; these will be the true values. If we do not know the law, then, even if we know the second magnitude, the problem is more complex and might seem at first sight incapable of definite solution. For whatever value of the unknown magnitude results from any process of combining the many inconsistent values, it will always be related to the known magnitude by some law; whatever process we adopt, there will be some numerical relation between the single value of the unknown magnitude and the associated value of the known. It is true that a limitation which we have already imposed on the numerical relations which can form part of a numerical law implies some limitation on the processes that can be adopted; we have concluded that the numerical relation must always be capable of being represented by an analytic function. It might turn out that only one process would lead to an analytic function; then only that process would be legitimate, and the law obtained by its adoption the only possible law. But we cannot be sure *a priori* that the solution will be unique in this manner, and it is very doubtful whether in any actual case it is unique; it is certain that there are cases in which it is not unique. It seems therefore that, if the problem is to be soluble, the law must be known. But how is the law to be known? Surely it can only be discovered and established in the first instance by just such investigations as we propose. The law which defines density can only be established by examining the relation between measurements of mass and measurements of volume; and if—as is probable—all such measurements on related mass and volume display some inconsistency, the law can never be established definitely until the inconsistency is removed. The matter is still further complicated—but not seriously for our purpose—if we are ignorant of the second magnitude as well as of the law; the range of possible choices for the true values and for the form of the law is increased, but a mere increase of alternatives, of which there are already several, does not alter the position essentially. And yet there is no doubt that we do actually use the calculus of errors to achieve the result which this argument would seem to prove impossible, namely to determine the form of a law between two magnitudes, the measurements of both of which are affected by errors of inconsistency.

Like so many difficulties in sciences which formally appear insuperable, this difficulty is quite easy to solve. The solution is to be found in a consideration on which much insistence has already been placed. No formal argument of any kind and no experiment however complete can ever certainly establish a law of any kind, numerical or otherwise; all that we can do is to suggest possible laws and investigate whether they are consistent with the facts. Such is the procedure we adopt here. Sometimes the law is suggested by a theory so well-established and so fundamental in science that it is impossible to doubt the law in any particular case. Laws of this kind form the equation of condition in surveying and (probably) in many astronomical observations. Again the form of the law may be known with certainty from other observations and only the derived magnitudes in it may be doubtful; such is the position when we are weighing measured volumes of a liquid; we shall see that this partial knowledge, though not equivalent to complete knowledge, aids in the solution of the problem. Lastly the crude observations, unanalysed by any calculus of errors, suggest that there is a law. The observational points plotted on a graph all lie close to some curve of simple form—there is no need to examine more nearly what is meant by "close". We inquire whether we can find a method of selecting a single value from each inconsistent collection such that the points plotted from these single values will lie accurately on the curve[1]. If we cannot, then either the suggested law is false, or the method of selecting the single values is wrong. If we can, then both the law and the method may be right, but there is still the possibility that both are wrong and that there is some other law and some other method which would also bring the points on the curve, but have a better claim to be the right law and the right method. Which of these alternative conclusions we shall adopt will depend on what we find in the examination of a large number of such problems. If we can find a method of selection, applicable to all instances, which in a great many cases brings the points on to the curve of the suggested law, then we shall doubtless consider that this method is the right one, and we shall judge the law to be right or wrong according as this method does not give points consistent with it. We shall be confirmed in this view if the method which thus turns out to be actually right can be explained satisfactorily; and if further, in those instances in which the method does not confirm the suggested law, there is some special reason for placing less than the ordinary reliance on the suggestion. If matters turn out in this way, then the method will represent a law, or at least its use will be justified by the same reasoning which justifies the use of any law. It will represent the facts adequately, and it will have the intrinsic value which attends a satisfactory explanation and a general coherence with all parts of physical knowledge.

Rule for finding true magnitudes. But can such a method be found?

---

[1] This statement requires slight amendment. There will be methodical errors and the measuring instrument will have a step. We have seen that there is no meaning in assigning to a magnitude one rather than another of the values between consecutive members of the standard series. Accordingly we shall be satisfied if the method of selecting the values gives single values within a step such that, if some other values within the same steps were selected, the points would lie accurately on the curve. For brevity we shall leave the methodical error out of account until, at the end of this chapter, we examine it again in the light of the theory of errors of inconsistency.

The general impression is that it can; and here a general impression is perhaps more important than a very rigid proof in certain selected instances; for the prevalence of such an impression indicates that our current practice does render our experience coherent and intelligible. But to rely completely on general impression is not satisfactory, for we have concluded in connection with this very matter that general impressions may be mistaken. On the other hand I do not think that an inquiry has been conducted in any particular case so complete that we could regard the method as established, even for that case, simply by experiment. It will be well therefore to consider the kind of inquiry which might lead to a substantially complete proof and leave the reader to judge how far the facts which would be necessary have actually been observed.

The prevalent belief is that if the observations fulfil the conditions stated in the opening paragraph of this chapter and a complete collection is obtained, then the true value to be selected from the inconsistent measurements is the arithmetic mean. Such was the doctrine on which Gauss founded his treatment of error. Subsequent discussion has occasionally suggested doubts; it has been asked whether it would not be wiser to take the most probable value or the probable value or, possibly, some mean other than the arithmetic. These questions have never been answered definitely for an obvious reason, namely that when the necessary conditions for answering the question are fulfilled these other suggested values are always (or nearly always) the same as the arithmetic mean. They differ notably only when the conditions are not fulfilled and the collections are not complete, so that the problem that we are considering does not arise. Accordingly for the present we shall suppose that the rule which is to be proved is that the arithmetic mean of the inconsistent measurements is the true value, and shall consider later what is to happen when that rule is doubtful.

A very simple proof of the rule may be obtained in some instances. If A, the magnitude of which the measurements are inconsistent, is related to B by a known law, and the measurements of B are not inconsistent, then the true values of A are known, and it can be asked immediately whether this true value is the arithmetic mean of the inconsistent measurements. Such an example can be very nearly realised. Suppose that we are weighing different volumes of a liquid by delivering quantities of it out of a graduated burette into a counterpoised vessel and measuring what volume has to be delivered to give a certain weight. Then the mass is the magnitude B, and it is probably possible to determine without inconsistency, and with only methodical error, the mass of liquid in the vessel at any given time; on the other hand the volume measured by the burette is the magnitude A, and repeated determinations of the volume that must be delivered to give a certain mass will be inconsistent (owing to change of temperature, adhesion of the liquid to the walls of the burette, and so on). If we make a sufficient number of determinations of volume for each mass we shall probably find that they form a complete collection. However we probably do not know the density of the liquid quite accurately and therefore cannot deduce immediately what is the true volume for each weight, but we are quite certain—as certain as we can be of any law—that there is a density, and that mass is proportional to volume. Accordingly, though we cannot test the proposed method by measurements of the volume corresponding to a single mass, we can test it by measurements of the volumes of several different weights. If it turns out that, after so many observations of each volume have been made that it can be shown that the difference between the arithmetic means of two collections of measurements can be made less than the step of the burette by increasing the number in those collections, these arithmetic means are proportional to the corresponding masses, then the selection of the arithmetic mean will have been shown to be justified. But it must be noticed that the proof is not complete. It must be shown also that no other function of the values of A which is not the same as the arithmetic mean will lead to proportionality. Of course if we took some other function, then even if we obtained proportionality, we should not obtain exactly the same value for the density; but it must be admitted that there is some slight uncertainty in the knowledge of the density and that more than one value would have to be admitted as possible.

Such is the most direct proof possible. A slightly less complete proof is obtained if B as well as A is liable to errors of inconsistency. Thus we might (as imagined before) determine the weight of liquid which would fill the vessel up to a certain mark, and then, by filling the vessel up to the same mark with the standard liquid and weighing it, determine the volume; both the weight and the volume would then be liable to inconsistency. We should then inquire whether, if a large number of observations were taken as before on each associated pair of volume and weight, the arithmetic means for the two members of the pairs were always proportional. If they were proportional we should have produced striking additional evidence that the method was right, but the possibility would again be left open that some other function of the inconsistent values would also be proportional and would give a slightly different, or even the same, value for the density. And here the doubt would probably be more serious; for—as the reader will see if he thinks of the matter in the light of the accepted theory—if in selecting values of both the weight and the volume, we chose a function which was always rather greater than the arithmetic mean, it might very well happen that the selected values would be found to be proportional, and even that the value of the density was exactly the same as if we chose the arithmetic mean. Accordingly the proof based on such observations will be rather less cogent.

To complete the proof the investigation should be extended to as many other cases as possible of other laws. If the selection of the arithmetic mean always proved satisfactory and if, further, investigations of the first type always shows that the arithmetic mean was the only possible function, then we should probably conclude that we had proved the suitability of that selection as completely as we could prove anything by mere experiment. I do not think such investigations have been carried out in a single instance.

But I do not mean to suggest that they ought to be carried out before we place any reliance on the selection of the arithmetic mean as a method of dealing with errors of inconsistency. Our reasons are probably sufficient for believing on other grounds that if they were carried out they would prove satisfactory, even to the extent of showing, in the first type of investigation, that the arithmetic mean was the only possible selection (if we except those which always give the same result as the arithmetic mean). But I wish to insist that they might be carried out, and that if they did not lead to the results we expect we should be forced to abandon that method of selection. The proposed method of selection can be proved satisfactory by purely experimental investigation and without any introduction of a theory to explain why errors of inconsistency occur in the manner in which they are actually found to occur. The recognition that there is a clear experimental foundation for the treatment that is actually adopted is essential to any clear understanding of the subject.

Systematic error. We will suppose then that it is proved experimentally that the arithmetic mean of a complete collection turns out to be the true value in a large number of typical cases. If in other cases it does not turn out to be the true value, the conclusion indicated is that the law which represents the equation of condition is not true. But we should not be prepared to accept that conclusion unless these cases were distinguished by some feature which made us more ready than we usually are to accept a disproof of the law suggested by the crude observations. It is difficult to say whether there are actually any cases in which complete collections can be obtained and yet the arithmetic mean does not turn out to be the true value, because in few, if any, cases have complete collections been investigated. On the other hand there certainly are cases in which we do not believe that the arithmetic mean is the "true value", or would be the true value even if the number of observations were increased indefinitely; these cases are usually described as affected by "systematic error". When we say that there is a systematic error, what we mean, expressed in terms of experiment and not in terms of theory, is that the observations are such that the arithmetic mean is not the true value which satisfies the equation of condition, however many observations we make. The proof that there is systematic error can only be based on such investigations as have just been described; and if we assert the existence of such error without making those investigations it is only because we believe that if we did make them the result would be different from that which establishes that the arithmetic mean is the true value.

However the use of the term, systematic error, would seem to indicate that we do not accept the conclusion which, it has been urged, should be drawn, namely that the law of equation of condition is not true; it suggests that we attribute the failure of the method of finding the true value to the presence of some new kind of error which is not "corrected" by that method. According to the theory of error which we shall examine immediately—we shall anticipate here in order to dispose of this matter finally—when there is systematic error, there is superimposed on the normal and characteristic casual error, affecting differently different observations, an error which affects all observations alike. Now the assertion that there is something affecting equally *all* observations is very similar to a law; it is actually part of a theory, but it is part of a theory which has value simply because it is so closely analogous to a law. We are practically saying that the observations are determined, not only by the law which is the equation of condition, but also by another law acting in conjunction with it and with equal regularity; for the purpose of the observations under examination the law of the equation of condition and the law which gives rise to systematic error are a single law. It may be convenient for purposes of exposition to divide it into two laws on the ground that in other observations one acts without the other. But such division does not alter the fact that in respect of the matters that are here under considera- tion the combination of the law giving rise to systematic error with the other is simply equivalent to a change in that law. It may be convenient to use the expression "systematic error", but its use does not really show that we refuse the conclusion that the law which we have stated as the equation of condition is not true, or is not the whole truth.

Perhaps an example will make the matter clear. Let us return to the experiments of weighing measured volumes of liquid delivered from a burette. If the burette has been calibrated with water and we are delivering mercury, we shall certainly find a systematic error; because, owing to the difference in the adhesion of the two liquids to glass, the proportion of the liquid contained in any segment of the tube which is delivered when that segment is "emptied" will be greater if the liquid is mercury than when it is water. The actual volumes of mercury we shall deliver will be generally greater than the volumes determined from the calibration. Accordingly if we state the law that mass is proportional to volume and if we mean by volume the magnitude determined by the emptying of the segments of the calibrated burette, that law is not true —which is also the conclusion indicated by the discrepancy between the arithmetic mean and the true value determined with that law as an equation of condition. If on the other hand we mean by volume something perfectly different and still use a law of the same form as an equation of condition, we must alter entirely the nature of the experiments. Any particular kind of experiment involves necessarily the use of a corresponding equation of condition; if we change the equation we must change the experiment. It is perfectly true that the experiments do not prove that a law is untrue in which something else is meant by volume than a magnitude defined by the delivery of the burette; but that is obvious, because the experiments cannot throw light of any kind on the law. The only law on which the experiments throw light is that in which volume is a magnitude so defined, and that law they show definitely to be untrue. Talk about systematic error does not alter that fact: it only suggests that, by recognising a systematic difference between two definitions of volume, we can explain why this law is untrue and yet some other closely similar law which is investigated in quite other experiments is true.

We shall regard then cases in which it is said that there is systematic error merely as a special, and not particularly important, class of cases in which the equation of condition is not true. All the remarks which will be made about determining whether the equation of condition is true apply to this class as to any other. Systematic error may be dismissed entirely from further consideration; the only conclusion to be drawn when the arithmetic mean is not the true value, even when an unlimited number of observations can be made, is that the equation of condition is false.

If the inconsistent measurements form a complete collection, the problem presented by them is now completely solved. We can determine the true value and can decide whether the law is true on which the meaning of that true value is based. But before we pass on it will be well to insist once more on the view on which our whole discussion is founded. It will be noticed that the rule for determining the true value does not depend on the nature of the equation of condition; it might be argued therefore that this true value is not, as has been maintained here, inseparably connected with that equation. But such an argument would be false. The fact that the rule is the same whatever the equation does not alter the fact that the quantity which the rule is directed to determine has no meaning apart from that equation; all that it shows is that there is some feature common to all equations of condition. And again it must be remembered that though the rule does not depend on the equation, the nature of the material to which it is applied does depend on it; the measurements turn out in the way that they do turn out because they are connected with other magnitudes by that equation. The conclusion at which we have arrived is in no way inconsistent with the fundamental considerations of our discussion.

The theory of errors of inconsistency. And now what problems remain? There are two problems. The first is to explain the basis of the rule. So far it is purely empirical; it is based on no theory of error; it will not be completely satisfactory unless it can be based on a theory, just as no law is completely satisfactory unless it is so based. The second is to find some rule for dealing with inconsistent measurements which do not form complete collections; for there are undoubtedly such measurements from which we wish to remove the inconsistency and to determine true values. It will be recognised that the solution of the second problem depends on the solution of the first, and accordingly to that we will direct our attention.

The theory by which we explain the occurrence of inconsistent measurements and of errors of inconsistency is based on the recognition of methodical errors. It is fundamental to every principle of measurement to maintain that it is possible to represent a magnitude, in some manner which has physical significance, by one numeral and by no other (the unit of measurement being always the same). It follows therefore, as has been urged before, that the inconsistent measurements must be measurements of different magnitudes; errors of inconsistency, once more, are not errors of measurement, but errors in an attempt always to realise the same magnitude for measurement. But how comes it that there should be errors in such an attempt; how can we fail to distinguish magnitudes that are different? The theory of methodical errors gives the answer. That theory involves the view that several systems, all of which have the same measured magnitude, and are therefore indistinguishable by any process of measurement, may have different real magnitudes. It is real magnitudes that are related by a numerical law; the crude measured magnitudes may suggest the law; but when we assert the law in a definite numerical form by a mathematical function, it is the real magnitudes, and not the measured, that we are asserting to be related by that function. Since many systems, all having the same measured magnitude, may have different real magnitudes, they may be connected by the numerical law to different real magnitudes of another kind. Now these other real magnitudes, all different, may or may not correspond to the same measured magnitude. If they do correspond to the same measured magnitude, each measured magnitude of one kind will be related to one and only one measured magnitude of the other kind; but if they do not, each measured magnitude of one kind may correspond to many measured magnitudes of the other kind and there will be an appearance of inconsistency.

Let us put the matter formally. The magnitudes a and b are related by a numerical law which states of the real magnitudes A and B that $A = F(B)$. a is measured by an instrument with step α, b with an instrument of step β. Consequently a measurement which gives a value b_1 for b indicates only that the real magnitude of this system lies between $b_1 + \beta$ and $b_1 - \beta$; the real magnitude of the corresponding a must lie between $F(b_1 + \beta)$ and $F(b_1 - \beta)$, or, if β is sufficiently small, between $F(b_1) \pm \beta F'(b_1)$. If $\beta F'(b_1)$ is less than α, these real magnitudes will all correspond to the same measured magnitude; but if $\beta F'(b_1)$ is greater than α they will correspond to different measured magnitudes a, and we shall find the kind of inconsistency which results from a single measured magnitude b_1 being associated with several measured magnitudes $a_1, a_2, \ldots$, although the function in the numerical law is single-valued and only one real magnitude A can be associated with each real magnitude B.

We may interpret according to this view the examples that have been considered. Thus suppose again that we are weighing the quantities of liquid which fill a flask up to a certain mark on the neck. In filling it we are, in effect, making a measurement of volume. For we may imagine that, in place of the single mark on the neck, there are five marks, very near together, marked 1, 2, 3, 4, 5, and that we are filling to the mark 3. If the marks are sufficiently near together we shall find that the contents of the vessel filled up to mark 2 are equal to those of the vessel filled up to mark 3, and those up to mark 3 equal to those up to mark 4. In arriving at this result we must be measuring volume as a fundamental magnitude by noticing what vessels can be filled by the same contents; we shall have found that the contents up to 2 and the contents up to 3 both fill some vessel, and that the contents up to 3 and those up to 4 both fill some other vessel. But no vessel can be found which will be filled both by the contents up to 2 and the contents up to 4. The law of equality fails in the manner typical of methodical errors. Accordingly we must now separate out the marks until the law of equality is just always true, and the distance between the marks now represents the steps of the instrument for measuring volume. Although the marks other than 3 are not actually present on the neck, when we are making our measurements of mass, we are, in each filling, imagining that there are such marks, and we judge the vessel filled when the surface coincides more nearly with mark 3 than with either of the marks on the two sides of it which we can imagine just distinguished from it. We find that at successive fillings our measurements of mass are inconsistent, and this inconsistency we attribute to the fact that volumes which are indistinguishable when measured as volumes, because their surfaces lie between two barely distinguishable marks, are distinguishable by their masses. α, the step of the instrument for measuring mass, is so small or $F'(b)$ so large that, though x is less than β, the step of the instrument for measuring volume, $x.F'(b)$ is greater than α.

The theory is readily extended to inconsistent measurements of magnitudes which are related by the equation of condition to more than one other magnitude; in our example the mass will be related not only to the volume but also to the temperature. Inconsistency may arise from similar methodical errors in any of these other magnitudes and the total error of our magnitude will be the sum of "partial errors" due to the others. In fact, if the equation of condition is $A = F(B, C, D, ...)$, and the steps of the instruments measuring $a, b, c, d, ...$ are $\alpha, \beta, \gamma, \delta, ...$, the same argument shows that the measurements should be consistent or inconsistent according as

$$\beta \frac{dF}{dB} + \gamma \frac{dF}{dC} + \delta \frac{dF}{dD} + ... < \text{or} > \alpha.$$

Such, I believe, are the ideas which underlie our general notion of how errors of inconsistency arise and of how they may be explained. Errors of consistency are regarded as nothing but errors of method magnified until they can be directly detected by experiment. The magnification is effected through the equation of condition, and results either from the addition of several partial errors of method, each of which could not be detected separately, or from the transference of the error from a magnitude less accurately measurable to one which is more accurately measurable. The explanation is theoretical, and indeed the theory is nothing but an immediate extension of the theory of errors of method; it requires only the addition to the hypothesis that the real magnitudes corresponding to the inconsistent measured magnitudes are related by the equation of condition. If the theory turns out to be true, it will provide a very notable confirmation of the theory of methodical errors according to the principles of Chapter VI. For the addition to the hypothesis (or the part that is common to all additions, namely that numerical laws relate real magnitudes) is inevitably suggested by the analogy on which the hypothetical ideas are based; and with this addition we deduce a new experimental proposition, namely that there should be errors of consistency related to the steps of the measuring instruments and to the derivatives of the equation of condition. If this experimental proposition turns out to be true, the theory is confirmed.

But is it true? Again I do not think that systematic experiments have been made which admit of a direct answer to the question, but again I think that the general experience which has accumulated indicates very strongly that a systematic research would confirm the theory. It would require, of course, the determination of the proper steps of the measuring instruments used in determining the related magnitudes, and this task is not easy. But there seems little doubt that these steps could be fixed with an exactitude sufficient to show that the magnitude of the errors of consistency is not inconsistent with possible values of those steps. Thus, to take the example of density once more, we should have to determine (1) within what distance of the mark on the neck of the vessel we could be sure of adjusting the level of the liquid, (2) what error of temperature might occur in filling the vessel, (3) what errors might occur in other magnitudes determining the quantity of liquid put into the vessel. The density of the liquid would then tell us the partial error of inconsistency which would arise from the partial error of method (1), and the coefficient of expansion of the liquid the partial error of consistency that would arise from the partial error (2), and so on. We should have to inquire then whether errors of consistency were ever observed which were greater than the sum of these partial errors or, on the other hand, whether they were always very much less. I think it is quite certain that a test of this nature would generally confirm the theory. I do not pretend that the theory of error has been actually proved by experiment, but only that it could be, and that no known facts are inconsistent with it; it is capable of direct experimental confirmation as much as any other theory.

The errors of consistency that we have been discussing occur when successive measurements are made on a system which, at every measurement, is in exactly the same state in respect of all relevant properties, so far as experiment can tell. But sometimes, owing to the impossibility of controlling accurately the experimental conditions, it is necessary to make measurements when it is known that the conditions are not always the same; such a necessity arises most often in the observational sciences. The differences between successive measurements in such circumstances are often called "errors", and the considerations which have just been presented show that they are very similar to errors of consistency; they differ only in the fact that the differences in the other magnitudes involved in the equation of condition can be detected by experiment. But in such cases we do not usually speak of the "true" value of the magnitude which has to be deduced from the varying measurements, but rather of its "average" or "mean" value. The importance of this mean value is that it will be independent of the exact variation of the uncontrollable conditions. As we are going to conclude that the real magnitude, when there are true errors of consistency, is also a mean value[1], the resemblance between the two classes of cases is very close. Nevertheless for our present purpose it is necessary to distinguish them; in what follows we shall always suppose that the systems of which the inconsistent measurements are made are really indistinguishable by experiment.

We have now examined the theory of errors of consistency. But of course that theory does not so far answer the question we are considering; it does not tell us why the arithmetic mean is the true value. If it is to tell us that, we must introduce into our theory the additional hypothesis, which in our previous discussion we left over for further consideration, stating the "law" of errors of method. We are in a better position to discuss the matter now, for our view that errors of consistency are simply magnified errors of method will enable us to apply some experimental tests to any law the theory may suggest. For if we know the true value, we know by what error each of the inconsistent measurements is affected, and from the distribution of these measurements in a complete collection we can deduce the distribution of the errors. Our conclusion that the arithmetic mean is the true value immediately determines the distribution of errors of inconsistency in a complete collection; if we know the derivatives of the equation of condition we can determine the distribution of methodical errors. However our immediate purpose is not to determine the errors but to explain them; for this and other reasons it will be well to start at the other end and see if we can devise a law of errors which will explain the distribution found and at the same time be in harmony with the fundamental ideas of the theory.

The law of errors of method. We have already seen that the supposed distribution of the measurements in a complete collection is such that the conception of probability is applicable to them. We propose therefore at once to base our law of errors on that conception. We concluded also in Chapter VII that any theory of probability will be ultimately satisfactory only if the hypothetical ideas are analogous to those which arise from the observation of the arbitrary actions of an intelligent being; it is for this reason that all theories involving probability tend to analyse unequal probabilities into the equal probabilities of random events. It is easy to devise a theory of methodical errors which fulfils these necessary conditions. When we are dealing with methodical errors only, just as when we are dealing with such errors magnified into errors of consistency, the circumstances are always such that we are trying in our experiments to realise a system with some definite real magnitude; we are making a large number of systems in

---

[1] Indeed so much seems involved in the meaning of the word "mean". A mean generally is a function of a number of values that such, if all the values were the same and equal to a, the function would also be equal to a. The mean of $a_1, a_2, a_3, \ldots$ is a function $F(a_1, a_2, a_3, \ldots)$ such that $F(a, a, a, \ldots) = a$. If the errors, or differences between $a_1, a_2, a_3, \ldots$ are small compared with the values, there is some reason quite apart from experiment for choosing the arithmetic mean rather than any other. For if F_1 and F_2 are two means, $F_1 - F_2$ will always tend to zero as the values $a_1, a_2, \ldots$ tend to equality. But if F_1 is the arithmetic mean and F_2 any other, it is easy to prove that $(F_1 - F_2)/(a_1 - a_2)$ also tends to zero; it follows that, if the errors are small, all other means approach more rapidly to the arithmetic mean than they do to each other.

the hope that one of them will have the real magnitude we desire. Owing to methodical errors, it is not possible to tell precisely when we have made such a system, but it is possible to exclude definitely certain systems as not having the real magnitude, those namely the measured magnitude of which differs from the values assigned to the desired real magnitude by more than E. We may suppose that we are making the systems entirely at random, and subsequently rejecting some of them because they have clearly not the right real magnitude. Now acting at random in this manner means that it is equally probable that we shall make any system; that is what we mean fundamentally by equal probability; the criterion of equal probability discussed on pp. 168–174. is a mere indication that we are acting in this way. The number of systems having different real magnitudes within the range B to $B + dB$ is proportional[1] to dB; accordingly the probability that we shall make a system within the range B to $B + dB$ is proportional to dB, for it is the sum of equal probabilities, the number of which is proportional to dB. If the step were perfectly sharp, and we could be sure of rejecting any system of which the real magnitude differed from that required (B_1) by as much as E, then the only systems which would be retained would lie within the range $\pm E$, and the probability of a value in a range dx within this range would be $dx/2E$. The probability of a value for the real magnitude of the system between $B_1 + x$ and $B_1 + x + dx$ would be $dx/2E$ if $\mid x \mid$ is less than E, and 0 if $\mid x \mid$ is greater than E. However the step is not perfectly sharp. Actually it is likely that we should reject some of the systems of which the errors were nearly as great as E. No single especially plausible hypothesis can be made about the probability of rejecting such systems, but it seems that, if we take them into account, the law of probability should be this: If $f(x)\,dx$ is the probability that the real magnitude of the system accepted lies between $B_1 + x$ and $B_1 + x + dx$, that is, the probability of an error lying between x and $x + dx$, $f(x) = 1/2E$ if x lies between $\pm \alpha E$, where α is some proper fraction; $f(x) = \phi(x)$, where $\phi \mid x \mid$ is less than $1/2E$ and ϕ' is always of the opposite sign to x, if $\mid x \mid$ lies between E and αE; $f(x) = 0$, if $\mid x \mid$ is greater than E. The theory will not assign

---

[1] This is an assumption which can certainly be doubted; indeed it is not certain that it means anything, for the number of real magnitudes in a finite interval, if it is anything, is infinite; and there is no such thing as an infinite number—though there may be infinite Numbers. The matter can be put more plausibly thus. The process of making systems with real magnitudes at random is analogous to that of placing points on a line at random. We find, by actual trial, that if all parts of the line are indistinguishable, the probability that a point will be placed on any segment of the line of length l is proportional to l. The analogy suggests that the probability of a real magnitude falling between x_1 and x_2 is proportional to the function of x_1 and x_2 which is analogous to the length of the segment, i.e. $x_1 - x_2$. It may be observed that it is not necessary to assume that the probability is proportional to the length, but only that it is some function of the length, so long as this function is analytic. For, by the meaning of probability, the probability that a point falls between x_1 and x_3 (x_3 not being between x_1 and x_2) is the sum of the probability that it falls between x_1 and x_2 and the probability that it falls between x_2 and x_3. Accordingly if $f(x_1 - x_2)$ is the probability that the point falls between x_1 and x_2, we must have

$$f(x_1 - x_3) = f(x_1 - x_2) + f(x_2 - x_3).$$

The only analytic function f satisfying this equation is $f = a(x_1 - x_2)$.

precisely α and ϕ; but since the whole of the error must be 1, there must be the relation

$$2\int_{\alpha E}^{E} \phi(x)\,dx + \alpha = 1.$$

The graph of $f(x)$ will have the form shown in Fig. 1, in which $\phi(x)$ is taken to be linear.

Now we must consider what will be the law of errors of consistency resulting from this law of errors of method. If $F'(B)$ is constant from

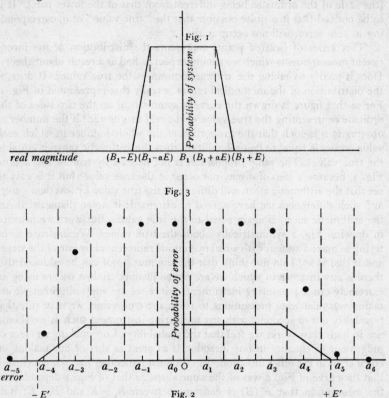

Fig. 1

Probability of system

real magnitude $(B_1-E)\,(B_1-\alpha E)\quad B_1\ (B_1+\alpha E)\,(B_1+E)$

Fig. 3

Probability of error

a_{-5} a_{-4} a_{-3} a_{-2} a_{-1} a_0 O a_1 a_2 a_3 a_4 a_5 a_6
error

$-E'$ Fig. 2 $+E'$

$B = B_1 + E$ to $B = B_1 - E$, the general form of the graph representing the law of errors of consistency will be exactly the same as that in Fig. 1; only the scale will be altered; the abscissae are multiplied by $F'(B)$, the ordinates divided by $F'(B)$. For the only effect of $F'(B)$ will be to magnify in the same ratio all the measurements; while the total probability must remain 1. Accordingly we get Fig. 2, E' being $E.F'(B)$. However we must remember that A will also be affected by methodical errors and that it is measured by an instrument with a step; only a finite number of values of a, the measured magnitude, will be possible. If a_0, a_1, a_2, a_3, ... on the axis of abscissae (Fig. 2) represent the steps of the instrument measuring a, all values of A lying between two of these points will give values of a equal to one or other of them. If we draw ordinates midway between a_0, a_1, a_2, ... the probability of the occurrence of each value of a will be the area of the curve included between the ordinates on either side of it. Accordingly the graph representing the probability of the various possible values of a will consist of a number of isolated points, such as are shown in the upper part of the figure (Fig. 3) (the scale of the ordinates being different from that of the lower part). It is to be noticed that it is quite possible that the "true value" of a, corresponding to zero error, will not occur at all.

This series of isolated points represents the distribution of the inconsistent measurements which we should expect to find as a result of our theory. Does it justify us taking the arithmetic mean as the true value? It does, if the distribution of the methodical errors is really that represented in Fig. 1. For as that figure is drawn the curve is symmetrical on the two sides of the ordinate representing the true value of the real magnitude; if the number of observations is such that the proportion of the whole number in which each value occurs is equal to its probability[1], then the arithmetic mean is equal to the true value. The same proposition is not necessarily true of the dots in Fig. 3, because a step of a may not occur at the true value; but it is easy to see that the arithmetic mean will differ from the true value by less than a step, and such differences we have agreed to disregard; if we so disregard them, the arithmetic mean is again equal to the true value. But were we justified in drawing Fig. 1 symmetrically about the true value? We are sure to be trying to make a system with a real magnitude represented by one of the steps; and if that is so, I do not think that the slightest proof can be adduced that there is any instance in which we are not so justified, unless we are using an extremely crude measuring instrument. Since we are supposing that we are taking very elaborate precautions to reach the true value, we may rule that possibility out of account; with any measuring instrument such as we should use in high class work, we feel that the probability of our making an error of judgement of equality in one direction is as great as that of our making an equal error in the other direction. But we must remember that our conclusion that the curve of Fig. 2 was of the same shape as that of Fig. 1 depended on the assumption that $F'(B)$ is constant between $B_1 + E$ and $B_1 - E$; it is more doubtful that this assumption is always true, and hence we may recognise that the theory suggests that it is possible that there should be cases in which the arithmetic mean is not the true value.

In this discussion it has been supposed that one of the related magnitudes, b, is free from errors of consistency; it may be asked how the law of error of a would be affected if measurements on b as well as those on a were incon-

---

[1] Not equal to its probability, but differing from it by less than any assigned magnitude. All such statements ought really to be expressed in terms of limit, but it is unnecessary here to sacrifice brevity to complete accuracy.

sistent. Inquiry into any particular case would always show that in such cases both a and b are related by a numerical law to some third magnitude x, which may not actually be measured, but, if it were, would be free from inconsistency; the true values of a and b are those which are related by this law to some special value of x. The errors of consistency of both a and b will represent, in the manner that has been discussed, the methodical errors of x; they are not connected and do not determine each other directly; they are connected only through x. Accordingly the errors of both a and b should be distributed in the way we have described; the fact that one of them is affected by errors of inconsistency will not alter the law of errors for the other. A simple example is that which we have taken before. The mass of the liquid which will fill the flask is measured (a) and also the mass of the liquid of standard density which fills the flask (b); b is called the volume. The errors of consistency of a will be distributed in exactly the same way as they would be if the volume b were measured as a fundamental magnitude and showed no errors of inconsistency but only errors of method.

Proof of the law of errors. But now the important question arises whether our theory is confirmed by experiment. Do we actually find that inconsistent observations are distributed as suggested by Fig. 3, or differing from it only by such a distortion as would result from a variation of $F'(B)$? Of course the conventional answer is, No. It is usually asserted that errors of inconsistency are distributed according to Gauss' Law, and the law we have proposed is not that law. It is recognised nowadays that Gauss' Law is a much less certain and obvious thing than was believed when it was first propounded; everyone admits that it is not always true and is, perhaps, never perfectly true. It is admitted too that all the attempts to prove that the law is true from *a priori* considerations are fallacious[1]. But nevertheless it is still usually asserted that as a matter of fact the law is very nearly true in a large number of cases, and examples are frequently quoted as evidence of its truth.

The question whether the distribution of inconsistent measurements is in fact that predicted by the theory can, of course, only be decided by experiment. And here, as almost everywhere else in the theory of errors, the researches that would be necessary to decide the question thoroughly have

---

[1] A point arises here which deserves notice. Gauss' original proof of the law was based on the proposition that it was the only law that led to the result that the arithmetic mean is the true value. It is known now that the proof is fallacious. The chief objections are that two tacit assumptions are made, namely that the true value is the most probable value, and that the probability of the occurrence of a value x, when the true value is z, is some function of $(z - x)$ rather than of z and x as independent variables. We have suggested another law which also makes the arithmetic mean the true value. The fact that it is not Gauss' Law is due partly to the denial of the second assumption (the first will be considered presently), but it is well to notice that there is another tacit assumption that we have also denied; namely that the probability function is everywhere continuous and has everywhere a differential coefficient. This assumption is not true of our function. So far as I can make out nobody has actually pointed out that it might not be true, though that possibility can hardly have escaped the notice of anyone who has thought about the matter.

not been carried out with any completeness; perhaps they cannot be carried out. For we are assuming that the conditions stated at the beginning of this chapter are realised, and it is certainly not easy to realise them completely, as we shall see immediately. Accordingly the matter can only be discussed generally and indications given of well-known facts which, though they do not settle the matter, seem to point in one direction or the other.

In the first place, then, we may examine rather more closely the examples which are so often given of instances in which Gauss' Law of errors is true. Among all the examples that I have been able to find there is not one which clearly satisfies the conditions of the problem; none of the collections of "measurements" which are distributed according to Gauss' Law appear to be really measurements. For it is quite certain that all actual measuring instruments are characterised by a step; the step may not always be connected with the maximum error in the way suggested by the theory of errors of method, but there is a step, and only a finite number of values possible within any given range for the result of a measurement. Further it may be asserted safely that no measuring instrument has a step so small that it enables us to measure a magnitude to one part in ten million (a possible exception may have to be made in favour of instruments for measuring very long times). Accordingly if we find that the supposed "measurements" of an angle of nearly 90° are recorded to hundredths of a second, we may be sure that the figures recorded are not those which result from direct measurements; either each "measurement" is really the mean of a large number of true measurements, or "corrections" have already been applied which increase very greatly the number of possible values. If this criterion is applied to the examples of Gaussian errors usually quoted, I think it will be found that, even when the exact source of the figures given is not stated, it may be concluded confidently that they do not represent direct measurements and therefore have no bearing on the problem before us.

Another "proof" of Gauss' Law is sometimes based on the analogy of shots fired at a target. Of course the conditions here are utterly different from those in any physical experiment, and yet they may seem to have a bearing on the matter. For it might be urged that a marksman firing at a target is in the same position as an experimenter trying to realise a system with a given real magnitude, and that the errors of one are likely to be distributed in the same manner as the errors of the other. But the analogy is false. In the analysis of the marksman's shots every shot that he fires is accepted and included, even though many of them are clearly not in the bull. But the experimenter (when, for instance, he is filling a vessel to a given mark) rejects totally all the "shots" which he can clearly determine do not reach the "bull"; the only shots he accepts are those which, so far as he can tell, have reached the bull. If the two cases are to be analogous, we must reject all those shots of the marksman which we are certain do not pass through the very centre of the bull; and if we reject all but these, the analysis of the remainder tells us, of course, nothing whatever about the distribution of errors.

The whole theory of methodical errors is based on the idea that there are errors which cannot possibly be determined directly by any process of measurement; they can only be determined by the aid of the theory, whether it is confined to methodical errors or extended so as to explain errors of consistency.

On such grounds I conclude that the proofs so often offered, though they may prove something (that we must inquire into presently), do not afford the slightest evidence concerning the question which is at present under discussion; that question is how the inconsistent measurements are distributed which result directly from the attempt to measure the magnitude of a system, which is defined by its relation, expressed by an equation of condition, to some other magnitude. But some evidence on the matter is at the disposal of everyone who has done any experimental research. He must have made such direct measurements—experimental research consists of little else than making them—and he must have found them often inconsistent. He has probably seldom repeated the same observation so often that the measurements will form a complete collection, so that the conditions are present for the establishment of a definite probability for each value, but he has probably sometimes repeated it often enough to be certain that the arithmetic means of several independent collections of the observations do agree within the step of his measuring instrument—which he will probably call his "experimental error". And even when his observations have been less numerous, they will often be sufficient to indicate how a continuation of them might have been expected to turn out. Let him then examine his note books; I suggest that he will find usually that the distribution of measurements is much more like that of Fig. 3 than that given by Gauss' Law. He will find that there are certain measurements, all within a fairly definite range, which occur, as far as he can tell, with almost equal frequency; there is no reason to believe that if he continued the observations, the frequencies of these measurements would diverge. Outside this range the frequencies of the observations decrease. Further there is every indication of a maximum error and of measurements lying so far outside the first range that they never occur. And when I say "never" I mean never. If I am filling a 100 c.c. flask with water, I am as certain as I can be of anything in the world that I shall never observe a mass outside the range 99 to 101 grammes; if I did I should be perfectly certain something was "wrong" with the observation. There is such a thing as absolute certitude—and it may be felt about something which ultimately turns out to be wrong—and it is something quite different from the attitude towards even a million to one chance.

Such observations every physicist will find in his note books, and I believe that they will be found to occur more often than any other kind. But undoubtedly there are instances in which a distribution much more like Gauss' Law is found. Such occurrences are not inconsistent with our theory, though, if there were no others, it would be difficult to adhere to it. For Fig. 2 was deduced on the assumption that the equation of condition was $A = F(B)$. If it had been of the form $A = F(B, C, D, \dots)$ the curve would have been more complex. Its ordinates would have been the sum of those of many curves each of the general shape of Fig. 2, but differing, according to the maximum errors of $b, c, d, ...$, in the length of the horizontal portion and, perhaps, in the shape of the terminal portions; and its shape would have approached more nearly to that of the Gauss curve as the number of the $b, c, d, ...$ increased. Indeed it is well-known that the curve which is the sum of a large number of curves, each symmetrical about the same ordinate, which is the maximum ordinate for each and nearly the same in each, will approach indefinitely nearly to the Gauss curve as the number of curves added is increased[1]. In fact, this is held by many persons to be the most convincing proof of Gauss' Law. That law, or something very like it, is bound to be true so long as each "observed" error is the sum of a very large number of partial errors, all of the same order of magnitude and all equally likely to be positive as negative. It is said that observed errors always are the result of a summation of such partial errors.

Here again we arrive at a question of fact. It is true that all measurements we make do depend to some extent on a very large number of conditions, that is a very large number of other magnitudes. But we know roughly both the maximum errors of these other magnitudes and the various derivatives of $F(A, B, C, D, ...)$. We can determine then whether the partial errors are in fact all about the same order of magnitude. And I think we shall find that in most cases they are not; that there is usually one partial error which altogether outweighs the others. Thus, in the example which we have taken so often, the mass of the filled vessel doubtless depends on the temperature of filling, on the estimate of the density of the air in which it is weighed, on the neighbourhood of other bodies which alter the gravitational acceleration, on the evaporation which takes place during weighing, on dust settling on the pans and on many other things. But all errors from these sources, if reasonable care is taken, are outweighed by the error arising in filling the vessel exactly to the mark. If the distribution of errors followed Gauss' Law, it would not confirm but refute the theory of errors which has been proposed. But actually I do not think it would; the distribution would be much more like that of Fig. 3. Doubtless in other cases, and especially in the determination of surveyor's angles from which examples are so often taken, the position is reversed; the partial errors are of the same order of magnitude and a much nearer approximation to Gauss' Law is found.

There seems then no reason to believe that our theory is not in accordance with the facts, and that there is not a law of error more fundamental than Gauss' Law, which, if it is ever true, merely represents an extremely complicated combination of the more fundamental laws. Of course this conclusion is inconvenient, for our law of error is not expressed by a definite mathematical function; even if the curved portions in Fig. 2 could be abolished and we could believe that the "curve" was a straight line terminating abruptly at

---

[1] The proof usually offered seems to involve the assumption that the added curves can all be represented by analytic functions.

the two ends, the mathematical function representing it would be, as we shall see, much less tractable than that of Gauss. But the conclusion seems to me unavoidable and we must accept it.

Before we pass on one point should be noted. The original object of the theory was to explain the facts; is the explanation satisfactory and is it ultimate? I think it is. We have discussed in Chapter VII the conditions which a theory, involving the conception of probability, must fulfil in order to be completely satisfactory. If the events are to be regarded as "due to chance"—and it is only if they are so due that probability can be introduced—the theory must indicate that the distinguishable "chance" events are the effects of indistinguishable causes. This feature is found in our theory; the distinguishable errors of consistency are the effects of the indistinguishable errors of method. Again we concluded that the theory would not be satisfactory unless events of unequal probability were shown to be compounded of events of equal probability. This condition is not completely fulfilled. In Fig. 1 the errors of method are divided into two classes, one class all equally probable, the other varying in probability, and we have not analysed the second class. But it must be remembered why we imposed that condition; it was because "chance" can only result from the arbitrary action of a voluntary agent, and such action will always produce equally probable alternative events. Now in making the systems the agent is acting arbitrarily and all the systems he produces are, we suppose, equally probable. Unequal probability is introduced only when he rejects some of them, and here he is not acting arbitrarily; the unequal probabilities represent unequal certainties of judgement, unequal degrees of knowledge. This significance of probability is more fundamental than that based on frequency of occurrence; it is the fundamental significance of probability. To explain probabilities that are unequal in this sense by reference to occurrences of equally probable events would be the reverse of explanation. On the other hand when the law of errors is more complex owing to the presence of several important partial errors, and when it approximates to Gauss' Law, then we do explain unequal probabilities by analysis into equal probabilities. The exact explanation need not be stated here; it is too familiar; the derivation of Gauss' Law from the theory which regards observed errors as compounded of partial errors is given, with varying degree of accuracy, in every text-book. The criteria for a satisfactory theory of errors, based on probability, are satisfied.

Incomplete collections. We have now disposed entirely of the problem of errors of consistency in complete collections. We have found a rule, supported if not actually proved by experiment, for finding the true value; we have invented a theory for explaining how such errors arise, have deduced from it a law relating the size of the errors to their probability, and have again shown that this law, though not definitely proved by experiment, is quite concordant with it. Now we must turn to the second outstanding problem, which is practically much the most important problem connected with errors, and has inspired all the elaborate theories of error. We have hitherto supposed that so many observations of the inconsistent magnitude have been made that all the data are available for determining the probabilities of each of the alternative values; the arithmetic means of any two collections can then be made nearly equal and either of them gives directly the true value. In practice this condition is not fulfilled. It requires immense labour to attain and therefore is to be avoided if any other means of attaining the same results can be discovered. Sometimes it is actually impossible to attain, because by their very nature the experiments cannot be repeated indefinitely; for instance it is usually possible only to make one experiment to determine when a comet has a certain right ascension and declination. The question arises therefore whether, when it is not possible to make so many observations that the arithmetic means of different collections of them are nearly equal, any method can be found for selecting the true value and deciding whether or no the proposed equation of condition is correct.

In certain circumstances a method seems indicated by the theory. Suppose that we know that certain real magnitudes $(X_1, X_2, X_3, ...)$ are related by one or more numerical laws $f(X_1, X_2, X_3, ..., a, b, c, ...) = 0$, where a, b, c are the constants (other than formal constants) of the law. We measure values of the magnitudes $(x_1, x_2, x_3, ...)$, so that if the measured magnitudes· were the real magnitudes we should have $f(x_1, x_2, x_3, ..., a, b, c, ...) = 0$. We find actually that this equation is not true. We might (and probably should) find this result even if there were no errors of inconsistency; we might find that if we measured two sets $(x_1, x_2, x_3, ...)$ and $(x_1, x_2, x_3, ...)'$ with the system characterised by the law in the same state, we should always obtain the same values for the magnitudes, and yet (owing to errors of method) that these values did not satisfy the equation. But for the present we are going to imagine that there are errors of inconsistency, and that in the same state of the system, we obtain at successive measurements different sets $(x_1, x_2, x_3, ...)$, $(x_1, x_2, x_3, ...)'$, $(x_1, x_2, x_3, ...)''$, etc. The problem is to determine from these measured sets the true values of the real magnitudes $(x_1, x_2, x_3, ...)$.

If the collections $(x_1, x_1', x_1'', ...)$, $(x_2, x_2', x_2'', ...)$ were all complete, the problem would be that which we have considered already and the true real magnitudes would be the arithmetic means of the measured magnitudes. If they are not a complete collection the theory still suggests a process. Suppose for the moment that we know the true real magnitudes. From these and the measured magnitudes we calculate the errors $\delta x_1, \delta x_1', \delta x_1'', ..., \delta x_2, \delta x_2', ...,$ where $\delta x_1 = x_1 - X_1$ and $\delta x_2' = x_2' - X_2$, etc. Now we may have reason to believe (and the method is only applicable if we have such reason) that if we could make a complete collection of the errors of x_1, $\delta x_1, \delta x_1', \delta x_1'', ...,$ and another of the errors of $x_2, \delta x_2, \delta x_2', ...$ or any other x, then the errors in these two collections of x would be distributed according to the same law. The number of observations made on all the x's taken together will be greater than the number of those made on any one x, and it is possible that, though the number made on any one x is so small that it would not provide a complete collection, the number that we have made on all the x's together is so great that, if they had all been made on the same x, they would have provided a complete collection. That complete collection, made up of measurements on different magnitudes, we assume would be such that the errors would be distributed according to the law which is characteristic of the errors made in measurements on each of these different magnitudes.

The assumption is founded on the expectation that the actual errors, although they are errors in different magnitudes, will occur with the same frequency as if they were errors of the inconsistent measurements of the same magnitude. It is an obvious application of the ideas underlying the theory; it involves an addition to the theory, but only one which is suggested immediately by the analogy on which it is founded. Just as I expect the distribution of cards drawn to be the same whether I continue to draw cards from the same pack (replacing the card after each draw) or draw successive cards from different packs, so, if the law of errors is the same throughout, I expect the distribution of errors of the different magnitudes to be the same as would be the distribution of errors of a single magnitude. But it should be noticed that, if the law of errors were that of Fig. 3, a discontinuous series of points, it would hardly be possible that the laws should be the same for every x_1 and the same for every x_2; it would only be so if all the true magnitudes fell in the same position in the interval between steps of the measuring instrument. That might happen, but it would be quite illegitimate to assume that it would happen. The conditions could only be realised if the law of errors is taken to be Fig. 2 and not Fig. 3; we must neglect totally in the application of the rule the errors of methods which are superimposed on those of consistency. A source of uncertainty is thereby introduced into our arguments, but we shall see that there are so many other sources of uncertainty that it may be left on one side for the present. We shall suppose that the law of error is always represented by a continuous graph of some kind.

Accordingly if we knew the true values we should expect to find the errors distributed in a certain way. It is a natural consequence that we should frame the rule that we select the errors so that they are distributed in that way. Such is doubtless the basis of the rule actually adopted; but in the application a difficulty immediately arises. We might interpret the phrase "distributed in that way" to mean "occurring with the frequencies corresponding to the probabilities given by the law of error". Unfortunately, owing to the nature of probability, that rule can never in practice indicate the selection to be made. If the conception of probability is applicable, the errors must be "due to chance" and we must never know what the next error is going to be. Accordingly (as we argued on p. 173) at any trial any error with a probability not zero must be possible, and any collection of errors must be a possible collection. Whatever observations have been made, any selection of true values is possible so long as it makes all the errors less than the maximum error (and if a law is adopted which gives no maximum error even this restriction is removed). The case is hardly altered if we limit the choice of possible distributions by denying the occurrence of extreme coincidences. There will certainly always be more than one selection of true values possible. The rule would give a result only if it could be assumed that the frequency with which an event of probability p occurs in N trials is exactly pN; that assumption is not legitimate however great is N; in fact it is self-contradictory, and if we made it should find generally true values could not be chosen so that the errors were distributed according to the law of errors; the process would break down from the start. The assumption that the errors are distributed in a manner consistent with the law of errors does not lead to an unique determination of the true values. In order to choose true values uniquely we have to select one out of the sets of errors which the law permits as possible.

The "most probable distribution" of errors. Some further criterion is therefore necessary. Our idea is that the errors are to be distributed as nearly as possible in accordance with a certain law; we must give a definite meaning to "as nearly as possible". The universally accepted rule is that we should choose that set of true values which makes the distribution of errors the most probable. Now it may be admitted at once that if we are going to choose one set rather than another on the ground of their probabilities, it would be highly unreasonable to choose any set but the most probable[1]. But

---

[1] It has been urged that not the most probable value, but the probable value, should be taken as the true value; but if such a suggestion is made here I think it would be founded on a misunderstanding. When it is made, the circumstances which are usually contemplated are that a collection of measurements have been made on a single magnitude and that the true value is to be selected from them. If the collection is complete, we have decided that the true value is the arithmetic mean: if the probabilities are determined, it will be found that the arithmetic mean is the value with the greatest probability; it will also be the probable value. That is the result which is predicted by any theory of errors that anyone has proposed —except in so far that our theory would make the arithmetic mean, not the only most probable value, but one of a set of values all of which were equally probable and more probable than any other values. If the collection were complete and we did not find that the arithmetic mean, the most probable, and the probable values all coincided, then we should doubtless revise our whole theory of errors; and it is quite likely (see p. 511) that we should still take the arithmetic mean even if it were not the most probable value or, if we did not, the probable rather than the most probable value. If the collection is not complete, then none of the values have a definite probability at all; there is no means of determining probability unless the number of observations can be extended indefinitely. The most probable value is not that which has occurred most frequently, unless there is every reason to believe that it would always occur most frequently if the observations were continued indefinitely.

This point is overlooked when the choice of the probable as against the most probable value is urged. As an example favouring the choice of the former rather than the latter might be given such a collection of observations as 1, 2, 2, 2, 3, 3, 4, 4, 5, 5, 6, 6, 7. Here 2 occurs most frequently, but the arithmetic mean, and the value which would be the probable value if frequencies were probabilities, lies between 3 and 4. It would certainly be unreasonable to choose 2 from such a collection, but then as the collection is obviously incomplete it would be unreasonable, according to any rule we have established so far, to choose anything. If we did not choose 2, it would be on the grounds that the collection was not complete and that further observations would alter the distribution. Such grounds are inconsistent with the attribution to 2 of any probability whatever, whether greater or less than the probability of 3.

But all this is really irrelevant to the matters we are going to discuss. For we shall find that the most probable value which it will appear reasonable to select is not the most probable of a complete collection of values, but a value which is most probably the cause of the

the alternative must not be overlooked that it may not be desirable to choose at all on the ground of probability in this technical and complicated sense. If I have to choose a day for a garden party a year ahead, it will be reasonable to choose it on the ground of the probability of the day being fine (or, if I am an unsociable person, wet), this probability being estimated by the observed frequencies of fine weather on various days of the year; for there is no other ground on which to choose. But if I can wait until nearer the date before choosing, it will be wiser to choose by a meteorological forecast, which is not based on considerations of probability at all And the alternative will be still more plausible if I find that the records are so incomplete that there is great difficulty in estimating the probability. Let us therefore inquire rather more closely how the probability of a distribution of errors is estimated.

The problem is one of the probability of causes. I know that I have certain effects, namely certain observed values of the magnitudes. I know that the causes are (1) some true values of these magnitudes which are not known, (2) a certain law of the probabilities of errors, or differences between the observed and true values; this law is supposed known. If I assume certain true values, I can calculate the errors from the observed magnitudes. Thus, if I assume that the true values are $(X_1, X_2, X_3, ...)$, I know the errors $\delta x_1, \delta x_1', ..., \delta x_2, \delta x_2', ...$ From the law of errors I know the probabilities of the occurrence of these errors; let them be $p_1, p_1', ..., p_2, p_2', ...$ It is assumed that the errors are independent, so that the probability of the occurrence of an error δx_1 in one measurement is independent of the occurrence of an error δx_2 in the other; the assumption is not indubitable, but we will accept it. (It is probably a necessary consequence of our fundamental assumption that all the errors in any magnitude of the same kind are distributed according to the same law.) Then P, the probability that all the errors will occur, is

$$p_1 \cdot p_1' \cdot .... \cdot p_2 \cdot p_2' \cdot ....$$

According to the discussion in Chapter VII, if Q is the probability *a priori* of the true values I have assumed, then R, the probability that the errors which have actually occurred have occurred as the effect of these true values, is $QP/\Sigma QP$, where Σ is the sum of QP for all possible sets of true values. Since we only require to compare the probabilities that the errors have resulted from different sets of true values and since the denominator ΣQP is the same for all, the conclusion at which we arrive is that the true values are that set which makes QP a maximum.

---

distribution of that collection. This is quite a different conception, as we decided in Chapter VII. If we have to select one event rather than another as the cause of a known effect, we shall undoubtedly choose the most probable cause. Nobody, I think, would propose to choose under any circumstances the probable cause—and the best proof of that statement is that the phrase "probable cause", as distinguished from "most probable cause", is never used. Moreover the reason why it is never used is obvious after our discussion in Part I. The calculation of the probable cause—defined analogously to the probable event—would involve a knowledge of the numerical values of the probabilities of different causes. We concluded that such numerical values have no physical meaning; it is only the order of probabilities that is significant.

It is always assumed that all sets are equally probable *a priori* and all Q's the same. Then the true values are those for which P is a maximum. If Gauss' Law for the probability of the individual errors is accepted—and it always is accepted when this method is adopted—then P is a maximum when

$$h_1^2 \Sigma \overline{\delta x_1^2} + h_2^2 \Sigma \overline{\delta x_2^2} + h_3^2 \Sigma \overline{\delta x_3^2} + \dots$$

is a minimum. h_1 is here the measure of the precision of the measurements of x_1 and $\Sigma \overline{\delta x_1^2}$ is the sum of the squares of the errors made in all measurements of x_1. But our fundamental assumption, that the law of errors is the same for $x_1, x_2, x_3, \dots$, means that $h_1 = h_2 = h_3$. The rule therefore to which we are led is that those true values should be selected for which

$$\Sigma \overline{\delta x_1^2} + \Sigma \overline{\delta x_2^2} + \Sigma \overline{\delta x_3^2} + \dots = \Sigma \overline{\delta x^2}$$

is a minimum.

The question whether it is legitimate to assume that all the *a priori* probabilities of the true values are equal has often been discussed. It appears to me that it is usually legitimate—so far as anything is legitimate in connection with the very difficult and uncertain theory of the probability of causes. All that we know about the true values is that they satisfy the equations of condition; when we have set up a state of the system and before we make measurements, we do not know anything about it except that the true values will satisfy these conditions. The *a priori* probabilities of all such values are therefore equal. But in the subsequent argument we shall definitely exclude any values which do not satisfy the equations; therefore all the remaining values are equally probable *a priori*. It is true that after we have made the measurements some true values are more probable *a priori* than others, namely those somewhere near the measured values; and we do not actually begin to think about true values until we know the measured values and our state of mind—on which *a priori* probability depends—has changed. But we ought to think about them before, and deduce a rule which will be applicable whatever the measured values actually turn out to be; that seems to be the position which the calculation of the probability of causes assumes.

If this argument is not sufficient, the assumption of equal *a priori* probabilities can be justified in two other ways, which are really expressions of the same point of view. On the ground of some previous knowledge derived from any source we may consider that all proposed true values are not equally probable *a priori*. But let us assign to them for trial the same *a priori* probabilities, and let us calculate the most probable distribution. Now either the most probable distribution so calculated is one to which we attach a very high *a priori* probability, or it is not. If it is, then it is clear that the distribution would not be made less probable *a posteriori* by assigning the *a priori* probabilities in the manner we propose and giving it a high probability *a priori*. Since we are only concerned to know which is the most probable distribution and not precisely what the probability of that distribution is, we shall come to the same conclusion whether or no we assign unequal probabilities *a priori*. If it is not, then there is a clear conflict between the evidence derived from these measurements and the knowledge on which the *a priori* probabilities were based, and we shall have to investigate the discrepancy.

The matter may be put another way. What we are concerned to know is the evidence which is given by the measurements we have made for one set of true values rather than another. It is right then to investigate this matter without reference to anything but these measurements, and to assume that all results are *a priori* equally probable. If our conclusion based on that assumption is inconsistent with evidence based on any other source, then we shall have to make up our minds which source is the more reliable and whether in any manner we can resolve the discrepancy. In any case it is well to know whether there is or is not discrepancy and we can only know that certainly if we put all *a priori* probabilities equal. This argument (which, it may be noted, applies as well to any consideration of the probabilities of causes, involving *a priori* probabilities) is the best way of justifying the assumption that is always made; it appears to me sound so long as the conditions supposed are fulfilled.

The Method of Least Squares. Such is the basis of the familiar rule which is embodied in the formalism of the Method of Least Squares. The rule is that the true values in the conditions which have been supposed are such that the sums of the squares of the errors is a minimum for changes in those true values, the errors being the differences between the true and the measured values, and the reduction to a minimum being made subject to the true values satisfying the equations of condition. The formalism by which the method is applied does not concern us directly; the problem is purely mathematical. So long as the equations of condition are linear (as they almost always are in practice), the method of "undetermined correlatives" provides the solution; if it is not linear, devices are available for making them linear (see p. 515). But it is well to note that a method is sometimes used which is not analytically legitimate. In this method the results of the measurement are stated in "observational equations" of the form $x_1 = N_1$, $x_1 = N_2$, ..., $x_2 = M_2$, ..., etc., where the N's and M's are numerals. By means of equations of condition, which are of the form $ax_1 + bx_2 + ... = 0$, as many of the variables $x_1, x_2, ...$ are eliminated as there are equations of condition. The true values, $X_1, X_2, ...$, are then taken to be such that the sum of the squares of the residuals of the remaining equations is a minimum for variations of these true values; the residuals being the quantities by which the two sides of the equations differ when the true values are substituted for the measured values. Formal rules are available, consisting in the formation and solution of "normal equations", for determining these true values which make the residuals a minimum.

This alternative method deserves notice because it is very similar to that adopted in the solution of another problem which will concern us later; but, as has been said, it is not really legitimate in general. It is only legitimate and gives the same result as the method of undetermined correlatives, if (1) all the coefficients in all the equations of condition are equal—or rather if all their moduli are equal, (2) all sums of products of errors of the form $\Sigma dx_1 . dx_2$ are zero. The first condition is very often fulfilled, for all the coefficients are often $+ 1$ or $- 1$. The second would doubtless be fulfilled if the measurements on each of the magnitudes x formed a complete collection. But if they did form a complete collection, there would be no need for the application of adjustment at all, for their arithmetic mean would be the true value; the adjustment is valuable only when the measurements on each of the magnitudes do not form a complete collection, but the measurements on all the magnitudes taken together form a complete collection. Accordingly (2) is never true, and examination will show that the two methods do usually give rather different results. However this criticism of actual practice is not important at present; the first method is an adequate expression of the theory on which the treatment rests, and we may suppose that it is always used.

But is that theory true? It involves intimately the assumption that the errors are distributed according to Gauss' Law; for if that law is not assumed there is no reason for believing that the solution which makes the sum of the squares of the errors a minimum is the most probable solution and gives the true values. I have already given reasons for believing that the law is not true; it cannot possibly be true if, as seems certain, all measuring instruments are characterised by steps and only a finite number of values can be observed; the admission that the number of possible values is finite is sufficient to destroy all belief in the law, even if the further proposition that there is a definite maximum error is not admitted. On the other hand, in discussions of the adjustment of observations examples are always given to show that the law is true; what are we to make of these examples? The answer has been given already; what are called in these examples "measured values" are not measured values; they are almost always arithmetic means of large numbers of measured values. In the circumstances in which this method of adjustment is applied, each of the magnitudes $x_1, x_2, \ldots$ have been measured many times; in place of treating each measurement as independent in the process of adjustment, the practice is always adopted of first taking the arithmetic mean of all the measurements on each magnitude (and possibly "correcting" it) and treating these arithmetic means as the observations to be adjusted. When it is said that the errors obey Gauss' Law, what is meant is that the differences of these means from the calculated true values obey that law. This statement may be true, but it is quite irrelevant; even if it is true, it provides not the slightest basis for the application of the Method of Least Squares. We cannot base that method on a law of error proved *a posteriori*; the law must be known before the justification of the method begins.

For let us follow out once more the argument which led to the view that the distribution of errors is most probable when the sum of the squares of the errors is a minimum. We now propose to assume that we know, not that the errors of the individual measurements are distributed according to Gauss' Law, but that the residuals, or the difference between certain calculated true values and the measured values, are so distributed. But now the "cause" of the occurrence of any residual is not simply certain true values and certain measured values; it is also the process of calculation. It is true that the presence of this additional cause does not alter the probability *a priori* that a proposed true value is acting as a cause or the probability that a given measured value will result from that true value; for since the method of calculation is always "acting", its *a priori* probability is 1 and the probability that any residual will result from it is also 1. But the additional cause does mean that additional alternatives have to be considered; we must consider the possibility of the same true values but a different method of calculation. But since the method of calculation is an expression of the law of errors, a change in it means a change in the probability that a given measured value will result from a given true value. The numerator on p. 489 will become $QP + Q_1P_1 + Q_2P_2$, where the Q's are the probabilities *a priori* of the different laws and the P's the probabilities that the given measured values result from the proposed true values according to those laws. There is no method of estimating the Q's and, even if we put them all equal to 1, the P's are very difficult to estimate because all the laws are not represented by simple mathematical functions. But even if we overcame these difficulties it is certain that the rule at which we should arrive for finding the most probable distribution would certainly not be that of making the sum of the squares of the residuals a minimum; for that rule is characteristic of Gauss' Law alone.

But—it may be said—this argument, if pressed, could be applied to a law of individual errors as well as to a law of residuals. No; for the argument depends on the fact that the law is only known after the calculation is completed; we have seen that a law of individual errors might be determined directly by experiment without any calculation at all. It was on the assumption that it is so known that the deduction of the Method of Least Squares was based; and that assumption can be maintained only if the errors are really errors of individual measurements in a complete collection. All the evidence that is available seems to prove that Gauss' Law cannot be true for such individual errors; and therefore the Method of Least Squares loses all theoretical justification[1].

---

[1] It may be observed in passing that even if the law of errors of individual measurements were that of Gauss, the practice of taking means before proceeding to adjust would be quite illegitimate. Let X_1', X_2', ... be the arithmetic means of the measured values of x_1, x_2, ..., and X_1, X_2, ... the true values which are proposed; let the measured values of x_1 be $X_1' + dx_1$, where dx_1 varies. Then if dx_1 is distributed according to Gauss' Law, the quantity which should be made a minimum is $\Sigma (X_1 - X_1' - dx_1)^2$ which, since $\Sigma dx_1 = 0$, is equal to $\Sigma (X_1 - X_1')^2 + \Sigma dx_1^2$. On the other hand, by taking means before adjusting the quantity which is made a minimum is $\Sigma (X_1 - X_1')^2$. Accordingly the prevalent practice is illegitimate even if the individual errors are distributed according to Gauss' Law; but if they were so distributed, it could be made legitimate by adjusting before and not after taking means. The process would be much more complex, but it could be carried out.

Again it will be well to note here that if it is true that the residuals of the means of the observations are distributed according to Gauss' Law, it follows at once that the individual errors of the means are not so distributed (see p. 503). The discovery that residuals are distributed according to that law does not prove that the law is true for errors, as is commonly suggested; it proves exactly the contrary.

Is the Method of Least Squares right? However, even if the Method of Least Squares is not theoretically justified, it is still possible that it may lead to the right result. For either the theory may be wrong, or, though it does not directly justify the Method, it may not be inconsistent with it. The question whether it does lead to the right result is obviously very important, and needs careful consideration.

It will be well to have clearly in our minds the kind of observations to which the Method is likely to be applied. We must note at once that they are not likely to be such as are important in pure physics. In pure science we are seldom, if ever, concerned to determine very accurately the true value of a measured magnitude; for such a value is necessarily the property of some individual body or system. Pure science is concerned with laws, which are propositions true of all bodies or systems of a certain class, and not with propositions which distinguish members of a class which are all subject to the same laws. Nevertheless the consideration which is to be given to the matter is justified, because of the light that it will throw on problems of a different nature which are important to pure physics and will receive attention later.

The examples of the application of the Method of Least Squares in the form which we are considering, ordinarily given in text-books on the Method, are derived from surveying; and such examples will serve our purpose admirably. We will suppose that the observations to be adjusted are those of a levelling survey. We have measured with all possible accuracy the vertical distances $z_{12}, z_{13}, ..., z_{23}, ...$, between certain points 1, 2, 3, ... The equations of condition which these observations have to satisfy are of the form

$$z_{pr} = z_{pq} + z_{qr}.$$

These equations are not satisfied by the observations, even when z_{pr} is the mean of all the observations made of the distance between p and r. It is required to adjust the z's so that the equations of condition are satisfied.

We must start as usual by inquiring what we mean by the "true values" and the "right result". In our discussion of the complete collection of measurements on a single magnitude, we concluded that the true value was that value which is connected with some other magnitude by means of the equation of condition. But here the method of adjusting which is proposed is such that it is mathematically necessary that the adjusted values should satisfy that equation; we adjust them so that they do satisfy it. Whatever law of errors we assumed, and whatever the process to which it led, the adjusted values must be in this sense the true values and the right result; the fact that the adjusted values satisfy the equation of condition does not indicate that the proposed method, as distinguished from any other which makes use of the equation of condition in the process of adjustment, gives the right result. What then is meant by the question?

The fundamental assumption is that the measurements on each z do not form a complete collection; it is only the collection of all measurements on all z's that is complete. On the other hand, if the collection of measurements on any z was complete, the mean of that collection would be the true value of z. Accordingly our question should be, Does the process of adjustment lead to the result which would be obtained if we so increased the collection of measurements on each z that each such collection was complete? The answer must clearly be given independently of any theoretical considerations by a simple and direct examination of the facts. For we are asking what would be the result of certain additional observations, and no theory can be used to predict observations until it is completely established; and we have already had reason to doubt the theory. But it is easy to see that no simple and direct examination of the facts can give an answer, for the reason that, in the circumstances contemplated, it is impossible to obtain a complete collection of measurements on any z and so to find its true value. For in such examples the measurements on the various z's that are to be adjusted are always the most accurate that can be made. If by increasing the number of his observations the surveyor thought that he could increase the accuracy of his result, he would take the additional observations necessary for that purpose. The fact that, when he has made the most accurate measurements he can, these measurements do not satisfy the equation of condition shows that by no process of simple observation can he arrive at true values; if he could arrive at true values, they would, by the definition of "true values", satisfy the equation of condition and no adjustment would be necessary[1]. The only circumstances in which adjustment is necessary are those in which the test whether the adjustment gives the right result cannot be applied. Moreover the assumption on which we have so far founded the Method of Least Squares is that all the observations taken together form a complete collection, though the observations on each magnitude do not. But if we cannot form complete collections for each magnitude however numerous they are, can there be any reason for assuming that the collection for all of them together is complete?

I conclude then that, in such an example as we have considered, experimental as well as theoretical evidence must necessarily be lacking for an assertion that the Method gives the right result. And this conclusion is important, for it is on such examples that the evidence for the method is usually based (by pointing out that the residuals obey Gauss' Law). Nevertheless it may be urged that the example is unfavourable; that cases could be found in which complete collections of observations are obtainable and, therefore, true values; that we might then split up these collections into several which were not complete; and, by combining these incomplete

---

[1] It may be said that a previous conclusion has been forgotten. The mean of a complete collection is not necessarily actually the true value; it is only a value differing from that true value by less than the least physically significant difference. But this admission does not alter the position. If the most accurate values of individual z's were always within the least significant difference of the true values, the discrepancy in the satisfying of the equation of condition would also be less than that difference. What would be the object of adjusting to avoid a discrepancy that is physically insignificant? It might be practically convenient to adjust in order to satisfy the equations formally, but the adjustment could have no significance and there could be no question of whether it was right. Really, of course, the discrepancy is always greater than the least significant difference.

collections on the different magnitudes by the Method of Least Squares, inquire whether that Method gave the right result. It must be admitted that such examples probably could be found[1]; I do not think that any of them have been carefully investigated, but I am not disposed to dispute that it is highly probable that, if the Method were investigated by means of them, it would be found generally to give the right result. I do not really wish to prove that the prevailing method of adjustment leads to the wrong result, but only to destroy the arguments by which it has been maintained that it must lead to right results. It is important to destroy those arguments, primarily because they are fallacious, but also because they might hinder the consideration of other methods of adjustment which possess equal or greater advantages.

The Method of Least Squares is really used in such processes of adjustment because it is a convenient method of getting an unique result. A surveyor naturally and properly wants to make the results of his survey look neat and tidy; it would not be neat and tidy to give values for the height of 1 above 2 and of 2 above 3 which did not add up to the height of 1 above 3; the Method gives him a way, easy and universally adopted, for avoiding such discrepancies. But it is very doubtful whether he regards the adjusted values as more accurate in any important sense than those by which he replaces them. And perhaps the best proof of that statement is that surveyors, who are not less intelligent than physicists, often employ this method of adjustment when the most superficial examination must show that there cannot be the smallest theoretical foundation for its use. One example of this nature is sufficiently interesting to merit brief notice.

It occurs in the adjustment of angles, say the angles of a plane triangle. The equation of condition here is that the three angles have to add up to $180°$. The measured values are actually found to add up to $180 - d$. The rule of adjustment indicated by the Method of Least Squares is that $d/3$ should be added to each of the measured values. All the errors are therefore of the same sign in every adjustment; the sign may be sometimes positive and sometimes negative, but it is always of the same sign in all of any set of adjusted angles. Such a result is clearly contradictory to the law of errors on which the method of adjustment professes to be founded; there must be a fallacy in an argument which leads to a conclusion contradicting the premises. The fallacy is obvious; it is introduced in assuming that all values of the real magnitudes are equally probable *a priori*. For here we cannot investigate the real values indicated by the measurement under the assumption that we are completely ignorant of everything but these measurements. For the

---

[1] Probably weight would be the best magnitude on which to conduct the investigation. We might weigh a set of bodies on a very accurate and sensitive balance, and then weigh them, singly and in combination, on a much less sensitive balance; we might then adjust the weights so that the weights of the combinations were the sums of the weights of the components, and investigate whether these adjusted weights agreed with the true weights determined, first on the sensitive balance, second as the mean of a large number of observations on the insensitive.

circumstance which makes us want to adjust the values at all is not any inconsistency or uncertainty about the values themselves; it is simply the fact that, when compared with what is known from other experiments or from theory, they appear on the whole too small (or too large). If they did not appear too small we should not want to adjust them at all. And if we only want to adjust them because they appear too small, it is clearly ridiculous to start by assuming that an adjustment which makes them smaller will be as acceptable and as probable *a priori* as one that makes them larger. In this form of the problem, Gauss' Law is not applicable and indeed no law is applicable which assumes that positive and negative errors are equally probable; systematic error must be recognised. It is quite possible that the rule to which the conventional method leads is as good as any other; it is unlikely that it could ever be shown not to lead to the right result. But it is clear that the method must be regarded simply as an empirical rule adopted for convenience because *some* rule is necessary, and that it cannot be founded on a theory of error which is directly contradicted by the facts to which it is applied.

The probable error. The conclusion at which we have arrived is generally reached by every inquirer into the basis of the usual methods of the adjustment of observations. But it may be urged that the theoretical considerations on which it was originally based, although they are certainly inadequate, have been made to appear worse than they really are, because it has been supposed that the Method of Least Squares pretends to achieve a result which it does not really pretend to achieve. Much of the criticism has been directed against the view that the values which result from the adjustment are "true values", and differ from the real true values which satisfy the equation of condition by an amount which is physically insignificant. The Method of Least Squares, it may be said, does not profess to achieve such a result and arrive at absolutely right values; the values adjusted are nothing but what they are said to be, namely the most probable values. It is admitted that they may differ from the true values; all that is asserted is that they are the best results we can arrive at from the consideration of observations which are insufficient to establish complete certainty.

This assertion is expressed by the addition to every statement of adjusted values of a probable error. The probable error r of an adjusted value X is defined to be such that the probability that the true value lies within the range $X + r$ to $X - r$ is equal to the probability that it lies without that range. Its introduction shows that it is not asserted that X is the true value, but only that the probability that the true value differs from X by any assigned amount z is less than the probability that the true value differs from any value other than X by the same amount z. Let us examine this conception of a probable error.

A distinction is always made between the "probable error of a single observation" and "the probable error of the general mean" (i.e. of the adjusted value). The two errors are supposed to be closely related, but they

are essentially distinct; the determination of the second depends on a knowledge of the first. Let us therefore consider first the probable error of a single
observation.

If we know the errors and if the collection of them is complete, then we
can determine the probability that any error will occur as the result of a
single measurement; for a complete collection is one from which we can
determine probabilities. We are assuming that, though the collection of
errors of a single magnitude is incomplete, it is permissible to group together
all the measurements on different magnitudes, and that this collection is
complete. If we can determine the true magnitudes, then the residuals, v,
of the observational equations are the errors of the measured magnitudes.
However these errors are distributed we can determine the probable error r
which is such that the probability that an error lying between $+r$ and $-r$
is $\frac{1}{2}$. If we know that the distribution is that of Gauss' Law, the determination
is very simple; for it can be shown that h, the measure of precision, is $\sqrt{2\Sigma v^2/n}$,
where n is the number of observations, and that $hr = 0.4769$. All this is
perfectly clear and involves nothing that is not implied by the statement that
the collection of the observations is complete and that the probability of the
various errors can be determined.

But now what is the probable error of the adjusted value? It is obviously
zero. For in the calculation of the probable error of a single observation we
have assumed that we know the true values; there is no probability that they
are the true values; they *are* the true values, and there is no more to be said.
If on the other hand we do not know the true values, we have no means of
calculating the probable error of a single observation, and since on this
probable error depends the probable error of the adjusted values, we have
no means of determining that probable error.

However we may try to avoid this dilemma by noticing that the admission
that we do not know the true values and that they have a finite probable error
is equivalent to the admission that the collection of measurements is not
complete. Our consideration has been based so far on the assumption
that it is complete; we must now consider how it is affected by the denial of
that assumption.

The following is a paraphrase of the argument which underlies the conventional deduction of the probable error of the general mean. Let us suppose
that we have a complete collection of measurements, and let us choose out
of it at random smaller incomplete collections each of n measurement. From
each incomplete collection let us determine an adjusted value or "mean"
by the Method of Least Squares. Since the collections are incomplete, these
means will differ; they, like the original measurements, will be distributed
according to a law of errors[1]; there will be a function $f(x)$ such that $f(x)\,dx$
is the probability that the mean of the incomplete collection differs from the
true value, or the mean of the complete collection, by an amount lying between
x and $x + dx$. There will be therefore a quantity r such that the probability

---

[1] But not in general the same law of errors. (Cf. p. 503.)

is $\frac{1}{2}$ that any mean of an incomplete collection of n measurements differs from the true mean by not more than r. If we know $f(x)$, we can determine this r; for r is such that $\int_{-r}^{+r} f(x)\,dx = \frac{1}{2}$. Then r is, by definition, the probable error of the mean. Now we have an incomplete collection of observations which may be taken as selected at random; therefore r is the probable error of our adjusted value. That, I think, is the argument; for the methods adopted for finding the probable error of the general mean are those which, applied to a complete collection, would determine such an r.

But of course the obvious criticism is that, *ex hypothesi*, they are not applied to a complete collection; if the collection were complete there could be no object in applying them. But if it is not complete there is no method of determining $f(x)$. For $f(x)$ can be determined only in two ways. First, if we had a number of incomplete collections which, taken together, formed a complete collection, then we could find the probability of various errors of the means of the incomplete collection just as we found the probability of the errors of individual measurements in a complete collection of them. But, of course, if we had a sufficient number of incomplete collections to make up a complete collection we should not attempt to deduce an adjusted value from one of these incomplete collections only; the problem that we are considering does not arise except when we have one incomplete collection only. Second, $f(x)$ is known if we know the distribution of the errors of the individual measurements; for from that distribution we can calculate the probability of any given collection of measurements affected by given errors and the probability of that collection will be the probability of the error x in the adjusted mean, where x is the difference between the true mean and the mean derived from adjustment of that collection. But again to determine the distribution of the individual errors we must have a complete collection of them; if we had a complete collection we should know the true values and there would be again no need of adjustment.

In the method of calculation of the probable error according to the ordinary rules, these difficulties are avoided by simply applying to the incomplete collection the formula which would be applicable if the collection were complete and the errors of individual measurements distributed according to Gauss' Law[1]. It is unnecessary to insist that the method is unjustified. On the other hand it may be admitted that, if the conception of the probable error of the mean has any significance at all, the usual formula will give some approximation to it, so long as the observations are fairly numerous.

---

[1] This statement is not strictly accurate. The ordinary formula for the probable error of a single observation is $r = 0.6745 \sqrt{\Sigma v^2/(x-q)}$, where q is the number of magnitudes of which the values are adjusted. The formula if the collection were complete would be obtained by putting $q = 0$. The probable error of the mean is taken to be $r/\sqrt{p}$, where p is the weight of the mean (see p. 502). The introduction of q is justified on grounds which depend on the recognition that the collection may be incomplete, but no attempt is made to offer any sound theoretical basis for it. Again, it is recognised that the probable error itself has a probable error; but if we once start on such a regression, where are we to stop?

It is possible therefore that, like the adjusted values, the probable error may be regarded as a conventional method of obtaining an unique value for a quantity which must be measured somehow; if that is so, no objection can be raised to its use.

But has the conception of the probable error of the mean any significance? Suppose that the probable error could be calculated in a manner free from objection, what would it mean? The considerations on which its calculation is based show that it would mean this. When we say that the probability is P that the mean of an incomplete collection differs from the true value by x, we are asserting that if N, the number of incomplete collections examined, were increased sufficiently, the number of them giving means differing from the true value by x would tend to P/N as N tends to infinity. r, the probable error, would be such that the number giving means differing from the true value by not more than r would tend to $\frac{1}{2}N$ as N tends to infinity. That is the information that would be provided by a statement of the probable error if it could be calculated rightly. But such information is utterly irrelevant. We do not want to know what would happen if we were examining one out of a very large number of incomplete collections; for, once more, if we were, we could obtain a complete collection and true values; there would be no need for adjustment and no probable error. What we want to know is the value which we are to adopt from a single definite collection which is known to be incomplete and must remain incomplete. We have supposed—this is the foundation of all our discussion—that we are to adopt the value which is the most probable cause of the observations. We are now proceeding to ask what is the probability that the value which we have selected is—

Well, what? The true value? But the true value is, according to our assumption, the most probable value. The most probable value? Of course the most probable value is the most probable value. We cannot even ask the question which is supposed to be answered by a statement of the probable error without assuming that there is some method other than that of the adjustment of inconsistent observations for determining the true value. But there is no such method; if there were we should never adjust observations. The whole idea underlying the introduction of probable error at all is based on inextricable confusion of thought.

The difficulties with which we are faced are really those which have already been considered generally in Chapter VII. The probability of a proposed value being the true value is a probability of causes of the second kind, and not, as is generally suggested, of the first kind. We concluded that such a probability has no significance except as a vague indication of degree of certainty, and that it has this significance only in so far as the probability of an event is a measure of degree of certainty. But the probability of an event is such a measure only when the event represents an extreme coincidence; the only knowledge associated with probability is the knowledge that coincidences do not happen. Accordingly all the estimates of probability can tell us is that no value can be the cause of the observations or can be the true value which is such that the probability of its occurrence, estimated by the formula of the probability of causes, is so small that its occurrence would represent an extreme coincidence. On the other hand no difference in degree of certainty is to be attributed to values none of which constitute an extreme coincidence.

It is possible that such considerations might lead to introducing into the statement of our results some quantity not very different from the probable error. If we revert to the formula for the probability of a proposed value being the cause of the observations, we shall see that the probability is always infinitely small, if Gauss' Law, or any other reasonable law, of errors is accepted. Accordingly the acceptance of any exact value as the true value is impossible, for it would always be an extreme coincidence. On the other hand, the probability of one of a set of values within a finite range being the cause would in general be finite[1]. We might inquire therefore how great the range had to be in order that the probability of the cause lying within it became so large that it ceased to be that of an extreme coincidence. Of course, as we cannot define numerically what is an extreme coincidence, it is impossible to calculate such a range, but we may consider how it would vary with those quantities which determine the probable error. The range would decrease with the average residual and would decrease as the number of observations increased. In these respects then it would vary in the same way as the probable error. Accordingly if we do not regard the precise numerical value of that error but only the general mode of its variation, we can attribute to it a definite significance. It measures roughly the range within which the observations permit the true value to lie. Now this is really all the meaning that anyone does attach to the probable error[2]; it is merely regarded as an indication of what deviation from the adjusted value is permissible. But this agreement with current practice is no objection, but rather a support to the views that have been urged. I am not anxious to prove, here or in most other places, that the prevalent practice of physicists leads to fallacious results; I only want to inquire into the basis of the practice and ascertain why it is justified. If the probable error is interpreted in the manner just stated, it is a very useful conception (though it would probably be better to replace it by the "huge error"); but we must never forget exactly what is its significance. It is clear that the arguments that have been advanced for its use do not justify in any way a preference for the actual adjusted values over any others which are permitted by the criterion; so long as none of them represent

---

[1] This result would follow if the probability of either *A* or *B* being the cause of an event were the sum of the probability that *A* is the cause and the probability that *B* is the cause. This proposition has not been introduced before, and I do not see that there is any evidence that it is true; it is difficult to establish any proposition about the numerical values of degree of knowledge. However the probability of *A* or *B* is almost certainly greater than that of *A* or that of *B*; this assumption might be sufficient to justify the argument given in the text.

[2] This meaning is attached rather to the "huge error" than to the probable error but the former is a constant multiple of the latter.

extreme coincidences we have no reason to prefer one to the other. And again we must remember that there may be many other ways of arriving at adjusted values, and the permissible range about them, which have just as much claim to adoption as that usually adopted. If one method is to be preferred to another, it must be on some ground other than that of strict theoretical validity.

This last conclusion is important. We have seen into what a tangle of difficulties we are led by our fundamental assumption that the adjusted values of inconsistent observations should be the most probable values. The assumption appears very obvious at the start, but the more we inquire the less obvious it becomes. Its initial obviousness is, I believe, due merely to our habit of using "probable" in both a technical and in an untechnical sense. In the former it merely implies a high degree of mental confidence, and is applicable to events and propositions of all kinds. In the latter it is directly and strictly applicable only to events which form complete collections and to propositions about them. All our difficulties arise from the attempt to apply conceptions suitable only for complete collections to collections that are essentially incomplete. It is worth while, therefore, to retrace our steps and to see if we cannot find some method of adjusting observations which possesses the practical advantages of the Method of Least Squares, but avoids the very difficult theory of probability on which it is based. Such an attempt will be made; but before we proceed to it, it will be well to notice some other features of the Method of Least Squares which were left on one side in order that the main argument might not be interrupted.

The weight of observations. First, a word is necessary on the "weight" of an observation. Strictly speaking, the weight of an observation ought only to be introduced when several observations have been made each of which gives precisely the same result. If there are p such observations, then it is easily seen that the same results will be obtained if, instead of writing p identical observation equations, a single observational equation is written in which both sides are multiplied by p. Actually the conception is used in other circumstances. If p dissimilar observations have been made on the same magnitude, the arithmetic mean of their results is taken, and this mean is used to state a single observational equation which is multiplied throughout by p. But this procedure is strictly illegitimate. The part of Σv^2 which arises from these observations is $\overline{\delta x_1}^2 + \overline{\delta x_2}^2 + \overline{\delta x_3}^2 + \dots + \overline{\delta x_p}^2$; for this sum we substitute $p^2 \delta x^2$, where

$$\delta x = \frac{\delta x_1 + \delta x_2 + \dots + \delta x_p}{p}.$$

The two will not be identical unless $\Sigma \delta x_r \delta x_s = 0$, a condition which will not be fulfilled unless the arithmetic mean of the p observations is also the true value determined from these and the rest of the observations.

Weight is also used in other circumstances which are equally questionable. Suppose that some of the observations have been made in more satisfactory conditions than the remainder. Then it may be supposed that the measure of precision, h, is greater for these than for the remainder. Accordingly if y denotes the good, x the bad observations, the quantity which has to be made a minimum is $h_x{}^2 \Sigma \overline{\delta x^2} + h_y{}^2 \Sigma \overline{\delta y^2}$, where h_y is greater than h_x. If h_x and h_y were known, we could write $h_y = ph_x$, and the quantity to be made a minimum would be $h_x{}^2 (\Sigma \overline{\delta x^2} + p^2 \Sigma \overline{\delta y^2})$, the good observations could be regarded as having a weight p; they would have the same influence on the result as if each of them consisted of p identical bad observations. So far the procedure is legitimate; but in practice there is usually no way of determining h_x and h_y; the value of p is simply guessed. The result depends on the predilections of the guesser and not only on things determined experimentally. This course of uncertainty is, of course, always recognised; but it removes still further the result obtained from that which is indicated by strict theory and experiment.

And here a curious fallacy which seems often overlooked should be noted. The problem is often raised what is r, the probable error of y, when y is known to be a function of x_1 and x_2, $f(x_1, x_2)$, and the probable errors of x_1 and x_2 are r_1 and r_2. The answer given is that

$$r^2 = (f_{x_1}' r_1)^2 + (f_{x_2}' r_2)^2.$$

The answer is based on the deduction that, if δx_1, δx_2 are the errors of x_1 and x_2, δy, the error in y, is $f_{x_1}' \delta x_1 + f_{x_2}' \delta x_2$; accordingly, it is said, the probable error in y must be given by $r^2 = (f_{x_1}' r_1 + f_{x_2}' r_2)^2$; and this, if $\Sigma \delta x_1 \delta y_1 = 0$, reduces to the expression given. But one very obvious consideration is overlooked. The entire argument which leads to the determination of probable error is based on the assumption that the errors follow Gauss' Law; it is only if this is true that there is any reason for believing that the true value of y is that which makes the sum of the squares of its errors a minimum. But if the errors in x_1 and x_2 follow that law, the measures of precision being h_1, h_2, the errors in y cannot generally follow that law. For if p_1, p_2 are the probabilities that the errors in x_1 and x_2 are δx_1, δx_2, the probability that the error in y is δy, where

$$\delta y = f_{x_1}' \delta x_1 + f_{x_2}' \delta x_2, \text{ is } \frac{h_1 h_2}{\pi} e^{-h_1{}^2 \delta x_1{}^2 - h_2{}^2 \delta x_2{}^2}.$$

But this is not of the form $h\pi^{-\frac{1}{2}} e^{-h^2 \delta y_2}$; consequently the errors in y do not follow Gauss' Law. This appears to me the most serious objection to the law that can be raised; if the law is true for the actual observations, it cannot be true for any function of those observations. But one measured magnitude is often a function of other measured magnitudes; all measured magnitudes cannot therefore obey Gauss' Law. Perhaps this argument is rather too crude. It shows, for instance, that if area is measured as the product of two lengths, the errors in determination of area, so measured, cannot be distributed according to Gauss' Law, if the errors in length are so distributed. But it does not prove that if area is measured directly as a fundamental magnitude, the errors in its measurement might not be so distributed. But nevertheless it does show that the domain of Gauss' Law is much more restricted than is usually supposed. If all fundamental measurements are liable to errors distributed according to that law, no derived magnitude can have errors so distributed.

The adjustment of derived magnitudes. Before the lengthy discussion which has just ended was begun it was observed that the problem to be discussed was not really of much interest in pure science. It concerned the adjustment of magnitudes measured directly, either as fundamental magnitudes or as quasi-derived. The knowledge of such magnitudes is only a means to an end; the end is the determination of true derived magnitudes (with which we will include for the present the constants of an empirical law). In the problem which we have just left, which will be called problem 1, the constant coefficients of the equation of condition are accurately known, usually because there is only one law, with one set of coefficients, of the form of the equation of condition. Thus in all laws relating the heights z_{pq}, z_{qr}, z_{pr}, the constant coefficients are unity; there is no law of the same form in which those coefficients have any other value. But in the problem to which we are about to proceed, there are many laws, all of the same form, but differing in the constant coefficients; these coefficients are then derived magnitudes. Thus we know that the mass and the volume of many systems are related by a law, or equation of condition, of the form $m = \rho V$; but different systems are characterised by different values of ρ, the density. The problem, which will be called problem 2, is to determine these coefficients.

It may be stated generally thus. Suppose now that we know that the system is characterised by the magnitudes $x, y, z, \ldots$ (corresponding to $x_1, x_2, \ldots$ in problem 1) related by the equation, which must again be linear, $ax + by + cz + \ldots + m = 0$. In different states $(1, 2, 3, \ldots)$ of the system we measure associated sets of the magnitudes $(x, y, z)_1, (x, y, z)_2, \ldots$. Whatever values we assign to $(a, b, c, \ldots m)$, the measured values, inserted in the equation of condition, do not satisfy it but leave on the left side "residuals" $v_1, v_2, \ldots$. Accordingly the measured values cannot be true values; we want to find the true values and from them the values to attribute to $a, b, c, d, \ldots$. The solution which the theory indicates is that which makes the distribution the most probable; it appears then that we should proceed thus. Choose some values for $a, b, c, \ldots m$, and then solve problem 1, determining the true values $(X, Y, Z)_1, (X, Y, Z)_2, \ldots$, which make the distribution of the errors the most probable on the assumption that these are the true values of $(a, b, c, \ldots m)$. If h_x, h_y, h_z are the measures of precision of the magnitudes (Gauss' Law being still assumed true), these values will be such as to make

$$h_x{}^2 \Sigma \overline{\delta x^2} + h_y{}^2 \Sigma \overline{\delta y^2} + h_z{}^2 \Sigma \overline{\delta z^2}$$

a minimum, subject to

$$aX_1 + bY_1 + cZ_1 + \ldots + m = aX_2 + bY_2 + cZ_2 + \ldots + m = \ldots = 0.$$

Let R be the probability calculated as on p. 489 that these true values are the cause of the distribution of errors. Now choose another series of values for $a, b, c, \ldots m$ and calculate R again. Then that set $a, b, c, d, \ldots$ should be adopted which makes R a maximum.

Such seems the process indicated by the theory. It involves two separate operations, first that of adjusting the true values to the assumed values of the constants, second choosing the true values of the constants so that the adjusted true values may give a probability of the actual distribution of errors which is a *maximum maximorum*. On the other hand the process adopted in the ordinary Method of Least Squares consists of a single operation which is to choose $a, b, c, d, \ldots m$ so that $\Sigma v^2 + v_1{}^2 + v_2{}^2 + v_3{}^2 + \ldots$ is a minimum for variations in these constants. How far does this process agree with that indicated by the theory?

Suppose that we knew the true real magnitudes $(X, Y, Z)_1, (X, Y, Z)_2, \ldots$, and consequently the errors $(\delta x, \delta y, \delta z)_1, (\delta x, \delta y, \delta z)_2, \ldots$; then since, by hypothesis, $aX + bY + cZ + \ldots + m = 0$, we have $v_1 = a\,\delta x_1 + b\,\delta y_1 + c\,\delta z_1 + \ldots$ The criterion that Σv^2 is a minimum is equivalent to the criterion that the following expression is a minimum

$$a^2 \Sigma \overline{\delta x^2} + b^2 \Sigma \overline{\delta y^2} + c^2 \Sigma \overline{\delta z^2} + \ldots + 2ab\,\Sigma \overline{\delta x \delta y} + 2bc\,\Sigma \overline{\delta y \delta z} + 2ca\,\Sigma \overline{\delta z \delta x} + \ldots.$$

If it is to be identical with the criterion that $h_x{}^2 \Sigma \overline{\delta x^2} + h_y{}^2 \Sigma \overline{\delta y^2} + h_z{}^2 \Sigma \overline{\delta z^2}$ is a minimum we must have (unless there is some purely fortuitous connection between the h's and the coefficients a, b, c[1]) (1) $a = b = c$ and $h_x = h_y = h_z$, (2) $\Sigma \delta x \delta y = \Sigma \delta y \delta z = \Sigma \delta z \delta x = 0$, which, since $\delta x, \delta y, \delta z$ are independent, implies in general $\Sigma \delta x = \Sigma \delta y = \Sigma \delta z = 0$. If the measurements are so numerous that the collections are complete, it is likely that (2) will be fulfilled, but there is never the smallest reason for supposing that (1) is fulfilled, for, except by mere chance, it will never happen that $a = b = c$.

Again, the theory suggests that we ought first to reduce Σv^2 to a minimum in respect of changes of the true values and then reduce it further to a minimum in respect of changes of the coefficients. But the process of forming and solving the normal equations consists simply in reducing Σv^2 to a minimum for changes in the coefficients, while it is assumed, during the process, that the measured values are the true values of the magnitudes; it would be legitimate only if it were true that the values of the coefficients which make Σv^2 a minimum are the same whatever values are selected for the true values. But this is not true; for of course if we inserted in place of the measured values any other values we should arrive at different values for the coefficients. It is entirely impermissible to make Σv^2 a minimum for changes of the coefficients until we are sure that the values (x, y, z) in the equations have been

---

[1] It might be thought at first sight that a connection between the h's and the coefficients would not be purely fortuitous, because our discussion of the relation between errors of consistency and methodical errors showed that this relation was dependent on the derivatives of the equation of condition. But it was noticed on p. 481 that if two of the magnitudes are liable to errors of consistency it must be because, in the conditions of the experiment, they are related by laws to some third magnitude. This third magnitude is not concerned in the equation of condition we are considering here, and it is not the derivatives of that equation which will determine the precision of the measurements.

replaced by true values. There is again not the smallest reason to believe that
the procedure of the Method of Least Squares will lead to those values of
the coefficients which represent the most probable of all most probable
distributions; nothing in the theory we have discussed gives any foundation
for the adoption of that Method.

As usual, when we reach the conclusion that some practice widely adopted
is wrong, we have to inquire how it came to be adopted; without the most
careful examination it is illegitimate to conclude that men of science have
simply made a blunder. But in this case I cannot help thinking that there has
been real confusion of thought, which arises largely from a formal similarity
of problem 2 with problem 1, if the solution of the latter is conducted by the
method (not strictly legitimate) of observational equations. For then we
have a number of linear equations in which the coefficients a, b, c, ... are
given and the variables x, y, z, ... have to be determined; the solution is
obtained by making Σv^2 a minimum for changes in the variables. In problem
2 we have similar linear equations in which the variables x, y, z, ... are given
and the coefficients have to be determined; it is concluded that the solution
is obtained by making Σv^2 a minimum for changes in the coefficients. But
there is this difference; in problem 2, the variables, though "given", are
not known; it is just because they are not known accurately that it is
necessary to solve the problem at all. Another reason for the acceptance
of the Method is probably to be found in the fact that the residuals of
the equations, when the adjusted values of the coefficients are used, appear to be distributed roughly according to Gauss' Law; it is therefore
concluded rashly that these residuals are the errors which, according to the
theory, are to be reduced to a minimum. Such an argument is obviously
inadmissible.

A third reason for adopting the conventional practice is more weighty.
If only one of the magnitudes x, y, z, ... (say x) is liable to error, so that
$\delta y = \delta z = ... = 0$, then the Method is an adequate expression of the theory.
For $\Sigma v^2 = a^2 \Sigma \delta x^2$, and $h_x{}^2 \Sigma \delta x^2$ will be a minimum when Σv^2 is a minimum.
Further, since now the real magnitudes Y, Z, ... are known, the choice of the
coefficients fixes definitely the true values X; the reduction of Σv^2 to a minimum in respect of the coefficients can only be effected in such circumstances
that the x's in the equation of condition are true magnitudes. Accordingly
when only x is liable to error, the Method does give a result in accordance
with the theory; and it is generally recognised that it is only in these circumstances that the Method is strictly applicable. Nevertheless it is most
certainly applied, and applied frequently, in other circumstances. It has
been proposed then to use methods of successive approximation, depending
on the determination of the coefficients first when one magnitude and then
when another is supposed to be the only one liable to error; but such methods
are extremely cumbrous and they profess to provide nothing but a rather
better approximation to the right result. Actually they are seldom employed,
and it is quite common to see the Method of Least Squares used in the simple

form to determine coefficients when the equations relate several magnitudes all of which are known to be liable to errors of inconsistency.

Nor is this all. For the application of the Method strictly it is necessary to know, not only that one of the magnitudes is alone liable to error, but which is this magnitude. In the equation of condition given so far there are $n + 1$ constants and n variables; the constants can be reduced to n by dividing the equation by one of them and so making the coefficient of one of the variables unity. Thus in place of $ax + by + cz + \ldots + m = 0$, we must write $x + b'y + c'z + \ldots + m' = 0$, or $a''x + y + c''z + \ldots + m'' = 0$. But the results obtained will not be exactly the same in the two cases; e.g. a'' will not be exactly $1/b'$ or c'' exactly c'/b'. If the collection of observations is complete, they will be (in our special sense) nearly the same; but if they are not complete, they may differ appreciably. If the argument on which the Method is based is examined, it will be found that it applies strictly only when the variable of which the coefficient is made unity is that which is alone liable to error; and accordingly, if there is any possibility of applying the Method to collections that are not complete, we must know which this variable is.

The choice of the variable liable to error may appear very simple, but I believe it is often made wrongly. In making measurements we usually fix, or try to fix, the values of all but one of the associated magnitudes, and measure that remaining, x. It is this remaining magnitude in which the errors of inconsistency appear. But our arguments show that it is not this magnitude that is really liable to error, but those that are fixed; the errors of inconsistency in x are due to errors of method in y, z, ... Thus, when we fix the volume and measure the mass, the errors in consistency of the mass are due to errors of method in the volume, and it is the volume (which is fixed and therefore usually assumed to be liable to no error) which is really liable to error. The only exception to this rule that it is the magnitudes which are fixed that should be regarded as affected by error—and the exception is important—is when the equation of condition is not really complete. Thus if we are measuring the variation of the activity of a radioactive substance with the time, we probably fix the time and measure the activity. But here the errors of consistency in the activity are not due to errors of method in the time so much as to errors in the instrument for measuring the activity, which are not mentioned in the equation of condition at all. If we have really to determine which of the magnitudes is liable to error, the matter requires much more attention than is usually given to it.

It seems then that the application of the Method of Least Squares to problem 2 is even more unjustified than its application to problem 1; for in the former it can definitely be shown that the Method is not that indicated by the theory, and that the method which is indicated by the theory would be bound to give slightly different results. But it is still possible that the difference may be less than that which is physically significant and that the Method, though not theoretically correct, may work with sufficient accuracy in practice. And as before, the matter might conceivably be tested experimentally. For this purpose we should have to make so many measurements on each associated set $(x, y, z, ...)$ that the collection of them was complete and the mean of their values the true values. If such a collection could be made, it would be found that the true values (or values differing from them by less than the least significant amount) would all satisfy the equation of condition if certain values were adopted for the coefficients; these values would then be true values, and they could be compared with those derived from the adjustment of collections of observations each of which was incomplete. I do not know of any evidence sufficiently complete to permit of such a test of the method, but it is quite probable that the test would turn out satisfactorily. Once more it is not asserted that the conventional method actually leads to wrong results, but only that there is no reason for believing that it is the only method that leads to right results, or that it is necessarily preferable to any other method.

It may be noted that in one respect the application of the Method to problem 2 is more legitimate than the application to problem 1. The condition which we imagined the observations to fulfil is that while the measurements on a single magnitude, or (in problem 2) on a single associated set $(x, y, z, ...)_1$, do not form a complete collection, the measurement on all magnitudes or on all sets do form such a collection. In problem 1 it is unlikely that this condition is fulfilled in the circumstances in which the Method is usually applied; it is much more likely that it is fulfilled in problem 2. For here it often happens that we only make a single measurement of each associated set, corresponding to a single state of the system, while we make measurements of a very large number of different sets, corresponding to different states of the system. We fail to make a complete collection on each state, not, as in problem 1, because we find that however many measurements we make the collection does not become complete, but because it is quite impossible to make more than one, or a very small number, on each state. These circumstances always occur when one of the variables is the time, for it is impossible to make more than one measurement at a given instant. Thus, in the example of radioactive decay, it is possible that if we could stop the decay for a period of time long enough to make a large number of measurements of the activity at a given stage in the decay, we should find that such a collection was complete and that the mean of such collections fitted accurately to the theoretical curve. But since we cannot stop the decay the only method of obtaining enough measurements to form a complete collection is to make them at different stages in the decay; but there is no reason to believe that, if we make sufficient measurements at various stages, the collection of the whole of them will not be complete. Accordingly if a method could be found which is an adequate expression of a theory, on the assumption that this condition is fulfilled, that method could be applied legitimately to the solution of problem 2, in many very important cases.

It is unnecessary to repeat here all that was said before concerning the probable error which is usually associated, in this problem also, with the results obtained by adjustment by the Method of Least Squares. The circumstances are rather more complex, but precisely the same arguments could be used. The probable error was considered chiefly in order that the difficulties might be brought to light which are inseparable from any attempt to apply the conceptions of probability to the adjustment of errors of inconsistency. We have admitted that, if those conceptions are to be applied at all, it is quite likely that the Method of Least Squares provides as near an approach to a theoretically valid method as is consistent with practical convenience and general applicability. But we have yet to ask whether it is really necessary to introduce those conceptions at all. In order to arrive at the result which is "most probable" in the untechnical sense of "worthy of the greatest degree of confidence", is it necessary to take the value which is, in the strictly technical sense, most probable?

An alternative method of adjustment. To answer this question we must start again at the beginning. The fundamental fact in the whole theory of errors of inconsistency is that the true value of a complete collection of inconsistent measurements on a single magnitude is the arithmetic mean. If the collection (still consisting of measurements on a single magnitude) is incomplete, then we cannot determine the true value; that is really all that there is to be said about it. It may be convenient for some strictly limited purpose to express the results by a single numeral, and, if that is so, we shall probably select again the arithmetic mean as that numeral; but it cannot be too strongly insisted that the selection of that numeral does not imply a belief that it is a true value. If we cannot determine the true value, we cannot, and we must not pretend that we can. However, as we have noted, if there are other measurements available on magnitudes related to that on which the incomplete collection has been made, it may be possible, according to the theory, to convert the many incomplete collections into a single complete collection. The question that we are asking is what method we are to adopt in order to select the true value from this new complete collection. The general answer has already been given; it must be such that the errors, determined after the true value has been found, shall be distributed in a manner as similar as possible to that characteristic of the errors of the complete collection on a single magnitude. An attempt to define more strictly the expression "as similar as possible" led us before to select the value which gave the most probable distribution. We are now going to try another definition.

The whole difficulty arises from the fact that, whatever value is selected, the actual distribution cannot be made exactly the same as that of the assumed law of errors. If it could be made exactly the same, then if we made the actual distribution the same as that given by the law in one respect, it would be the same in all; if, for instance, we chose the true value so that the sum of the squares of the errors was a minimum, then the arithmetic sum of the errors would be zero. But as it cannot be made exactly the same, the obvious course suggested is to make the actual distribution the same in respect of some one selected feature and to ignore differences in respect of the other features. Further it seems reasonable to allow our choice of this feature to be dictated by the fundamental fact of the whole theory, namely the choice of the arithmetic mean of a complete single collection. The feature to be selected should be one which seems closely connected with that choice. Of course the arithmetic mean will, as a matter of fact, be a true value such that, in a complete single collection, the errors agree with the law in respect of all features; but agreement in respect of some of them will appear more closely connected with the choice of arithmetic mean than agreement in others. In other words, let us consider what reasons might lead us to select the arithmetic mean as the true value, if we knew nothing about errors of inconsistency except that they exist, and choose our true value in the new circumstances for reasons as closely similar as possible.

Now it has been held that this suggestion leads to the choice of the true value which makes the distribution the most probable, and that the arithmetic mean is selected simply because it is the most probable "cause". But I venture to think that this view is based on confusion and misunderstanding. Before we can say what value is the most probable we must determine the probabilities of various errors; and again before we can determine those probabilities we must know what the errors are. Now we do not know the errors until we know the true value. Once we have selected the true value we know actually what the errors are; different individual errors, as alternatives to other imaginable individual errors, are seen to have different probabilities, but the probability that all the errors have the values which they actually have—that is not a probability at all; it is a certainty; there is no alternative. Once we have selected the true value the errors must have those values; an alternative arises only if we select another true value. Then we should get other errors and another law of errors, but again the probability that these errors should have the value they actually have is not a probability but a certainty. When it is said that the arithmetic mean is the most probable value, it is supposed that the law of errors is known. But if it is to be known from any kind of experimental investigation and not merely evolved out of our minds by pure thought, then we must first know what the errors are and therefore what the true value is. The true value is not the most probable value but something fixed by a definite assertion which must be made before any considerations of probability can arise.

But it may be said that it is permissible to "evolve the law of errors out of our mind by pure thought", because, as we have seen, the fundamental ideas of the theory suggest a particular law—which may be Gauss' Law if we introduce into the theory the idea of observed errors being compounded of many equal partial errors. We may start therefore with the supposition that the law is known. We now add the supposition that the true value is that which makes the actual distribution of errors most probable on the assumption that the probabilities of the individual errors are given by this law. We shall find that the true value so obtained is the arithmetic mean, and shall find further by experiment that this true value is really the true value in the sense of p. 463. We have therefore proved the suppositions made. But this argument has force only so long as other suppositions, with the same kind of *a priori* support, do not lead to the same conclusion. I think that many other laws of error, combined with the supposition that the true value is such as to make the actual distribution most probable, would lead to exactly the same result; almost any law symmetrical about the arithmetic mean would do so. No evidence is therefore attained for Gauss' or any other such law; and while the law is uncertain it is absurd to talk about most probable distributions, for the probability of any actual distribution depends on the law.

I cannot help thinking that the readiness with which the assumption of the most probable distribution is accepted is partly due to a very elementary blunder—so elementary that I should hardly dare to notice it were there not passages in the writings of the most distinguished authors which might seem to give countenance to it. The law of errors suggested by the theory will always be one in which the true value is the most probable value (or one of the most probable values) for the result of one of the inconsistent measurements; it is at least as probable as any of the other measurements that are alternative to it. But this fact has nothing whatever to do with the assumption we are considering. We are asking, not whether one result of an individual measurement is more probable than another result, but whether the whole collection of errors, as a whole, is more probable than any other collection of errors. Even if the arithmetic mean were not the most probable result of a single measurement (if, e.g., the curve of errors were symmetrical about a minimum and not about a maximum) the argument, such as it is, for the true value being that which gives the most probable distribution would be unaltered.

I conclude then that, though the arithmetic mean is that value which makes the actual distribution of the errors most probable, if Gauss' Law of individual errors is assumed, this fact cannot provide any reason for the selection of that mean as the true value. Our reason for selecting it and expecting that experiment will show that it is the true value can have nothing to do with considerations of probability, because we must *know* what the true value is before we can enter on them. The reason seems to me much simpler and much more cogent. Though the theory does not suggest precisely the form of the law of individual errors, it does suggest very clearly that this law must have one definite feature, namely that the curve of errors will be symmetrical on both sides of zero error, and that positive and negative errors of the same magnitude will occur with equal frequency in a complete collection. If this suggestion is accepted it follows that, when the number of errors is so large that the collection is complete, the algebraical sum of the errors must be zero. If we take the arithmetic mean as the true value the algebraic sum of the errors will always and necessarily be zero, and the actual distribution of errors will agree in this very important respect with the distribution indicated by any law of errors which could be consistent with the theory. These considerations seem to provide the most simple and direct justification for the selection of the arithmetic mean; the choice of that mean will always make the actual distribution of errors agree with that of the law in one important respect. Its choice rids us of all necessity of determining definitely the law of errors, a task that is almost impossible to perform quite satisfactorily; it requires us to know nothing about that law except that it would make positive and negative errors equally probable.

And if this is our reason for selecting the arithmetic mean of a complete collection of inconsistent measurements on the same magnitude, it is surely natural and right that the same considerations should determine our choice when the collection is incomplete and we are endeavouring to complete the collection by including in it measurements made on different magnitudes. Again we should choose such true values that the algebraical sum of the actual errors is zero. I really cannot conceive of any reason why anyone should imagine that this rule is less plausible than that which is conventionally adopted. Everyone admits that the evidence for Gauss' Law being the precise law of errors is very slight; everyone admits that the evidence for the law being such that the algebraic sum of the errors is zero is very strong. Surely therefore it is reasonable to adopt a rule which is founded on the evidence which is admittedly strong and does not require that which is admittedly weak.

Application of the alternative method. But is the principle possible to apply in practice? Certainly; nothing could be easier. Consider problem 2 of p. 504. We have to determine the coefficients in $ax + by + cz + m = 0$. We measure N associated sets of (x, y, z) and insert them in the equation; we then add all the equations so obtained, one for each associated set, and obtain $aX' + bY' + cZ' + Nm = 0$, where $X' = \Sigma x$, etc. If the N sets form a complete collection, the arithmetic sum of the errors is zero, and $X' = NX$, where X is the true real magnitude. Consequently if we divide through by N, we get $aX + bY + cZ + m = 0$, which must be accurately true. In order to find a, b, c, d we have only to make in a similar way n of these equations, where n is the number of the coefficients a, b, c, d, and solve them as a set of simultaneous equations. Accordingly the rule is: If there are n coefficients, and N observations, divide the N observational equations into n sets, add each set, and solve the resulting equations for the n coefficients.

But, it will be objected, the result we shall obtain will depend on the way in which we divide the N observational equations into n sets. True; but if this occurs when we have made the number in each set as nearly equal as possible (or exactly equal if n is a factor of N), what is indicated is that we have not made enough observations to get n complete collections; if we want an unique result, we must simply take more observations. The fact that the results do not agree is a direct proof that the collections are not complete and that true values cannot be determined; our method, instead of concealing this very important fact in a mass of incomprehensible symbolism about probable errors, forces it on our attention. That is one of the chief advantages of the method. But—the objector will continue—however many observations we take, the results of dividing the N observations in different ways will never lead to exactly the same result. True again; but then we are not concerned that it should lead to exactly the same result. There is always some difference ϵ between alternative values which is so small that it has no physical significance; in fundamental measurement it is the step of the most accurate instrument, for derived magnitudes it is the difference arising from a difference of one step in the fundamental measurements by which it is measured. So long as the observations are such that we can divide them in several ways into n sets and yet always get values for the coefficients which agree within less than ϵ, then we shall have achieved everything that has any physical significance.

However though the results of all methods of grouping the observations are admissible as solutions (it must be remembered that the Gaussian method admits any solution as possible so long as the probable error is finite), it does not follow that they are all equally reliable. Investigation will show that, given a certain set of errors, the consequent error in the adjusted results varies with the method of combination into sets. In general that result will be the more reliable for which this consequent error is less. It is desirable therefore to combine the observations in a manner so as to make this consequent error small; and rules can be devised by means of which this result can be achieved[1]. When it is desirable to select one value only to represent the result, it should be one obtained according to these rules. But the adoption of a single value must not be allowed to disguise the fact that there is a finite range of values all of which are equally admissible, and between which, so long as the collection of observations is incomplete, there is no reason whatever to choose. This conclusion was also reached on p. 501.

The method may also be applied to solve problem 1, although here its advantages over the Method of Least Squares are smaller[2]. By the use of the equations of condition as many magnitudes as there are equations are eliminated. The observations are then stated in the form of observational equations; these are divided into n sets, if there are n magnitudes, and each set is simply added, and the resulting m equations solved. The magnitudes obtained are such that the arithmetic sum of the errors of the observed magnitudes is zero and such that they satisfy the equations of condition. Again it may happen that division of the observational equations into sets in different ways leads to different results; but again the difference, if exceeding the least significant difference, indicates only that the observations are incomplete and lead to no true values. If the observations are sufficiently numerous and the errors

---

[1] The practical application of the method here described is discussed rather more fully in the *Philosophical Magazine* for 1920.

[2] It cannot be used to adjust the errors of the angles of a triangle (see p. 496); for since it is assumed that the sum of the errors is zero, the sum of the adjusted values will differ from 180° by as much as the sum of the observed values. But here the assumption is illegitimate. The sum of the errors of a complete collection is zero only so long as there is no systematic error and the equation of condition is strictly true. The observations here indicate strongly that there is systematic error—if the discrepancy is physically significant; there must be some source of error in the measurements which tends to make the errors all of the same sign.

are really of the nature we have considered, it will be possible by increasing their number sufficiently to reach a stage when several different divisions will give results differing by less than the least significant difference.

I cannot conceive what objection can be raised to this method by anyone except a computer likely to be thrown out of his job. It is based on the same theory of error as the conventional method, but is an accurate expression of that theory in all cases, and not only in a few very exceptional cases. It leads to values which do really obey the equations of condition. It gives a direct indication whether the observations are complete and whether true values are obtainable. If they are not complete it is possible to indicate in some measure the degree of their incompleteness and, consequently, the degree of mental confidence to be placed in the result. Of this degree the difference in the magnitudes obtained by dividing the observations into sets in different ways (each containing as nearly as possible N/n observations) will be an indication. It is true that it cannot be stated definitely what degree of mental confidence is to be associated with what difference between the results of different divisions, but then again there is no pretence of a definite statement. The apparent, but wholly illusory, precision of the calculated probable error is avoided.

I have little expectation that any attention will be paid to these arguments. The Method of Least Squares is so firmly established that nothing short of a revolution in science could displace it. The only reasonable grounds I can find for continuing to use it are that, since so much work has been interpreted by its use, the adoption of any new method might produce an unconformity between the new and the old. But that is no reason why it should not be used in the more recent branches of science and especially in any that may yet be developed. But I maintain that the *onus probandi* lies entirely with those who maintain the old method; it is for them to justify the use of a method which they admit to be devoid of all theoretical foundation and full of inconsistency when another has been proposed which is free from these objections.

Nevertheless it may be well to notice one very simple instance when the rule here proposed gives a result in accordance with current practice, but not with the Method of Least Squares, and at the same time highly reasonable. Suppose we have to determine the coefficient a in the equation of condition $ay - x = 0$ (x might be a mass, y a volume, a a density). We measure associated values of x and y. The way in which I believe everyone would combine the measurements to obtain the density would be to add all the x's and all the y's, and to divide the sum of the former by the sum of the latter. This is precisely the procedure which the rule of making the sums of the errors zero indicates. But according to the Method of Least Squares, the density ought to be taken to be $\Sigma xy/\Sigma x^2$. I do not believe the firmest adherent to the Method would actually adopt that value; if he does not adopt it in the simpler cases, what justification has he for adopting it in the more complex? The only answer he can give is that here the simpler method, like the Method of Least Squares, gives a single definite result. But this definiteness is delusive; it does not mean necessarily that the density determined is certainly known to be a true value. To test whether it is a true value, determined from a complete collection, we ought to write the equation of condition $ay + bx = 0$. Then we require two sums to determine a and b, and have to divide up the observations into two sets. If, in whatever way they are divided up (into equal halves), the density determined is the same within the least significant difference, then, and then only, is the density a true value.

Lastly a word may be said on a matter that has been left on one side during our discussion. In order to apply either of the methods of adjustment that have been proposed, it is necessary that the equation of condition should be linear. If it is not linear, two methods are available for reducing it to the linear form. It is only necessary to state them for problem 2, for in problem 1 the equation of condition is almost always linear. (1) If the equation is $f(x, y, z, ..., a, b, c, ...) = 0$, it may be possible to find functions $x' = \phi_x(x)$, $a' = \phi_a(a)$, etc., such that $f(x, y, z, ..., a, b, c, ...) \equiv a'x' + b'y' + c'z' + ... = 0$. If such functions can be found, then it is usual in adjusting the observations to use the linear equation $a'x' + b'y' + c'z' + ... = 0$ and adjust $a', b', c', ...$ and not $a, b, c, ...$ Thus, if the equation is $y = be^{-ax}$, it can be reduced to the linear form by taking $y' = \log y$, $x' = x$, $b' = \log b$, $a' = a$. (2) Approximate values of $a, b, c, ...$ may be guessed; let them be $a_0, b_0, c_0, ...$ Then if the true values are $a_0 + da, ...$

$$f(x, y, z, ..., a, b, c, ...)$$
$$\equiv f(x, y, z, ..., a_0, b_0, c_0, ...) + da\left(\frac{\partial f}{\partial a}\right)_{a_0, b_0, c_0} + db\left(\frac{\partial f}{\partial b}\right)_{a_0, b_0, c_0} + ...$$

The equation is then linear in $da, db, dc, ...$ and the values of these differences may be found by the ordinary method.

Method (2) is formally legitimate, but is often extremely cumbrous in practice; accordingly (1) is always adopted whenever it is available. But if the Method of Least Squares is used, it is not legitimate for the reason discussed on p. 503. If the errors in $x, y, z, ...$ are distributed according to Gauss' Law, then the errors in $x', y', z', ...$ are not so distributed. And in fact it will often be found that methods (1) and (2) give results differing appreciably. It is an advantage of the method of adjustment here proposed that (1) is always legitimate if the errors are small; for since $dx' = \phi_x' . dx$ and ϕ_x' is constant for small errors, the solution which makes $\Sigma dx'$ zero will also make Σdx zero. This is quite an important argument in favour of this method.

The establishment of numerical laws. Much of the discussion of this chapter has been based on the view that the chief importance of accurate measurement is the establishment of numerical laws and the determination of the derived magnitudes defined by them. It will be well to consider what effect the conclusions we have reached have on those which were reached in Chapters XIII—XV.

On p. 474 it was remarked incidentally that numerical laws state relations between real magnitudes (and true real magnitudes) and not between measured magnitudes; that remark may seem inconsistent with the whole discussion of Chapter XIII in which it was supposed that a numerical law could be determined directly by the examination of measured magnitudes. Indeed it may seem to bring us once more face to face with the difficulty to which so much attention has been devoted, and which arose when we asked what were the terms between which the numerical relation of the law is asserted. It was hard to avoid the conclusion that they are Numbers, a conclusion which was objectionable because it indicated that all numerical laws were really theories. Now real magnitudes are essentially hypothetical ideas and derive their meaning from a theory of errors. If numerical laws state relations between real magnitudes, we must admit that they are theories even if we deny that they concern Numbers.

However the new difficulty is not very serious. It is quite true that a numerical "law", stated in the usual form as a mathematical relation, is a theory; but our discussion has shown that it is only a theory to explain the law which can be stated in terms of the measurements. The very fact that it is a theory indicates that it must explain laws and that there must be laws to explain. The experimental law we may suppose again to be established and stated by means of a graph. In our previous discussion it was supposed that the graph had to be drawn so that it actually passed through all the experimental points; but even if it has to be so drawn there is always room for choice of its precise form because the number of experimental points is finite. The only difference made by our recognition of error is that it is no longer necessary that the graph should be drawn through all the points; the latitude of choice is thereby increased, but the difference is one of degree and not of kind. And again when the graph is drawn the law will not state that any new experimental points must lie exactly on the graph, but only that they must lie very near it. This is the law which is explained by the theory which introduces real magnitudes and error. If we consider that the graph has been drawn as a smooth curve before it is discussed, all the conclusions of the previous chapters remain unaltered.

But if the law is to be significant, the expression "very near the graph" must be defined more closely. In seeking such a definition we are asking what is the greatest distance from the graph at which an experimental point may lie consistently with the acceptance of the law as true. This question is often very pertinent in connection with problem 2. In problem 1 it is supposed that the law which forms the equation of condition is known as certainly as anything can be known in science; it is always conceivable that new evidence, including the evidence that is being analysed, might lead us to abandon it, but abandonment would involve a reconstruction of all our ideas so revolutionary that nothing approaching to a formal process could be defined for conducting it. In problem 2 again the form of the law of which the coefficients are to be determined may sometimes be perfectly certain and to the same extent beyond dispute. If the arguments which we are about to explain would prove that the law is not true, then we have the alternative of denying that the theory on which the arguments are based is sound (or, more probably, that the conditions contemplated by that theory are fulfilled); we should probably adopt that alternative. It is almost inconceivable today that any mere measurements of mass and volume could convince us that pure substances are not characterised by a definite density and that mass is not proportional to volume; we should accept almost any alternative rather than abandon the law of density, unless observations of many different kinds conspired to make us alter all our theory of the structure of material bodies or of the relation of mass to that structure. But the form of other laws are not so certain. The law may be empirical and its constants not derived magnitudes; then the form of the law will be quite as doubtful as the numerical values of its coefficients; or, though we may be sure that the law is true in some circumstances, we may not be sure that those circumstances obtain in the condition of the experiment; thus we are sure that a pure radioactive substance decays according to a simple exponential law, but we may not be sure that the substance we are examining is pure.

It is in such circumstances that the question may arise whether the law to which we are fitting the observations by determining the coefficients is really correct. What criterion can be applied consistent with the theory of errors? The best and most stringent test is undoubtedly that, by the method described, it should be possible to determine true values of the coefficients. If sufficient observations can be made and it appears that the collection of them can be divided into n sets in several different ways so as to give the same true values of the coefficients, then it may be concluded that the law is correct. For it must be remembered that true values that are "the same" differ by less than the least significant difference, which is the step of the most accurate instrument. And by the most accurate "instrument" is meant, not merely a piece of apparatus which would ordinarily be called an instrument, but any arrangement whatever which permits measurement. If the most accurate means of detecting differences of magnitude fail to detect any discrepancy between different determinations, then no discrepancy can be detected, and it would be absurd to maintain (except perhaps on grounds purely theoretical and not experimental) that the law is not true.

But it may be impossible to make sufficient observations to apply this test. Then no test can be applied which is sufficient, but a test may be found that is necessary; we may be able to show that there is no evidence, derived from the measurements that have been made, that the law is not true, but it must remain open whether further measurements might provide such evidence. A test of this nature can readily be devised, if the view urged here as to the nature of the law of errors is accepted. According to that law there is for each of the measured magnitudes a maximum error, namely the step of the measuring instrument; let ϵ_x, ϵ_y, ... be these maximum errors. Then, if the values found for the coefficients are correct, the greatest possible residual will be $v_m = | a . \epsilon_x | + | b . \epsilon_y | + \dots$. After the coefficients have been determined, the residuals are calculated by the insertion of the measured values of $(x, y, z, \dots)$ in the equation of condition; if any residual is found to exceed this quantity, then it is impossible both that the law should be true and that the coefficients should be rightly determined[1]. If a discrepancy of this nature is found, either the law or the coefficients must be rejected. If it appears that no values of the coefficients, obtained from any division of the observations into sets, will remove the discrepancy, we shall suspect the law; if it can be removed by adopting other values consistent with the observations, then we shall probably suspect the coefficients. But it must always be remembered that certainty can only arise from the determination of true values, and that the only way to attain certainty is to increase the number of observations until true values can be determined.

Perhaps it is also well—since many widely used treatises overlook the problem—to consider what criterion should be applied if the Method of Least Squares is used for adjusting the observations. Of course, in view of the objections that have been urged against the method, any such criterion can only be regarded as very vague and unsatisfactory; but since I am not so sanguine as to believe that the Method will suddenly be abandoned, an attempt may be made to state one. The best I can find is this: I shall only state it—not defend it. Calculate in the ordinary way from the residuals v "the probable error of a single observation" (which would here be more accurately termed the probable error of a single residual). The probable errors r_x, r_y, r_z of a single observation of x, y, z must then be determined. They can be found by making a large number of measurements on a single magnitude of the kind x, taking the arithmetic mean, calculating the error of each observation and then finding the probable error by the ordinary formula from the sum of the squares of these errors. If, taking the calculated values of a, b, c, $\dots$, $ar_x + br_y + cr_z + \dots$ is found to be considerably less than r; then, as before, there is considerable evidence that either the law is false or that the coefficients have been wrongly determined. The distinction between these alternatives must be made on the same grounds as before.

The calibration of the standard series. And now we can return to the problem from which the whole of our discussion started in the previous chapter, namely the assignment of numerals to represent the magnitudes of the standard series. On p. 449 we arrived at a set of equations, involving the real magnitudes and the errors, which required to be solved in order that the real magnitudes might be determined. For the purpose of the solution some law of errors had to be stated; we have now discussed the law of errors, and can apply our results to the problem.

It is almost exactly similar to what has been called problem 1, when that

---

[1] If the law is not linear the test can be, and should be, applied to the law in its correct form and not in the perverted linear form which is necessary for the application of the methods of adjusting the observations.

problem is stated by means of observational equations. The equations of p. 449 are not strictly observational equations because they do not assign definite measured values to the magnitudes concerned; to only one of these is a magnitude assigned, namely to the unit which is involved in the equations; concerning the remainder only mutual relations are stated. But the equations resemble observational equations in that the residuals, obtained by substituting in the equations the values finally assigned to the magnitudes, are the errors. Any process of adjusting these residuals which may be adopted in problem 1 is also available for the solution of the problem of calibrating the standard series.

If we accept the arguments on which the Method of Least Squares is founded and consider them applicable to this special case, the true values which are to be assigned to the members of the series are those which make the sum of the squares of the residuals a minimum. This method is adopted in practice when the highest accuracy is required[1]. The conditions prevailing in practice are not exactly those which we have supposed. We have supposed that the weights of none of the members (except the unit) are known, so that all have to occur at least twice on the left-hand side of the equation. But if such complete ignorance is assumed, it becomes very difficult to find a series which gives a sufficient number of balancing combinations to enable the weights to be determined. Actually it is supposed that the weights of certain members of the series which are small compared with those which are to be adjusted are accurately known; thus, if we are adjusting a set of weights between 100 and 1 grammes, we shall suppose that the rider is accurate and that milligrams can be measured without error. We then place (say) the 50 gram weight in one pan, the 10 and two 20's in the other, and find the position of the rider necessary for a balance. If the position corresponds to a milligrammes, the corresponding equation is

$$(50) - (20) - (20)' - (10) - a = \epsilon_1.$$

This procedure simplifies the calibration enormously; indeed, without it the calibration would be practically impossible. It will be justified if the maximum error which can occur in a is sufficiently small compared to E, the maximum value of ϵ. The discussion on p. 448 of the determination of E shows that it is not certain that this condition must always be fulfilled, for if (as it must be) the nominal weight $a = 1/n$ is calibrated by balancing against the unit n bodies which balance each other, then it appears that the two such nominal weights might really differ by any amount not greater than E. However in practice the procedure is certainly justified on two grounds; first that E is not, as we assume, constant, but decreases with the

---

[1] The only other method which seems to be employed is to make the number of equations equal to the number of members of the standard series compared, by limiting the number of combinations that are balanced against each other, so that, if all the ϵ's are put equal to o, an unique solution is obtained. That solution is adopted. But nobody would defend that method as having any advantages other than practical simplicity; it will always lead to discrepancies when new combinations of the members are examined.

weights on the pans, so that it is much less for the small adjusting weight than for the relatively large weights which are adjusted; second that the adjusting weight is usually a rider; if the rider is in such a position that only a fraction α of its weight is effective, only a fraction α of its error can occur. It may be asserted confidently that any uncertainty introduced into the adjusted values by means of this necessary device is always very small compared with the average value of the errors ϵ, which it is the purpose of the adjustment to remove.

But of course we must question whether the use of the Method of Least Squares is justifiable. It seems to me impossible that there should be any case in which it is less justifiable. For here the errors are pure single errors of method. The only reason why there are any errors at all, which have to be removed by adjustment, is that the balance is not infinitely sensitive, and that it may not deflect appreciably when the loads on the pans are not "really" equal. (It is supposed of course that all possible precautions to avoid other errors are being taken.) It is impossible to believe that such errors are distributed according to Gauss' Law. There must be a maximum error; an error of a milligram on a first class balance is not merely very improbable; it is literally impossible. On the other hand, if the rider beam is only graduated to tenths of milligrams it is absurd to maintain that an error of a hundredth of a milligram is any less probable than an error zero.

Is it then possible to prove that the Method is false? It is certainly possible to prove that the result is not correct; for if we repeat the whole process, replacing some of the weights that have been adjusted by others, we shall not in general get exactly the same result as before for those that are the same in the two series. But this does not prove the Method is false; for it only pretends to lead to absolutely true values when the collection of measurements is complete. This condition is very seldom fulfilled. In order to get a collection of observational equations so large that it is complete, it would be necessary to find a very large number of balancing combinations, a number much larger than can be obtained with the members of an ordinary standard series, the values of which are selected largely with the view of being able to measure the greatest number of magnitudes with the smallest number of standard members. It is always possible in practice to attribute the discrepancies to an incompleteness of the collection (which will invalidate any method) rather than to a failure of the theoretical basis of the method.

Another way in which some methods of adjusting might be proved incorrect is that some of the residuals ϵ might turn out to be greater than the maximum error E. But here again it is very unlikely that the test will actually disprove the soundness of the method, even if it is actually unsound. For the method makes the sums of the squares of the errors as small as possible— smaller, if the method is incorrect, than the correct method. And if the sum of the squares is less, it is unlikely that the maximum error will be greater. Since the maximum error deduced by a correct method must be less than E, it is unlikely in any case that the maximum error of the Method of Least Squares will be greater than E.

Accordingly, even here, where everything is against the Method, it is almost impossible to prove that it is untrue. What then is the objection to using it? None, so long as no better method can be found. And since the impossibility of proving that the method is false depends on the essential incompleteness of the observational materials, it is unlikely that any method can be found which will always give better results in the matter of consistency of successive determinations. Nevertheless there does seem room here for further investigation; it might be worth trying the method of p. 512, although it is just when the material is very incomplete, and the number of observational equations not large compared with that of the variables to be adjusted, that it is least likely to be successful.

And now the final question to which all this discussion leads up. Is it possible to determine real magnitudes? If it is not possible in this case, the calibration of a standard series, it will certainly be impossible in any other. The answer that our discussion gives is clearly this. If we can obtain a complete collection of observations, and if we can determine the law of errors (or at least one of its features), then we can reduce the difference of the assigned value from the real value to less than any quantity we please. The second condition is fulfilled; there can be no doubt that in a complete collection of measurements made with an instrument of the highest quality positive and negative errors would occur with equal frequency; and we have found a method of adjustment which assumes that proposition concerning the law of errors and no other. On the other hand, it is improbable that a really complete collection can be obtained; the mere extension of a series of observations generally introduces new sources of error; if we excluded "accidental" errors by increasing sufficiently the number of observations, we should probably introduce "systematic" errors. On the other hand, it ought certainly to be possible to adjust the members of a standard series so that the difference between the true and assigned real magnitudes is so much less than E, the step of the most sensitive measuring instrument, that it is inappreciable in any experiment and therefore physically insignificant.

CHAPTER XVIII

MATHEMATICAL PHYSICS

Summary. Up to this point an effort has been made to show that certain parts of physics, including that which consists of measurement, though apparently dependent on mathematical conceptions are, in fact, wholly independent of those conceptions; they are purely experimental. But mathematical conceptions undoubtedly do play an important part in physics, and it is now time to consider exactly how they enter into the science.

The considerations are recapitulated which led to the conclusion that measurement has nothing to do with mathematics. It depends only on the physical magnitude, number, not the mathematical conception, Number.

Guided by these considerations we return to the problem, left unsolved in Chapter XIII, of determining whether numerical laws involve mathematical conceptions. It is concluded that the facts expressed by numerical laws can be expressed as laws, and that these laws can be used to define derived magnitudes and for any other purposes for which any other laws are used, without any introduction of mathematical conceptions. They can even be expressed as relations between numerals without introducing such conceptions. On the other hand if we inquire how we obtain the numerals by which numerical laws are expressed, then we are bound to introduce the mathematical conception of Number.

But mathematical conceptions enter unavoidably and characteristically only when we attempt to explain numerical laws. The explanation is effected by mathematical theories, which usually involve, beside the simple conception of Number, the more peculiarly mathematical conceptions of limits, continuity, derivatives, and integrals. The supreme use of numerical laws is to test theories, and this use of them necessarily involves mathematics. It is here that mathematics enters as an essential part of physics.

Mathematical theories were discussed so fully in Chapter VI that it is only necessary to add a few remarks on questions that have been raised since by our discussion of numerical laws.

The use of derivatives in the hypotheses of mathematical theories suggests the question to what laws these hypotheses can be analogous. In answering this question we are led to the conception of a physically significant derivative of a mathematical function used in stating a numerical law. The conception is examined carefully, and the necessary conditions for physical significance explained; they are fulfilled only for a comparatively small proportion of the derivatives actually employed in physics. Velocity is a physically significant derivative; but the dispersion coefficient is not. Derivatives have to be distinguished carefully from derived magnitudes, with which, however, they are closely associated. A derivative can be measured experimentally in the same way as a derived magnitude.

Mathematical derivatives are possessed only by continuous functions. Though actually only continuous functions are used in mathematical physics, it is worth while to inquire why this is so, and whether in any circumstances discontinuous functions could occur. These questions, though not important in their applications, have some intrinsic interest.

The application of the conception of continuity to physics is discussed. It is found that we have to distinguish sharply and clearly between continuous or discontinuous *functions* and essentially continuous or discontinuous *magnitudes*. For discontinuity can enter either through the function or the magnitude. Contrary to what might be expected, if it enters through one it generally does *not* enter through the other. Discontinuous functions are usually (but not always) functions of essentially continuous magnitudes; and essentially discontinuous magnitudes are often related by continuous functions. Physical number is the characteristically discontinuous magnitude, and theory (but not experiment) tends to reduce all other discontinuous magnitudes to number. Time is the characteristically continuous magnitude. The tendency of theoretical physics at the present day is to reduce all theoretical magnitudes to number and time. The question that suggested this discussion is not answered definitely, but left to be examined in particular instances. But there appears to be no simple reason why a continuous function of a discontinuous magnitude should not have a physically significant derivative; on the other hand, of course, a discontinuous function cannot have a derivative at all at points where it is discontinuous.

Measurement and mathematics. Throughout this Part, whenever it has appeared at first sight necessary to introduce into physics conceptions distinctively mathematical, an attempt has been made to show that the introduction can be avoided. The reason for such attempts is the decision in Chapter VI that such conceptions are essentially hypothetical ideas which can be involved in a theory but not in a law; if this decision is correct—and I can find no reason for doubting it—all parts of physics which are in any way logically subsequent to the first introduction of mathematical conceptions must be theoretical and cannot consist of true laws. Such parts therefore cannot rest only on the external judgements which are peculiarly characteristic of science and concerning which true universal assent can be obtained. It is clearly desirable to make as large a part of physics as possible rest on such judgements, and accordingly the introduction of mathematical conceptions must be postponed as long as possible. On the other hand, there doubtless is such a branch of knowledge as mathematical physics in which all the instruments developed by pure mathematical analysis are employed in the service of physics; to reject entirely the ideas of pure mathematics as foreign to physics is utterly impossible, even if it were desirable. But it is very important to know at exactly what point of our study those ideas must be introduced; and this is the most convenient stage at which to examine the matter. For I believe that we shall find that this point has now been reached; that we can measure fundamental magnitudes, and can employ them to state numerical laws, to measure derived magnitudes and to make deductions in the way described in Chapter XV, without any use of distinctively mathematical conceptions; but that any further developments in which measurement and magnitudes are involved introduces those conceptions.

Before we proceed with the discussion it will be well to recapitulate and to notice once more how we avoided the use of mathematical conceptions where they appeared to be necessary. First of all they appeared necessary in the process of measurement. The primary object of measurement is to find a way of assigning to each of an ordered series of magnitudes a numeral, so that to each magnitude is assigned one and only one numeral and so that the order of the numerals is the order of the magnitudes. For this purpose we must find rules whereby we shall know by what numeral to represent a magnitude connected by known physical relations to other magnitudes to which have already been assigned numerals. Thus we want a rule by which to know what numeral we are to assign to the magnitude that is connected to the magnitude represented by 2 and 3 by the physical process of addition, or to assign to the magnitude which is such that a collection of magnitudes equal to it possessing the number 3 (each magnitude being a unit) and added together physically are equal to the magnitude represented by 2. The rules that were suggested at first were based on the properties of the Numbers (mathematical conceptions) represented also by numerals. In the first instance we adopted the rule that the numeral to be assigned was that which represented the Number that is the mathematical sum of the Numbers 2 and 3; in the second instance the rule that the numeral was that which represented the Number of which the mathematical product with the Number 3 was equal to the Number 2. Mathematical arithmetic tells us that the first numeral is 5, the second 2/3, and the information that is required is thus obtained. We find that, if such rules are adopted, they lead to the results which we desire of a process of measurement, so long as the process of physical addition obeys certain laws and so long as all the objects characterised by the ordered magnitude are enumerable.

But on further inquiry we found that we could dispense with Numbers altogether, by introducing the physical magnitude number. So long as we were concerned only with the assignment of the integral numerals, all the rules that had been deduced from the arithmetic of Number could be deduced equally well from the laws of number, established by the process of counting, together with the law that all units of magnitudes are enumerable objects and possess a number in terms of one of them as unit. From these laws, together with the fundamental laws of addition and equality involved in measurement, the requisite rules could be obtained. When we introduced fractional numerals to fill up the gaps in the series of ordered magnitudes some difficulties appeared, because these fractional numerals are not applicable to number. But we found that it was only necessary to add to our previous laws a law that is the converse of the second law of addition, in order to establish a law which would give the rules that are required. Accordingly the whole process of assignment of numerals to represent magnitudes in the manner desired involves no process of deduction and no conceptions that are not intimately involved in the notion of a law and so essential to all physical reasoning. The deductions required consist in the combination of laws to form other laws in the manner discussed in Chapter V and in the deduction of the statement of a particular instance from the law regarding all instances. Nothing logical or mathematical is required, except in so far as logic or mathematics employs processes of reasoning characteristic of science and uses propositions which, though they may be established by other means, can also be established by experiment and observation; all the propositions were of the nature of those for which true universal assent can be obtained.

On the other hand when we discussed numerical laws we found it hard to avoid the conclusion that they could only be interpreted to mean propositions about Number; for (e.g.) cos y would seem to mean nothing at all unless y is a Number; it means nothing if y is a number or any other kind of magnitude. But it seemed also that this conclusion must be wrong, because everything that is physically important and stated by numerical laws seemed also expressible in terms of the purely experimental properties of graphs. The apparent contradiction was not resolved; it was only shown that our first conclusion must be wrong.

The position is not greatly changed by the introduction of experimental error and the recognition that numerical laws state relations between real magnitudes. It must be noticed that the graph does not determine the derived magnitude precisely or even show indubitably that the law is of one form rather than another; there is always room for difference of opinion exactly which curve fits best the experimental points. If reasons are to be assigned for choosing one curve rather than another it can only be based on the theory of probability applied to the theory of real magnitudes. A derived magnitude is theoretical to exactly the same extent as a fundamental magnitude; the assignment of exactly one value rather than another can only be based on theory, but the assignment of a value within certain limits is determined wholly by experiment. Moreover—and this is the most important point— the discovery that there is a derived magnitude, a concept defined by a law, is as purely experimental as is the discovery of any other concept; the regularity of the points which is shown by the graph does provide a reason, and the only kind of reason there can be, for the recognition of a law; and the difference of the graphs, all of the same form, for different systems is a necessary and sufficient basis for regarding the derived magnitude as characteristic of the system. There is no reason why we should alter our conclusion that graphs do determine derived magnitudes in a manner that makes them as purely experimental concepts as fundamental magnitudes.

The establishment of numerical laws. But, once again, what of the numerical law; does not the proof of the existence of a derived magnitude by means of a numerical law require the introduction of Number in a manner in which it is not required for the proof of the existence of a fundamental magnitude? No, it does not. For the relation stated by a numerical law can be regarded with perfect sufficiency as a relation between numerals. What we mean when we say that $y = y_0 \cos at$ is simply that the numeral representing the magnitude of y is the same as the numeral connected by a purely formal rule with the numeral y_0 and a and the numeral representing the magnitude t. It is unnecessary even to know what is the formal rule; all that is required will be obtained if we have a book of tables giving for all values of y_0, a, t a single numeral corresponding to them, so long as everybody else has access to a similar book of tables. The only advantage of knowing the rule is that any person can prepare the tables for himself.

This statement may appear rather startling; and it is difficult to prove it definitely, for the proof would be of a negative proposition, namely that we do not mean anything more than what is asserted here. But perhaps the truth of the statement will be realised if the process of determining the derived magnitude from the numerical law is compared with that of determining it from the graph. In the latter process we imagine ourselves provided with a set of curves each marked with some sign denoting the form and with one or more numerals distinguishing the curve from others of the same form; just as we try which of these curves will fit the graph, so in the same way we try which set of tabulated numerals will fit the numerical law. Somebody must have drawn the curves according to some rule, just as somebody must have prepared the tables according to some rule; but when we are fitting the graph or numerical law to a curve or table, we are not in the least concerned to know what those rules are; a knowledge of the rule does not help in the fitting and the rule is not necessarily expressed when the fitting is complete.

Nor is a knowledge of the rule necessary for the use of the numerical law when it is once established. For the uses of numerical laws, as such, are two. First they define derived magnitudes; if it is found that, when we change from one system to another, we have to change from the page of the tables marked a to that marked a', and that the order of a, a' is always the same as the order of some magnitude characteristic of the system, then a, a' will measure a derived magnitude. Second, they give rise to other numerical laws by combination; the example taken before was that of the path of a particle $x^2 = cy$ obtained by combination of the laws $y = at^2$ and $x = bt$. In this case we shall have two sets of tables, one (A) giving the numerals y which correspond to various values of t, the other (B) giving the numerals x which correspond to various values of t. The combination is effected by taking from A and from B numerals corresponding to the same numeral t, and asserting that the value of y represented by the numeral from A is simultaneous with the value of x represented by the numeral from B; we can prepare a new table from the numerals corresponding to the same t in A and B, and this table will establish the numerical law which gives the path of the particle.

I think it is important to realise how completely independent of all mathematical conceptions is the process of establishing a numerical law and of using it in any manner which involves no assumption except that it is a law. The independence is apparent when we employ graphs, but, though less apparent, it is equally complete when we use numerical tables. It is less apparent when tables are used because we are in the habit of calculating our tables as we go along in certain exceptional but very important cases. We do not actually draw up tables of the function $y = ax$ for all values of a because it is less trouble to reproduce the tables whenever we want them by calculation than to print and to consult them. On the other hand we do print and consult tables of the function $y = y_0 \cos ax$* because it is considerable trouble to reproduce them by calculation; and it will be realised that they can be used without any knowledge of the rule by which they were made; in fact very few of the people who actually do use them know exactly how they were prepared. Nor is it necessary to know anything whatever about the mathematical properties of the function $\cos x$. If we all used the same edition of the same tables, and in this edition a misprint occurred, resulting in the systematic interchange of $\cos x$ and $\sin x$, we should find a law $y = y_0 \sin ax$ where we now find $y = y_0 \cos ax$. But if we made no application of the numerical law other than the two just considered we should never suspect any "error". For the purpose of these two applications, "$\cos x$" is merely an arbitrary name for a particular set of tables, which might equally well be called "$\sin x$" or "Jones' function" or any other arbitrary name.

However of course it is a matter of some importance in what way the tables are prepared, though it is not important that, in establishing the law, we should know how they are prepared. Unless the tables were prepared in certain ways we should not find numerical laws at all or the numerical laws we should find would be empirical and would not define derived magnitudes. It is a remarkable fact that it is only rules of certain kinds which lead to tables which, in their turn, lead to the establishment of true numerical laws, but this is one of those inexplicable facts that were discussed in Chapter IX. It is only rules which are suggested by comparatively simple mathematical functions which are of this kind; and a knowledge of the rules is so far important that, if we had two sets of tables each of which would fit equally well the observed numerical values of y and t, we should, if we knew the rules, be inclined to choose that of which the rule was the simpler. Let us therefore consider the rules rather more closely.

When it is said that a rule is suggested by the mathematical function x^2, it is meant that the rule must be such that there appears in the tables corresponding to the numeral which represents the Number x the numeral which represents the Number x^2. But how are we to find this numeral? The Number x^2 is defined as (Number x) $\times$ (Number x), where the operation sign $\times$ is defined as obeying the laws of multiplication discussed in Chapter XII †. It follows that the numeral representing the Number x^2 will be that representing the magnitude of a system which is equal to a collection of x systems added together, each of them having the magnitude x. Since we have given a meaning to this expression in the case of magnitudes other than number, even when x is fractional, we might always find the numeral x^2 by the process

---

* Of course we actually use tables of $y = \cos x$. The establishment of the law then really requires three sets of tables. Given a value of x we extract a value from the table $y = ax$; with this value we extract a value from the table $y = \cos x$; and with this value extract a value from the table $y = y_0 x$. But for the first and last tables we substitute calculation.

† I am not sure that these propositions are really definitions; but they are true, and that is all that we require.

of measuring a magnitude such as weight. But since the measurement of number requires much less elaboration than any other and is, moreover, free from the complications arising from experimental error, it would be extremely convenient if we could employ number as the magnitude for determining the numeral x^2. But we cannot do so directly because x has no meaning for number unless it is integral and we require a value when x is fractional. However it can be proved purely logically from the properties of multiplication that $q/p \times q'/p' = (q \times q')/(p \times p')$. Now $q \times q'$ and $p \times p'$ can be determined from q, q', p, p' by means of the properties of number and the operation of counting. Accordingly by means of that operation we can determine x^2, although our knowledge that the numeral obtained by that operation will always represent the Number x^2 depends on purely logical and mathematical deduction. We can perform the actual operation of drawing up our table without the use of any mathematical conception, just as we can draw our standard curves for use in connection with graphs by the use of experimental data only. In fact the drawing up of the tables can be effected by the working of an actual piece of mechanism, a calculating machine; but the correlation of the table thus drawn up with the function x^2 requires, as might be expected, mathematical conceptions. It is here and here only that mathematical conceptions enter in connection with numerical laws; we do not require them in the actual process of establishing the law; but we do require them if we ask why we choose to draw up our tables in one way rather than another, and we require them if it is asked if one rule is simpler than another.

If the mathematical function by which the rule is suggested is $x^{\frac{1}{2}}$ or $\cos x$, the position is slightly more complicated. For it can be shown (mathematically) from the definitions of these functions that the numeral which should represent the Number is not in general one which can be obtained by any process of multiplying or adding the number x; that is to say, it is not the numeral $(x.x + x)$ or $(x.x + x)/x.x$ or any other numeral of that form. It cannot be obtained by any operations which depend upon counting. On the other hand it can be shown that a numeral determined by the operations of counting can be obtained which differs from the numeral representing the function by less than any assigned numeral; that is to say, assuming certain formal rules for the handling of the operation signs $+$ and $\times$, a numeral r can be found such that $r = (x^{\frac{1}{2}}) + \epsilon$, where $(x^{\frac{1}{2}})$ is the numeral which should represent $x^{\frac{1}{2}}$, ϵ a numeral as small as we please to choose, and r a numeral q/p where both q and p are numerals which represent the number of some system derived from a system of number x by the physical processes of addition and multiplication. Accordingly though we cannot determine by counting, or by the mechanical operations of the calculating machine, the numeral which should represent $x^{\frac{1}{2}}$, we can by such processes determine a numeral which differs from that numeral by as little as we please. The numerals that we shall insert in the table will be those which differ from the "true" numerals by a numeral representing a magnitude less than the experimental error. The conclusions that we shall arrive at in establishing the law will then be exactly the same as if the true numeral were inserted. It is to be observed again that all these complicated considerations can be neglected entirely in the actual establishment of the law; they are important only if we ask why we insert in the tables the numerals which we actually do insert. It is a fact that we shall find numerical laws defining derived magnitudes only if we choose our rules with reference to mathematical conceptions, but it is a fact which is perfectly inexplicable and the truth of which is in no way involved in the actual establishment or use of the laws.

Numerical laws and mathematical theories. We conclude then that mathematical conceptions, even such simple conceptions as Number, are not necessary in the establishment of numerical laws or in their use to define derived magnitudes. Numerical laws, like other laws, are established by experiment and experiment only. But mathematical conceptions are necessary to explain numerical laws. If all numerical laws were capable of explanation our previous efforts to exclude mathematical conceptions would have been wasted, for at some stage in dealing with them such conceptions would have had to have been introduced. It is well therefore to note that all numerical laws are not explained, or conceivably explicable. An example of an inexplicable law (at least according to nineteenth century physics) is the law of a falling body which defines the derived magnitude, uniform acceleration. We do not explain or attempt to explain that law; we rather regard it as a basis of all other explanations. It is of course because inexplicable laws are used to explain others that they are of so great an importance; it is in connection with them that it is so desirable to realise that they are purely experimental. Nevertheless we shall see immediately that though they are purely experimental their use as bases for explanation involves the recognition of a relation between them and mathematical conceptions.

The explanation of numerical laws is effected by mathematical theories. Concerning such theories so much has been said in Chapter VI that there is little to add here. There is only one feature that calls for additional comment. It is not always recognised that Number is a mathematical conception; it is more often confused with number or even with numeral; but it is recognised that limits, continuity, derivatives, integrals, and all the conceptions of the infinitesimal calculus are peculiarly mathematical. It is these that we usually mean when we speak of mathematical conceptions. All mathematical theories[1] involve these conceptions; but they involve them in a peculiar way. The mathematical conceptions are involved in the hypothesis of the theory but not in the dictionary. The hypothesis of the theory is almost always expressed in the form of a differential equation, but the propositions deduced from the hypothesis are always obtained by a process which consists, in part at least, of the integration of the equation and the removal of all derivatives. The derivatives themselves (or any other characteristically mathematical

---

[1] At any rate until recently, when a tendency has arisen to invent theories involving discontinuous theoretical magnitudes to which these conceptions are not applicable.

ideas) are purely hypothetical ideas; not only have they, like all hypothetical ideas, no meaning apart from the theory, but even with the theory they have no meaning standing alone; they have meaning only in the particular connection which makes the hypothesis of the theory. The importance of this conclusion will appear immediately. For the present we are concerned only with the propositions which result from the hypothesis by the integration of the differential equations and their connection with numerical laws by means of the dictionary.

The integrated equation will state a relation between the variables of the differential equations, the constants of those equations and certain "arbitrary constants". The dictionary will state that the variables "are" (in the sense of p. 124) the real magnitudes characteristic of the various states of some system, and that the constants, or some functions of them which occur in the integrated equation, are magnitudes characteristic of all states of that system. The statements of the dictionary about the arbitrary constants will be of a different nature in different theories; all that will be common to all is that for each particular system some values must be assigned to these constants. But the general physical meaning attributed to these constants by the dictionary is indicated by their mathematical significance. They are Numbers such that, whatever value they may have, the integrated equation is a consequence of the hypothesis. Accordingly their physical meaning must be such that the truth of the theory is unaffected by the value attributed to them. If they represent at all any magnitude characteristic of the system it must be some magnitude determined by some considerations which lie outside the province of the theory and which the theory does not profess to explain. In a great number of theories, perhaps the majority, one of the variables is the time. Now no law is true for all values of the time. When we are stating a law in which one fundamental magnitude is the time, we are usually considering a case in which some process is set going; the law states what happens when once it is going. The law is not true for any time before it was set going, but only for later times, but the law will usually differ in some way according to the exact manner in which it was set going; it will depend, as we say, upon the initial conditions. The initial conditions are not usually determined by law at all, but by the arbitrary action of the experimenter; they cannot therefore be explained by any theory; a theory to be adequate must be true whatever the initial conditions. It is for this reason that, in theories which involve the time as one variable, the arbitrary constants represent the initial conditions. The arbitrary constants are something such that, whatever they are, the theory is true; and the same statement is true of the initial conditions.

But the dictionary does not only state what the variables, the constants, and the arbitrary constants "are"; it must also give a physical meaning to the relation between them expressed by the integrated equation. This relation always includes uniform association, though it may (and usually does) include other physical relations also, such as simultaneity. When such meaning is attributed to the relation the dictionary is complete; the integrated equation can be translated entirely and directly into physical statements, and since those statements include assertions of uniform association it will be a law. It will also, of course, be a numerical law. It will assert not only that a particular value of the magnitude x is uniformly associated and otherwise physically related to a particular value of the magnitude y, but also that any value of x is related in this way to that value of y which is such that the Numbers, represented by the numerals representing these values of x, y, and the constants, are connected in the manner stated by the integrated equation deduced from the hypothesis. Experiment can now determine whether this statement is true; according as it is true or false the theory is true or false. If it turns out to be true we shall conclude that the function of the constants of the hypothesis that are related by the dictionary to the constants of the numerical law "are" the derived magnitudes defined by that law; and, conversely, we may be able to express the constants of the hypothesis as functions of the derived magnitudes and so determine the numerical values to be attributed to each of them. This manner of measuring a theoretical magnitude has already been noticed in Chapter VI.

It has been argued that theories are the only part of science which have true intrinsic importance. If this be so, the use of numerical laws to test theories and to attribute numerical values to theoretical magnitudes must be their highest use to which all others are subsidiary. It must be noted therefore that this use is only possible if the numerical law is established by means of tables of which the rule is known; it requires the knowledge and acceptance of the mathematical reasoning which underlies the rule; it is not possible if the law is established by a graph or by tables of which the rule is not known. So long as we are concerned only with laws, there appears to be no reason why a graph should not be in every way as valuable as a numerical law; it permits prediction, the derivation of laws by combination and the discovery and measurement of derived magnitudes. But it offers no point of contact with a mathematical theory; the conceptions of one cannot be related to those of the other—except by means of the "equation to the graph", the use of which at once converts the graph into a numerical law established by known mathematical rules. It is because we are so accustomed to use numerical laws to test theories, more accustomed than we sometimes think, that numerical laws have become so closely associated in our minds with mathematical reasoning; and it is because mathematical reasoning has thus become so closely associated with what are undoubtedly experimental laws that the division between law and theory is so often overlooked. It is forgotten that mathematical reasoning is not applicable to any of the concepts derived directly from experiment, and paradoxes arise from the attempt to apply it to propositions which deny implicitly its fundamental assumptions. Mathematical physics consists of theory alone; experimental physics has no more connection with mathematics than with theology.

Physical derivatives. It has been said that the propositions that are derived from the hypothesis of a mathematical theory and interpreted by the dictionary are always deduced by integrating the equations of the hypothesis and thus removing all derivatives and other distinctively mathematical conceptions. If this statement is true, it follows that no numerical law explained by a theory can involve any magnitudes that are connected by the dictionary with derivatives; derivatives would seem to be conceptions wholly foreign to any numerical law. But on the other hand, it was maintained in Chapter VI that the hypotheses of theories are valuable only if they are analogous to laws. If the hypotheses of theories involve derivatives, a conception wholly foreign to laws, how can they be analogous to laws?

The answer is that conceptions closely analogous to derivatives are involved in some laws and, perhaps, even in laws explained by mathematical theories. But any law involving such conceptions can also be expressed in a form that does not involve them, and it is always expressed in the form without derivatives when it is desired to test it for the purpose of proving a theory; though it may be used in the form with derivatives to suggest the hypothesis of the theory. This matter is important and must be considered carefully.

Suppose we have a law expressed by a graph; then by a purely experimental process we can draw tangents to the graph; we cut the outline of the graph in a sheet of metal and press a straight edge against it. We can then measure the angle which the straight edge makes with the axes when it is pressing against the outline at various points, and form a new graph by plotting these angles against the abscissae of the points. Such a process can be applied to any graph; it can be applied again to the new graph that we have produced. The carrying out of the process involves no knowledge except the bare form of the graph; it does not even require that we should know that physical nature of the magnitudes of which the graph represents the relation. But it may happen that the new graph determined by the angles of the tangents is of the same form (or can be made of the same form by a suitable choice of scale in plotting) as that expressing some other law characteristic of the system of which the original law was characteristic. As we have expressed the matter, such a result will probably never happen; but if we plot, instead of the angle made by the tangent with the axis, some other geometrical magnitude defined by the tangent (e.g. the ordinate to the tangent at a point separated by a fixed distance along the axis of abscissae from the point where the tangent cuts that axis, or the area of the triangle bounded by this ordinate, the tangent and the axis), then in certain cases, but not in all, we shall find that the result will happen. Thus if the system we are investigating is a charged condenser shunted by a high resistance, and the original graph represents the relation between the time since the experiment began and the charge which has passed from one plate of the condenser to the other, then the derived curve (choosing the ordinate to define the tangent) will be of the same form as the graph relating to the same time the potential difference between the plates of the condenser; further, if we have sufficiently sensitive methods of measuring the magnetic intensity at some point near the shunting resistance, it will have the same form as the graph relating this magnetic intensity to the time.

Accordingly the geometrical magnitude defining the tangent has in such cases a distinct physical significance. The fact that, by suitable choice of scale, the graphs can be made of the same form shows that there must be some law between the magnitude characteristic of the tangent and the potential difference between the plates of the condenser or the magnetic intensity near the connecting wire; it could be proved by experiment that the graph relating them is a straight line, and this straight line will define a derived magnitude characteristic of the system. By the use of the tangents we have obtained a new derived magnitude which further investigation would show to be important; we have arrived at results of considerable physical significance.

These very familiar matters have been expressed thus fully and in this particular form in order to show that the proof that the magnitude characteristic of the tangent has a distinct physical significance is purely experimental; the law relating this magnitude to others characteristic of the system is as much a law as any other. But to any one to whom they were not familiar (if he could understand the matter at all) the whole procedure would appear entirely artificial; he would ask how we ever thought of trying such a process for the discovery of new laws. In answering his question we should have to introduce considerations that are not purely experimental. Our reasons are of this nature. If the law expressed by a graph were expressed by a numerical law $E = f(t, a)$, then by regarding E and t for the moment as mathematical variables and a as a mathematical constant, we could form the derivative dE/dt, and deduce an equation $dE/dt = f'(t, a)$, where f' is another function of t and a. Now we know (we need not inquire at present why) that the numerical law $y = f(t, a)$, if expressed by a graph with suitable scale, would have the same form as the graph relating the ordinate of the tangent and the time. Accordingly this last graph may be regarded as the graph of dE/dt, and it will have physical significance if dE/dt is related by a law to the potential difference between the plates or the magnetic intensity. But why do we expect dE/dt to be related by a law to these magnitudes? If instead of allowing the charge on the condenser to leak away through the high resistance we kept it connected to a suitable source of electricity, we should get in place of the

law $E = f(t, a)$ [where $f(t, a)$ is a matter of fact $E_0(1 - e^{-\frac{t}{CR}})$] the law $E = a'.t$,

defining a derived magnitude a'. Now here experiment would show that the magnitude a' is characteristic of the high resistance and the potential across it and also of the magnetic field surrounding it. But when the law is of this form, $a' = dE/dt$; accordingly we expect in general that dE/dt will be a magnitude characteristic of the same properties of the system.

Of course there is a great assumption, at first sight very rash, in the last stage of the argument. When the law is of the form $E = a'.t$, a' is equal not only to dE/dt, but to innumerable other derivatives and functions of derivatives. The assumption cannot be avoided and therefore had better be expressed baldly. But some support for it is often derived from the familiar conception that a law of any form other than $E = a'.t$ may be reproduced, with any accuracy that we desire, by a combination of laws of this form, each of these laws being characterised by a different value for a'; and further that these values of a' may be made to differ by as little as we please from the values of dE/dt for the values of t corresponding to each of these values of a'; in other words, a polygon formed by tangents to the graph may be made to approach as closely as we desire to the actual graph. But it is generally recognised now that such considerations provide no certain basis for the assumption that we are making, namely that dE/dt has the same physical relations as the derived magnitude to which it reduces when the form of the law is such that dE/dt is constant. The mere fact that dE/dt is *not* constant introduces a new feature into the case. We are assuming practically that the processes which are represented by the law are such that they are determined by the simultaneous values of the magnitudes that are being measured, and not at all by the magnitudes at an earlier time. That assumption may be true, but there is no guarantee that it is always true; and if it were not true dE/dt, when changing, would not have the same physical relations as it has when it is constant. The experiments with the graphs, from which our discussion started, show that it is true in this particular instance; but similar experiments will always be required to prove it in any other instance.

Significance of derivatives. We conclude then that a derivative can be determined by experiment, through the use of graphs, as well as by a mathematical process from the corresponding numerical law; but that, whichever way it is determined, further experiment is needed to prove that it has physical significance. But here we must distinguish. A derivative always has *some* physical significance if determined from a numerical law; for there will be a statement about the derivative which is simply equivalent to the numerical law from which it is determined. The statement that $dy/dx = f'(x)$ is experimentally the same thing as the statement that $y = f(x)$; it states the same experimental facts; if $y = f(x)$ is physically significant, so is $dy/dx = f'(x)$. For even if the law is expressed by a graph, the statement about the derivative is equivalent to the statement of the law from which it is derived; from a knowledge of the relation between magnitudes defining the tangent and the magnitude represented by x, the curve to which the tangents are tangents can be constructed. But this is not the physical significance that makes a derivative important. A derivative is physically significant only if a law involving it can be found which is not the law from which it was determined; it must enable us to state some new law. In our previous example, the derivative dE/dt, in virtue of the law from which it was determined, was related by a law to t and the derived magnitude of the original law (CR). The law which gives to dE/dt its importance is not this law, but the law that $dE/dt = RV$, where V is the potential difference at the ends of the high resistance, and the law that $dE/dt = b.H$, where H is the magnetic intensity at some point near the resistance. These are new laws, totally different from that whereby the derivative was determined; they involve altogether new magnitudes.

Since the matter is important, it may be useful to make the matter clear by yet another and more familiar example. If the distance a body has travelled (s) is related to the time occupied in travelling it (t) by any relation of the form $s = f(t)$, we can determine the derivative ds/dt, which we call the velocity (v). If the only laws we knew about velocity were $v = f'(t)$, one such law corresponding to each law $s = f(t)$, then velocity would be a very unimportant conception. But we know other laws involving v; for instance we know that the energy of a body (a measurable magnitude) is proportional to v^2 and that a body carrying a charge e in a magnetic field H is subject to a force proportional to Hev; and we know that this law is true, whatever is the form of $f(t)$ in the law from which v was determined as a derivative. We probably established the law first when $f(t)$ was simply $a.t$, and the derivative equal to the derived magnitude a, the uniform velocity; the considerations which have been mentioned suggest to us that the law will be true also when f is not of this form; but we cannot be certain that the law will be true until we have examined many other forms of f. The fact that ds/dt is equal to a when $f(t)$ is $a.t$ does not give of itself the slightest proof that all laws involving a will remain true, if for a is substituted ds/dt, when ds/dt is not equal to a. Nor again does a proof that one such law remains true necessarily prove that any other will remain true. For strict proof new experiments are needed for each law. But it is only if the law remains true that ds/dt is physically significant.

These considerations may be generalised. It will be seen that they lead to the conclusion that a derivative will be physically significant if the following conditions are fulfilled: (1) That a system under certain circumstances is characterised by a numerical law $y = f_1(x, a, b, c)$, where y and x are the fundamental magnitudes, a, b, c the derived; and (2) that f_1 is such that some one of the derivatives f_1^n is equal to one of the derived magnitudes a; and (3) that this derived magnitude is related by some other numerical law $F(a, u, v, w) = 0$ to other magnitudes u, v, w; and (4) that by changing the circumstances a system can be obtained characterised by the law $y = f_2(x, a, b, c)$, the nature of the magnitudes and the physical relation between them being unchanged; (5) that the derivatives of this law are connected with the magnitudes u, v, w by the law

$$F[f_2^n, u, v, w] = 0.$$

It is important to notice that there are many cases, indeed a majority of cases, in which these conditions are not fulfilled. Thus (2) is not fulfilled in the law, $I = I_0 e^{-\lambda t}$, for the decay of a radioactive substance. But perhaps a refusal to attribute physical significance on this score is unduly narrow, for, though no derivative of I is equal to λ or I_0, the combination $\dfrac{1}{I}\dfrac{dI}{dt}$ is equal to λ. If the other conditions were fulfilled, we should have to admit that this function of the variables and the derivatives had physical significance. But here (4) is not fulfilled, and therefore (5) cannot be; there is no pure radioactive substance under any conditions which decays according to any other law; and if we include mixtures, decaying according to the law

$$I = I_1 e^{-\lambda_1 t} + I_2 e^{-\lambda_2 t},$$

then (2) is not fulfilled. It is not easy to find a case in which (3) is not fulfilled; for even if a law between a derived magnitude and other magnitudes is not actually known, one is usually suspected; thus, in this example, though λ is not definitely known to be related to other magnitudes, it is suspected that it is related to the range of the particles emitted. But the important cases to notice are those in which all the other conditions are fulfilled and only (5) is lacking. A good example of such cases is provided by the derivative dp/dT from the gas equation (T is absolute temperature). So long as the equation is that of a perfect gas (e.g. hydrogen at low pressure), $dp/dT = R/V = b$ (say). b is a derived magnitude connected by known law with the mass of the gas, which is not necessarily involved in the equation between p and T. Under other circumstances (e.g. smaller volume) the relation between p and T is not of the same form. But now (5) is not fulfilled; dp/dT is no longer related by the same law to the mass of the gas. Accordingly dp/dT has not, in our sense, physical significance. This conclusion, in a slightly different form of words perhaps, is generally recognised; it is known that dp/dT is not in quite the same position as velocity. But even if the conclusion is obvious it is well to make the reason for it clear.

Such is the meaning of the physical significance of a derivative and the conditions that it should exist. When they are fulfilled, there is a natural tendency to overlook the distinction between the function of the derivatives and the derived magnitude to which, if the numerical law is of the form f_1, they become equal; this tendency is especially marked when this "function" is simply one of the derivatives, as it is in the case of velocity and acceleration. We call the derived magnitude a (when the law is of the form $s = a.t$) and the derivative ds/dt (when the law is not of this form), indifferently by the name "velocity", and regard a merely as a form of "velocity" which happens to be uniform. Now if the condition (5) has been proved to be true, whatever the form of f_1, the identification of the derivative and the derived magnitude is completely justified; for there is no important difference between them; both can be determined experimentally and both have everywhere the same physical significance. But such proof is very seldom available. Owing to experimental difficulties we almost always prove the law involving u, v, w, much more thoroughly when the derived magnitude, and not the derivative, is related to them. For instance, I do not think that many, if any, of the laws between velocity and other magnitudes have been subjected to such examination as would give us any adequate reason for believing them, unless we knew that they were true for uniform velocity. Certainly at the present time we should without the slightest hesitation regard as true of a non-uniform velocity any new law which we had proved of uniform velocity. Our practice in this matter is justified by its success; we never have found, as we might have done if the practice had not been justified, that conclusions founded on our assumption lead us into error.

Such confusion as there is in the matter is largely due to the practice of using derivatives even when they have no physical significance. The practice is often convenient and quite harmless when proper attention is paid to the whole matter. It is sometimes convenient, in order to display analogies, to write a numerical law in the form $y' = f'(t)$, rather than $y = f(t)$. The numerical values of a derivative which has no physical significance are also sometimes tabulated, e.g. those of dp/dT or of $dn/d\lambda$ (dispersion). But the fact that any numerical law determines derivatives, and that those derivatives have usually *some* importance, must not be allowed to conceal the more interesting fact that only a small number of them have the peculiar importance that we have called physical significance and permit the statement of laws, valid for all derivatives of the type, which cannot be stated without their help.

Before we leave this subject one question concerning derivatives should be asked. Is a derivative a magnitude; and, if so, is it a fundamental or a derived magnitude? At first we might be inclined to answer that it is a derived magnitude, but further reflection must make us abandon that answer. For it is a characteristic of a derived magnitude that it has a definite numerical value in virtue of some law; the statement that it has a certain numerical value is simply equivalent to saying that a law of a certain form (and with certain values of the constants, if these are not regarded as part of the form) is true. Now this is not the meaning of a statement of the numerical value of a derivative. The laws $s = 3t^2$, $s = 2t^3$ are perfectly different laws, but for each of them the derivative ds/dt may have the same numerical value; further it has the same numerical value for the same value of t, when $t = 0$ or 1, and the values through which the derivative passes between $t = 0$ and $t = 1$ are precisely the same in the two laws. Any law $s = f(t)$ gives a derivative and, for an indefinite number of different forms of f, some derivative given by one form of f will have the same numerical value as some derivative given by any other. The assertion of a particular numerical value for a derivative does not, therefore, tell us anything whatever about the form of the law from which it arises; it does not tell us even if the derivative is physically significant, for the numerical values of any derivative may be interesting.

It is equally obvious that a derivative is not a fundamental magnitude. But we have recognised a third kind of magnitude, called a defined magnitude, which is such that it is defined to be some function of two other magnitudes (if the defined magnitude is to have any significance these magnitudes must be connected by a law). A derivative is clearly such a defined magnitude. The assertion that velocity is the derivative ds/dt is a pure definition; it states nothing that is true or false, but merely an arbitrary assertion on which we are agreed; it does not imply the truth of a law, like the assertion that density is mass/volume. If we only used physically significant derivatives, then the assertion that velocity is a derivative would imply that it is physically significant and involve the assertion that the necessary conditions were fulfilled. But since we do not so limit ourselves (and it would be undesirable to limit ourselves) we must regard derivatives as pure defined magnitudes, and add, in certain cases, the statement that they are physically significant. But they are obviously closely allied to derived magnitudes; as indeed must follow from the fact that they sometimes become identical with them; they have dimensions and the fixing of their numerical values raises exactly the same problems as those which we considered in Chapter XIV.

And now, having considered derivatives so thoroughly, we can answer the question from which we started. The laws which suggest the hypotheses of mathematical theories are those relating physically significant derivatives, determined by some numerical law, to magnitudes which are not involved in that law. The hypotheses differ from the laws that suggest them in two respects. First the derivatives are not, by the nature of the case, susceptible of experimental determination; second some connection, not discoverable by experiment, is asserted between the magnitudes. A very simple example will be sufficient to illustrate these differences. All dynamical theories are suggested by the law that a force acting on a body produces an acceleration proportional to the force. This law has been proved with some certainty when the acceleration is the derived magnitude, uniform acceleration; it is assumed to be true when the acceleration is not uniform. The hypothesis of a dynamical theory always contains equations of the form $m \cdot d^2s/dt^2 = F$. The remainder of the hypothesis consists of assertions that F is related in a certain manner to s and possibly to t; the relation being once more suggested by known laws concerning forces, distances and times. We thus arrive at equations of the form $m \cdot d^2s/dt^2 = f(s, t)$. The proof of the theory consists in the integration of these equations, the interpretation of the result by the dictionary, and the comparison of the resulting numerical law with experiment.

Continuity. All the questions that have occurred to me, relating to measurement and calculation, that are of any importance in any actual physical problem, have now been discussed. But it may be worth while to discuss here some other questions which seem to have intrinsic interest. They are suggested by the fact that only such functions of mathematical variables possess derivatives as satisfy the mathematical definition of continuity. All functions that are expressed by any physical law, if applied to mathematical variables, do satisfy that definition. This, in itself, is a fact of some interest, suggesting the inquiry whether any explanation of it can be offered. If it cannot be explained, the further question arises whether there could be any meaning in a derivative of a discontinuous function, and, if there is such a meaning, whether such a derivative could have physical significance in the sense that has been explained.

Mathematical continuity is defined thus: $f(x)$ is continuous for $x = \xi$ if, given ϵ, we can choose η so that $| f(x) - f(\xi) | < \epsilon$ if $| x - \xi | < \eta$. It follows that if $f(x)$ is continuous in the interval between x_0 and x_1, $f(x)$ must assume once at least every value between $f(x)$ and $f(x_1)$ as x varies from x_0 to x_1. The converse of this proposition is not necessarily true, but it is true for any function that occurs in any physical law or theory. The definition quoted may be paraphrased with sufficient accuracy for our purpose by the statement that y is a continuous function of x if, by making the difference between x_0 and x_1 small enough, we can make the difference between y_0 and y_1, the corresponding values of y, as small as we please.

Now it is clear from the discussion of Chapter XVI that no magnitude that is a function of another, defined by a numerical law, can be continuous in this sense. For we have seen that the number of values which either of the magnitudes can assume in any given range is finite, and is fixed by the experimental error of the process of measurement. If we cannot detect the effect of adding a magnitude ξ to x when $x = x_0$, then x can only have one value within the range $x_0 - \xi$ to $x_0 + \xi$. There can be no physical meaning whatever in asserting that x has more than one value in this range; the statements that $x = x_1$ and $x = x_2$, where x_1 and x_2 are both within the range, can only assert precisely the same experimental facts; experimentally there can be no distinction whatever. Accordingly without considering the relation of x and y we can assert definitely that neither can be a continuous function of the other or of any other magnitude, for under no conceivable circumstances can y have every value between any two assigned values.

But of course the recognition of these facts, intimately involved in the conception of experimental error, leads us at once to turn to the idea of "real magnitude" which was introduced to explain the facts. It is not inconsistent with all that was said in Chapter XVI to ask whether one *real* magnitude may be a continuous function of another *real* magnitude if the two are related by a numerical law. However we have concluded that there must always be some uncertainty in the assignment of the values of the real magnitude. It is impossible therefore to conclude definitely that one real magnitude is a continuous function of another at all points within a given range, but it may be possible in some cases to conclude definitely that it is not a continuous function.

Suppose that we are determining a numerical law between magnitudes x and y. We set up our apparatus, including instruments for measuring x and y, and we make alterations in some part of it which generally lead to changes in x and concomitant changes in y. But we shall not find that every change in the apparatus produces a change either in x or in y. If ξ is the step of the instrument measuring x in the neighbourhood of x_0 and η that of y in the neighbourhood of a concomitant value y_0, then, as a result of the change in the apparatus three alternative things may happen to x: (1) x may not change at all, (2) x may change from x_0 to x_1 where $x_1 = x_0 \pm \xi$, (3) x may change to x_1, where $x_1 = x_0 \pm n\xi$, where n is greater than 1. There are three similar alternatives for y, and any one of the alternatives for x may happen with any one of the alternatives for y. The question we have to ask is which of the nine alternatives are consistent with Y being a continuous function of X, where X, Y are the real magnitudes. We will suppose that there are no errors of consistency and that whichever of the alternatives happens is repeated at any subsequent trial.

Let us plot on a graph two points representing the two pairs of associated values of x and y, and with each of these points as centre draw a rectangle of sides 2ξ and 2η, parallel to x and y. Then it is clear that we may, consistently with the observations, attribute to the real magnitudes, X and Y, represented by the points, any values which lie inside these rectangles; but of course, since there are only two states of the system concerned, we can only attribute to X and Y two pairs of associated values, one lying inside each rectangle. Now starting from the same initial condition, x_0, y_0, we make a slightly different alteration in the apparatus; again any one of the nine alternatives may happen, and it may or may not be the alternative which happened at the first trial; if it is not the same we draw a rectangle round the new pair x_1, y_1. And so we proceed until we have made a very large number of trials. There are now two alternatives. If we suppose that the area covered by each rectangle is shaded, it may be possible to draw a line from x_0, y_0 to one of the values x_1, y_1 without going outside the shaded portion of the diagram, or it may not; in other words, one or more of the rectangles round x_1, y_1 may touch or overlap the rectangle x_0, y_0 or there may be a gap between the rectangle x_0, y_0 and any of the rectangles x_1, y_1. If the first alternative happens, it is possible that Y is a continuous function of X; if the second alternative happens (and continues to happen however long we continue the trials), then Y cannot be a continuous function of X. For, if our experiments are exhaustive, Y (or X) cannot have any value for those values of X (or Y) which correspond to points in the gap; if X varies from a point in one shaded area across the gap to the other shaded area, Y cannot vary over all values between that associated with the first value of X and that associated with the second. According to the definition of continuity, Y cannot be a continuous function of X. But if the first alternative happens, then since our experiments are consistent with the assignment to X and Y of any values within the shaded areas, we may assign those values so that they are all different and all lie along a continuous curve from x_0, y_0 to x_1, y_1; and by making a sufficient number of trials we may place as many different points as we please on this curve and can place them in any position on that curve. By placing two points sufficiently near together on the continuous curve (that is by making $X_1 - X_2$ or $Y_1 - Y_2$ small enough) we can always make $Y_1 - Y_2$ or $X_1 - X_2$ as small as we please; Y may be made a continuous function of X. It should be mentioned that there is one condition which has been silently assumed to be fulfilled (and always is fulfilled if the other conditions are), namely that as the number of trials is increased indefinitely the number of points falling within *each* of the rectangles increases indefinitely;

for if that were not so there would be no evidence that we could place as many points representative of X, Y within that rectangle as we please.

The argument may easily be generalised and we may conclude that Y may be regarded as a continuous function of X within any range x_0 to x_1 if by making a sufficient number of trials and drawing "rectangles of error" round the points characteristic of their results, we can obtain a shaded area extending without gaps from the point x_0, y_0 to the point x_1, y_1. In terms of the nine alternatives which may happen as the result of any one trial, this condition means that there must be some trials at which one of the alternatives involving (2) happen. If at every trial y either does not change at all or, if it changes, changes by an amount greater than 2η, then the real magnitude Y must be a discontinuous function of the real magnitude X; on the other hand, so long as at some trials (the number of these trials increasing indefinitely as the number of trials increases) y increases by an amount less than 2η, then Y may be a continuous function of X. This is a definition of continuity completely in accordance with practice and with common sense. But it must be noted that no experiments can prove that Y is a continuous function of X. We have no means whatever of distinguishing between any curves all of which fall within the shaded area; and we can draw a discontinuous curve keeping within that area just as well as we can draw a continuous curve. And this conclusion is only to be expected; for the real magnitudes are hypothetical ideas and any proposition concerning them is a theory. No experiments can establish completely the truth of a theory; they can only show that the facts are consistent with the theory, although they may also be consistent with other contradictory theories.

It is clear that the judgement whether Y can be regarded as a continuous function of X will depend upon the values of ξ and η, the steps of the measuring instruments. By sufficiently increasing the steps and the areas of the rectangles, the shaded areas can always be made to overlap. We shall not therefore consider that we have obtained any evidence that the function can be regarded as continuous until we have reduced the steps to the smallest that are possible. But the criterion remains perfectly definite, because there is a definite limit to the step; this limit is fixed by the condition that the consecutive members of the standard series which define the step are such that they are not equal, but are both equal to some third magnitude. It is only if the step of the measuring instrument fulfils this condition that experiments give any evidence for continuity; though, of course, if a function is shown to be discontinuous with an instrument of larger step it will also be discontinuous if the step is reduced.

Essential continuity. We have spoken so far of Y being a continuous function of X, and this mode of expression is necessary if we are to apply the mathematical definition of continuity. For no mathematical variable is continuous or discontinuous *per se*; it is one or the other only in so far as it is a function of some other variable. A mathematical variable by its very nature must be capable of assuming all values whatever; it is only when those values are limited by the condition that it is a function of some other variable that there can be any question whether it can or cannot assume certain values. Here the conception of a continuous magnitude differs from that of a continuous variable; for we undoubtedly do think and speak of physical real magnitudes as being essentially discontinuous and as incapable by their very nature of assuming certain values under any conditions whatever and not merely because they occur in connection with other magnitudes. Thus, according to modern theory, the electric charge on a body is an essentially discontinuous magnitude; however we alter the charge on a body, it can assume only certain values. We might attempt to bring this conception into line with mathematical continuity by saying that when we state that the physical real magnitude is essentially discontinuous, we mean that it is a discontinuous function of every other magnitude. But the attempt is not wholly successful, for a real magnitude is only a function of another if it is related to it by some numerical law. Our definition could only be applied to variations of the magnitude which are determined by some law; but such a definition is not wide enough, for we can vary a magnitude in ways which involve no law at all. Thus we can vary the charge on a body by touching it with a stick of sealing wax rubbed with silk, and, if our methods of measurement were sufficiently accurate, we should expect to find that only certain values of the charge ever occurred; but in such experiments we are not tracing a numerical law between the charge and any other magnitude. If we attempted to trace such a law completely we should fail; we might trace a law relating the charge left on the body to the previous condition of the body and of the sealing wax; but if we went still deeper and attempted to predict what would be the state of the sealing wax at each trial, we should find no law, for that state results from the characteristically arbitrary actions of the experimenter. And this feature is common to all experiments; even when we are deliberately investigating a numerical law between x and y, the changes that are made and produce in their turn concomitant changes of x and y are completely arbitrary. Ultimately therefore the variation of every magnitude is determined by some arbitrary variation with which it is not connected by a law, and of which it is not a function. There is a sense then in which a magnitude can be physically discontinuous which involves in no way ideas of functionality and of numerical laws.

We might attempt to define such essential discontinuity by the statement that a magnitude is essentially continuous or discontinuous over the range x_1 to x_2, according as by some means or other a series of the magnitude can be found including x_1, x_2 and all steps of any measuring instrument between x_1 and x_2. But according to that definition all magnitudes would be continuous, for we have supposed that the steps are defined by realised members of the standard series, and the mere fact that there are such steps means that a system having the magnitude associated with each of them can be found. There are various ways in which we might overcome this difficulty but the best is to return to the fundamental idea of experimental error. We were led to recognise such error by observing that the law of equality is not always, or indeed usually, true; we can usually find three systems, x_1, x_2, x_3, such that $x_1 = x_2$, $x_2 = x_3$, but $x_1 \neq x_3$. If we can find an indefinite number of systems x_2 fulfilling this condition (and if we can find one such system we can always find any number that we please), then we can attribute to each of these systems a real magnitude which may be anything between X_1 and X_3. Accordingly we can attribute to the real magnitude of some system any value between X_1 and X_3; we can fill up the gap between X_1 and X_3 with as many real magnitudes as we please and assert that each of these real magnitudes is characteristic of some system. X can have any value between X_1 and X_3, and this is what we mean when we say that X is essentially continuous. On the other hand if the law of equality is always obeyed and no system can be found which is equal to both x_1 and x_3, if $x_1 \neq x_3$, then there is nothing to suggest a distinction between real magnitudes and magnitudes; there is nothing to suggest that the real magnitudes are not the same as the magnitudes, and since there is a gap in the magnitudes between x_1 and x_3 we must also recognise a gap in the real magnitudes, if we introduce that conception at all.

Accordingly we arrive at the following definition of essential continuity: A magnitude is essentially continuous within the range x_1 to x_2, if, and only if, a series of systems having the magnitude can be found, including x_1 and x_2, such that each is involved in a set of propositions of the form $x_r = x_s$, $x_s = x_t$, $x_r \neq x_t$; in other words, if the magnitude is continuous we must be able to pass from x_1 to x_2 through a series of systems each of which is equal to its immediate predecessor and immediate successor. This is (slightly altered in wording) the definition given by Poincaré, to whom all this treatment of physical continuity is due. It will be seen that it does not introduce any ideas that are not expressible in terms of experiment alone; essential continuity and discontinuity are not, like the continuity and discontinuity from which we started, hypothetical ideas. Continuous magnitudes are simply those for which the purely experimental law of equality is not true. On the other hand it is impossible to explain why we regard such magnitudes as continuous without introducing the idea of a real magnitude; it is "really" the real magnitude, not the magnitude, that is continuous.

Most of the magnitudes which we have considered so far are, in this sense, essentially continuous. There is only one that is both fundamental and essentially discontinuous, namely number; the essential discontinuity of number is expressed, as we saw before, by the fact that number is subject to no experimental error. But many derived magnitudes are discontinuous; for instance Faraday's constant, or refractive index (in the neighbourhood of that of diamond), or density of a liquid at a temperature of 20° C. (in the neighbourhood of that of mercury). For many purposes, and especially those with which we are concerned in this chapter, the discontinuity of derived magnitudes is of the same nature and involves the same consequences as that of fundamental magnitudes. But it may be noted that if a derived magnitude is discontinuous, it does not mean necessarily that its determination is free from experimental error; for such error is introduced by the experimental errors of the fundamental magnitudes by which it is determined.

On the other hand there are many theoretical fundamental magnitudes that are regarded as essentially discontinuous; that is to say, there are many hypothetical ideas that are analogous to essentially continuous fundamental magnitudes and yet are stated by the hypothesis to be discontinuous in the sense that they are capable of having only an assigned number of values separated by finite intervals; they would be completely analogous to the fundamental magnitudes if these were discontinuous in a certain manner. Thus, according to the atomic theory mass must be discontinuous, and modern theory is constantly adding to the number of discontinuous theoretical magnitudes. In fact at the present time there seems to be only one theoretical magnitude which there is no tendency to regard as discontinuous, namely time; a discontinuous time seems to us as impossible a conception as did a discontinuous energy a few years ago. Now the equations involved in the hypothesis of a mathematical theory are always analogous to numerical laws; and though there are few numerical laws which involve essentially discontinuous magnitudes, it is useful to consider what would be the nature and properties of such laws if they were known, because in so doing we are considering what form of equations are permissible in the hypothesis of a theory involving essentially discontinuous theoretical magnitudes. We should note then that if a theoretical magnitude is asserted by the hypothesis to be discontinuous, it is always also associated very closely with a number, the one essentially discontinuous magnitude; it is usually asserted that if one of the possible values of the magnitude is taken as unit, the remainder can be represented by the values which are possible to numbers, namely all integral positive values. This assumption is, of course, not in the least necessary; a discontinuous magnitude might have the values 1, $1\frac{1}{2}$, 2, $2\frac{1}{3}$, ... the smallest magnitude being taken as unit; it would then be impossible by taking any of the values as unit to represent the others by integers. But such assumptions are never made, and the fact that they are never made almost justifies us in saying that in theories, as in laws, the only discontinuous magnitude is number. Theoretical mass is simply not a magnitude at all; if mass were actually analogous to the essentially discontinuous theoretical mass we should hardly recognise it as a magnitude at all; the results which at present we express in terms of mass we should express in terms of number and a universal constant which would be what we now call the mass of the unit body. On the other hand, essentially discontinuous derived magnitudes are usually not associated with number, for it is usually not possible by taking one system as unit to express all the remainder by integers. But in many cases we do not regard such derived magnitudes as "really" discontinuous when we come to assert theories about them; it is "a matter of chance" that certain values and only these occur. But here we are anticipating too much the result of future discussions; with this hint, which will probably tell the reader what is meant, we must leave the matter. It is only important to insist once more that whenever essentially discontinuous magnitudes are discussed or used, the magnitude number is of peculiar importance.

Before we leave the definition of essential continuity one further remark should be made. It is sometimes said that a magnitude is continuous if, given two systems possessing it, a third can always be found such that its magnitude is between those of the other two. By "between" is meant "greater than one and less than the other", where greater and less are used, in the generalised sense of p. 273, for the characteristic relation generating order and its converse. Now if this definition be adopted, no magnitude is continuous, unless by magnitude is meant real magnitude. It is impossible to find a body of which the weight is between the weights 1 gramme and 1·000001 gramme, if by weight is meant what is directly measured on a balance. If, however, magnitude is to be interpreted as real magnitude, then much of the definition is unnecessary. For only continuous magnitudes possess real magnitudes at all; and instead of saying complicated things about real magnitudes it would be sufficient to say simply that they exist.

Continuity of functions and magnitudes. Having examined the conception of essential continuity we may return once more to that of continuous functions involved in numerical laws. There is a close connection between the two conceptions, but it is precisely the contrary to that which might seem natural at first sight. To a casual observer it might seem that discontinuous functions would be necessarily associated with essentially discontinuous magnitudes, but a very little thought will show that it is usually continuous magnitudes that are involved in discontinuous functions and *vice versa*. For consider a simple case of a discontinuous function. If I supply electricity at a constant rate (e.g. by means of a Wimshurst machine) to a condenser in parallel with a spark gap, and measure the relation between the time and the charge that has been received by the low potential side of the spark gap, I shall find that the relation shows all the features of discontinuity. While the condenser is charging up the charge received does not change, but as soon as the sparking potential of the gap is reached, the charge changes suddenly by an amount, equal to the product of the capacity of the condenser and the spark potential, which may well be greater than the step of the instrument for measuring charge. The curve which I shall get relating the time t to the charge Q will consist of a succession of straight portions parallel to the axis of t, separated from each other by finite intervals parallel to the axis of Q. But now suppose (the conditions are of course actually incapable of realisation) that the condenser and the spark gap are so small that Q_0, the charge that passes at each spark, is equal to the steps in the series of the magnitude, charge, an essentially discontinuous magnitude. Then again I shall get precisely the same form of curve as before, but the steps in the curve will be equal to the essential steps of the magnitude. In the first instance I should regard the law discovered as showing the presence of a discontinuous function; in the second instance I should not. For in this second instance, I should regard the absence of certain values of Q as determined, not by some special connection between Q and t, but by the essential nature of Q; the curve is discontinuous because Q is essentially discontinuous, not because there is any discontinuity about the process that is represented by the law. In the first instance, however, Q is essentially continuous so far as can be indicated by the instrument measuring the charge; nothing in the nature of Q indicates why certain values of it do not occur; the absence of these values must be determined by something discontinuous in the process involved, and this process is therefore properly represented by a discontinuous function. It is only because the magnitudes involved are essentially continuous that I conclude that the function relating them is discontinuous.

These conclusions, which would undoubtedly be drawn from the experiments, follow directly from the definition of the discontinuity of a function. In the first instance the increases in Q are greater than the step of the measuring instrument; in the second they are not greater, because the step of the measuring instrument must be at least as great as the intervals between the values of the discontinuous magnitude. It is for this reason that the definition was stated in terms of this step, rather than in terms of the closely associated experimental error. For while an essentially discontinuous magnitude must have a finite step in any measuring instrument used in connection with it, it has no experimental error. If we had said that the function was not continuous unless the change in y were not greater than the experimental error, then it would have been necessary to conclude that every function involving an essentially discontinuous magnitude was discontinuous. But the examples quoted show that such a conclusion would have been unfortunate, and that a discontinuous function has a definite physical significance which may be important whether the magnitudes related are essentially discontinuous or continuous; a discontinuous function indicates an important peculiarity in a process which may be present whatever the nature of the systems undergoing that process.

However it should be noted that, according to our definition (which represents the common sense view of the matter much more closely than one founded on experimental error), an essentially discontinuous magnitude may be involved in a discontinuous function. For the intervals by which y always changes, if it changes at all, may still be greater than the step of the magnitude which defines its essential discontinuity; y may miss out several steps. That would occur in our first example if we could decrease the step of the measuring instrument so far that the essential discontinuity of charge was revealed while the experiment was otherwise unaltered; the absence of the missing steps could not be accounted for by the nature of the magnitude, and we should again be led to regard the discontinuity of the function as indicating a discontinuity of the process investigated. But such instances do not often occur in actual laws, because so few magnitudes are (apart from theory) essentially discontinuous. Discontinuous functions are almost always found experimentally in connection with continuous magnitudes; and for this reason the discontinuity found is always of a special kind. Our general definition indicates the possibility that there should be gaps in the values of x as well as in the values of y, but since the magnitudes are always essentially continuous, it is always possible to conduct the experiments so that all values of one of them occur, and it is only values of the other that are missing. Discontinuous curves might occur in which the observations were only to be represented by isolated points dotted over the graph; but actually those that occur consist almost always of a series of continuous branches separated from one another by displacement parallel to one of the axes. But this feature is not in any way necessary, and examples might be devised (though they would be hard to realise) in which more general forms of discontinuity occurred.

We see then that the occurrence of a discontinuous function usually implies that the magnitudes involved are essentially continuous; it should also be observed that a function of discontinuous magnitudes is often and usually continuous. Suppose for example that we are observing the relation between the time and the number (essentially discontinuous) of alpha particles emitted from a radioactive substance. Then, if there were no "Schweidler's fluctuations", we should find $n = a \cdot e^{-\lambda t}$, and the expression of the relation in this manner by a continuous function would convey extremely important information. As a matter of fact, owing to the fluctuations, we do not find that relation; the function which actually represents the relation, though it may be continuous, is not analytical. From this fact again we draw important conclusions, but it must be observed carefully that these conclusions would not be valid, unless it were recognised that, in spite of the essentially discontinuity of n, the relation between n and t might have been represented by a continuous and analytical function.

A more striking illustration of the association of discontinuous magnitudes and continuous functions may be obtained by observing that it is often possible to substitute a continuous for a discontinuous function by substituting a discontinuous for a continuous magnitude. Thus in our example of the charge conveyed across the spark gap in parallel with the condenser, the charge is represented by a discontinuous function only so long as the magnitude of which it is a function is essentially continuous. If, instead of plotting charge against time (continuous), we plotted it against number of sparks across the gap (discontinuous), then, applying our definition, we should find that the function was continuous. The gaps in y would appear to be due simply to the fact that the missing values cannot appear because the values of x to which they would correspond (if the function were continuous) cannot occur at all owing to the essential discontinuity of x. There would be no need to imagine that the absence of those values was due to any discontinuity in the process taking place. We should write $Q = a \cdot x$, where x is the number of sparks and a a constant (a derived magnitude); we should represent the relation between Q and x by a continuous function and feel that that mode of expression accurately conveyed the important facts. It is only so long as we express Q as a function of the continuous magnitude, time, that we feel that the expression of the relation between the two by a continuous function is essentially misleading[1].

Continuity and derivatives. This long discussion has been intended chiefly to direct attention to the important distinction between the two kinds of physical discontinuity. There is the discontinuity of a function, which represents a characteristic of the process represented by the law in which the function is involved; and there is the essential discontinuity of a magnitude. The question that led to the discussion is now split into two. Can a discontinuous function have a derivative and, if so, can that derivative be physically significant? and can a continuous function of an essentially discontinuous magnitude have a derivative and, if so, can that derivative be physically significant?

The answers to the questions are different. No discontinuous function can have a derivative at a value where it is discontinuous, for there is simply no means of determining such a derivative; but it can have a derivative at a value where it is continuous. Such a derivative might have a physical significance; but as a matter of fact I do not think that it ever has. However this fact is not sufficient to distinguish discontinuous and continuous functions, for the derivatives of many continuous functions have no physical significance. Again a continuous function of a discontinuous magnitude can clearly have a derivative; we can always by the usual rules determine the derivative at any point, even if it is not occupied by one of the values of the discontinuous magnitude. But it is more difficult to determine whether this derivative can have any significance. In one case it certainly can; that is when the form of the law is such that the derivative is identical with a derived magnitude. Thus, in the law $Q = a.x$ relating the charge that has passed across the spark gap to the number of sparks that have passed, $dQ/dx = a$, which is an important derived magnitude equal to CV, the product of the capacity of the condenser and the spark potential of the gap. I can think of no instance in which the derivative is not identical with the derived magnitude and yet has any significance, either the significance of an important numerical value, or the full physical significance which we have discussed. On the other hand it does not seem to me clear that in no case could it have such a significance, at least at points occupied by values of the discontinuous magnitude.

---

[1] And yet we often do so express it in graphs. ("We" here includes I, for I have been guilty of the error.) Instead of leaving the separate branches of the curve separate, we often join them up by lines parallel to the axis. These lines represent nothing whatsoever that we observe in our experiments; they are apparently inserted because there is a mistaken belief that no physical function can be truly discontinuous. It certainly can be discontinuous so far as any experiment can tell; whether theory can admit discontinuous functions (especially of the time) is another question. The most familiar example of the error is in representing the isothermal of a substance below its critical temperature; a line parallel to the axis of volume is usually drawn connecting the volumes of the liquid and gaseous phases. But there are no observations corresponding to points on this line.

However it is difficult to discuss discontinuity adequately in general, for its importance arises chiefly in connection with theories. And in a theory questions concerning it are apt to be inextricably mixed with special considerations which affect the particular theory. Some of the most important of these considerations arise from the introduction of conceptions arising from the study of statistics. Accordingly we shall leave the matter here, and revert to the discussion at later stages when they become relevant.

APPENDIX

As is explained in the preface, this volume was written on the assumption that it would include Part III of the treatise. It may therefore be well to indicate very briefly a few of the conclusions which would have been attained in that Part in order that various references to it may be comprehensible. A few words will also be added on matters which belong to Part IV.

Time. All temporal conceptions depend on the immediate judgements of "before", "after", and "simultaneous with". These are fundamental judgements concerning which there is universal agreement, and the combined field of these relations includes all other judgements on which physics is based.

The relations are of the kind which can generate order in accordance with the principles of Chapter X; all physical judgements can therefore be ordered in respect of time. But the establishment of this order does not lead immediately to a system of measuring "time", because no satisfactory method of addition can be found. There is no rule whereby I can combine an event that occurs at 3 a.m. with one that occurs at 6 a.m. to make an event which occurs at 9 a.m. (When I speak of an "event" I am referring to a set of uniformly associated judgements that are simultaneous; but it is impossible to give any definition of the term beginning "an event is...".)

The measurement of "time" is effected by means of "periods" which are properties of systems or individual bodies. I can find certain systems which are such that one of the uniformly associated properties A is uniformly before another of the uniformly associated properties B; if the properties are really uniformly associated the system is then said to have a period. The periods of two systems, characterised in this manner by the events A, B and A', B' respectively, are equal if, when A is simultaneous with A', B is simultaneous with B'. The period of a third system characterised by A'', B'' is the sum of these two periods if, when A'' is simultaneous with A, and A' with B, then B'' is simultaneous with B'. These definitions turn out to be satisfactory in the special sense of Chapter X and suitable for establishing a system of fundamental measurement. All periods are measurable on that system; there are no negative periods.

The realisation of the standard series is made easy by the discovery of isoperiodic systems, namely such as are characterised by a series of events A, B, C, D, ..., which may be made as long as we please, the periods AB, BC, ... being all equal (tested against some other period). Accordingly in such systems the periods AB, AC, AD, ... provide the integral members of the standard series. The fractional members are provided by other isoperiodic systems, one event of these periods being made simultaneous with a member of the integral series. Pendulums and clocks are isoperiodic systems; but the ultimate isoperiodic system providing the unending series of events, is the rotating earth.

When the standard system of periods is established—but not before—it is possible to measure magnitudes, called time-intervals, relating events that are uniformly associated and therefore cannot define periods, which are necessarily properties of systems, characterised by uniformly associated properties. If C, D are any two events, and if, when C is simultaneous with the event A of the standard series, D is simultaneous with B, then the time-interval between C and D is equal to the number of unit periods which, added together, are equal to the period AB. Further, if we choose as C one particular event and estimate for another event, X, its time-interval CX, then CX is a numeral characteristic of the events X; it is called the time at which X happens. The order of these numerals is the order in which the events X would be placed by the generating relation before-and-after; it is therefore the magnitude which is suggested by our original observation that all events can be placed in an order by that generating relation. But it is essential to observe that it is a defined magnitude (not derived—for its measurement involves no law other than those involved in the measurement of periods), and depends entirely on the previously established fundamental magnitude, period.

It is often convenient to measure periods indirectly through the times at which the events that characterise them happen. If we know the times at which two events happen and know that they are uniformly associated, so that they define a period, then that period is simply the difference of the times at which they happen. It is because periods are usually measured in this way that the necessity for founding all temporal measurements upon periods is sometimes overlooked. It is a fundamental assumption of physics—and one of the very highest importance—that "times" can enter into a law only as differences, which measure periods. The assumption may also be expressed by saying that the laws of physics are independent of the time at which the events concerned happen; it is only the differences of the times of the events concerned in the law, and not the times themselves, which are significant. A denial of that assumption would undermine the use of the relation of uniform association, which includes an element of invariability, which again means nothing but such independence of the "time".

The difficulties and paradoxes often associated with the temporal conceptions arise mainly from two circumstances. First, there are complications arising (as we say now) from the finite velocity of propagation of all signals. It is a consequence of this finite velocity that the definitions for the equality and addition of periods are not satisfactory (in the special sense) unless the two systems of which the periods are compared and the observer by whom they are compared are very near together. (It is possible that other conditions beside that of propinquity have to be fulfilled, e.g. relative rest.) It is difficult always to fulfil this condition. But when it cannot be fulfilled certain rules can be laid down—and are found satisfactory—for determining how the judgements of simultaneity of a distant observer would be related to the temporal judgements of an observer on the spot. The actual working out of these rules and the presentation of the evidence for them is a matter of considerable complexity; nevertheless the rules themselves in their final form are simple—so simple that their use is now instinctive. It is important to notice that, in current practice, the rules are used to re-define simultaneity, which no longer means the immediate and fundamental judgement on which all temporal conceptions ultimately rest. The neglect to notice that the meaning of this important word has been changed is the source of much confusion.

The second circumstance, complicating temporal conceptions, is even more important and more difficult to treat adequately in a summary. It may perhaps be stated in the form that, besides our immediate and instinctive judgements of before, after, and simultaneous with, we have other instinctive temporal judgements of the "passage of time", which lead us to regard events as happening at "instants of time", each of which is unique and sharply distinguished from any other instant of time.

But such an idea of separate instants, each distinguished *per se* from the other, is precisely contradictory to the fundamental physical idea of the significance of differences of times, though not of the times themselves. On the other hand, of course, it is intimately involved in our attitude towards all our personal experience, towards history, and to all those judgements of the external world which we decided in Chapter I must be excluded from the domain of science. I shall go to my laboratory tomorrow, fully confident that I shall repeat the observations that I made today (unless I am still doubtful whether those observations indeed represent a law); so far as any part of my scientific experience is concerned, today and tomorrow are the same thing; but so far as my non-scientific experience is concerned, they are poles asunder. To pure experimental science, past, present, and future represent distinctions so trivial that it is doubtful if they can be defined satisfactorily in terms of the concepts it employs; to all experience that is not purely scientific, there are no distinctions that are more vitally important.

It can be urged, and has been urged, that the difference between the scientific and non-scientific views of time is not really fundamental; that even in non-scientific experience the apparently essential difference between past and future is not an intrinsic difference in instants of times, but merely, as is the view of science, a difference in the relations of events which occur at those instants. But though it may be true that we can thus "explain" the contradiction, though it may be true that my instinctive feeling that 1814 and 1914 are intrinsically different is merely due to the fact that I was born and came to consciousness between those dates, even then it is none the less true that I have that instinctive feeling and that my ultimate judgement on the matter is no less vital to me than other ultimate judgements which can be accepted as the basis of science. However much we protest, we must all feel that a view of "time" in which no place was allowed to an intrinsic difference of instants would not afford that intellectual satisfaction which it is the primary object of science to attain.

The difficulty can be and is solved by taking advantage of the distinction between laws and theories, between concepts and hypothetical ideas. It is only in laws and in the concepts based on them that the fundamental principles of science forbid us to recognise intrinsically distinguishable instants of a continuously changing time; there is nothing to prevent us recognising the idea in our theories; indeed we are almost compelled to recognise it there, for no theory is satisfactory ultimately unless the ideas involved in it are analogous to those that have ultimate validity and importance. And as a matter of fact we do introduce into our theories a "time" closely analogous to the time of history and of personal experience. The "time" of our theories is, as has been noticed before, the pre-eminent independent variable. But an independent variable is simply something of which all the values differ *per se* and not because they are differently related to other values. Newton was perfectly right when he spoke of physical time as "evenly-flowing" in an independent stream, but he was right only if he meant the time of our theories and not of our laws. For the hypothetical time always occurs in differential coefficients; it is not until the differential equations in which those coefficients are involved have been integrated that the propositions of the hypothesis can be translated into laws by the dictionary. But when they have been integrated, the independent variable time never occurs, except in a function of the differences of times. Now differences of physical times (i.e. time-intervals since a fixed datum) are concepts, namely periods; and these periods are the same, for a given difference, from whatever fixed datum the times of which they are the difference are reckoned. We can omit from our minds everything about the datum, except, if we are stating experimental propositions, the fact that there is some datum. It is easy to remove this remaining limitation so far from our minds that we cease to be spontaneously conscious of it, and to imagine that the times in the integrated equations, of which the differences represent the periods of laws, are reckoned from no datum whatever, and that different values of those times represent not different relations of instants to the datum, but intrinsic differences in those instants.

When we have schooled ourself to this point of view (and the non-scientific view in this matter is so much more familiar than the scientific that any schooling required is rather in the reverse direction), we have obtained a complete psychological reconciliation between the evenly flowing independent time of theory, consisting of intrinsically distinguishable instants, and the time of laws, consisting of time-intervals since a datum measured by periods which are invariable, and therefore "time-less", properties of systems.

It is difficult in the few words that can be devoted to the matter here to expound fully so recondite a matter. But I think it will be found that many difficulties will disappear if it is clearly recognised that the "t" which occurs in all our theories is a pure hypothetical idea, unrelated directly by the dictionary to any concept; and that it is precisely because it cannot be directly related to concepts that it is valuable and satisfies our intellectual desires. And of course if time is a purely hypothetical idea, the fact is of the utmost importance for the analysis and criticism of all the propositions in which it is involved. Incidentally we shall be prepared for the view that any science (such as geology) in which the conceptions of past and future are fundamental must consist mainly of theory.

Space. The scientific conceptions of space differ from those of time in a much longer and more elaborate development from the fundamental judgements on which they rest. The characteristically temporal relation of simultaneity is directly established by immediate and fundamental judgements; but any relations that can be regarded as characteristically spatial are not fundamental, but are established only by an elaborate comparison of fundamental judgements, none of which, by themselves, would be regarded as spatial.

These fundamental judgements doubtless arise, as Poincaré has pointed out, from the sensations accompanying muscular movement. The first difficulty in understanding the development and meaning of spatial conceptions appears when we inquire why many kinds of muscular sensations which seem to differ in their psychological character completely give rise to the "same space". For example, the difference in experience when I move my leg and when I "accommodate" my eye seems as great as the difference in experience when I see a light and when I hear a sound. Nevertheless we recognise what is often called "an identity of tactual and visual space", but we insist on the complete differentiation of sound and light.

The solution of the difficulty is to be found in the observation that all muscular sensations, whether of the limbs or of the eye, are characterised by a relation which may be called "betweenness". Judgements of "between" are perfectly fundamental as are judgements of before and after. The remarkable fact which leads to the identity of the many kinds of muscular space is that judgements of between made in respect of one muscular sensation are uniformly associated (in certain conditions) with corresponding judgements of between in respect of any other muscular sensation. Accordingly if all spatial conceptions and laws are developed solely from judgements of between, it will not matter what muscular sensations we employ in our experiments; all will lead to the same laws of the "same space".

Guided by such considerations we shall try—and, I believe, succeed—to express the elementary spatial conceptions in terms of judgements of between. These conceptions are boundaries (distinguished into surfaces and lines), the intersection of boundaries, and direction. The last is certainly the most difficult conception to describe. It is not pretended that the process of development traced is that which has actually occurred in the history of either the race or the individual; it is intended only to show how the universally accepted propositions concerning space might be founded on truly immediate and fundamental judgements concerning which the universal agreement characteristic of science can be obtained.

We now proceed to metrical geometry, a branch of experimental science intimately connected with the existence of rigid bodies. We find a method of defining a plane and a straight line (we conclude that the former is really the more fundamental conception), and thence discover satisfactory methods of measuring as fundamental magnitudes the length of a straight line, the area of a plane surface, and the angle between two straight lines. These magnitudes (like the period of a system, but unlike time-intervals and distances) are properties of a system. In all cases equality is judged by superposition. The plane geometry which we develop is thus very similar (as might be expected) to that of Euclid's *Elements*, the axioms and postulates of which correspond closely to the laws on which the satisfactoriness of these systems of measurement depends.

As usual a difficulty arises in stating something to correspond to the axiom of parallels; this difficulty is intimately connected with those encountered in all discussions of "direction". It appears that the law that we need will state that by turning a straight line in a plane successively through a number of angles, it can be made to coincide once more with its original position; and that the sum of the angles (in the sense of physical addition) through which it is turned in the process is the same whatever (within very wide but definite limits) are the details of the process. This is an experimental proposition which could not be predicted *a priori;* if the permissible limits of the process are as wide as they have usually been assumed to be, then it is an experimental fact that "space is Euclidean". But if it were found that they had to be narrowed somewhat, then we should be forced to the conclusion that space is non-Euclidean—so long, of course, as we are determined to retain unaltered our specification of the physical addition of angles.

The geometry, which has so far been confined to rectangular figures, can be extended without difficulty to plane curves. Thus the length of a plane curve is also a fundamentally measurable magnitude in virtue of the fact that there are flexible but unextensible tapes, in the same sense that there are rigid bodies.

The laws of plane geometry, to state which these systems of measurement are propounded, assert relations between the lengths, areas and angles characteristic of certain figures. They are true experimental laws, although the realisation of their experimental character is often rendered difficult by the usual mode of expression. The conclusions of Chapter II should be borne in mind; the experimental properties of the circle (e.g.) are but stated in the form, There are circles. Some of these laws are used, in modern practice, to measure areas and angles as quasi-derived magnitudes in terms of length. But it must never be forgotten that area (e.g.) does not mean the product of the lengths of two sides of a rectangle, or angle the ratio of the arc to the radius of a circle; it is an experimental law that areas and angles are so related to lengths in certain figures, and that the law could not have been established unless areas and angles were measurable as fundamental magnitudes[1].

---

[1] Cf. p. 382. Of course the laws form part of the general propositions, There are rectangles or circles. The question whether it would be possible to dissociate the uniform association in virtue of which the area of a rectangle is proportional to the product of the length of its sides and yet leave other uniform associations sufficient to define a concept that might reasonably be called a rectangle—this is one of the questions which are too complex for discussion in a summary.

And here a word may be said on the difficulty of "incommensurable" magnitudes— though, of course, it arises in the law $s = \frac{1}{2}gt^2$ as much as in the law $A = al^2$. There are no in-

The extension of geometry of this kind to surfaces which, though not plane, are made up of a finite number of plane surfaces, is relatively easy. We require to change our definition of angle somewhat to include an angle between planes and also our definition of area. Far greater difficulties arise when the surfaces are continuously curved. It seems that we can only elaborate a purely experimental geometry of such surfaces by means of difficult and artificial propositions about their relations to sets of plane surfaces into which they can be "developed" or by which they can be closely circumscribed. But the discussion of these matters cannot be summarised.

The importance for most physical purposes of boundaries that are surfaces, but not plane surfaces, is their connection with the magnitude, volume. Volume is a fundamental magnitude, equality in respect of which is judged by means of "occupation" by an incompressible fluid, just as equality of length and area is judged by superposition on a rigid plane surface. Just as there are laws, involving universal constants characteristic of all rigid bodies, relating areas, angles and lengths, so there are laws, involving universal constants characteristic of all incompressible fluids, relating volumes, areas, angles and lengths. It is with these laws that the experimental part of solid geometry is concerned; and, if the magnitude volume is added to those mentioned previously, all the statements made about plane geometry are applicable also to solid.

But volume has a further significance, connected with the properties of rigid bodies rather than with those of incompressible fluids, which may be roughly expressed by the statement that the volume of a body is a measure of the space that it occupies. This conception of the occupation of space (it may be noted that it is only in this connection that it is necessary to introduce the word "space" at all) needs very careful consideration; for on it depend most of the historical difficulties and paradoxes of the subject.

The conception arises from the fundamental sensations in which, as we hold, all geometrical notions are founded. If I am alone in an empty room there are certain muscular motions which I can make and which I cannot make if the room is crowded with furniture. The presence of rigid bodies in my neighbourhood prevents me from moving my limbs in certain ways. But the states which I reach as a result of different motions differ for me simply because the motions differ; we are accustomed to express the difference by saying that the different motions lead to different positions in space. It is a natural consequence of that mode of speech to say that the rigid bodies which prevent certain motions occupy the space corresponding to the motions which they render impossible. Further it appears that in the vague sense which alone is possible before the establishment of true measurement, the amount of muscular motion excluded by a body is indicated by its volume, measured by means of an incompressible fluid.

These ideas appear to be inherent in the earliest geometrical conceptions of solid bodies, but they do not and cannot become of scientific importance before the development of coordinate geometry. The introduction of coordinates permits us to accept the general notion of a difference between different positions in space that is independent of their occupation by one material system rather than another, and yet to substitute, in the expression of this difference, measurable magnitudes in place of the vague and subjective conceptions based immediately on muscular sensations. It appears as an experimental fact that to every position in space,

commensurable magnitudes; there cannot be, by the very meaning of fundamental measurement; but there may be incommensurable *real* magnitudes; and numerical laws, we concluded, always state relations between real magnitudes.

defined by muscular motion, corresponds (if the system of coordinates is rightly chosen) one and only one set of coordinates. These coordinates are magnitudes, either angles or the lengths of lines or, possibly, areas.

Having developed a system of coordinate geometry under the influence of these ideas, we can use it to replace entirely the older form. All the laws of the properties of figures can also be stated as laws between coordinates. The exact analysis of the processes involved in the translation of the propositions of one kind of geometry into propositions of the other and the precise statement of the laws (for of course there must be such laws) which permit the translation to be made are problems of great interest. They raise, incidentally, the question of the meaning and the foundation of the proposition that space is three-dimensional. But they are very complex and must be considered in full detail if the discussion is to have any value; they must therefore be left untouched here.

The change in geometry consequent on the substitution of coordinate for classical geometry is very similar to that in the study of time consequent on the substitution of "times" for periods. First it leads to the measurement of truly fundamental magnitudes as quasi-derived and thus to a tendency to forget that they are truly fundamental. If we state the propositions of classical geometry (for instance, any of the properties of a conic section) in terms of coordinate geometry[1], the lengths, angles and areas of the conic section appear as functions of differences of coordinates, or of "distances between points". But a distance between points, like a time-interval, is not and cannot be a fundamental magnitude, because it is not the property of a system; it is measured by means of a fundamental magnitude which is a property of a system, namely the length of the straight line the ends of which coincide with those points; but, since it is something which is supposed to be independent of the presence of the measuring rod, it is not a property of that rod.

However the second change is more important. Spatial conceptions cease to be concepts and become hypothetical ideas; we are now dealing with a theory of space from which the laws of classical geometry are deduced. A full discussion would be necessary to show that the new spatial conceptions are indeed hypothetical; here a mere indication must suffice. In classical geometry "a point" is the common part of two linear boundaries. The experimental fact that any two such points, having the same coordinates, are coincident is the basis of coordinate geometry. But now the "generalisation" is made that any set of coordinates represents a point. If the meaning of "point" is left unchanged, the proposition is simply untrue; the vast majority of sets of coordinates do not correspond to points; and many sets are not capable of realisation at all (because, as we say now, they correspond to points inside a rigid body). If we seek a new definition of point we shall find none that will serve except simply the assertion that a statement about a point means a statement about a definite set of coordinates. But a very important proposition is added, namely that, though with any one system of coordinates, a point is simply a set of those coordinates, if we change the system (e.g. by changing our axes) to every point on the new system corresponds a point on the old. The properties of any collection of points are unchanged by a change in the system of coordinates. The reader will realise easily that this is not a law, but the proposition of an hypothesis. The points concerning which it is made are not concepts, but hypothetical ideas; they belong moreover (like instants of time) to the class of hypothetical ideas which is not related by the dictionary directly to any concept. In the laws deduced from the theory, interpreted by the dictionary,

---

[1] In what follows it will be supposed for brevity that the coordinates are always rectangular.

the set of coordinates of a point never appears singly[1]; what appears is always the difference (or some other function) of the sets of coordinates belonging to two points; it is these functions of two or more points that alone are related by the dictionary to concepts.

Of course, in accordance with the principles that have been maintained throughout, the fact that coordinate geometry, unlike classical geometry, leads at once to a physical theory is one of its greatest advantages. But theories, unless they are recognised as such, are likely to be harmful rather than valuable; we must never forget that our 3-dimensional, homogeneous, continuous space, "occupied" by material bodies, is as purely a hypothetical idea as is the continuous and evenly flowing time of Newton. Both ideas are intensely valuable, but no direct statement about either of them is capable of being either proved or disproved by experiment.

Perhaps a word should be added about vectors. They represent, of course, from this point of view merely a new system of coordinates. But they are interesting for our purpose because of their bearing on the doctrine of fundamental measurement; they represent the discovery of a new physically satisfactory process of addition. The process (e.g.) of combining two vectors in a plane, according to the parallelogram law, to give a third has the character required for physical addition; for if we first combine A and B and then combine the resultant with C, we reach the same result as if we combine A and C and then combine the resultant with B. The second law of addition is true, and so is the first. The difference from the process so analysed in Chapter X is that, if by equality we mean (as we do) equality in scalar magnitude and in direction, then only a very limited selection of vectors will be equal to any member of the standard series prepared by combination of equal vectors. We cannot therefore measure all vectors in terms of a single unit; we must have at least 3 units; sometimes it is more convenient to have an indefinite number of units. The peculiarity of vectorial addition is that it is usually accompanied by a change of unit.

Motion. There are many interesting questions to be discussed in connection with motion which were raised, or ought to have been raised, in treatises of a generation ago. We have to inquire exactly what is meant by the statement that a body moves, how the measurable concepts connected with motion (velocity and acceleration are the chief) are measured, and what general laws of motion, independently of the circumstances in which it occurs, can be stated. Thus we must ask what is the foundation, experimental or other, for regarding kinematic magnitudes as vectors, to be added by the parallelogram law, or what is the justification for using the term "relative velocity", which seems to imply that the velocity of A relative to B is the same as the velocity of B relative to A.

But today an attempt to touch any of these questions would at once lead to a discussion of the Principle of Relativity. Of course that Principle is one of the things which it must be the purpose of such a treatise as this to consider; and more than half of Part III, as it stands at present, is devoted to a consideration of it. But, unlike most of the other topics that have been considered, it has been discussed very fully in the last few years in the spirit of criticism which is the object of this treatise; and though personally I cannot accept all the conclusions which have been advanced, or even all of those that seem generally accepted, it would be absurd to pretend that anything serious could be added to that discussion in a few pages of an anticipatory appendix. It is best therefore to dismiss all these

---

[1] Of course an apparent exception sometimes occurs, e.g. when the origin of rectangular coordinates happens to coincide with a physical point characteristic of the system of which the laws are stated.

matters with the briefest mention—a course which I adopt with great regret; for by the time that Part III appears everything that I should like to say now will probably have been said, all the difficulties which at present attend the Principle will have vanished, and it will have become one of the commonplaces of physical thought.

Nevertheless I cannot refrain from raising an objection and making a suggestion, which arise directly from conclusions about the distinction between laws and theories and about the nature of spatial and temporal conceptions that have already been advanced.

The Fundamental doctrine of the Principle of Relativity is often expressed in some such words as these: It is possible to express the laws of physics in such a form that this form is unaltered if for one set of coordinate axes to which they are referred is substituted another set, moving relatively to the first set. (At first a restriction was imposed on the form of motion permissible; this has been partially removed, and it is felt that it may be removed entirely. But its presence or removal does not affect the point made here.) The significance and the truth of this proposition must depend on the precise meaning given to the terms "laws" and "form" of laws. I have tried to give very definite meanings to those words; it is not certain that those meanings are universally accepted; but it seems to me that some very definite meaning must be given to these terms in the statement of the doctrine unless it is to be almost self-contradictory[1].

For there is one law that cannot be unchanged by the change of axes, namely the law which is involved in the decision that the axes have been changed for a set moving relatively to the first set. Suppose that I change my axes from a body A to a body B which is moving relatively to A. Then the principle asserts that all laws are unchanged. But, if they are unchanged, how can I know that B is moving relatively to A? Something which can be observed must have been changed during the transference; if it is not the laws of the system A–B, what is it? The answer will doubtless be made that the statement that A is moving relatively to B, or, in a particular instance, that a ship is moving relatively to the land, is not a law; it is a statement of the properties of an individual system. That is perfectly true; but the example is irrelevant; it is not in such cases that the Principle is applied. It is not applied to the transference of axes from a ship to land, but from the earth to the sun. The statement that the earth is moving in a particular way relative to the sun is also not a law in our special sense, but it is a statement that can only be made in virtue of laws; there is no evidence for it unless certain laws (and, we must add, theories) are true. If the motion of the earth relative to the sun had been capable of determination in the same simple and direct way as the motion of the ship relative to the land, Galileo would never have quarrelled with the Inquisition. We say that the earth moves relatively to the sun simply because we believe that certain laws would be altered if our axes were transferred from the earth to the sun; to say that the earth moves relatively to the sun and to say at the same time that these laws would be unaltered by the transference of the axes is to talk nonsense, pure and unadulterated. If the Principle of Relativity is to mean anything, serious attention must be given to the distinction between the "laws" to which it does and does not apply.

As a matter of fact, I do not believe that the Principle is true of any laws; it is only true of theories. And it is not true of all theories, but only of certain theories. I believe that an adequate statement of the Principle would be this: No physical

---

[1] The objection about to be raised has been raised previously in a much less general form (*Phil. Mag.* April, 1911, p. 503). No attention seems to have been paid to the criticisms advanced there, but I still venture to think they are important.

theory is to be regarded as ultimate, and as incapable cf further explanation, unless it is such that its form, including the numerical value of any constants involved in it, would be unchanged by a transference of the axes to which it is referred to another set moving relatively to the first set. (Strictly speaking, it must be remembered that the axes are hypothetical ideas and differ not in motion, which is an experimental conception, but in a way analogous to motion.)

If the Principle is expressed in that form, I think it will lose none of its generality; for the propositions in connection with which it is applied are characteristically ultimate theories, capable of no further explanation; they are the equations of the electron theory and of dynamics. At the same time most of the paradoxes vanish when it is realised that the ideas discussed are exclusively hypothetical ideas, and, moreover, pure hypothetical ideas, not directly connected by the dictionary with any experimental concepts. With such a mere hint, the matter must be left.

Force. Part IV, which treats of Force, is as yet only sketched; but a few conclusions may be stated in order to explain some references in the text of this volume.

The idea of force arises, as is well known, from the sensation of muscular exertion. Scientific terminology connected with force and, to some extent, the conceptions which it is used to denote bear clear marks of this origin. It is extremely interesting, and indispensable for any clear understanding of the matter, to trace the steps by which we have passed from the idea of force as something detected by direct and instinctive judgement to the elaborate idea called by the same name in modern analytical dynamics. But here I want only to make clear a very important difference between the force of statics and the force of dynamics; for I believe that in the appreciation of that difference lies the solution of many of the difficulties which attend an accurate formulation of the foundations of either branch of science.

Statical force is a fundamental magnitude, measurable (if not actually measured) according to the principles of Chapter X. It is always the property of a system in a given state, and its nature will be clear if it is always called the force exerted by that system. Thus a stretched spring with a given extension is characterised by the property of exerting a certain force on any body to which its free end is attached. For the measurement of this property definitions of equality and of addition are, as usual, necessary. Forces exerted by two systems are equal when, if exerted on the same body in opposite directions (here is a slight elaboration which need not detain us), the body remains at rest. Forces are added when they are both exerted in the same direction on the same body; thus the forces of two stretched springs are added and applied to a body when the free ends of both springs are attached to that body and the extensions are in the same direction.

These definitions can be shown to be satisfactory. It will be seen that the proposition of the independence of forces is a part of the definition of addition. When we have established this satisfactory way of measuring the force exerted by a system, this force being a definite property of the system, uniformly associated with its other properties and independent of the body on which the force is exerted, then we can establish the laws of statical force—the law of the lever and so on. It is obviously a consequence of the definition of force that if equal forces in opposite directions are applied to a body it remains at rest, and that the converse proposition must also be true, that, if it remains at rest, the algebraic sum of the forces applied in opposite directions must be zero.

It now turns out that in certain important conditions, force so measured determines the motion of a body that is not at rest; and in particular that the uniform acceleration of a body on which a given force is exerted is proportional to the force exerted. Thus, if a small body be attached to the end of a very long stretched spring and be not attached to anything else, it can be shown experimentally to move in the direction of the force with an acceleration which, over any small part of its course, is uniform and proportional to the force corresponding to the extension of the spring at that part of its course. But the value of the acceleration depends on the nature of the body as well as the magnitude of the force; it is the product of the force by a constant which is a characteristic property of the body.

But when we try to generalise this result and to interpret all acceleration as due to the action of statical forces, three main difficulties arise. The first is peculiar to gravitation, but none the less important; for gravitational force is the only form of force on which really accurate fundamental experiments can be made. It is that the body on which force is exerted appears to be the same as the system which exerts force. A heavy body is a system characterised by the exertion of a force on any other body just as is a stretched spring, but when it falls its motion seems determined by the very force which it exerts on others. Of course nowadays we say that the force of a heavy body is not so much a property of that body as of the gravitational field of the earth in which it is placed; but it required the genius of Newton to develop and state clearly that conception. Second, the motion of a body may be accelerated even when it is apparently under the action of no system which would exert statical force on it if it were at rest; thus a body set moving in a liquid of the same density is accelerated (for of course acceleration includes deceleration) and yet when it is at rest it shows no signs of being acted on by force. We are led to the conception of forces that act on bodies in virtue of the fact that they are in motion; but, from the nature of the definition, such forces cannot possibly be measured as are statical forces. Third, two bodies may both be accelerated by their mutual action, as when two elastic bodies collide; they are then both presumably acted on by forces; but the forces which can be considered as responsible for their accelerations will depend upon the way in which their mutual acceleration is divided up into two partial accelerations. If one body is considered at rest and all the acceleration allotted to the other, it must be considered as subject to no force; in what way should mutual accelerations be divided up so that the two partial accelerations are proportional to the forces?

These difficulties are met by a theory of dynamics which introduces hypothetical forces. The hypothesis states that (1) all systems are composed of particles to each of which is assigned a characteristic constant, its mass; (2) that the force on any particle is determined in some stated way by its relations to other particles; (3) that the acceleration of any particle is the ratio of the sum of the forces exerted on it by other particles to the mass of that particle; (4) that the force exerted by the particle A on B is equal and opposite to that exerted by B on A. The dictionary asserts that the integrated equations of motion derived from the hypothesis are the experimental equations of motion referred to some frame of coordinates.

The difficulty remains that the theory is indeterminate. If we refer our experimental motion to one frame we have to assign the hypothetical forces in (2) in one way; if we choose another frame, we have to assign them in another way. But the discussion of this difficulty would lead us much too far. The point on which it is important to insist is that whereas statical force is an experimental concept and a magnitude, dynamical force is a hypothetical idea. It cannot be determined directly by experiment, but only by the introduction of those analogies and considerations of simplicity which determine the meaning of theories and not the truth of laws.

INDEX

Heavy type denotes a definition